MORE TOPICS
IN MATHEMATICS

FOR
ELEMENTARY
SCHOOL
TEACHERS

THIRTIETH
YEARBOOK

NATIONAL COUNCIL OF TEACHERS OF MATHEMATICS

PREFACE

The extensive curriculum changes in school mathematics during the past dozen years involve both new material and a more penetrating treatment of familiar material. Many teachers have found that their professional education did not give them sufficient breadth and depth of understanding of mathematical concepts to match these rapid changes.

It can now truly be said, however, that the outstanding and continuing success of the program is in large measure a result of the eternally youthful spirit with which the elementary and secondary school teachers set about retooling their mathematical background by seeking and assimilating the newer mathematical expositions.

One of these expositions was the Twenty-ninth Yearbook (1964). The material in that book first appeared, earlier that year, in the form of eight separate booklets:

Booklet No. 1: *Sets*
Booklet No. 2: *The Whole Numbers*
Booklet No. 3: *Numeration Systems for the Whole Numbers*
Booklet No. 4: *Algorithms for Operations with Whole Numbers*
Booklet No. 5: *Numbers and Their Factors*
Booklet No. 6: *The Rational Numbers*
Booklet No. 7: *Numeration Systems for the Rational Numbers*
Booklet No. 8: *Number Sentences*

Because of the enthusiasm with which this material was received, it was felt that an extension of subject matter would be valuable.

The material in the present yearbook also first appeared in the form of separate booklets. Like the earlier units, the present ones are written for elementary school teachers rather than their pupils. The topics were chosen especially with a view to providing background material for introducing to children in their early school years some of the *central unifying concepts in mathematics*. It is the hope of the authors and of the NCTM that this yearbook may be helpful to all who are interested in improving mathematics instruction.

The ten booklets that constitute the present yearbook are the product of a summer (1966) writing session. The project was initiated at a meeting arranged by Kenneth B. Henderson and William Wooton, chairmen

iii

of the NCTM Supplementary Publications Committee for 1962–64 and 1964–66, respectively, and attended also by Edwin F. Beckenbach. A later planning session included, in addition, George Arbogast, Marguerite Brydegaard, and Lenore S. John. The writing was sponsored by the 1965–66 NCTM Supplementary Publications Committee and financed by the NCTM. The Committee consisted of William Wooton (chairman), Don E. Edmondson, Marian A. Moore, Thomas L. Reynolds, Seaton E. Smith, Jr., Anne Peskin, and John Fujii. The booklet manuscripts were read critically by the members of the 1966–67 NCTM Supplementary Publications Committee: Seaton E. Smith, Jr. (chairman), Thomas L. Reynolds, Anne Peskin, John Fujii, John L. Marks, Marilyn J. Zweng, and Herman Rosenberg.

The Thirtieth Yearbook Editorial Committee (composed of the members of the original writing group) is grateful for the warm support given this project by Bruce E. Meserve, NCTM president, 1964–66; Donovan A. Johnson, NCTM president, 1966–68; and Julius H. Hlavaty, NCTM president, 1968–70. The Editorial Committee is also grateful for the many valuable suggestions made by members of the two NCTM Supplementary Publications Committees and for the assistance of the NCTM Washington office. The writers herewith express their deep appreciation to the following persons for reading parts of the manuscripts and consulting with the writers during the preparation of the material: Joseph M. Trotter, Jr., principal of San Luis Rey School, and Bonita Trotter, teacher at Laurel School, both of the Unionside Union School District, California; John M. Hoffman, director of the Community Educational Resources Section of the San Diego County Department of Education; and James E. Inskeep, Jr., professor of mathematics education at San Diego State College. The writers are especially indebted to Alice C. Beckenbach for extensive help in organizing and editing the material for several of the booklets. They are most grateful, also, to Elaine Barth and her fine staff of typists for their excellent work in manuscript preparation.

The Editorial Committee

George Arbogast	Joseph Hashisaki
Manuel P. Berri	Lenore S. John
Marguerite Brydegaard	David Johnson
Louis S. Cohen	Robert H. Sorgenfrey
Helen L. Curran	J. Dean Swift
Patricia Davidson	William Wooton
Walter Fleming	Edwin F. Beckenbach, *Chairman*

CONTENTS

BOOKLET NO. 11: *THE SYSTEM OF REAL NUMBERS*

BOOKLET NO. 15: MEASUREMENT

BOOKLET NO. 17: *HINTS FOR PROBLEM SOLVING*

BOOKLET NO. 18: *SYMMETRY, CONGRUENCE AND SIMILARITY*

BOOKLET NUMBER NINE:

THE SYSTEM OF INTEGERS

INTRODUCTION

To a vast majority of people, numbers and the properties of numbers are important only insofar as they are useful in describing real-life situations or in solving practical problems in which "quantities" of some kind are involved. The housewife who wants to cut a recipe for eight servings to proportions for six servings would like to be able to multiply by 6/8 or 3/4. The grocery clerk who does not have access to a cash register that automatically computes change would like to be able to subtract $3.47 from $5.00 in order to make change for a five-dollar bill, or at least to be able to determine how much money must be added to $3.47 in order to obtain $5.00.

Indeed, anyone who is aware of the nature of our present-day civilization can hardly fail to realize how deeply numbers and their properties affect our daily lives.

Numbers, however, like any other abstractions (for the concept of "number" is an abstraction), are useful in a practical sense only to the extent that they parallel some real-life situation. For example, were it not true that adding two cups of milk to three cups of pancake flour produces the same kind of pancake, except for quantity, as adding three cups of milk to four and one-half cups of pancake flour, the mathematical fact that

$$\frac{2}{3} = \frac{3}{4\frac{1}{2}}$$

would be of no help in adapting a recipe to increase the number of servings. The point is that numbers are useful because they (and many of the properties associated with their sums, products, differences, and quotients) lend themselves to the study of a very wide variety of physical situations.

1

Moreover, we use different kinds of numbers for different aspects of the real world.

The numbers most frequently used in coping with quantitative problems in everyday life are the whole numbers, such as 0, 1, 2, and 3, and the numbers named by fractions, such as 3/4, 2/5, and 21/6, or by decimals, such as 0.12, 2.305, and 71.6. Whole numbers help us deal with ideas of "how many." Numbers named by fractions are useful in measurement; they help us answer questions about "what part of" or "how much." Accordingly, these are the numbers that receive the greatest attention in the early years of our lives and that are, in a sense, of the greatest importance to most of us.

In addition to those aspects of the physical world that can be studied or dealt with by using whole numbers and fractions, there are other aspects that demand attention. Many everyday situations involve the idea of *directed* quantities, that is, quantities that can be referred to as being on opposite sides of a given reference point. Just as there are temperatures above 0° Fahrenheit, so also there are temperatures below 0° Fahrenheit; just as there are altitudes above sea level, so also there are altitudes below sea level; and just as a milepost may be located two miles west of a given point on a straight road, so also a milepost may be located two miles east of the given point. These kinds of situations are concerned not only with magnitudes but also with what might be described as *opposite directions*. Neither the natural numbers nor numbers such as 3/2, 2.7, and 0 possess properties that parallel this notion of "oppositeness." Therefore, if we are to be as practical about models of such things as thermometers, or about profits and losses in business, as we are about recipes and making change, we need to employ numbers that somehow reflect "oppositeness" as well as magnitude. There are several systems of numbers that have the desired characteristics. Because we wish to keep an introduction to the properties of such numbers as simple as possible, let us consider the simplest such system, the system of *integers*. We shall designate the set of elements in this system—that is, the set of integers—by J.[1]

THE INTEGERS

Something Old

Prompted by the notion that it is always (or nearly always) a good idea when beginning something new to start with something old and

---

[1] When the elements of a set of numbers are considered along with their properties under such operations as addition and multiplication, the set and the operations together are called a *system*. (For a discussion of sets, see Booklet No. 1: *Sets*.)

familiar, let us open this discussion by recalling two sets of numbers that are used by most of us every day. These are the set N of *natural numbers*,

$$N = \{1, 2, 3, 4, \cdots \},$$

and the set W of *whole numbers*,[2] which consists of N and one additional number, 0:

$$W = \{0, 1, 2, 3, 4, \cdots \}.$$

In each of these sets there is no last member. This fact is indicated by using three dots (ellipses) in the notation, as shown. The things we want to recall about these sets include the following.

A. Both are ordered sets. This means that given any two (different) numbers in either set, it is always true that one of the numbers is less than the other. For example, in either set, 2 is less than 3, 3 is less than 4, and so on. The symbol $<$ (read "is less than") is used to denote this relationship. Thus, "2 is less than 3" is represented by "$2 < 3$." If the symbol $<$ is reversed, then the resulting symbol appears as $>$ and denotes "is greater than." Thus, "$4 > 1$" is read "4 is greater than 1."

B. Each of the sets N and W can be pictured by using a number line, as shown in Figure 1. Recall that the heavy dots on the lines in the

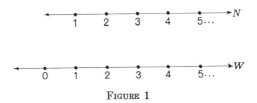

FIGURE 1

figure mark the points we call the *graphs* of the numbers. The number paired with a point is called the *coordinate* of the point. Arrowheads are included at the ends of the picture to denote the endless extent of the line, and the ellipses following the numeral 5 are intended to suggest the endless succession of numbers in both N and W.

C. In both N and W, there are two *basic* operations, addition and multiplication, and two *associated* operations, subtraction and division. These operations have some basic properties with which you are

---

[2] See Booklet No. 2: *The Whole Numbers*; Booklet No. 3: *Numeration Systems for the Whole Numbers*; Booklet No. 4: *Algorithms for Operations with Whole Numbers*.

probably familiar, and which, in any event, we shall later discuss briefly in connection with integers.

To keep the distinction between N and W clear, just remember that the set N does not contain the number 0, while W does; otherwise, they contain the same members. In practical situations the set W is of course the more convenient, because it is frequently necessary to use a number to describe such things as how many dollars one has on hand the day before payday or how many times one has been to Peru, when "none" and "never" are the *words* describing these things. Notice that the *words* "none" and "never" do not name a number, but the word "zero" and the symbol "0" do. You should not confuse the number 0 with what it describes. Figure 2 suggests how useful "0" can be under certain circumstances.

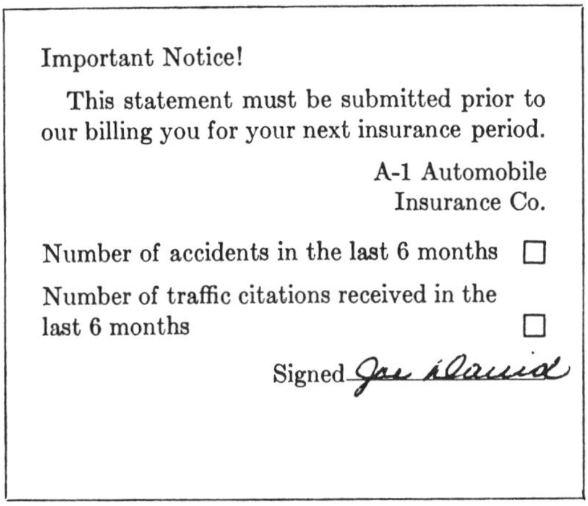

Important Notice!

    This statement must be submitted prior to our billing you for your next insurance period.

                                   A-1 Automobile
                                     Insurance Co.

Number of accidents in the last 6 months ☐

Number of traffic citations received in the last 6 months ☐

                Signed *Joe Blauid*

FIGURE 2

The natural numbers and the whole numbers are the numbers we use to describe "how many." You use these numbers to help you answer such questions as the following:

(1)   If tennis balls cost $2.00 per can, how much do four cans cost?

(2)   If an automobile moves at a constant speed of 50 miles per hour, how long does the automobile take to complete a trip of 200 miles?

(3)   John weighs 160 pounds and Jane weighs 100 pounds. Can they safely cross a bridge together if the bridge will support a load of no more than 250 pounds?

To answer question (1) you would, of course, multiply the whole number 4 by the whole number 2 to obtain the whole number 8; and then you would answer the question by saying, "Eight dollars." Similarly, because the whole number 200 divided by the whole number 50 yields the whole number 4, you would answer question (2) by saying, "Four hours." Although question (3) does not actually ask for a quantity of some kind, you can nevertheless use the set of whole numbers to help you answer it appropriately. Because $100 + 160 = 260$, and $250 < 260$, you can reply to question (3) with a simple "No."

Notice that no idea of opposites is involved in any of the foregoing real-life situations. Consider, however, a fourth question with real-life significance (at least for some people):

(4) A check for $200 was written on a bank account containing $180. If the bank honored the check, what would be the new balance?

To answer this question with a number only, we shall have to look elsewhere than in set N or set W.

Exercise Set 1

1. N = set of natural numbers.

   W = set of whole numbers.

   Complete (see Booklet No. 1: *Sets* for set notation):

   a. $N \cup W =$ ____.

   b. $N \cap W =$ ____.

2. Explain why the set of natural numbers is a proper subset of the set of whole numbers.

3. Arrange the following from least to greatest:
$$7, 5, 19, 0, 3$$

4. Which of the following are names for whole numbers?

   a. $3 + 5$ **d.** 2×4

   b. $5 - 7$ **e.** $8 \div 8$

   c. $19 - 6$ **f.** $16 \div 3$

5. Complete: The number associated with a point on the number line is called the ____ of the point.

6. Complete: The point associated with a number on the number line is called the ____ of the number.

7. What are the two basic operations in the set of whole numbers?

8. Can the following problems be solved using the set of whole numbers and the operation of addition? Why?

   a. My friend and I live on the same street. She lives 3 blocks away from me. A new girl who just moved to our street lives 5 blocks from my friend. How far away from me does the new girl live?

b. This morning the temperature changed 8 degrees between seven o'clock and noon. Since noon it has changed 3 degrees. By how much does the temperature now differ from the temperature at seven o'clock this morning?

Something New

Suppose a mirror is held with its edge passing through the point 0 of Figure 3 and with its face perpendicular to the number line, as suggested

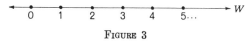

FIGURE 3

by Figure 4. Now, if the part of the line held to the mirror and the line's

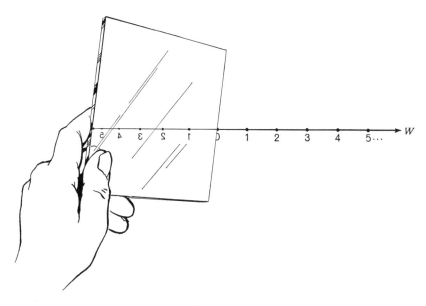

FIGURE 4

reflection are thought of together as representing a single line, you have the number line pictured in Figure 5. This might be described as a sort of

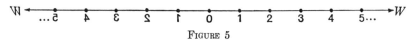

FIGURE 5

"through-the-looking-glass" extension of the set of whole numbers, where endlessly many new numbers are now graphed endlessly to the left of the origin (the graph of zero).

Of course, these new "numbers" are thus far quite meaningless, and it is only when we decide how to compare them and to perform operations using them that they become meaningful and valuable. Since examining these matters is the chief purpose of this booklet, however, we shall henceforth refer to them as *numbers* and shall consider them to have a claim to this name that is just as valid as the one we presume the whole numbers to have. Decisions regarding these numbers are made because they are consistent, seem reasonable, and are useful. It should constantly be kept in mind, though, that these decisions constitute *definitions;* we do not *prove* how to compare or perform operations with these new numbers.

Notice that we can separate the set

$$\{\cdots, \mathtt{2}, \mathtt{4}, \mathtt{E}, \mathtt{S}, \mathtt{r}, 0, 1, 2, 3, 4, 5, \cdots\}$$

of numbers, some of whose graphs are shown in Figure 5, into three distinct and nonoverlapping sets (disjoint sets). These are the set

$$N = \{1, 2, 3, 4, 5, \cdots\}$$

of natural numbers with which we began; the set {0}, whose only member is 0; and the set

$$\{\cdots, \mathtt{2}, \mathtt{4}, \mathtt{E}, \mathtt{S}, \mathtt{r}, \}\,,$$

of those numbers whose graphs appear to the left of 0 on the number line and therefore opposite the graphs of the members of N. Notice that we have pairs of numbers in this extended set—for example, 1 and $\mathtt{r}$, 2 and $\mathtt{S}$, 3 and $\mathtt{E}$—whose graphs are "mirror reflections" of each other from the point of origin, 0.

Now, by changing some symbols we can go directly from the set we obtained with the help of a mirror to the set J of integers.

To begin with, let us agree that for the numbers whose graphs occur to the left of the origin on the number line, we shall use the symbols $^-1$ (read "negative one") instead of $\mathtt{r}$, $^-2$ (read "negative two") instead of $\mathtt{S}$, $^-3$ (read "negative three") instead of $\mathtt{E}$, and so on. Thus, by prefixing a raised minus sign to the numeral for a natural number, we shall name its "mirror image." Any number whose graph is to the left of the origin on the number line will be called a *negative number*, and the set

$$\{\ \cdots\ , \ ^-5, \ ^-4, \ ^-3, \ ^-2, \ ^-1\}$$

of all these new numbers we have introduced will be represented by J^- (read "jay negative") and called the set of negative integers. (If it seems strange to place the minus sign on the right-hand side of the letter J to name the set of negative integers and, on the other hand, to place the minus sign on the left-hand side of a numeral to name a negative integer such as ⁻2, you should adjust to the fact that mathematicians as well as other people can behave strangely. There is no particular significance to this order of symbols; it is simply customary. This also applies to the symbols J^+ and ⁺2 to be introduced next.)

In keeping with the designation of their new partners, we shall also refer to the set N of natural numbers as the set J^+ (read "jay positive") of *positive integers*. Sometimes, when we wish to put particular emphasis on the fact that a given number is a positive integer, we use symbols such as ⁺1 (read "positive one"), ⁺2 (read "positive two"), and so on, in place of the familiar symbols 1, 2, and so on. When this is done, you should bear in mind that ⁺1 and 1 designate the same number; only the name has been changed. We shall not give a name to the set {0}, whose only member is 0; but it is important to observe that the number 0, although an integer, is neither a positive nor a negative integer and is the only integer with this property.

Therefore, the union of the sets J^+, {0}, and J^- is the set J of integers, which is sometimes represented as

$$J = \{ \cdots, {}^-3, {}^-2, {}^-1, 0, 1, 2, 3, \cdots \},$$

where the three dots at each end indicate that these numbers continue endlessly in both positive and negative directions. (See Fig. 6.)

FIGURE 6

Exercise Set 2

1. What are the members of the set J^- called?

2. What are the members of the set J^+ called?

3. List any integers that are not members of either J^- or J^+.

4. To which set does each of the following belong, to J^- or J^+ or {0}?

a. $6 - 2$ d. ⁻36

b. ⁻4   e. $16 + 4$

c. $6 - 6$ f. 9

5. In which of the following situations might you need the set of integers? In which would the set of whole numbers suffice?

a. Computing the enrollment of a school, given the number of children in each class

b. Making a thermometer

c. Indicating a change in the price of a stock

d. Recording the altitude of the continental shelf off the coast of Africa, which is 4,000 fathoms below sea level

6. Use an integer to express each of the following.

a. 5 points "in the hole"

b. A loss of $500

c. 9 seconds before "blast off"

d. A loss of 5 yards by a football team

Opposites

If 0 is excluded, then the integers can be sorted into *pairs* of numbers that have graphs on the number line and are located the same number of unit segments from the origin, but on opposite sides of it. Some examples of such pairs are ⁻1 and 1, ⁻2 and 2, and ⁻3 and 3. We say that ⁻1 is the *opposite* of 1; 1 is the opposite of ⁻1; ⁻2 is the opposite of 2, and so on. (See Fig. 7.) Since the graph of 0 is zero units in each of the two directions on the line from the origin, we say that 0 is its own opposite.

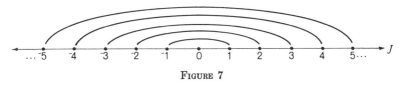

FIGURE 7

Because integers can be used to describe quantities that are of the same magnitude but that are in opposite directions from a reference point, the system of integers is useful in many practical ways. For example, on page 5 a question was asked about a bank balance after a check for $200 had been honored by the bank for an account containing $180. Having the integers at our disposal makes it possible to assign a number to the resulting state of the account; namely, we can say that the resulting balance is ⁻$20.

You should recall that a *variable* is a symbol that represents an unspecified element of some set. Usually a lowercase letter, such as a, b, n, or x, is employed for this purpose—although a box, □, or triangle, △, or some other simple figure may also be used. Thus, to say that a is a member of J means that you are using the symbol "a" to name an integer, such integer being unspecified. The set J is called the *replacement set* of the variable a.

Now, it is often necessary to refer to the opposite of a particular integer. So it is useful to have a symbol that represents the opposite of an integer named by a variable, such as a. Accordingly, we define the symbol $°a$ (read "the opposite of a") to represent the *opposite* of a. Thus, if $a = 4$, then $°a = {}^-4$, while if $°a = 3$, then $a = {}^-3$. Therefore, the statement

$$°({}^+3) = {}^-3, \text{ or } °3 = {}^-3,$$

means that the opposite of positive three is negative three; and the statement

$$°({}^-4) = {}^+4, \text{ or } °({}^-4) = 4,$$

means that the opposite of negative four is positive four.

An important point to remember about the use of a variable and the symbol for "opposite of" is this: you cannot assume that if a names an integer, then it must name a positive integer; you also cannot assume that if $°a$ names an integer, then it must name a negative integer. The symbols a and $°a$ when used to name integers may name either positive integers, negative integers, or 0. Thus you can be sure that if a is positive, then $°a$ is negative; if a is negative, then $°a$ is positive. In set symbols you might represent this certainty by writing "If $a \; \varepsilon \; J^+$, then $°a \; \varepsilon \; J^-$" (read "If a is a member of jay positive, then the opposite of a is a member of jay negative") and "If $a \; \varepsilon \; J^-$, then $°a \; \varepsilon \; J^+$."

The one integer that is neither positive nor negative is 0. Moreover, as we observed earlier, 0 is its own opposite; you can see by considering the number line that it is the only integer that is its own opposite. Hence, if a names an integer such that $°a = a$, then a must name the integer 0.

Exercise Set 3

1. Write the opposite of each integer below.

   a. 2   d. ⁻768
   b. ⁻8   e. 45
   c. 0   f. ⁻30

2. Complete the following:

   a. °7 = _____   d. °(6 × 3) = _____
   b. °(⁻3) = _____   e. °(6 + 2) = _____
   c. °0 = _____   f. °(5 − 2) = _____

3. Complete the following table of selected values for a and $°a$.

a	2	-5	4	-3	0				1	-9	
$°a$	-2	5				6	-8	-15			-10

4. Complete: If a names a positive integer, then $°a$ names a _____ integer.

5. Complete: If $°a$ names a _____ integer, then a names a negative integer.

6. Complete: If $°a = a$, then a names the integer _____.

Arrow Representation of Integers

Because we can pair each whole number with a selected point on a line, we can construct a number line and then can use the graphs of the whole numbers to help us study the properties of whole numbers. (See Booklet No. 2: *The Whole Numbers.*) We can similarly use the graphs of integers on a number line to help us study and understand the properties of integers.

There is also another pairing we can make to help us visualize the properties of whole numbers and of integers: We can picture a whole number or an integer in terms of a *movement,* or *translation,* along the number line. This is particularly true of the integers because they incorporate the idea of opposite directions with the idea of magnitude. For example, we can think of the positive integer 2 as being represented by a movement of 2 units to the *right* along a horizontal line and the negative integer ⁻3 as being represented by a movement of 3 units to the *left* along the line. Such a movement, or translation, can in turn be pictured by using an arrow drawn above the number line, pointing in the direction of the movement, and having as its length the number of units involved in the movement. Actually, the arrow should be thought of as lying directly *on* the number line; it is pictured above the line only for visual convenience. Thus each arrow in Figure 8 represents the positive

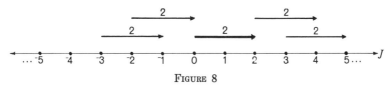

Figure 8

integer 2 because it points to the right and is 2 units long. Each arrow in Figure 9 represents the negative integer ⁻3 because it points to the

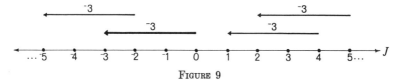

Figure 9

left and is 3 units long. Notice that the location of the arrow on the
line has no bearing on the number represented, since the representation
is accomplished by using only the length and direction of the arrow. In
more advanced mathematics these arrows are referred to as geometric
vectors. In order to ensure that each integer has an arrow representation,
we call the arrow representation of 0 a *point arrow;* we conceive it to be
an arrow with either a positive or negative direction, as seems convenient, and to have a length of 0 units.

Of all the arrows representing a given integer, the one with its initial
point (tail) on (or directly above) the origin has its terminal point (head)
on (or directly above) the graph of the integer on the number line; for
this reason the arrow is said to be in *standard position*. Thus the heavy
arrows in **Figures 8** and **9** are in standard position.

Another way to think of these translations is in terms of walking back
and forth along a straight path running east and west. Two steps to the
east could represent the positive integer 2, and 3 steps to the west could
represent the negative integer ⁻3. The integer 0 would be represented by
no movement along the path, although you can think of a person facing
either east or west without moving; this corresponds to the notion of
having an arrow without length represent 0, but still being able to assign
one of the two directions on the line to the arrow.

Exercise Set 4

1. Look at the arrows on the number line below.
  a. How are they alike?
  b. How are they different?
  c. What integer does each arrow represent?

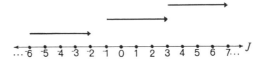

2. Look at the arrows on the number line below.
  a. How are they alike?
  b. How are they different?
  c. What two different integers are represented by these arrows?
  d. Which arrow is in standard position?

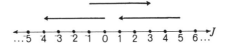

3. Draw a number line. Label it with integers. Draw three arrows, each representing ⁻4, that begin at the graphs of ⁻4, 7, and 0, respectively.

4. Label each arrow below with an integer.

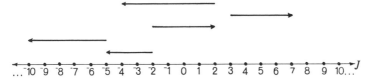

Absolute Value

If a scientist wished to keep a container at a temperature within 3 degrees of 0° centigrade, he might arrange a thermostat that started a refrigeration unit at 3° above 0° and a heating unit at 3° below 0°. (See Fig 10.) Each unit would be turned off when the temperature

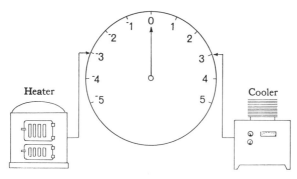

FIGURE 10

reached 0°. Thus a change of 3° from 0° in either direction would be enough to start a countermovement of the temperature. In such a situation the *direction* of the change in temperature would be important only insofar as it resulted in an appropriate action by the heater or cooler; the main concern is that a *change* of 3 degrees from 0° should produce a corrective activity. Mathematically speaking, the scientist is interested in what is called the *absolute value* of the integers 3 and ⁻3. As you will see later, this concept has an important role to play in the operations of addition, subtraction, multiplication, and division of integers; accordingly, we shall look at the idea in several ways.

To explain what is meant by the *absolute value* of an integer, let us turn again to thinking about integers in terms of arrow representations. The arrow representations of 1 and ⁻1 are alike in one respect, namely length. They are opposite, however, in direction. Similarly, the arrow representations of 2 and ⁻2 have the same length but are opposite in direction, and those representing 3 and ⁻3 are equal in length but opposite in direction. In general, for every given integer the arrow representations of the integer and its opposite have the same length but have opposite direction (Fig. 11). Of course, our agreement to assign

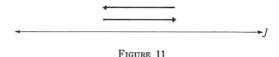

FIGURE 11

either direction to an arrow representation of 0 is in recognition of the fact that 0 is its own opposite. With the foregoing facts in mind, let us define the absolute value of an integer in terms of the length of an arrow representation of the integer:

> *If a is an integer, then the* absolute value *of a is the non-negative (positive or zero) integer that gives the length of an arrow representation of a.*

The absolute value of a is denoted by $|a|$. For example,

$$|{}^-7| = 7, |7| = 7, |{}^-8| = 8, \text{ and } |0| = 0.$$

Alternatively, by agreeing that the graph of any integer is located a distance from the origin that is a nonnegative integer number of units, we can define the absolute value of an integer as follows:

> *If a is an integer, then the absolute value of a is the nonnegative integer that gives the distance of the graph of a from the origin.*

Figure 12 illustrates this definition of $|a|$, first with $a < 0$ and then with $a > 0$.

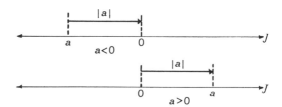

FIGURE 12

We can give still another definition of absolute value, a definition that does not depend on the number line or on arrow representations. Let us begin by observing once more that the symbols a and $°a$ represent *opposites,* so that regardless of the integer denoted by a, $°a$ denotes its opposite and regardless of the integer denoted by $°a$, a denotes its opposite. Then consider the following definition:

> *If a is an integer other than 0, then the absolute value of a is the positive one of a and $°a$. The absolute value of 0 is 0.*

Now let us give some examples to interpret what this means. If $a = 3$, what is $|a|$? The integer 3 has an opposite, namely ⁻3; and 3 and ⁻3 form a pair of opposites. Of these, 3 is nonnegative (actually positive) and ⁻3 is negative. Therefore, by the foregoing definition $|3| = 3$. On the other hand, suppose you wish to identify $|⁻10|$. The integer ⁻10 has an opposite, namely 10; and 10 is the nonnegative member of the pair 10 and ⁻10. Therefore, by the definition $|⁻10| = 10$.

Exercise Set 5

1. Complete:

    a. $|⁻3| = $ _____

    b. $|0| = $ _____

    c. $|4 - 3| = $ _____

    d. $|9| = $ _____

2. Which arrow represents the integer with greater absolute value:

    a. An arrow drawn from ⁻3 to 7 or an arrow drawn from 3 to 7?

    b. An arrow drawn from 9 to ⁻1 or an arrow drawn from 9 to 1?

    c. An arrow drawn from 0 to 4 or an arrow drawn from ⁻6 to 0?

    d. An arrow drawn from 6 to ⁻2 or an arrow drawn from ⁻2 to ⁻6?

3. Write the value of each of the following:

    a. $|17|$ **c.** $|⁻7| + |3|$

    b. $|⁻10|$ **d.** $|⁻6| \times |⁻11|$

4. Write the value of each of the following:

    a. $°|2|$ **c.** $|°3|$

    b. $°|⁻4|$ **d.** $|°(⁻7)|$

5. Complete: If the integer a is not zero and if $|a| = a$, then a must be a _____ integer.

6. Complete: If the integer a is not zero and if $|a| = °a$, then a must be a _____ integer.

Order in the Set of Integers

On page 3 it was observed that the set of whole numbers is ordered. This property is reflected on the number line by the relative location of the graphs of the whole numbers: Of the two whole numbers a and b, the graph of the greater lies to the right of the graph of the lesser on the number line (Fig. 13). Let us retain this notion of the location of the

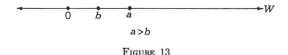

$a > b$

FIGURE 13

graphs of two numbers as establishing the order of two numbers and define order in the set of integers as follows:

If a and b are integers, then $a > b$ if and only if the graph of a lies to the right of the graph of b on a horizontal number line.

Thus, when you look at Figure 14, it is apparent that ‾4 is greater than ‾5, ‾1 is greater than ‾4, and 0 *is greater than every negative integer.*

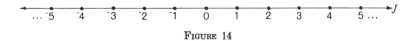

FIGURE 14

An alternative but equivalent way of defining order in the set of integers will be considered on page 47, after we have defined addition and subtraction in this set.

As remarked earlier, the symbols $<$ and $>$ mean "is less than" and "is greater than," respectively. Two other symbols frequently used in discussing order are $\leq$ (read "is less than or equal to") and $\geq$ (read "is greater than or equal to"). Each of these symbols is a condensation of two statements connected by the word *or*. Thus,

$$a \leq b$$

means that

either $a < b$ or $a = b$;

and

$$a \geq b$$

means that

either $a > b$ or $a = b$.

When you see statements such as $6 \leq 8$, you know there is no intent to assert that 6 is equal to 8. The statement is a true statement because only one of the statements,

$$\text{either } 6 < 8 \quad \text{or} \quad 6 = 8,$$

needs to be true in order for the combined statement to be true; and $6 < 8$ is, in fact, true. Similarly, $8 \leq 8$ is a true statement, not because $8 < 8$ is true (which it is not), but because $8 = 8$ is true; $8 \leq 8$ simply asserts that one or the other of the statements, either $8 < 8$ or $8 = 8$, is true.

You can use order symbols to identify variables that represent only positive integers instead of integers in general. Thus, if a names an integer, then the sentence

$$a > 0$$

means simply that a names a *positive* integer, because only positive integers are greater than 0. Similarly, to say that a names an integer and that

$$a < 0$$

means that a names a *negative* integer, because only negative integers are less than 0. If, however, a names an integer, then the statement

$$a \geq 0$$

does not assure you that a names a positive number, for it may name 0. What this statement asserts is that a names a *nonnegative* integer; that is, a names an integer that is not negative. Similarly, if a names an integer and if

$$a \leq 0,$$

then a names either a negative integer or 0. In this case you say that a names a *nonpositive* integer.

All of the foregoing discussion of positive, negative, nonpositive, and nonnegative integers is built on the fact that the sets J^+, $\{0\}$, and J^- are disjoint but make up all of J; that is, each integer belongs to one and only one of these sets.

To say that an integer a is negative is to say that it is a member of J^- and not a member of $\{0\}$ or J^+. To say that an integer is nonnegative is to say that it is *not* a member of J^-; therefore, it is either 0 or a member of J^+. For integers in general, we have the same *trichotomy property of order* (see Booklet No. 2: *The Whole Numbers*) as we do in W. Thus:

If a and b are integers, then one and only one of the following statements is true: $a < b$, $a = b$, or $a > b$.

Exercise Set 6

1. How does the term "nonnegative" differ in meaning from the term "positive"?

2. How does the term "nonpositive" differ in meaning from the term "negative"?

3. In each pair of integers below, which is the greater integer?

  a. ⁻14, 14   **d.** ⁻2, 6
  b. 5, ⁻5   **e.** 9, 0
  c. 0, ⁻7   **f.** 3, ⁻7

4. I am thinking of two integers, a and b. If I make the true statement that $a > b$, what true statement can you make about $°a$ and $°b$?

5. Specify the reading that marks the warmer temperature in each of the following:

  a. 60°, 50°
  b. 10°, ⁻5°
  c. ⁻4°, 0°
  d. ⁻20°, ⁻10°

6. Arrange from least to greatest:

$$4, \ ^{-}8, \ 0, \ 6, \ ^{-}5$$

7. Use the symbols $>$, $<$, or $=$ to make each of the sentences below true.

  a. If $a > 0$ then $°a \ \square \ 0$.
  b. If $a < 0$ then $°a \ \square \ 0$.
  c. If $a = 0$ then $°a \ \square \ 0$.

8. Mark each statement below true (T) or false (F).

  a. Every negative integer is less than every positive integer. _____
  b. The opposite of each integer is less than the integer itself. _____
  c. Zero is a nonnegative integer. _____
  d. Every integer is a negative integer. _____

9. Use one of the symbols $>$, $<$, or $=$ to make each of the following sentences true.

  a. $|^{-}7| \ \square \ ^{-}7$ **c.** $|^{-}5| \ \square \ 4$
  b. $|3| \ \square \ ^{-}13$ **d.** $|9| \ \square \ |°9|$

10. From $|n| = 2$ can you determine what integer n names? Why or why not?

11. Mark each of the following true (T) or false (F).

   a. $|^-2| = 2$ ____   **d.** $|5| = {}^-5$ ____

   b. $|^-7| < 7$ ____   **e.** $|a| \geq {}^\circ a$ ____

   c. $|3| = {}^-3$ ____   **f.** $|9| < {}^\circ 9$ ____

ADDITION OF INTEGERS

The Sum of Two Whole Numbers

When pupils are first learning the operation of adding two whole numbers, it often helps them to visualize the concept if they combine two sets of familiar objects, such as blocks or apples, and then count the number of objects in the union set. For example, the fact that a set of three blocks combined with another set of two blocks produces a set of five blocks makes the mathematical statement $3 + 2 = 5$ physically meaningful. Also, by combining such sets in various ways the pupil can discover certain basic properties of addition in the set of whole numbers. These properties are shown in Table I.

TABLE I

ADDITION PROPERTIES IN THE SET W OF WHOLE NUMBERS

Property	Physical Representation
1. Closure EXAMPLE: $2 + 3 = 5$, and 5 is a whole number.	1. When two sets of blocks are combined, the result is a set of blocks.
2. Commutativity EXAMPLE: $2 + 3 = 3 + 2$	2. Combining a set of two blocks with a set of three other blocks produces the same set you get by combining the set of 3 blocks with the set of 2 blocks.
3. Associativity EXAMPLE: $(2 + 3) + 1$ $= 2 + (3 + 1)$	3. Combining a set of 2 blocks with a set of 3 other blocks and then adjoining a set of 1 more block produces the same set you get by combining the set of 3 blocks with the set of 1 block and then adjoining all of these to the set of 2 blocks.
4. Additive Identity (addition property of 0) EXAMPLE: $3 + 0 = 3$	4. Combining a set of 3 blocks with a set of no blocks produces a set of 3 blocks.

Thus, the process of combining two sets of blocks provides a physical model of the mathematical concept of adding two whole numbers. Con-

versely, the process of adding two whole numbers can be considered
a mathematical model of the physical process of combining two sets of
blocks. Some other examples of how the operation of addition relates to
the physical world are the combining of mileages between towns on a
trip or of the pennies from two piggy banks.

The number line offers a particularly clear and simple visual model
of the mathematical operation of addition. Figure 15 shows how you can

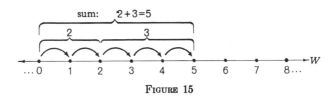

FIGURE 15

picture the sum 2 + 3 by starting at the origin and counting to the right
a number of unit intervals corresponding to the first addend, 2. From that
point you continue counting to the right a number of unit intervals corresponding to the second addend, 3. The coordinate of the point you thus
reach will be 5. This model illustrates that the sum of 2 and 3 is 5.

Still another number-line model of addition involves arrow representations of whole numbers. For example, to show the sum 2 + 3, the tail of

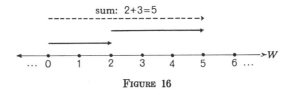

FIGURE 16

the arrow representing the first addend is directly above the origin and
the head of the arrow directly above the point with coordinate 2, so
that the arrow is in standard position. Then the arrow for the second
addend starts directly above the head of the first arrow and extends three
units farther to the right. (See Fig. 16.) Finally, the dashed arrow in
standard position represents the sum. It starts over the origin and

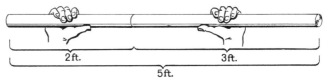

FIGURE 17

extends to a point directly above the head of the second arrow. Since this arrow is 5 units long, we have a pictorial representation of the fact that $2 + 3 = 5$. Instead of counting intervals and combining them as in the previous model, the arrow model combines two line segments having lengths that correspond to the two addends. The latter idea is much like putting together a stick 2 feet long and another stick 3 feet long to form a stick 5 feet long. (Fig. 17.)

Exercise Set 7

1. Represent each sum on a number line by drawing arrow diagrams.
   a. $7 + 3$
   b. $3 + 7$

2. Look at your diagrams for exercise 1.
   a. What is your first pair of addends?
   b. What is your second pair of addends?
   c. How are the two pairs of addends alike?
   d. How are the two pairs of addends different?
   e. What do you observe about the names you found for the two sums?

3. Represent each sum on a number line by drawing arrow diagrams.
   a. $(4 + 3) + 5$
   b. $4 + (3 + 5)$

4. Look at your diagrams for exercise 3.
   a. What was the result of adding 3 to 4?
   b. What was the result of adding 5 to this sum?
   c. What was the result of adding 5 to 3?
   d. What was the result of adding this sum to 4?
   e. What do you notice about the results in exercises 4b and 4d?

5. Represent the sum $7 + 0$ on a number line by drawing an arrow diagram.

6. Look at your arrow diagram for exercise 5. What do you notice about the renaming of $7 + 0$?

7. Mark the following statements true (T) or false (F).
   a. If you add two positive integers, the sum is always a positive integer.   _____
   b. The sum of any positive integer and zero is zero.   _____
   c. The order of adding two positive integers cannot be changed without changing the sum.   _____

d. The regrouping of addends does not change the sum of
three or more positive integers.   _____

The Sum of Two Negative Integers

Addition in the set of integers is defined in a way that is consistent
with the addition of whole numbers. The number line will serve as a
model in making this extension of the notion of addition. In this section
you will see how this is done when both addends are negative. In the
next section the extension will be completed by considering the case
where one addend is nonnegative and the other negative.

Just as we can represent the addition of two positive integers on the
number line by starting at the origin and counting unit intervals to the
right, so (by suitably extending the definition of addition) we can add
two negative integers by starting at the origin and counting unit intervals
to the left. Figure 18 illustrates that the sum of $^-3$ and $^-5$ is $^-8$. We start

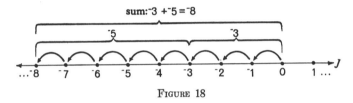

FIGURE 18

at the origin and count 3 units to the left and then continue from that
point to count 5 more units to the left. The point we arrive at is the
graph of $^-8$, which is located 8 units to the left of the origin.

By means of arrow representations Figure 19 pictures the fact that

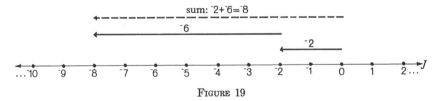

FIGURE 19

$^-2 + {}^-6 = {}^-8$. Notice that the procedure for picturing the sum of two
negative numbers by means of arrows is the same as that for two
positive integers, except that in this case the arrows all point to the left.

Since successive countings to the left of the origin will always bring
us to a point to the left of the origin, it is evident that the sum of two
negative integers is always a negative integer. Moreover, the number
of unit intervals we count for a given integer addend is equal to the
absolute value of that integer. Combining these two facts, let us see if

we can describe how to find the sum of any two negative integers in terms of their absolute values. Consider, for instance, the sum of ⁻7 and ⁻8. To picture this sum on the number line, we would first count 7 units to the left from the origin and then count 8 more units to the left. The total number of unit intervals counted in this process would be 7 + 8. In terms of absolute value this is |⁻7| + |⁻8| = |15|. Since the counting was done to the left, however, the point representing the sum will have the coordinate °(|⁻7| + |⁻8|), or ⁻15. Hence we can write

$$⁻7 + ⁻8 = °(|⁻7| + |⁻8|) = ⁻15.$$

In general, we can say:

The sum of two negative integers is equal to the opposite of the sum of their absolute values.

For example, to find the sum ⁻214 + ⁻373, we add |⁻214| and |⁻373| to obtain 587. Then the opposite of this, namely ⁻587, is the desired sum; that is,

$$⁻214 + ⁻373 = ⁻587.$$

Exercise Set 8

1. Use an integer to make each of the following a true sentence.

a. |⁻7| = □   **e.** |⁻7| + 8 = □

b. |⁻8| = □   **f.** |⁻5| + 2 = □

c. |5| = □   **g.** ⁻7 + ⁻8 = °(7 + □)

d. |2| = □   **h.** ⁻1 + ⁻6 = °(□ + 6)

2. Study the diagrams below; write a mathematical sentence for each.

a.

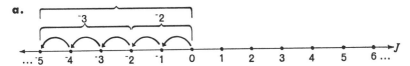

b.

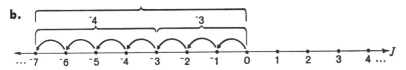

3. Rename the following sums with simple names of integers.

a. ⁻43 + ⁻59   **d.** ⁻36 + ⁻97   **g.** ⁻936 + ⁻425

b. ⁻17 + ⁻18   **e.** ⁻28 + ⁻11   **h.** ⁻12 + ⁻957

c. ⁻427 + ⁻582   **f.** ⁻69 + ⁻75

The Sum of a Whole Number and a Negative Integer

To define the sum of a whole number and a negative integer (that is, of a nonnegative and a negative integer), such as $3 + {}^-7$, we can use either the process of counting unit intervals along the number line as shown in Figure 20(a) or an arrow representation as shown in Figure 20(b).

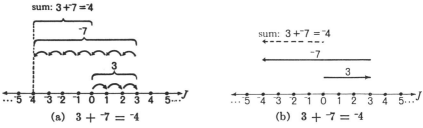

(a) $3 + {}^-7 = {}^-4$ (b) $3 + {}^-7 = {}^-4$

FIGURE 20

As you look at Figure 20(b), you should note certain general features of the process of graphical addition with arrows:

1. Arrows always point to the right for positive addends and to the left for negative addends.
2. The arrow for the first addend is in standard position. It starts just above the graph of zero.
3. The arrow for the second addend starts just above the *head* of the arrow for the first addend.
4. The dotted arrow representing the sum is in standard position. It starts above the graph of zero and ends just above the head of the arrow for the second addend. The sum is given by the coordinate directly below the head of the dotted arrow.
5. The arrows should be thought of as being actually on the line, of course. They are shown above it merely for easy visualization.

For either the counting or the arrow representation of Figures 20(a) and 20(b), the procedure is the same as that used earlier for the sum of two positive or two negative integers. In this case, however, the two countings, or the two arrows for the addends, go in opposite directions. As a result, the coordinate for the sum may be either positive, negative, or zero. In general, the sum of a positive and a negative integer is positive or negative according as the integer with the greater absolute value is positive or negative. If both addends have the same absolute value, the sum is 0.

Figure 21 shows arrow representations of the sums ⁻6 + 2 and 5 + ⁻3. You can see that in both cases the absolute value of the length of the

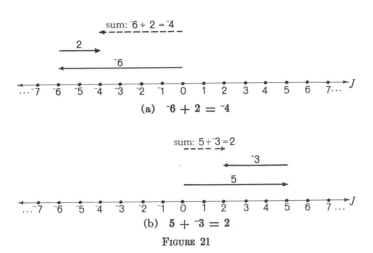

(a) ⁻6 + 2 = ⁻4

(b) 5 + ⁻3 = 2

FIGURE 21

arrow for the sum is simply the *difference* between the absolute values of the lengths of the arrows for the two addends. In the sum ⁻6 + 2, the arrows for the two addends have length |⁻6| and |2|, respectively. Then the arrow for the sum has length |⁻6| − |2| = 4. In the sum 5 + ⁻3, the arrows for the two addends have respective lengths |5| and |⁻3|. Hence the arrow for the sum has length |5| − |⁻3| = 2. In each case the arrow for the sum has the same *direction* as the arrow representing the addend having the greater absolute value.

Here are two more examples of similar sums:

EXAMPLE 1: ⁻15 + 8 = ____

Longer arrow has length   15.
Shorter arrow has length   8.
Sum arrow has length   7.
Longer arrow has negative direction.
Sum arrow has negative direction.

Therefore: ⁻15 + 8 = ⁻7.

EXAMPLE 2: 25 + ⁻17 = ____

Longer arrow has length   25.
Shorter arrow has length   17.
Sum arrow has length   8.
Longer arrow has positive direction.
Sum arrow has positive direction.

Therefore: 25 + ⁻17 = 8.

Since the length of an arrow is equal to the absolute value of the integer it represents, we can summarize the facts above so as to define the sum of a nonnegative and a negative integer in terms of absolute value, as follows:

1. The absolute value of the sum of a nonnegative integer and a negative integer is the whole-number difference in the absolute values of the addends (lesser subtracted from greater).
2. If the addend of greater absolute value is positive, then the sum is positive. If the addend of greater absolute value is negative, then the sum is negative. If the two addends, one positive and one negative, have the same absolute value, the sum is zero; for example, $5 + {}^-5 = 0$.

Here are two examples of determining sums by applying these two principles:

EXAMPLE 3: Simplify the sum: ${}^-28 + 3$.

(a) $|{}^-28 + 3| = |{}^-28| - |3|$
$= 28 - 3$
$= 25$.

(b) Since $|{}^-28| > |3|$, the sum is negative.

Therefore: ${}^-28 + 3 = {}^-25$.

EXAMPLE 4: Simplify the sum: $19 + {}^-11$.

(a) $|19 + {}^-11| = |19| - |{}^-11|$
$= 19 - 11$
$= 8$.

(b) Since $|19| > |{}^-11|$, the sum is positive.

Therefore: $19 + {}^-11 = 8$.

Applications of the addition of integers are to be found in many places. If you represent bank deposits in dollars by using positive integers and withdrawals by using negative integers, then identifying the balance in the account is a matter of adding all (positive) deposits to all (negative) withdrawals. You will see in the next section that the order in which the terms are added does not affect the sum. For example, if deposits of $150, $200, and $50 are made in an account and withdrawals are made of $70, $80, and $130, then the number of dollars in the balance would be

$$150 + 200 + 50 + {}^-70 + {}^-80 + {}^-130,$$

so that the balance would be $120.

As another example, the degrees of rise and fall from a given air temperature can be represented by positive and negative integers. If the temperature in a certain place is ${}^-5°$ and if it subsequently falls 6 degrees, then the resulting temperature is obtained by computing ${}^-5 + {}^-6 = {}^-11$. Thus the resulting temperature is ${}^-11°$.

Exercise Set 9

Study the diagrams below. Write a mathematical sentence for each.

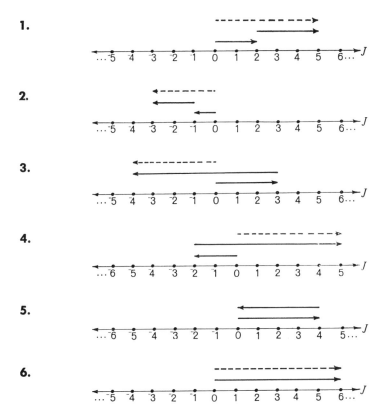

Properties of Addition in the Set of Integers

On page 19, we observed that the addition of whole numbers, and hence of nonnegative integers, has the properties of closure, commutativity, and associativity, and that 0 serves as the identity element for addition because $n + 0 = n$ for every nonnegative integer n. By using either the counting model or the arrow model that we used for defining addition in the set J of integers, we can display examples exhibiting the fact that these properties are true for *all* integers. The arrow diagram can become quite complicated, however, in the case of the associative property. Therefore, rather than drawing pictures to illustrate this property, we shall simply present numerical examples; you might yourself supply the diagrams for these, as an exercise.

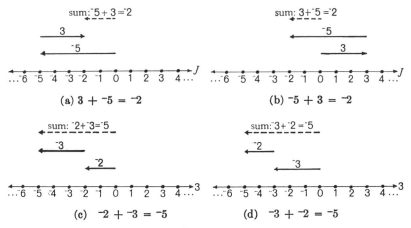

FIGURE 22

Since every integer has an arrow representation and since combining any two arrows in the way described earlier would determine another arrow representing an integer, it seems reasonable to conclude that addition is closed in *J*—that is, that the sum of any two integers is an integer.

Figures 22(a) and 22(b) show that the sum $3 + {}^-5$ is the same as the sum ${}^-5 + 3$, namely ${}^-2$; Figures 22(c) and 22(d) show that the sum ${}^-2 + {}^-3$ is the same as the sum ${}^-3 + {}^-2$, namely ${}^-5$. These figures, along with the fact that addition of nonnegative integers is commutative, illustrate that the addition of integers is commutative.

Now, consider the two sums

$$(3 + {}^-2) + 4 \quad \text{and} \quad 3 + ({}^-2 + 4).$$

Upon simplifying these you find that

$$(3 + {}^-2) + 4 = 1 + 4 \qquad 3 + ({}^-2 + 4) = 3 + 2$$
$$= 5, \qquad\qquad\qquad = 5.$$

Hence,

$$(3 + {}^-2) + 4 = 3 + ({}^-2 + 4).$$

For another example, we have

$$({}^-2 + 3) + {}^-4 = 1 + {}^-4 \qquad {}^-2 + (3 + {}^-4) = {}^-2 + {}^-1$$
$$= {}^-3 \qquad\qquad\qquad = {}^-3.$$

Therefore,

$$({}^-2 + 3) + {}^-4 = {}^-2 + (3 + {}^-4).$$

The two examples above illustrate that addition is associative for all integers.

The fact that the arrow representation of 0 is a point arrow, or arrow with length 0, suggests that combining this arrow with any other given arrow in the way described earlier will simply result in the given arrow. This, in turn, suggests that for every integer a, $a + 0 = a$.

To summarize, we have illustrated the following properties of addition, which hold for all integers.

1. *Closure Property:* If a, b, and c are integers, then $a + b$ is an integer.
2. *Commutativity Property:* If a, b, and c are integers, then $a + b = b + a$.
3. *Associativity Property:* If a, b, and c are integers, then $(a + b) + c = a + (b + c)$.
4. *Additive Identity:* If a, b, and c are integers, then $a + 0 = a$.

The term "additive identity," when applied to the property $a + 0 = a$, stems from the fact that adding 0 to a given integer produces identically the given integer. Accordingly, 0 is called the *additive-identity element* in J. The property that $a + 0 = 0 + a = a$ is sometimes called the *addition property* of 0.

As you will have observed, the four properties listed above are exactly the same as the properties of addition in the set of whole numbers. In the set of integers, however, addition has one particularly useful property that the set of whole numbers does not have.

Figures 23(a) and 23(b) illustrate this property of addition in the

(a) $a < 0$ (b) $a > 0$

FIGURE 23

set of integers. You can say that for every given integer there is one, and only one, integer whose sum with the given integer is 0. Of course, as Figures 23(a) and 23(b) suggest, these integers are opposites. This property can be formally stated as follows:

5. *Additive Inverse:* If a is an integer, then there exists a unique integer $°a$ such that $a + °a = 0$.

This expresses the *additive-inverse property* for integers. Each of the integers a and $°a$ is called the *additive inverse* of the other. This, incidentally, provides us with another phrase for the "opposite" of a number —namely, the phrase "additive inverse" of the number. Thus "the opposite of $^-5$" and "the additive inverse of $^-5$" both name the same number, 5.

The additive-inverse property and the associative law can be used to simplify sums of certain integers. For example, consider the sum $10 + {}^-18$. Since you know that $^-18 = {}^-10 + {}^-8$, you can write

$$
\begin{aligned}
10 + {}^-18 &= 10 + ({}^-10 + {}^-8) \\
&= (10 + {}^-10) + {}^-8 \quad \text{(by the associative property)} \\
&= 0 + {}^-8 \quad\quad\quad\;\; \text{(by the additive-inverse law)} \\
&= {}^-8.
\end{aligned}
$$

Here are two more examples of the use of the additive-inverse property:

$$
\begin{aligned}
{}^-7 + 16 &= {}^-7 + (7 + 9) \\
&= ({}^-7 + 7) + 9 \\
&= 0 + 9 \\
&= 9.
\end{aligned}
\qquad\qquad
\begin{aligned}
{}^-18 + 5 &= ({}^-13 + {}^-5) + 5 \\
&= {}^-13 + ({}^-5 + 5) \\
&= {}^-13 + 0 \\
&= {}^-13.
\end{aligned}
$$

Exercise Set 10

1. Use a diagram on a number line to help you find a value for n in each of the following:

   a. $^-4 + {}^-11 = n$ **d.** $3 + {}^-5 = n$
   b. $7 + 15 = n$ **e.** $^-7 + 0 = n$
   c. $^-9 + 2 = n$ **f.** $^-8 + 8 = n$

2. Rename each integer in Column A by matching it with another integer in Column B.

	Column A	Column B
a.	$7 + 3$	$^-11$
b.	$^-2 + {}^-9$	$^-3$
c.	$5 + {}^-3$	0
d.	$^-4 + 1$	10
e.	$^-6 + 6$	5
f.	$5 + 0$	2

3. Assume that you have a balance of $50.00 in your bank account. Let the positive integers represent deposits and the negative integers represent withdrawals. Complete the equivalent mathematical question, "$50 + \cdots = ?$" and find your balance in each case if you—

   a. Deposited $6.00.

   b. Deposited $7.00 and withdrew $10.00.

   c. Deposited $15.00 and withdrew $8.00.

   d. Withdrew $9.00 and then withdrew $6.00.

   e. Withdrew $28.00 and then deposited $18.00.

   f. Deposited $11.00 and then withdrew $11.00.

4. Complete the grid for basic addition facts in the set of integers. A few sums, for example, $2 + 5 = 7$ and $^-3 + {}^-4 = {}^-7$, have already been filled in.

Second addend

First addend

Second addend	-9	-8	-7	-6	-5	-4	-3	-2	-1	0	1	2	3	4	5	6	7	8	9
9																			
8																			
7																			
6																			
5												7							
4			-3																
3								1											
2															7				
1																			
0	-9	-8	-7	-6	-5	-4	-3	-2	-1	0	1	2	3	4	5	6	7	8	9
-1																			
-2													1						
-3																			
-4							-7												
-5													-2						
-6																			
-7																			
-8																			
-9																			

5. Use the chart of basic addition facts of exercise 4 to help you complete the following.

a. The sum of zero and any integer k is _____.

b. The sum of any pair of opposites is _____.

c. When two integers are added, the result is always an _____.

d. The order in which two integers are added does not change the _____.

e. The sum of ⁻2 and 3 is ____.

f. The sum of ⁻1 and 4 is ____.

g. The sum of 3 and 4 is ____.

h. The sum of ⁻2 and 7 is ____.

i. The sum of (⁻2 + 3) and 4 is ____.

j. The sum of ⁻2 and (3 + 4) is ____.

MULTIPLICATION OF INTEGERS

The Product of Two Whole Numbers

As indicated above, pupils first learn the operation of adding whole numbers by combining sets of familiar objects, such as blocks or apples. The learning experience is extended to the operation of multiplying whole numbers through the consideration of sums of equal addends. This leads to the discovery of the basic properties of multiplication in the set of whole numbers, discussed in Booklet No. 2: *The Whole Numbers.*

1. *Closure Property:* The product of any two whole numbers is a specified whole number.
2. *Commutative Property:* If a and b are any whole numbers, then $a \times b = b \times a$.
3. *Associative Property:* If a, b, and c are any whole numbers, then $(a \times b) \times c = a \times (b \times c)$.
4. *Identity Element:* One is the identity element for multiplication; for any whole number n, $n \times 1 = 1 \times n = n$.
5. *Distributive Property of Multiplication over Addition:* If a, b, and c are any whole numbers, then $a \times (b + c) = (a \times b) + (a \times c)$.
6. *Distributive Property of Multiplication over Subtraction:* If a, b, and c are any whole numbers and $b - c$ is a whole number, then $a \times (b - c) = (a \times b) - (a \times c)$.
7. *Multiplicative Property of Zero:* If a and b are any whole numbers, then $ab = 0$ if and only if at least one of a and b is 0.

We shall now see how the operation of multiplication can be extended to the entire set of integers in a consistent, reasonable, and useful way.

The Product of a Whole Number and a Negative Integer

If in conducting a business there is a daily expenditure of \$20 for some particular purpose, then on the books of the company this might be represented by using the integer ⁻20. If, however, expenditures were to be entered only on a weekly basis, then for five business days the total of such expenditures would be represented by the sum

$$^-20 + {}^-20 + {}^-20 + {}^-20 + {}^-20.$$

This sum, of course, is ⁻100, so that the book entry in dollars would simply be ⁻\$100.

It would certainly seem advantageous if instead of working with the sum

$$^-20 + {}^-20 + {}^-20 + {}^-20 + {}^-20$$

we could, as we do when working with profits only, use a product. That is, just as when one earns \$20 per day, the earnings for a five-day period amount to 5 × 20, or \$100, so it would be sensible to say that expending \$20 per day for five days would result in a net expenditure of 5 × 20, or \$100. In terms of negative integers, though, this would imply that

$$5 \times {}^-20 = {}^-100.$$

Such is indeed taken to be the case. More generally, this line of reasoning strongly suggests that the product of a positive and a negative integer ought to be a negative integer.

Let us turn to the number line for further guidance in this matter. Figure 24 shows the arrow diagram depicting the sum of five whole numbers, namely, $2 + 2 + 2 + 2 + 2 = 10$.

Since we know that, for whole numbers, $2 + 2 + 2 + 2 + 2 = 5 \times 2$, and since our nonnegative integers are the whole numbers renamed, the arrow depiction in Figure 24 can be construed, by definition, to apply to the nonnegative integers as well. Thus, if we wish to preserve the notion that a product such as $5 \times n$, where n is any integer whatever, is the same as the sum of five addends each equal to n, then we would want to view $5 \times {}^-2$ as equal to $^-2 + {}^-2 + {}^-2 + {}^-2 + {}^-2$. An arrow de-

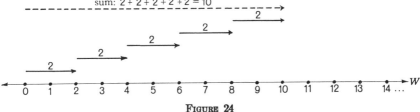

FIGURE 24

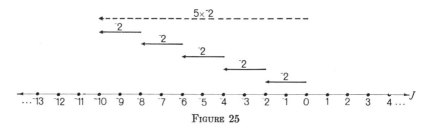

FIGURE 25

piction of this notion is shown in Figure 25. This picture clearly parallels the commonsense situation, discussed earlier, regarding the product 5 × ⁻20 as ⁻100 on the books of a company.

In general we can define the product of any positive integer a and any negative integer b as the sum of a addends, each equal to b (Fig. 26).

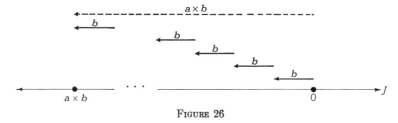

FIGURE 26

For $a = 1$, there is just one "addend," of course, and the "sum" is b; that is, $1 \times b = b$.

We can extend this definition to all whole numbers a by considering that for $a = 0$ we have *no* addends, so that the product of 0 and b is 0; that is, $0 \times b = 0$.

The Product of a Negative Integer and a Whole Number

For the product ba of a negative integer b and a whole number a, the intuitive situation is perhaps a bit less simple. Following the agreement given above, in which ab is defined to be the sum of a addends, each equal to b, we might want to say that ba is the sum of b addends, each equal to a. But what would we mean by a *negative* number b of equal addends? Let us apply the guidelines that operations in the system of integers should be consistent, reasonable, and useful.

CONSISTENT

We have seen (p. 32) that multiplication is commutative in the system of whole numbers. If this property is to hold in the system of integers, then there is no problem in determining the value of the product ba of a negative integer b and a whole number a. Namely, under this agreement we have $ba = ab$, to which we have assigned the value of the sum of a addends, each equal to b. For example, with $b =$ ⁻2 and $a = 5$, we have ⁻2 × 5 = 5 × ⁻2 = ⁻10.

That the commutative law should hold is not an overriding virtue, however, and we would not use this consideration in defining the product of a negative integer and a whole number if the value obtained were not also reasonable and useful. (You may know, for example, that multiplication is defined in the system of matrices in a way that is reasonable and useful, and this definition is retained *in spite of the fact* that under it multiplication is not, in general, commutative.)

REASONABLE

The negative integers are not counting numbers. You can nevertheless use them in "counting backward" by ones from 4 to ⁻4:

4, 3, 2, 1, 0, ⁻1, ⁻2, ⁻3, ⁻4.

You can also count backward by fives:

20, 15, 10, 5, 0, ⁻5, ⁻10, ⁻15, ⁻20.

These processes can be represented on the number line; the second is illustrated in Figure 27. Notice that you have:

$$20 = 4 \times 5.$$
$$15 = 3 \times 5.$$
$$10 = 2 \times 5.$$
$$5 = 1 \times 5.$$
$$0 = 0 \times 5.$$
$$^{-}5 = ? \times 5.$$
$$^{-}10 = ? \times 5.$$
$$^{-}15 = ? \times 5.$$
$$^{-}20 = ? \times 5.$$

Notice also that the terms on the left go backward from 20 to ⁻20 by fives, and that the first factors on the right start us counting backward by ones from 4. What could be more reasonable than to continue counting backward by ones and to write the following?

$$^{-}5 = {}^{-}1 \times 5.$$
$$^{-}10 = {}^{-}2 \times 5.$$
$$^{-}15 = {}^{-}3 \times 5.$$
$$^{-}20 = {}^{-}4 \times 5.$$

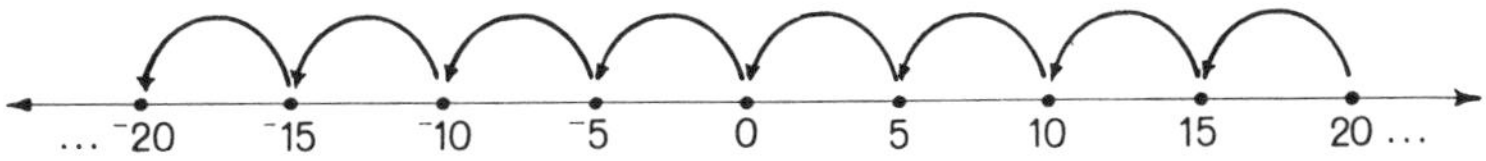

FIGURE 27

Thus the reasonable continuation of number patterns tempts us to define the product of a negative integer and a whole number in such a way that, for example,

$$^-2 \times 5 = ^-10.$$

USEFUL

John has deposited $5 in his savings account each week for 4 weeks. He now has $38 in the account. At this rate of depositing, how much will he have in the account 3 weeks hence? 8 weeks hence? How much did he have in the account 2 weeks ago?

Counting deposits and future times positively, and past times negatively, you would answer the first two of these questions thus:

$$38 + (3 \times 5) = 38 + 15 = 53;$$
$$38 + (8 \times 5) = 38 + 40 = 78.$$

Therefore in 3 weeks he will have $53 in his account, and in 8 weeks he will have $78 deposited there. You know that the answer to the third question must be $28. Accordingly, you would want

$$38 \text{ plus} \quad (^-2 \times 5) \quad \text{to equal } 28.$$

But since

$$38 \text{ plus} \quad (^-10) \quad \text{equals } 28,$$

again you would want $^-2$ times 5 to equal $^-10$.

Thus the definition toward which we are working is useful in solving practical problems. This definition, which applies both to the product of a whole number and a negative integer and to the product of a negative integer and a whole number, is the following:

The product $a \times b$ of two integers a and b, one of which is negative and the other a whole number, is given by

$$a \times b = {}^-(\, |a| \times |b| \,).$$

Exercise Set 11

1. Write one addition and one multiplication sentence represented by each of the arrow diagrams below.

a.

b.

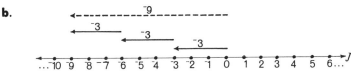

c.

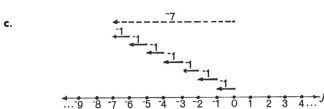

2. Use an arrow diagram on a number line to show each of the following products as a sum.

a. 5 × ⁻7   c. 2 × ⁻6
b. 4 × ⁻3   d. 6 × ⁻1

3. Complete:

a. 5 × ⁻3 = □ × 5.   c. 4 × ⁻6 = □ × 4.
b. ⁻7 × 2 = □ × ⁻7.   d. ⁻8 × 9 = □ × ⁻8.

4. Fill in the chart below:

Factor	Factor	Product
9	2	
9	1	
9	0	
9	⁻1	
9	⁻2	
2	9	
1	9	
0	9	
⁻1	9	
⁻2	9	

5. Simplify the following product expressions.

    a. $^-25 \times 7$ **d.** $1 \times\ ^-74$

    b. $6 \times\ ^-49$ **e.** $^-58 \times 62$

    c. $^-38 \times 1$ **f.** $70 \times\ ^-4$

The Product of Two Negative Integers

To decide what we shall mean by the product of two negative integers, let us once more call on our criteria of consistency, reasonableness, and usefulness.

CONSISTENT

We have seen that the distributive law holds for whole numbers (p. 32). When this law is applied twice, it yields

$$(a + b) \times (c + d) = [a \times (c + d)] + [b \times (c + d)]$$
$$= (a \times c) + (a \times d) + (b \times c) + (b \times d).$$

If this law is to hold also for the system of integers, then we must have, for example,

$$(8 +\ ^-5) \times (6 +\ ^-2) = (8 \times 6) + (8 \times\ ^-2) + (^-5 \times 6) + (^-5 \times\ ^-2)$$
$$= 48 +\ ^-16 +\ ^-30 + (^-5 \times\ ^-2)$$
$$= 2 + (^-5 \times\ ^-2).$$

But

$$(8 +\ ^-5) \times (6 +\ ^-2) = 3 \times 4$$
$$= 12.$$

Thus if the distributive law is to hold in the system of integers, then we must have

$$2 + (^-5 \times\ ^-2) = 12,$$
$$^-5 \times\ ^-2 = {}_{\iota}0.$$

REASONABLE

We have agreed to define multiplication in such a way that, for example,

$$^\circ5 \times 2 =\ ^\circ(5 \times 2).$$

It would seem reasonable, then, to extend the definition of multiplication in such a way that

(*) $$^\circ5 \times\ ^\circ2 =\ ^\circ(5 \times\ ^\circ2).$$

But we have agreed also to define multiplication in such a way that

(**) $$5 \times\ ^\circ2 =\ ^\circ(5 \times 2).$$

Substituting from (**) into (*), we see that we would like to have

$$°5 \times °2 = °(5 \times °2)$$
$$= °[°(5 \times 2)].$$

But

$$°[°(5 \times 2)] = 5 \times 2,$$

so we would like to have

$$°5 \times °2 = 5 \times 2,$$

or

$$^-5 \times {}^-2 = 10.$$

Number patterns also suggest the reasonableness of the same convention:

$$4 \times {}^-5 = {}^-20,$$
$$3 \times {}^-5 = {}^-15,$$
$$2 \times {}^-5 = {}^-10,$$
$$1 \times {}^-5 = {}^-5,$$
$$0 \times {}^-5 = 0.$$

At the left, we are counting downward by ones; at the right, upward by fives. Let us continue the same pattern:

$$^-1 \times {}^-5 = 5,$$
$$^-2 \times {}^-5 = 10,$$
$$^-3 \times {}^-5 = 15,$$
$$^-4 \times {}^-5 = 20,$$

and so on.

Tom has withdrawn $5 from his savings account each week for 4 weeks. He now has $38 in the account. At this rate of withdrawing, how much will he have in the account 3 weeks hence? 8 weeks hence? How much did he have in the account 2 weeks ago?

Counting deposits and future times positively, and withdrawals and past times negatively, you would answer the first two questions thus:

$$38 + (3 \times {}^-5) = 38 + {}^-15 = 23;$$
$$38 + (8 \times {}^-5) = 38 + {}^-40 = {}^-2.$$

Therefore in 3 weeks he will have $23 in his account, and in 8 weeks he will have ${}^-$2 (a negative amount, so that his account is overdrawn) deposited there. You know that the answer to the third question must be $48. Accordingly, you want

$$38 \text{ plus} \quad ({}^-2 \times {}^-5) \quad \text{to equal } 48.$$

But since

38 plus   10   equals 48,

again you would want ⁻2 times ⁻5 to equal 10.

It thus appears as consistent, reasonable, and useful that we should make the following definition:

The product a × b of two negative integers a and b is given by

$$a \times b = |a| \times |b|.$$

Exercise Set 12

1. Follow the form below to simplify each product expression.

⁻5 × ⁻6 = (⁻1 × 5) × (⁻1 × 6),
⁻5 × ⁻6 = (⁻1 × ⁻1) × (5 × 6),
⁻5 × ⁻6 = 1 × (5 × 6),
⁻5 × ⁻6 = 1 × 30,
⁻5 × ⁻6 = 30.

a. ⁻2 × ⁻4   **c.** ⁻78 × ⁻31

b. ⁻5 × ⁻9   **d.** ⁻650 × ⁻478

2. Complete the chart.

Factor	Factor	Product
2	⁻7	
1	⁻7	
0	⁻7	
⁻1	⁻7	
⁻2	⁻7	

3. In each sentence below, replace *n* with an integer that will make the sentence true.

a. ⁻54 × ⁻96 = *n*.

b. ⁻17 × ⁻23 = *n*.

c. 78 × ⁻65 = *n*.

d. 0 × ⁻32 = *n*.

e. $^-59 \times 38 = n.$
f. $^-714 \times {}^-293 = n.$

Properties of Multiplication in the Set of Integers

On page 32 we listed the closure, commutative, and associative properties of multiplication in the set W of whole numbers, noted that 1 is the multiplicative identity element in this set, and pointed out that multiplication distributes over addition and subtraction in this set.

We then defined multiplication in the set of integers in a way that seemed reasonable and useful. We also gave some indication that if the properties listed above are to hold in the set of integers, then products *must* be defined in precisely this way in the extended set.

We might, in fact, have *postulated* that the properties of addition and multiplication listed on pages 19 and 32 for the whole numbers hold also for the set extended to include additive inverses, and *on this basis* have *proved* that addition and multiplication must then be performed in the way we have described, and have *shown* that all the properties indeed are valid under the definitions of addition and multiplication as thus extended. This sort of concession to pure mathematical aesthetics is pleasing and orderly, of course; but without reasonable applications the development would be flat and sterile, indeed.

We shall not here complete the verification of the properties of multiplication in the set of integers, but shall content ourselves with listing them:

1. *Closure Property*: The product of any two integers is a specified integer.
2. *Commutative Property*: If a and b are any integers, then $a \times b = b \times a$.
3. *Associative Property*: If a, b, and c are any integers, then $(a \times b) \times c = a \times (b \times c)$.
4. *Identity Element*: One is the identity element for multiplication; for any integer n, $n \times 1 = 1 \times n = n$.
5. *Distributive Property of Multiplication over Addition*: If a, b, and c are any integers, then $a \times (b + c) = (a \times b) + (a \times c)$.
6. *Multiplicative Property of Zero*: If a and b are any integers, then $ab = 0$ if and only if at least one of a and b is 0.

Notice that we have not included a distributive property for multiplication over subtraction, since, as will be seen in the next section, in the set of integers the difference $b - c$ can be viewed as the sum $b + {}^-c$.

Exercise Set 13

1. Complete the chart of basic facts of multiplication in the set of integers below.

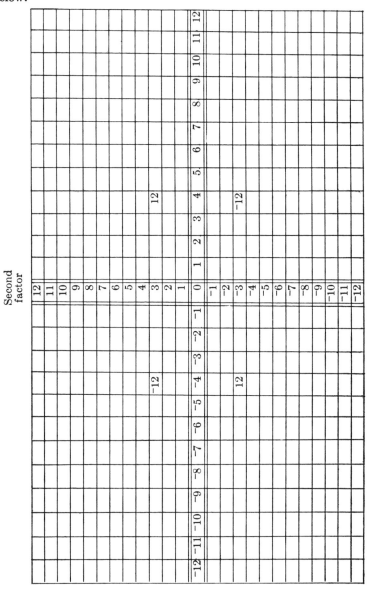

2. Use the chart completed in exercise 1 to help you in answering the following.

    a. Can the product of two integers always be expressed as an integer?

    b. $9 \times 9 = \square$.   **g.** $^-7 \times 12 = 12 \times \square$.

    c. $^-9 \times 9 = \square$.   **h.** $^-1 \times 7 = \square$.

    d. $^-9 \times ^-9 = \square$.   **i.** $8 \times ^-1 = \square$.

    e. $9 \times ^-9 = \square$.   **j.** $9 \times 1 = \square$.

    f. $5 \times ^-4 = \square \times 5$.   **k.** $1 \times 6 = \square$.

3. Complete the following, using your chart from exercise 1.

    a. $^-2 \times 3 = \square$.   **d.** $3 \times 4 = \square$.

    b. $^-6 \times 4 = \square$.   **e.** $^-2 \times 12 = \square$.

    c. $(^-2 \times 3) \times 4 = \square$.   **f.** $(^-2 \times 3) \times 4 = ^-2 \times (\square \times \triangle)$.

4. In the table below, identify the property of multiplication in the set of integers used to justify the given statement.

Statement	Property
a. $^-4 \times ^-5 = ^-5 \times ^-4$.	_____
b. $7 \times (^-6 \times 8) = (7 \times ^-6) \times 8$.	_____
c. The product of any two integers is always an integer.	_____
d. The product of any integer and 0 is always 0.	_____
e. The product of any integer and 1 is always the integer.	_____

5. A restaurant has hired an inexperienced waitress, who is very hard on the supply of cups. In fact, she has been breaking them at the rate of 5 cups a day.

    a. If she has been working 3 days, how does the number of cups before her arrival compare with the present supply? Write a product expression for this situation. Hint: Let past time be represented by the negative integers and future time be represented by the positive integers; and let numbers of broken cups be denoted by negative integers and numbers of unbroken cups by positive integers.

    b. If she continues in the same way, how will the supply 2 days from now compare with the present supply? Write a product expression for this situation.

6. Bill set out on a Scout hike with his canteen full, but the canteen leaked, and he lost water at the rate of 1 cup per mile.

   a. How will his water supply, after he has hiked another 2 miles, compare with his present supply? Write a product expression to describe this situation.

   b. How does the amount he had 2 miles back compare with his present supply? Write a product expression to describe this situation.

SUBTRACTION AND DIVISION OF INTEGERS

Subtraction

The familiar concept of subtraction as a process of "taking away" becomes meaningless if you wish to discuss the result, say, of subtracting 3 from 1. One cannot "take away" from something more than is there. It should be observed, however, that some people do not let this philosophical nicety bother them when they "take away," say, $50 from a bank account containing $40. In fact, since the set of integers is available, and since there is an alternative (and in many ways preferable) viewpoint one can take of subtraction, the logical problem involved in overdrawing a bank account can be resolved to the satisfaction of most persons who are not in the banking business.

Instead of viewing the difference $1 - 3$ as a matter of "taking away" 3 from 1, it is preferable to consider the expression $1 - 3$ as a name of the number n that must be added to 3 to obtain 1 as the sum, that is, the number n such that $3 + n = 1$. While no such number exists in the set of whole numbers, the integer $^-2$ does behave in this fashion; that is, you have $3 + {}^-2 = 1$. When subtraction is considered in this way, a *difference* is simply a *missing addend* in a sum. You may recall that this is the way in which we defined differences of whole numbers in Booklet No. 2: *The Whole Numbers.* We simply extend this definition now to the set J of integers.

If a, b, and n are integers, then $a - b = n$ if and only if $b + n = a$.

For example,

$$8 - 3 = 5, \quad \text{because} \quad 3 + 5 = 8;$$
$$7 - 12 = {}^-5, \quad \text{because} \quad 12 + ({}^-5) = 7;$$
$$7 - {}^-6 = 13, \quad \text{because} \quad {}^-6 + 13 = 7;$$

and

$$^-8 - {}^-9 = 1, \quad \text{because} \quad {}^-9 + 1 = {}^-8.$$

In mentally simplifying a difference such as $8 - ^-2$, you can ask yourself, "What number must I add to $^-2$ to obtain 8?" The answer, of course, is 10.

So closely bound to addition is the operation of subtraction that, with the existence of an additive inverse or opposite for every member in a set, a difference can be seen to be equivalent to a sum. Consider, for example, the difference $6 - 2$. An arrow picture of this difference is shown in Figure 28, where the broken arrow represents the difference $6 - 2$, or 4.

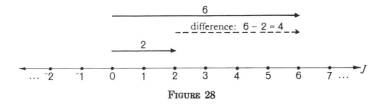

FIGURE 28

If you compare this figure with Figure 29, which shows the arrow picture of the sum $6 + ^-2$, you can see that the results are the same. Indeed,

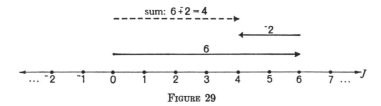

FIGURE 29

the arrow picture suggests that, in general, $a - b$ would have to be the same as $a + {}^\circ b$, because the only difference in any two such pictures must be the location and direction of the arrows for b and ${}^\circ b$. Given any

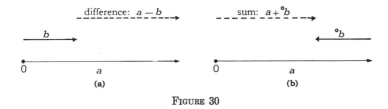

FIGURE 30

arrow for an integer a, and an arrow with the same initial point for the integer b, the arrow for the difference $a - b$ will run from the head of the arrow for b to the head of the arrow for a, as shown in Figure 30(a).

Also, the arrow for the sum of a and $°b$ must run from the tail of the arrow for a to the head of the arrow $°b$, when the tail of the arrow for $°b$ is at the head of the arrow for a, as seen in Figure 30(b). However, since the arrow for $°b$ has the same length as that for b but is opposite in direction and since these arrows are located with initial points at opposite ends of the arrow for a, it follows that the arrows for $a - b$ and $a + °b$ must be the same in regards to length and direction. Figures 31(a) and 31(b) show another case, in which b represents a negative integer.

FIGURE 31

Similar drawings, for cases in which a is negative and b is positive and negative in turn, should suggest strongly the truth of the following statement:

If a and b are integers, then $a - b = a + °b$.

Thus,

$$3 - 5 = 3 + {}^-5 = {}^-2,$$
$$6 - {}^-4 = 6 + 4 = 10,$$
$${}^-3 - {}^-7 = {}^-3 + 7 = 4,$$

and

$${}^-8 - 6 = {}^-8 + {}^-6 = {}^-14.$$

When subtraction is interpreted in terms of the addition of an opposite, the closure property for addition in J can be seen to apply also to subtraction. That is, we have the *closure property for subtraction of integers:*

If a and b are integers, then $a - b$ is an integer.

Addition and subtraction are called *inverse operations* because each can be looked upon as "undoing" the other. For example, the *addition of 3* to 5 yields 8, and the *subtraction of 3* from 8 yields 5. Figure 32 pictures this idea schematically.

Statements similar to those on page 23 and page 26 regarding the absolute value of addends and sums need not be given for subtraction, because subtraction in the set of integers is a matter of adding an opposite and the addition statements cover all such cases.

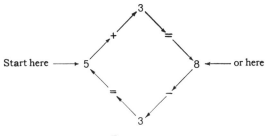

FIGURE 32

You will recall (p. 16) that $a > b$ if and only if the graph of a lies to the right of the graph of b. We have now seen that if arrows for a and b have the same initial point (Fig. 30)—say, if these arrows are in standard position—then an arrow for $a - b$ runs from the head of the arrow for b to the head of the arrow for a. It follows that $a > b$ *if and only if $a - b$ is positive*, that is, *if and only if $a = b + n$, where n is positive*.

Exercise Set 14

1. For each arrow diagram shown below, write the related subtraction sentence.

a.

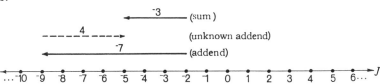

b.

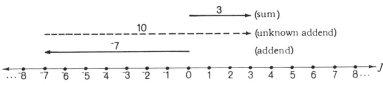

c.

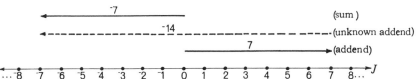

d.

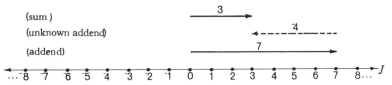

(sum)

(unknown addend)

(addend)

2. Complete:

  a. $17 - {}^-14 = 17 + \square$.

  b. ${}^-23 - {}^-6 = {}^-23 + \square$.

  c. ${}^-95 - 38 = {}^-95 + \square$.

  d. $89 - 108 = 89 + \square$.

3. Column A represents temperatures at 4:00 A.M. Column B represents temperatures at 6:00 P.M. Use an integer to indicate the amount and direction of change.

	A	B	Total Change
Monday	-5°	13°	_____
Tuesday	6°	-4°	_____
Wednesday	-2°	0°	_____
Thursday	4°	-7°	_____
Friday	-8°	10°	_____

Division

Just as subtraction is defined in terms of addition, so also division is defined in terms of multiplication. For example, we say that $8 \div 2 = n$, if and only if $2 \times n = 8$. A quotient thus can be viewed as a missing factor in the same way as a difference is thought of as a missing addend. Of course, if $8 \div 2 = n$, then n must name 4 because $2 \times 4 = 8$. In general, we say this:

  If a and b are integers, and $b \neq 0$, then $a \div b = n$ if and only if $b \times n = a$.

Additional examples of applying the definition to positive integers are

$$12 \div 6 = 2 \quad \text{because} \quad 2 \times 6 = 12,$$
$$25 \div 5 = 5 \quad \text{because} \quad 5 \times 5 = 25,$$
$$8 \div 1 = 8 \quad \text{because} \quad 1 \times 8 = 8.$$

It is at once apparent that in the set of integers not all pairs of integers have quotients, just as not all pairs of whole numbers have quotients, even when the divisor is different from 0. For example, the expression $8 \div 3$ does not name an integer because there is no integer n such that $3 \times n = 8$. Thus the set of integers is not closed with respect to division. This fact leads to a development of a new system of numbers called the system of rational numbers. (See Booklet No. 10: *The System of Rational Numbers.*)

Were it not for the need to discuss opposites in the set of integers, there would be nothing to say about division in this set, other than that it parallels division in the set of whole numbers. Indeed, there is very little to say anyway. The chief problem in simplifying quotients of integers lies in determining whether a given quotient is a positive or a negative number, and we can dispense with this problem by referring to what we already know about products of integers.

Consider the quotient ⁻12 ÷ 3. By our definition of quotient,

$$^-12 \div 3 = n \quad \text{if and only if} \quad 3 \times n = {}^-12.$$

Knowing that the product of two integers is negative only under the condition that one but not both of the integers is negative and knowing that 3 is not negative, we conclude that n must name a negative integer if $3 \times n$ is to equal ⁻12. Moreover, we know which negative integer is named by n because there is only one such integer for which $3 \times n = {}^-12$, namely ⁻4.

In a similar way, we can determine that

$$^-12 \div {}^-3 = 4 \quad \text{because} \quad {}^-3 \times 4 = {}^-12,$$
$$^-8 \div {}^-2 = 4 \quad \text{because} \quad {}^-2 \times 4 = {}^-8,$$
$$^-27 \div 9 = {}^-3 \quad \text{because} \quad 9 \times {}^-3 = {}^-27.$$

A general statement comparable to (and a consequence of) that on pages 36 and 40 regarding products of integers can be made as follows:

The quotient of two integers is—

1. Positive if both integers are positive or if both integers are negative.
2. Negative if one of the integers is positive and one is negative.

In discussing subtraction we did not formally state any rules involving absolute values of integers for use in simplifying differences. The situation surrounding division is a bit different. Once you can state that a difference $a - b$ is equal to the sum $a + {}^\circ b$, the absolute-value properties of addition are directly applicable to subtraction. The reason such a statement as

$$a - b = a + {}^\circ b$$

is true is that every integer b has an additive inverse $^\circ b$. A comparable situation does not exist for multiplication and division because division is not always possible in J. It is not difficult, however, to restate the absolute-value rules on pages 36 and 40 in terms of division, so let us do so.

To begin with, we know that for any integers a and b, with $b \neq 0$,

$$a \div b = n \quad \text{if and only if} \quad b \times n = a.$$

Now, according to the property stated on pages 36 and 40, we can say that if b and n are integers, then

$$|b| \times |n| = |b \times n|,$$

or, because by assumption $b \times n = a$, we can say

$$|b| \times |n| = |a|.$$

But by the definition of division ($|n|$ is a missing factor) this implies the following:

If a, b, and n are integers, with $b \neq 0$, and $a \div n$, then $|n| = |a| \div |b|$.

This fact, together with the statement on page 49 regarding positive and negative quotients, provides us with all we need to determine exactly which, if any, integer corresponds to a given quotient of integers:

Suppose a, b, and n are integers, with $b \neq 0$, and $a \div b = n$. If a and b are both positive or both negative, then $n = |a| \div |b|$; but if one is positive and the other negative, then $n = {}^-(|a| \div |b|)$. If $a = 0$, then $n = 0$.

For example, to identify the integer corresponding to $^-153 \div 9$, we first divide $|^-153|$, or 153, by $|9|$, or 9, to obtain the positive integer 17. Then, since $^-153$ is negative and 9 is positive, the quotient we seek is the *negative* number $^-17$.

Just as addition and subtraction are inverse operations, so are multiplication and division. For example, if 4 is multiplied by 5, the result is 20; and if 20 is divided by 5, the result is 4. Figure 33 depicts these operations schematically.

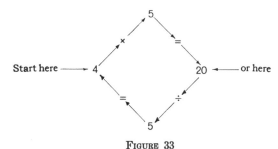

FIGURE 33

Just as in the set of whole numbers, quotients involving 0 require special consideration in the set of integers. No difficulty is presented by quotients of the form $0 \div a$, where a is any integer except 0. Thus, for every nonzero integer a,

$$0 \div a = 0 \quad \text{because} \quad a \times 0 = 0.$$

For example, $0 \div 3 = 0$ because $3 \times 0 = 0$, and $0 \div {}^-7 = 0$ because ${}^-7 \times 0 = 0$. However, 0 as a divisor is not permitted. To identify a quotient when ${}^-7$ is divided by 0, you encounter the problem of identifying a number whose product with 0 is ${}^-7$. That is,

$${}^-7 \div 0 = n \quad \text{if and only if} \quad 0 \times n = {}^-7.$$

For every integer n, however, $0 \times n = 0$; and so there is no integer n for which $0 \times n = {}^-7$. This means that ${}^-7 \div 0$ does not name an integer. To identify the quotient $0 \div 0 = n$, you encounter the uncomfortable fact that n can name *every* integer, because $0 \times n = 0$ for every integer n. Accordingly, just as in W, we simply exclude division by 0 as a legitimate operation in J, and assert:

In J, division by 0 is undefined.

Exercise Set 15

1. Rewrite the following division sentences as multiplication sentences:

   a. ${}^-24 \div 6 = n$ e. ${}^-312 \div 1 = n$

   b. $36 \div {}^-6 = n$ f. ${}^-96 \div 8 = n$

   c. ${}^-42 \div {}^-7 = n$ g. $144 \div {}^-12 = n$

   d. $512 \div 8 = n$ h. ${}^-840 \div {}^-24 = n$

2. Compute to find the integer represented by n in each of the following:

   a. ${}^-18 \div 3 = n$ d. ${}^-682 \div {}^-31 = n$

   b. $768 \div 16 = n$ e. ${}^-864 \div 12 = n$

   c. ${}^-760 \div {}^-19 = n$ f. $224 \div {}^-16 = n$

SOME NOTES ON NOTATION

One Symbol or Three Symbols for Three Meanings

Throughout our discussion of the set of integers, we have consistently used two symbols for concepts associated with integers that are not associated with whole numbers. These symbols are the raised minus symbol, "⁻," used before numerals to indicate negative numbers and the symbol "°" to mean "opposite of." For subtraction, we have used the standard subtraction symbol "−."

The symbols "⁻" and "°," however, are not universally standard symbols as are such symbols as "+," "−," "×," "=," "<," and the absolute-value symbol, "| |." In some textbooks, for example, the raised minus symbol must serve two roles: to designate negative numbers, as in $^-7$ or $^-3$, and also to mean "the opposite of," as in $^-(^-7)$ and $^-(3)$. Where in this pamphlet you encounter $^\circ 2$, you might elsewhere see $^-(2)$; or where we use $^\circ (^-7)$, other authors might use $^-(^-7)$. Similarly, the opposite of a number x would be written ^-x instead of $^\circ x$.

On the other hand, some writers employ the standard subtraction symbol in two ways, to indicate the operation of subtraction as in $7 - 5$, and also to mean "the opposite of," as in $-(^-7)$. Thus, where in this booklet you would find $^\circ 3$ and $^\circ(^-1)$, elsewhere you might find $-(3)$ and $-(^-1)$. Instead of $^\circ x$, in this context you would see $-x$.

Traditionally, in algebra texts and in most of advanced mathematics the subtraction symbol serves *three* purposes. One use is to denote subtraction, as in $5 - 3$. In this booklet, we have used the symbol exclusively for this purpose. A second use of the symbol "$-$" is to denote negative numbers. Where we have used $^-3$ and $^-7$, the symbols -3 and -7 are traditionally employed. A third use of the symbol is to represent "the opposite of." Where we have written $^\circ 3$ or $^\circ(^-7)$, the symbols -3 and $-(-7)$ are ordinarily employed. In fact, this usage is so widespread it is worth exploring a little further here.

In the first place, by defining "opposite of" to mean "additive inverse of," the symbolism we have used in this pamphlet would, in the case of the positive integer 4, for example, be written $^\circ 4 = ^-4$; that is, the opposite of positive 4 is negative 4. If, instead of the symbol "$^\circ$" for "opposite of," the subtraction symbol is employed, then $^\circ 4 = ^-4$ would appear as $-4 = ^-4$. Both equations mean that the opposite of the positive integer 4 is the negative integer $^-4$. Once one has gone this far, it is apparent that if -4 is equal to $^-4$, then it makes sense simply to use -4 to mean both the opposite of 4 and negative 4 and forget about the symbol $^-4$. Furthermore, since the statement of a difference such as $5 - 4$ is defined to mean (and here we use standard symbols) $5 + (-4)$ no ambiguity exists as regards subtraction either; so the single symbol "$-$" can play all three roles. Then, when an expression such as $5 - (-4)$ is encountered, one can reason as follows:

$$5 - (-4) \text{ means, by definition, } 5 + [-(-4)].$$

(In words this means "The difference when negative 4 is subtracted from 5 is the same as the sum of 5 and the opposite of negative 4.")

Since the opposite of negative 4 is positive 4, the symbol $-(-4)$ can be replaced with 4, and you have

$$5 - (-4) = 5 + 4.$$

The question of whether this is simpler symbolism than, for example,

$$5 - (^-4) = 5 + [^\circ(^-4)] = 5 + 4$$

is debatable, but there can be no question about the fact that if you can, without confusion, make one symbol do the work of three, you are that much ahead.

Reading for Meaning

A final word of advice: In reading any material where symbols are employed it is a good idea to know precisely what the symbols mean. More than this, it is helpful to establish the practice of reading a collection of symbols such as $5 - (^-4)$ for meaning the first few times it is encountered. By "reading for meaning" is meant actually translating the symbols into words mentally or even orally.

Symbolism is treacherous because as more and more of it is used, we become tempted to glance at it superficially and to take the word of the writer that it is meaningful and appropriate to the occasion of its use. Thus a writer will say to himself, "I can save some time and effort by writing something like

$$\begin{aligned}
18 + 9 &= (1 \times 10) + [(8 + 9) \times 1] \\
&= (1 \times 10) + (17 \times 1) \\
&= (1 \times 10) + [(1 \times 10) + (7 \times 1)] \\
&= [(1 \times \!0) + (1 \times 10)] + (7 \times 1) \\
&= [(1 + 1) \times 10] + (7 \times 1) \\
&= (2 \times 10) + (7 \times 1) \\
&= 20 + 7 \\
&= 27
\end{aligned}$$

to explain why $18 + 9$ is 27, instead of explaining every step of the work with words." The reader, if he is not careful, may be tempted to say to himself, "Yes, yes. Of course, $18 + 9 = 27$," and that will be the sum and substance of the communication between writer and reader in this instance.

Obviously, if the writer were not trying to say something using symbolism, all of the complicated-looking expressions in the chain would not be there. For his part, the reader of such things must be presumed to be reading with the purpose of understanding what the writer is saying; but only through diligent attention to the *meaning* of every symbol will such chains of symbols produce satisfactory communication. In short, reading mathematics is a quite different process from reading other kinds of material, and the temptation to skim or skip things must be firmly resisted.

————————•••————————

For Further Reading

Among the various helpful references that deal with the subject here introduced are the following:

ADLER, IRVING. *A New Look at Arithmetic.* New York: New American Library, 1965. Pp. 309. Available from New American Library, 1301 Ave. of the Americas, New York, N.Y. 10019.

McFARLAND, DORA, and LEWIS, EUNICE M. *Introduction to Modern Mathematics for Elementary Teachers.* Boston: D. C. Heath & Co., 1966. Pp. 406. Available from D. C. Heath & Co., 285 Columbus Ave., Boston, Mass. 02116.

PETERSON, JOHN A., and HASHISAKI, JOSEPH. *Theory of Arithmetic* (2nd ed.). New York: John Wiley & Sons, 1967. Pp. 337. Available from John Wiley & Sons, Inc., 605 Third Ave., New York, N.Y. 10016.

WHEELER, RURIC E. *Modern Mathematics: An Elementary Approach.* Belmont, Calif.: Brooks/Cole, 1966. Pp. 438. Available from Brooks/Cole, 10 Davis Drive, Belmont, Calif. 94002.

ANSWERS TO EXERCISES

Exercise Set 1 (p. 5)

1. a. $N \cup W = W$.
   b. $N \cap W = N$.

2. Since $W = N \cup \{0\}$, you have $N \subseteq W$. Since $0 \notin N$, you have $N \neq W$. Hence, N is a *proper* subset of W, $N \subset W$.

3. 0, 3, 5, 7, 19

4. a, c, d, e

5. Coordinate

6. Graph

7. Addition and multiplication

8. No. To solve these problems, one needs numbers that show direction as well as magnitude.

Exercise Set 2 (p. 8)

1. Negative integers

2. Positive integers

3. 0

4. a. J^+ **d.** J^-
   b. J^- **e.** J^+
   c. $\{0\}$ **f.** J^+

5. a. Whole numbers   **c.** Integers
   b. Integers   **d.** Integers

6. a. $^-5$ **c.** $^-9$
   b. $^-500$ **d.** $^-5$

Exercise Set 3 (p. 10)

1. a. $^-2$ **d.** 768
   b. 8   **e.** $^-45$
   c. 0   **f.** 30

2. a. $^-7$ **d.** $^-18$
   b. 3   **e.** $^-8$
   c. 0   **f.** $^-3$

3.

a	2	⁻5	4	⁻3	0	⁻6	8	15	1	⁻9	10
⁰a	⁻2	5	⁻4	3	0	6	⁻8	⁻15	⁻1	9	⁻10

4. Negative

5. Positive

6. Zero

Exercise Set 4 (p. 12)

1. a. Each arrow is 4 units long and represents a movement to the right.

　b. Each arrow begins at a different integer and ends at a different integer.

　c. 4

2. a. Each arrow is 4 units long.

　b. Each arrow begins and ends at a different integer. Two arrows represent a movement to the left on the number line, and one arrow represents a movement to the right on the number line.

　c. Two arrows represent the integer ⁻4. One arrow represents 4.

　d. The arrow extending farthest to the left (from 0 to ⁻4) is in standard position.

3.

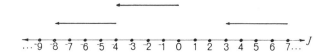

4.

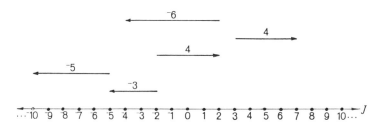

Exercise Set 5 (p. 15)

1. a. 3   **c.** 1
   b. 0   **d.** 9

2. a. An arrow drawn from $^-3$ to 7
   b. An arrow drawn from 9 to $^-1$
   c. An arrow drawn from $^-6$ to 0
   d. An arrow drawn from 6 to $^-2$

3. a. 17   **c.** 10
   b. 10   **d.** 66

4. a. $^-2$ **c.** 3
   b. $^-4$ **d.** 7

5. Positive

6. Negative

Exercise Set 6 (p. 18)

1. "Nonnegative" includes zero. "Positive" excludes zero.

2. "Nonpositive" includes zero. "Negative" excludes zero.

3. a. 14   **d.** 6
   b. 5   **e.** 9
   c. 0   **f.** 3

4. $^{\circ}a < {^{\circ}b}$

5. a. 60°
   b. 10°
   c. 0°
   d. $^-10°$

6. $^-8, ^-5, 0, 4, 6$

7. a. <
   b. >
   c. =

8. a. T   **c.** T
   b. F   **d.** F

9. a. >   **c.** >
   b. >   **d.** =

10. No, because it could name two integers, 2 and ⁻2.

11. a. T   **d.** F

   b. F   **e.** T

   c. F   **f.** F

Exercise Set 7 (p. 21)

1. a.

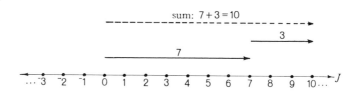

   b.

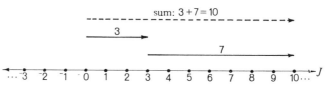

2. a. 7 and 3

   b. 3 and 7

   c. The integers are the same in both pairs.

   d. The order of the addends is different.

   e. The sums are the same.

3. a.

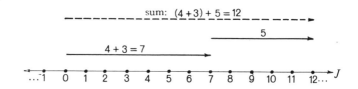

   b.

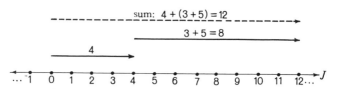

4. a. 7   **c.** 8

   b. 12   **d.** 12

   e. The grouping of addends may be changed without changing the sum.

5.

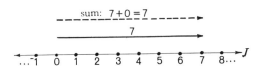

6. 7 + 0 is renamed 7.

7. a. T
  b. F
  c. F
  d. T

Exercise Set 8 (p. 23)

1. a. 7   **e.** 15
  b. 8   **f.** 7
  c. 5   **g.** 8
  d. 2   **h.** 1

2. a. $^-2 + {}^-3 = {}^-5.$
  b. $^-3 + {}^-4 = {}^-7.$

3. a. $^-102$ **c.** $^-1009$ **e.** $^-39$ **g.** $^-1361$
  b. $^-35$ **d.** $^-133$ **f.** $^-144$ **h.** $^-969$

Exercise Set 9 (p. 27)

1. $2 + 3 = 5.$
2. $^-1 + {}^-2 = {}^-3.$
3. $3 + {}^-7 = {}^-4.$
4. $^-2 + 7 = 5.$
5. $4 + {}^-4 = 0.$
6. $6 + 0 = 6.$

Exercise Set 10 (p. 30)

1. a.

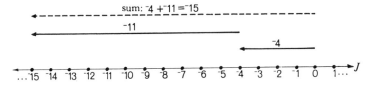

b.

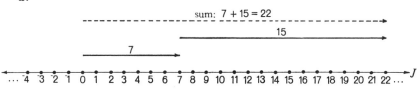

c.

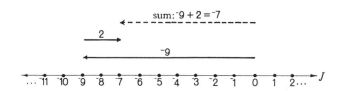

d.

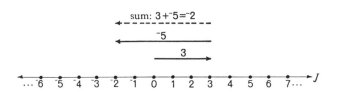

e.

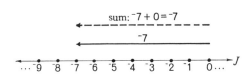

f.

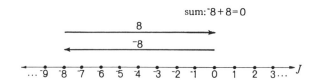

2. a. 10
  b. ⁻11
  c. 2
  d. ⁻3
  e. 0
  f. 5

3. a. 50 + 6 = _____; $56.00.
  b. 50 + 7 + ⁻10 = _____; $47.00.

c. $50 + 15 + {}^-8 =$ _____; \$57.00.

d. $50 + {}^-9 + {}^-6 =$ _____; \$35.00.

e. $50 + {}^-28 + 18 =$ _____; \$40.00.

f. $50 + 11 + {}^-11 =$ _____; \$50.00.

4.

Second addend

First addend

First \ Second	0	1	2	3	4	5	6	7	8	9	10	11	12	13	14	15	16	17	18
0	0	1	2	3	4	5	6	7	8	9	10	11	12	13	14	15	16	17	18
-1	-1	0	1	2	3	4	5	6	7	8	9	10	11	12	13	14	15	16	17
-2	-2	-1	0	1	2	3	4	5	6	7	8	9	10	11	12	13	14	15	16
-3	-3	-2	-1	0	1	2	3	4	5	6	7	8	9	10	11	12	13	14	15
-4	-4	-3	-2	-1	0	1	2	3	4	5	6	7	8	9	10	11	12	13	14
-5	-5	-4	-3	-2	-1	0	1	2	3	4	5	6	7	8	9	10	11	12	13
-6	-6	-5	-4	-3	-2	-1	0	1	2	3	4	5	6	7	8	9	10	11	12
-7	-7	-6	-5	-4	-3	-2	-1	0	1	2	3	4	5	6	7	8	9	10	11
-8	-8	-7	-6	-5	-4	-3	-2	-1	0	1	2	3	4	5	6	7	8	9	10
-9	-9	-8	-7	-6	-5	-4	-3	-2	-1	0	1	2	3	4	5	6	7	8	9
-10	-10	-9	-8	-7	-6	-5	-4	-3	-2	-1	0	1	2	3	4	5	6	7	8
-11	-11	-10	-9	-8	-7	-6	-5	-4	-3	-2	-1	0	1	2	3	4	5	6	7
-12	-12	-11	-10	-9	-8	-7	-6	-5	-4	-3	-2	-1	0	1	2	3	4	5	6
-13	-13	-12	-11	-10	-9	-8	-7	-6	-5	-4	-3	-2	-1	0	1	2	3	4	5
-14	-14	-13	-12	-11	-10	-9	-8	-7	-6	-5	-4	-3	-2	-1	0	1	2	3	4
-15	-15	-14	-13	-12	-11	-10	-9	-8	-7	-6	-5	-4	-3	-2	-1	0	1	2	3
-16	-16	-15	-14	-13	-12	-11	-10	-9	-8	-7	-6	-5	-4	-3	-2	-1	0	1	2
-17	-17	-16	-15	-14	-13	-12	-11	-10	-9	-8	-7	-6	-5	-4	-3	-2	-1	0	1
-18	-18	-17	-16	-15	-14	-13	-12	-11	-10	-9	-8	-7	-6	-5	-4	-3	-2	-1	0

5. a. k

  b. Zero

  c. Integer

  d. Sum

  e. 1

  f. 3

  g. 7

  h. 5

  i. 5

  j. 5

Exercise Set 11 (p. 36)

1. a. $2 + 2 + 2 = 6;$
    $3 \times 2 = 6.$

  b. $^-3 + {}^-3 + {}^-3 = {}^-9;$
     $3 \times {}^-3 = {}^-9.$

  c. $^-1 + {}^-1 + {}^-1 + {}^-1 + {}^-1 + {}^-1 + {}^-1 = {}^-7;$
     $7 \times {}^-1 = {}^-7.$

2. a. $5 \times {}^-7 = {}^-35.$

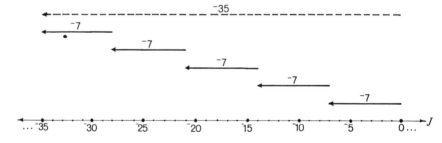

  b. $4 \times {}^-3 = {}^-12.$

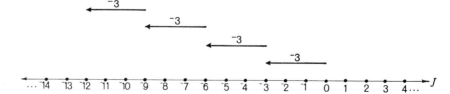

c. $2 \times {}^-6 = {}^-12.$

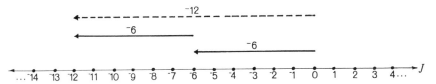

d. $6 \times {}^-1 = {}^-6.$

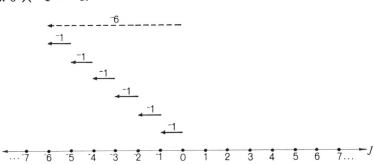

3. a. $^-3$ **c.** $^-6$
   b. 2 **d.** 9

4.

Product
18
9
0
$^-9$
$^-18$
18
9
0
$^-9$
$^-18$

5. a. ⁻175   **c.** ⁻38   **e.** ⁻3596
   b. ⁻294   **d.** ⁻74   **f.** ⁻280

Exercise Set 12 (p. 40)

1. a. ⁻2 × ⁻4 = (⁻1 × 2) × (⁻1 × 4),
   ⁻2 × ⁻4 = (⁻1 × ⁻1) × (2 × 4),
   ⁻2 × ⁻4 = 1 × (2 × 4),
   ⁻2 × ⁻4 = 1 × 8,
   ⁻2 × ⁻4 = 8.

b. ⁻5 × ⁻9 = (⁻1 × 5) × (⁻1 × 9),
   ⁻5 × ⁻9 = (⁻1 × ⁻1) × (5 × 9),
   ⁻5 × ⁻9 = 1 × (5 × 9),
   ⁻5 × ⁻9 = 1 × 45,
   ⁻5 × ⁻9 = 45.

c. ⁻78 × ⁻31 = (⁻1 × 78) × (⁻1 × 31),
   ⁻78 × ⁻31 = (⁻1 × ⁻1) × (78 × 31),
   ⁻78 × ⁻31 = 1 × (78 × 31),
   ⁻78 × ⁻31 = 1 × 2418,
   ⁻78 × ⁻31 = 2418.

d. ⁻650 × ⁻478 = (⁻1 × 650) × (⁻1 × 478),
   ⁻650 × ⁻478 = (⁻1 × ⁻1) × (650 × 478),
   ⁻650 × ⁻478 = 1 × (650 × 478),
   ⁻650 × ⁻478 = 1 × 310,700,
 • ⁻650 × ⁻478 = 310,700.

2.

Product
⁻14
⁻7
0
7
14

3. a. 5,184   **c.** ⁻5,070   **e.** ⁻2,242
   b. 391   **d.** 0   **f.** 209,202

Exercise Set 13 (p. 42)

1.

Second factor

144	132	120	108	96	84	72	60	48	36	24	12	12	-12	-24	-36	-48	-60	-72	-84	-96	-108	-120	-132	-144
132	121	110	99	88	77	66	55	44	33	22	11	11	-11	-22	-33	-44	-55	-66	-77	-88	-99	-110	-121	-132
120	110	100	90	80	70	60	50	40	30	20	10	10	-10	-20	-30	-40	-50	-60	-70	-80	-90	-100	-110	-120
108	99	90	81	72	63	54	45	36	27	18	9	9	-9	-18	-27	-36	-45	-54	-63	-72	-81	-90	-99	-108
96	88	80	72	64	56	48	40	32	24	16	8	8	-8	-16	-24	-32	-40	-48	-56	-64	-72	-80	-88	-96
84	77	70	63	56	49	42	35	28	21	14	7	7	-7	-14	-21	-28	-35	-42	-49	-56	-63	-70	-77	-84
72	66	60	54	48	42	36	30	24	18	12	6	6	-6	-12	-18	-24	-30	-36	-42	-48	-54	-60	-66	-72
60	55	50	45	40	35	30	25	20	15	10	5	5	-5	-10	-15	-20	-25	-30	-35	-40	-45	-50	-55	-60
48	44	40	36	32	28	24	20	16	12	8	4	4	-4	-8	-12	-16	-20	-24	-28	-32	-36	-40	-44	-48
36	33	30	27	24	21	18	15	12	9	6	3	3	-3	-6	-9	-12	-15	-18	-21	-24	-27	-30	-33	-36
24	22	20	18	16	14	12	10	8	6	4	2	2	-2	-4	-6	-8	-10	-12	-14	-16	-18	-20	-22	-24
12	11	10	9	8	7	6	5	4	3	2	1	1	-1	-2	-3	-4	-5	-6	-7	-8	-9	-10	-11	-12
12	11	10	9	8	7	6	5	4	3	2	1	0	-1	-2	-3	-4	-5	-6	-7	-8	-9	-10	-11	-12
-12	-11	-10	-9	-8	-7	-6	-5	-4	-3	-2	-1	-1	1	2	3	4	5	6	7	8	9	10	11	12
-24	-22	-20	-18	-16	-14	-12	-10	-8	-6	-4	-2	-2	2	4	6	8	10	12	14	16	18	20	22	24
-36	-33	-30	-27	-24	-21	-18	-15	-12	-9	-6	-3	-3	3	6	9	12	15	18	21	24	27	30	33	36
-48	-44	-40	-36	-32	-28	-24	-20	-16	-12	-8	-4	-4	4	8	12	16	20	24	28	32	36	40	44	48
-60	-55	-50	-45	-40	-35	-30	-25	-20	-15	-10	-5	-5	5	10	15	20	25	30	35	40	45	50	55	60
-72	-66	-60	-54	-48	-42	-36	-30	-24	-18	-12	-6	-6	6	12	18	24	30	36	42	48	54	60	66	72
-84	-77	-70	-63	-56	-49	-42	-35	-28	-21	-14	-7	-7	7	14	21	28	35	42	49	56	63	70	77	84
-96	-88	-80	-72	-64	-56	-48	-40	-32	-24	-16	-8	-8	8	16	24	32	40	48	56	64	72	80	88	96
-108	-99	-90	-81	-72	-63	-54	-45	-36	-27	-18	-9	-9	9	18	27	36	45	54	63	72	81	90	99	108
-120	-110	-100	-90	-80	-70	-60	-50	-40	-30	-20	-10	-10	10	20	30	40	50	60	70	80	90	100	110	120
-132	-121	-110	-99	-88	-77	-66	-55	-44	-33	-22	-11	-11	11	22	33	44	55	66	77	88	99	110	121	132
-144	-132	-120	-108	-96	-84	-72	-60	-48	-36	-24	-12	-12	12	24	36	48	60	72	84	96	108	120	132	144

First factor

2. a. Yes   **d.** 81   **g.** $^-7$ **i.** 9
  b. 81   **e.** $^-81$ **h.** $^-7$ **k.** 6
  c. $^-81$ **f.** $^-4$ **i.** $^-8$

3. a. $^-6$ **d.**   12
  b. $^-24$ **e.** $^-24$
  c. $^-24$ **f.** 3×4

4. a. Commutative property of multiplication
  b. Associative property of multiplication
  c. Closure property of multiplication
  d. Multiplicative property of 0
  e. Multiplicative identity of 1

5. a. $^-3 \times ^-5 = 15$. The restaurant had 15 more cups before the arrival of the waitress.
  b. $2 \times ^-5 = ^-10$. The restaurant will have 10 less cups.

6. a. $2 \times ^-1 = ^-2$. He will have 2 cups less.
  b. $^-2 \times ^-1 = 2$. It was greater by 2 cups.

Exercise Set 14 (p. 47)

1. a. $3 - ^-7 = 10$.   **c.** $^-7 - 7 = ^-14$.
  b. $^-3 - ^-7 = 4$.   **d.** $3 - 7 = ^-4$.

2. a. 14   **c.** $^-38$
  b. 6   **d.** $^-108$

3. Monday: 18°
  Tuesday: $^-10$°
  Wednesday: 2°
  Thursday: $^-11$°
  Friday: 18°

Exercise Set 15 (p. 51)

1. a. $6 \times n = ^-24$.   **e.** $1 \times n = ^-312$.
  b. $^-6 \times n = 36$.   **f.** $8 \times n = ^-96$.
  c. $^-7 \times n = ^-42$.   **g.** $^-12 \times n = 144$.
  d. $8 \times n = 512$.   **h.** $^-24 \times n = ^-840$.

2. a. $^-6$ **c.** 40   **e.** $^-72$
  b. 48   **d.** 22   **f.** $^-14$

BOOKLET NUMBER TEN:

THE SYSTEM OF RATIONAL NUMBERS

INTRODUCTION

The first set of numbers that a child learns to use is the set N of natural numbers, $\{1, 2, 3, 4, \cdots\}$. The next is the set W of whole numbers, $\{0, 1, 2, 3, 4, \cdots\}$. These are sufficient for many of the ways in which we use numbers. However, they are not sufficient for certain other purposes—for example, for the measurement of line segments in terms of a given unit segment. To record measures, we need the set of numbers which contains the whole numbers and also such numbers as $\frac{1}{2}, \frac{3}{4}, \frac{5}{5}, \frac{127}{10}$, namely, the set A of positive rational numbers. (In fact, in geometry we need still other numbers, such as $\sqrt{2}$, to express the true lengths of line segments. For example, if a square has sides of length 1, then the diagonal has length $\sqrt{2}$, which is not a rational number. (See Booklet No. 11: *The System of Real Numbers*.) These three kinds of numbers are still not sufficient for all purposes. In order to study and record changes that may occur in opposite directions—such as the rise and fall of prices, the expansion and contraction of metals, and the increase and decrease of populations—we need *negative* numbers. In Booklet No. 9: *The System of Integers*, we have already encountered a set of negative numbers, namely, the set J^- of negative integers, in which each number is the "opposite" of a positive integer. In this booklet we shall extend our consideration to include the opposite of each positive rational number. Since our discussion will include many points of reference to other "Topics" booklets, you would find it helpful to review some of them at this time—particularly Booklet No. 6: *The Rational Numbers*; Booklet No. 7: *Numeration Systems for the Rational Numbers*; and Booklet No. 9: *The System of Integers*.

In this study of the system of rational numbers, the first part is devoted to a review of what we have already learned about the *positive* rational numbers and what we know about operations with positive and negative integers and zero. From this information we can draw inferences

67

about what negative rational numbers should mean to us, and about ways in which we may operate with them.

The remainder of Booklet No. 10 is devoted to a more systematic treatment of the system of rational numbers. Definitions of the operations with rational numbers will be given in terms of *ordered pairs of integers*, and the properties of these operations will be justified through their origin in the properties of the operations with integers.

AN INTUITIVE LOOK AT THE RATIONAL NUMBERS

Suppose that the temperature has risen 3 degrees in 4 hours and that we wish to know the average increase in degrees per hour. We write the sentence

$$4 \times m = 3,$$

where m represents the average number-of-degrees rise per hour. This sentence has no solution in the set of integers, but in the set of rational numbers it does have a solution, namely $\frac{3}{4}$. For this problem the positive rational numbers, discussed in Booklet No. 6, are adequate. You will recall that a positive rational number is a number that can be represented as the quotient of two counting numbers; thus $\frac{2}{3}$ and $\frac{3}{2}$ are positive rational numbers; so are 1 and 2, since they can be represented as $\frac{1}{1}$ and $\frac{2}{1}$ (and as $\frac{2}{2}$ and $\frac{4}{2}$, and so on), respectively.

Suppose, however, that the temperature has *fallen* 3 degrees in 4 hours. Representing the drop in degrees by $^-3$, we now write the sentence

$$4 \times m = {}^-3.$$

To solve sentences like this, we need new numbers, which we shall call *negative rational numbers*. For our example we need a number that represents the same average change as $\frac{3}{4}$, but a change in the opposite direction. This number we shall call "negative three-fourths."

The Number Line

Let us begin by using a horizontal number line, as we did in Booklets No. 6, 7, and 9. We choose a point, called the origin, to represent 0, and a point to the right of the origin to represent 1. To the right of the origin we can now locate a unique point for each natural number and, indeed, for each positive rational number. Figure 1 shows the representation of some of these numbers by points. The points are the *graphs* of the corresponding numbers, and the numbers are the *coordinates* of the corresponding points.

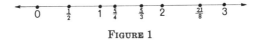

FIGURE 1

Now imagine a mirror, perpendicular to the number line at the origin, that reflects the right-hand side of the line onto the left-hand side of the line. Each point to the right of the origin will have a reflection point, or image, that appears to be to the left of the origin, the two points being the same distance from the origin, but in opposite directions. Let us use the symbol $^-(\frac{1}{2})$ as a label for the reflection of the point that represents $\frac{1}{2}$, the symbol $^-1$ (as in Booklet No. 9) for the image of the point that represents 1, the symbol $^-(\frac{5}{4})$ for the reflection of the point that represents $\frac{5}{4}$, and so on. We then have the picture shown in Figure 2.

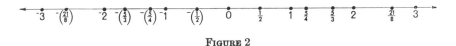

FIGURE 2

Just as we already associate a positive rational number with each of the labeled points to the right of the origin, we now associate a negative rational number with each labeled point to the left of the origin. With the point labeled $^-(\frac{5}{4})$, for example, we associate a negative rational number. The symbol $^-(\frac{5}{4})$ (read "negative five-fourths") is used as a name for this number.

Thus we have a pairing of rational numbers. Corresponding to each positive rational number there is a negative rational number such that the points representing these two numbers are reflections of each other.

In terms of the point of view stated on page 21 of Booklet No. 6: *The Rational Numbers*, we may generalize by saying: Just as the system of positive integers can be considered a subsystem of the system of positive rational numbers, so can the system of integers be considered a subsystem of the system of rational numbers. Accordingly, we shall speak of rational numbers 0, 1, $^-4$, $^-1$, and so on.

Let us again adopt the vocabulary of Booklet No. 9: *The System of Integers* and use the phrase "the opposite of" to replace the phrase "the reflection of," and the symbol "$^\circ(\frac{1}{2})$" to mean "the opposite of $\frac{1}{2}$." Thus

$$^\circ\left(\frac{1}{2}\right) = \ ^-\left(\frac{1}{2}\right),$$

which is read "the opposite of one-half is negative one-half." We also write

$$^\circ\left[\ ^-\left(\frac{1}{2}\right)\right] = \frac{1}{2},$$

which is read "the opposite of negative one-half is one-half." To determine $^\circ[^\circ(\frac{1}{2})]$, we can combine these two numerical statements to obtain

$$^\circ\left[\ ^\circ\left(\frac{1}{2}\right)\right] = \ ^\circ\left[\ ^-\left(\frac{1}{2}\right)\right] = \frac{1}{2}.$$

In general terms, the opposite of the opposite of *any* rational number is the number itself.

Just as the symbols $\frac{1}{2}$, $\frac{2}{4}$, $\frac{3}{6}$, and $\frac{4}{8}$ can be used as labels for the same point to the right of the origin on the number line and hence as names for the same (positive) rational number, so $^-(\frac{1}{2})$, $^-(\frac{2}{4})$, $^-(\frac{3}{6})$, and $^-(\frac{4}{8})$ all correspond to the same point to the left of the origin and are all names for the same (negative) rational number. In fact, if n is any natural number, then $^-(\frac{1 \times n}{2 \times n})$ names the same rational number as $^-(\frac{1}{2})$.

Order

You will recall that the positive rational numbers are "ordered"; that is, for two rational numbers such as $\frac{5}{4}$ and $\frac{7}{4}$, exactly one of three statements is true: either $\frac{5}{4} < \frac{7}{4}$ ("<" means "is less than") or $\frac{5}{4} = \frac{7}{4}$ or $\frac{7}{4} < \frac{5}{4}$. In this case the first of these is true and the other two are false. This is because there is a *positive* number, $\frac{2}{4}$, such that $\frac{5}{4} + \frac{2}{4} = \frac{7}{4}$.

If $\frac{a}{b}$ and $\frac{c}{d}$ represent positive rational numbers, the statement $\frac{a}{b} < \frac{c}{d}$ means that there is a positive number that when added to $\frac{a}{b}$ yields $\frac{c}{d}$. In other words, you must add a *positive* number to $\frac{a}{b}$ to get $\frac{c}{d}$. The order relation of any two positive rational numbers can be depicted very nicely on the number line. If $\frac{a}{b} < \frac{c}{d}$, then the point corresponding to $\frac{a}{b}$ on a horizontal number line is to the left of the point corresponding to $\frac{c}{d}$. For example, we know that $\frac{3}{4} < \frac{5}{4}$, and the point that represents $\frac{3}{4}$ is to the left of the point that represents $\frac{5}{4}$.

The notion of order can be extended to the negative rationals (we shall henceforth often use "rational[s]" for "rational number[s]") by noting the position of the corresponding points on the number line; namely, if r and s are any two rational numbers, we say that $r < s$, provided the point on the number line that corresponds to r is to the left of the point that corresponds to s. When (in the systematic treatment below) we define addition in the set of rational numbers, we shall see that our present way of looking at order agrees with the definition stating that $r < s$, provided there is a positive number t that when added to r yields s.

How are $^-(\frac{3}{4})$ and 0 related? The answer is "$^-(\frac{3}{4}) < 0$" because the point corresponding to $^-(\frac{3}{4})$ is to the left of the origin. The arrangement of points on the number line indicates that every negative rational is less than zero and that zero is less than every positive rational. Also, this arrangement indicates that every negative rational is less than every positive rational.

What about two negative rationals? Consider, for example, $^-(\frac{3}{4})$ and $^-(\frac{5}{4})$, which are the opposites of $\frac{3}{4}$ and $\frac{5}{4}$, respectively. The point representing $\frac{3}{4}$ is to the left of the point representing $\frac{5}{4}$ on the number line. But what about the reflections of these points? The point corresponding to $^-(\frac{5}{4})$ is to the left of the point corresponding to $^-(\frac{3}{4})$, and so $^-(\frac{5}{4}) < {}^-(\frac{3}{4})$. We see then that the process of reflection has the effect of "reversing the order."

Reflecting does not, however, reverse "betweenness." For example, we have $\frac{5}{8} < \frac{6}{8}$ and $\frac{6}{8} < \frac{7}{8}$. These inequalities are usually written together as $\frac{5}{8} < \frac{6}{8} < \frac{7}{8}$, and $\frac{6}{8}$ is said to be *between* $\frac{5}{8}$ and $\frac{7}{8}$. For the corresponding negative rationals, we have $^-(\frac{7}{8}) < {}^-(\frac{6}{8})$ and $^-(\frac{6}{8}) < {}^-(\frac{5}{8})$, which we write as $^-(\frac{7}{8}) < {}^-(\frac{6}{8}) < {}^-(\frac{5}{8})$; and $^-(\frac{6}{8})$ is between $^-(\frac{7}{8})$ and $^-(\frac{5}{8})$.

Absolute Value

Rational numbers can be represented by *arrows* on the number line, just as integers can be. The positive rational $\frac{5}{4}$ can be represented by an arrow pointing to the right and having length $\frac{5}{4}$, while the negative rational $^-(\frac{5}{4})$ can be represented by an arrow pointing to the left and also having length $\frac{5}{4}$. Such arrows are shown in Figure 3. The arrows in this figure start

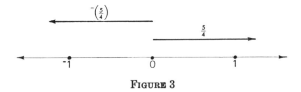

FIGURE 3

(have their tails) at the origin and end (have their heads) at the points whose coordinates they represent. For this reason these arrows are said to be in *standard position*. An arrow representing a rational number might, however, have its tail at any point on the line, provided it is of the same length and is pointed in the same direction as the corresponding arrow in standard position.

The length of the arrow used to represent a rational number is called the *absolute value* of that number. Thus, the absolute value of each of the numbers $\frac{5}{4}$ and $^-(\frac{5}{4})$, denoted by $|\frac{5}{4}|$ and $|^-(\frac{5}{4})|$ respectively, is $\frac{5}{4}$, since each number is represented by an arrow whose length is $\frac{5}{4}$. In general terms, any rational number and its opposite have the same absolute value; that is, if r is any rational number, then $|r| = |^\circ r|$.

Arrow Addition and Subtraction of Rational Numbers

We can define the sum of rational numbers in terms of arrows on the number line in the same way as we defined the sum of integers. Let us picture the addition of $\frac{3}{4}$ and $\frac{7}{4}$. (See Fig. 4.) The arrow for the first addend, $\frac{3}{4}$, is in standard position, with its tail at the origin; the arrow for the second addend, $\frac{7}{4}$, has its tail at the head of the first arrow. The dashed arrow for the sum of $\frac{3}{4}$ and $\frac{7}{4}$ is in standard position with its tail at the

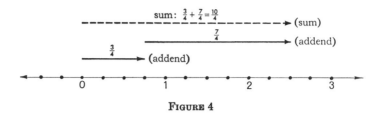

FIGURE 4

origin and its head even with the head of the second arrow. Note that the arrow for the sum extends from the origin to the point corresponding to $\frac{10}{4}$. Thus arrow addition gives us, for this example,

$$\frac{3}{4} + \frac{7}{4} = \frac{10}{4}.$$

The sum of $^-\left(\frac{3}{4}\right)$ and $^-\left(\frac{7}{4}\right)$ is pictured in a similar way in Figure 5. Note that Figure 5 may be thought of as the reflection of Figure 4 at 0.

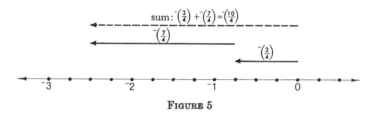

FIGURE 5

What happens when a positive rational and a negative rational are added? The two number lines in Figure 6 depict the two sums $\frac{5}{4} + \,^-\left(\frac{3}{4}\right)$

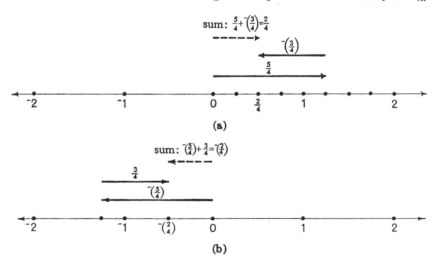

FIGURE 6

and $^-(\frac{5}{4}) + \frac{3}{4}$. Note that in each case the length of the arrow for the sum is equal to the difference between the lengths of the arrows for the addends: $(\frac{5}{4} - \frac{3}{4} = \frac{2}{4})$. The direction of the arrow for the sum is in each case the same as the direction of the longer of the two arrows for the addends.

The (rational) number 0 is the *additive identity element* in the system of rationals, just as it is in the system of integers. For example,

$$0 + \frac{2}{3} = \frac{2}{3} + 0 = \frac{2}{3}$$

and

$$0 + {}^-\left(\frac{2}{3}\right) = {}^-\left(\frac{2}{3}\right) + 0 = {}^-\left(\frac{2}{3}\right).$$

Figure 7 illustrates the sum of a rational number and its opposite,

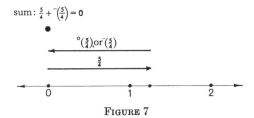

sum: $\frac{5}{4} + {}^-\left(\frac{5}{4}\right) = 0$

FIGURE 7

$\frac{5}{4} + {}^\circ(\frac{5}{4})$. The arrow for ${}^\circ(\frac{5}{4})$ (starting at the tip of the first arrow) extends to the origin. Thus the arrow for the sum of $\frac{5}{4}$ and ${}^\circ(\frac{5}{4})$ is the zero arrow and

$$\frac{5}{4} + {}^\circ\left(\frac{5}{4}\right) = 0.$$

The sum of any rational and its opposite is the additive identity element, 0. For this reason, we say that the opposite of a rational number is its *additive inverse*.

The *subtraction* of a second rational number from a first is now a simple matter; we just *add the opposite*, or additive inverse, of the second to the first number. (See pages 98–99 for an explanation of why this is so.) For example, we have

$$\frac{7}{4} - {}^-\left(\frac{3}{4}\right) = \frac{7}{4} + {}^\circ\left[{}^-\left(\frac{3}{4}\right)\right]$$
$$= \frac{7}{4} + \frac{3}{4}$$
$$= \frac{10}{4}.$$

Multiplication and Division of Rational Numbers

How do we multiply in the entire set of rationals? We already know how to find products of positive rationals. The product of $\frac{2}{7}$ and $\frac{3}{5}$ is $\frac{2\times3}{7\times5}$, which is $\frac{6}{35}$. What should the product of $\frac{3}{5}$ and $^-(\frac{2}{7})$ be? Recall that in the system of integers, discussed in Booklet No. 9, the product of 7 and $^-9$, for example, is the opposite of the product of 7 and 9. It is therefore reasonable that the product of $\frac{3}{5}$ and $^-(\frac{2}{7})$ should be the opposite of the product of $\frac{3}{5}$ and $\frac{2}{7}$. Hence, we decide that

$$\frac{3}{5} \times {}^-\left(\frac{2}{7}\right) = {}^\circ\left(\frac{3}{5} \times \frac{2}{7}\right)$$

$$= {}^\circ\left(\frac{6}{35}\right)$$

$$= {}^-\left(\frac{6}{35}\right).$$

What is the product of $^-4$ and $\frac{16}{7}$? It is the opposite of $4 \times \frac{16}{7}$, so

$$^-4 \times \frac{16}{7} = {}^\circ\left(4 \times \frac{16}{7}\right)$$

$$= {}^\circ\left(\frac{4}{1} \times \frac{16}{7}\right)$$

$$= {}^\circ\left(\frac{64}{7}\right)$$

$$= {}^-\left(\frac{64}{7}\right).$$

What about the product of two negative rationals? Consider the product $^-(\frac{4}{3}) \times {}^-(\frac{6}{5})$. Remember that the product of two negative integers equals the product of their opposites. Since we want the same rule to apply to negative rationals, we decide that

$$^-\left(\frac{4}{3}\right) \times {}^-\left(\frac{6}{5}\right) = \frac{4}{3} \times \frac{6}{5}$$

$$= \frac{24}{15}, \quad \text{or} \quad \frac{8}{5}.$$

The (rational) number 1 is the *multiplicative identity element* in the system of rationals, just as it is in the system of integers. For example,

$$1 \times {}^-\left(\frac{6}{7}\right) = \frac{1}{1} \times {}^-\left(\frac{6}{7}\right)$$

$$= {}^-\left(\frac{1 \times 6}{1 \times 7}\right)$$

$$= {}^-\left(\frac{6}{7}\right).$$

Just as in the case of integers, multiplication of a rational number by $^-1$ yields the opposite of that number:

$$^-1 \times \frac{4}{5} = {}^{\circ}\!\left(\frac{4}{5}\right), \quad \text{or} \quad {}^-\!\left(\frac{4}{5}\right); \qquad ^-1 \times {}^-\!\left(\frac{5}{3}\right) = {}^{\circ}\!\left[{}^-\!\left(\frac{5}{3}\right)\right], \quad \text{or} \quad \frac{5}{3}.$$

The system of rationals has an important property that the system of integers does not have. The property is this:

> For every rational number r, except zero, there is another rational number s, the reciprocal of r, such that $r \times s = 1$.

Since the product of any rational number r ($r \neq 0$) and its reciprocal is the multiplicative identity element, 1, we say that the reciprocal of a nonzero rational number is its *multiplicative inverse*. It is easy to see that the system of integers does not have this property. There is no integer x such that $8 \times x = 1$. Thus in the system of integers, 8 has no multiplicative inverse. As an element of the rational number system, however, 8 does have a multiplicative inverse, namely $\frac{1}{8}$, because $8 \times \frac{1}{8} = \frac{8}{8}$, which is 1. What is the multiplicative inverse of $^-(\frac{15}{9})$? The answer is $^-(\frac{9}{15})$, because

$$^-\!\left(\frac{9}{15}\right) \times {}^-\!\left(\frac{15}{9}\right) = \frac{9}{15} \times \frac{15}{9} = \frac{9 \times 15}{15 \times 9} = 1.$$

To summarize, if a and b are positive integers, then the multiplicative inverse of $\frac{a}{b}$ is $\frac{b}{a}$, and the multiplicative inverse of $^-(\frac{a}{b})$ is $^-(\frac{b}{a})$.

The *division* of a rational number by a nonzero rational number is now a simple matter; we just *multiply* the rational number by the reciprocal, or multiplicative inverse, of the nonzero rational number. (See pp. 110–12, below, for an explanation of why this is so.) For example, we have

$$\frac{7}{4} \div {}^-\!\left(\frac{3}{4}\right) = \frac{7}{4} \times {}^-\!\left(\frac{4}{3}\right)$$

$$= {}^-\!\left(\frac{7}{4} \times \frac{4}{3}\right)$$

$$= {}^-\!\left(\frac{7}{3}\right).$$

Exercise Set 1

1. Make an arrow diagram for each of the following sums:

   a. $\dfrac{7}{3} + {}^-\!\left(\dfrac{8}{3}\right)$ c. $^-\!\left(\dfrac{9}{8}\right) + \dfrac{5}{8}$

   b. $^-\!\left(\dfrac{5}{4}\right) + {}^-\!\left(\dfrac{3}{4}\right)$ d. $\dfrac{5}{6} + \dfrac{7}{6}$

2. Draw a number line with the unit segments separated into eighths. For each of the following numbers, locate and label its corresponding point and also the point for its opposite.

a. $\dfrac{5}{8}$ **c.** $^{\circ}\left[\,^{-}\left(\dfrac{9}{8}\right)\right]$

b. $^{-}\left(\dfrac{17}{8}\right)$ **d.** $^{-}\left(\dfrac{13}{8}\right)$

3. Choose a rational number and make an arrow diagram to show the sum of that number and its opposite.

4. Name each product by a simpler expression.

  a. $\dfrac{3}{5} \times \dfrac{7}{10}$ **c.** $^{-}\left(\dfrac{7}{9}\right) \times {}^{-}\left(\dfrac{5}{4}\right)$

  b. $^{-}\left(\dfrac{3}{5}\right) \times \dfrac{7}{10}$ **d.** $\left(\dfrac{11}{4}\right) \times {}^{-}\left(\dfrac{13}{5}\right)$

5. Write a simpler name for each of the following products.

  a. $4 \times {}^{-}\left(\dfrac{3}{5}\right)$ **e.** $0 \times {}^{-}\left(\dfrac{3}{5}\right)$

  b. $3 \times {}^{-}\left(\dfrac{3}{5}\right)$ **f.** $^{-}1 \times {}^{-}\left(\dfrac{3}{5}\right)$

  c. $2 \times {}^{-}\left(\dfrac{3}{5}\right)$ **g.** $^{-}2 \times {}^{-}\left(\dfrac{3}{5}\right)$

  d. $1 \times {}^{-}\left(\dfrac{3}{5}\right)$ **h.** $^{-}3 \times {}^{-}\left(\dfrac{3}{5}\right)$

RATIONAL NUMBERS NAMED BY FRACTIONS

Ordered Pairs of Integers

In our discussion so far, we have looked at the entire set of rational numbers by considering first the set of nonnegative rational numbers, or numbers that can be named by fractions of the form $\frac{a}{b}$, where b is a natural number and a is a whole number. The whole numbers 0, 1, 2, 3 are members of this set, since they can be named by such fractions as $\frac{0}{7}$, $\frac{2}{2}$, $\frac{6}{3}$, $\frac{3}{1}$. We considered the points on the number line which correspond to such numbers. We also noted that each fraction $\frac{a}{b}$ corresponds to exactly one point on the line and that if a is not equal to 0, then each of the numbers named by these fractions is greater than 0 and all the corresponding points lie to the right of the origin on the number line. We then imagined a mirror at the origin which reflected the right half of the number line into the left. The numbers corresponding to the reflections were then designated negative rational numbers. These numbers, together with zero and the positive rational numbers, make up the entire set of rational numbers. We saw, by using what we knew about the arithmetic of the nonnegative rationals and what we knew about the operations with positive and negative integers, how it would seem reasonable to add and multiply in the entire set of rational numbers.

Let us now look at the rational numbers from another point of view. When you first used a *fraction* (a symbol or name indicating the quotient of two numbers), such as $\frac{2}{3}$, you probably used it to designate part of an object, such as a square region. If the region is separated into three congruent, nonoverlapping regions and then two are shaded (Fig. 8), we say

FIGURE 8

that two-thirds of the region is shaded. The fraction $\frac{2}{3}$ is formed from a pair of numerals for natural numbers. The number 3 (the denominator) is the number of congruent regions into which the unit region is separated, and the number 2 (the numerator) is the number of congruent parts shaded. If the square region is taken as a *unit* region with measure 1, then the measure of the shaded part is the positive rational number $\frac{2}{3}$. It is called a *rational* number because it can be named in a way that indicates the *ratio* of the number of parts shaded (2) to the number of congruent parts in the unit region (3). Since the fraction $\frac{2}{3}$ names a different number from the fraction $\frac{3}{2}$ (which would suggest separating each of several unit regions into 2 congruent parts and shading 3 of the parts), a fraction is sometimes considered a name for an *ordered pair of numbers*. Thus, $\frac{2}{3}$ can be thought of as naming the ordered pair (2, 3) and $\frac{3}{2}$ as naming the (different) ordered pair (3, 2).

In thinking of fractions of the form $\frac{a}{b}$ as names for rational numbers, we have heretofore required that a be a member of the set W of whole numbers, $\{0, 1, 2, 3, \cdots\}$, and b a member of the set N of natural numbers. It is not reasonable to permit b to be zero, since (thinking again of a unit square region) we cannot conceive of the region being separated into zero regions.

We now wish to give meaning to the numbers named by fractions of the form $\frac{m}{n}$, where m is *any integer* and n is *any integer except* 0. For example, we shall have such fractions as $\frac{-4}{3}$, $\frac{5}{-7}$, $\frac{-2}{-3}$, $\frac{0}{-6}$, as well as the familiar fractions such as $\frac{12}{10}$. Numbers named by such fractions constitute the full set of rational numbers, and these numbers, together with the operations of addition and multiplication on them, constitute the *rational number system*.

The Number Line

Let us review the way in which the integers, $\{ \cdots, ^-3, ^-2, ^-1, 0, 1, 2, 3, \cdots \}$, are represented on a number line. A point, called the origin, is chosen to correspond to the integer 0. Next, a different point is chosen to correspond to 1. This may be anywhere on the line except at the origin but is usually chosen a convenient distance to the right of the origin (Fig. 9). The segment

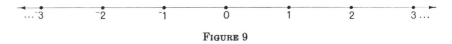

FIGURE 9

having the origin and the point corresponding to 1 as end points is called a *unit segment*, as is any segment congruent to it. Such a unit segment is used to mark off points to the right and to the left of the origin. The points to the right of the origin correspond consecutively to the positive integers $^+1$, $^+2$, $^+3$, $\cdots$; the points to the left of the origin correspond consecutively to the negative integers $^-1$, $^-2$, $^-3$, $\cdots$. For the positive integers we shall ordinarily use the notation 1, 2, 3, $\cdots$, instead of $^+1$, $^+2$, $^+3$, $\cdots$.

Suppose that a unit segment is separated into two congruent segments and that one of these shorter segments is used to mark off points to the right and to the left of the origin (Fig. 10). We label the points to the right of the origin consecutively with the fractions $\frac{1}{2}$, $\frac{2}{2}$, $\frac{3}{2}$, $\cdots$, which are read "one-half," "two-halves," "three-halves," or "one over two," "two over two," three over two," and so on. We label the points to the left of the origin consecutively with the fractions $\frac{-1}{2}$, $\frac{-2}{2}$, $\frac{-3}{2}$, $\cdots$, which are read "negative one-half," "negative two-halves," "negative three-halves," or "negative one over two," "negative two over two," "negative three over two," and so on. The origin is labeled $\frac{0}{2}$, this fraction being read "zero-halves," or "zero over two."

FIGURE 10

You will notice that each of the fractions appearing on the number line in Figure 10 has the integer 2 for its denominator. This reminds us that the segment used to mark off the equally spaced points was obtained by separating a unit segment into two congruent segments. What do the numerators signify? The numerator 3 of the fraction $\frac{3}{2}$, for example, indicates that the point bearing $\frac{3}{2}$ as its label is 3 half-units *to the right* of the origin. The numerator $^-4$ of the fraction $\frac{^-4}{2}$ indicates that the point labeled $\frac{^-4}{2}$ is 4 half-units *to the left* of the origin. What labels could be assigned to the two points that are 9 half-units from the origin? These labels should be $\frac{9}{2}$ and $\frac{^-9}{2}$. The label $\frac{0}{2}$ for the origin indicates that this point is 0 half-units from the origin.

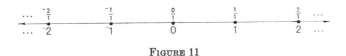

Figure 11

On the number line in Figure 11 new labels are given to the points corresponding to integers, as follows:

$\frac{1}{1}$, $\frac{2}{1}$, $\cdots$ to the points to the right of the origin,

$\frac{0}{1}$ to the origin,

$\frac{^-1}{1}$, $\frac{^-2}{1}$, $\cdots$ to the points to the left of the origin.

This labeling scheme is consistent with the scheme used in the preceding paragraph. The denominator 1 of each of the fractions indicates that a whole unit segment was used in marking off points. To each point corresponding to an integer we are giving a fraction symbol whose numerator is that integer and whose denominator is 1. The fraction $\frac{1}{1}$ might be read "one over one," $\frac{^-1}{1}$ read "negative one over one," and so on.

Equivalent Fractions

On the number lines in Figure 12, three different labeling schemes are shown. On (a), each *unit* segment has been divided into *two* congruent segments, and point R corresponds to $\frac{^-3}{2}$. On (b), each segment of length $\frac{1}{2}$ has been divided into *two* congruent segments, and point R corresponds to $\frac{^-(3\times2)}{2\times2}$, or $\frac{^-6}{4}$. On (c), each segment of length $\frac{1}{2}$ has been divided into *three* congruent segments, and point R corresponds to $\frac{^-(3\times3)}{2\times3}$, or $\frac{^-9}{6}$. We see that if a point corresponds to the fraction $\frac{^-3}{2}$, it also corresponds to the fractions $\frac{^-3\times2}{2\times2}$ and $\frac{^-3\times3}{2\times3}$. If we continue dividing segments of length $\frac{1}{2}$ into various numbers of congruent parts, R can also be shown to correspond to the fraction $\frac{^-3\times n}{2\times n}$, where n is any natural number. If a point on the number line corresponds to two different fractions, then we say that these fractions are *equivalent* to each other, or that they are *equivalent fractions*.

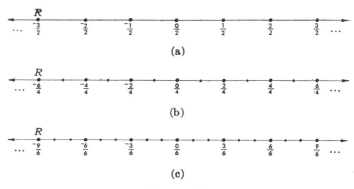

It will be useful for us to see in another way how the equivalent fractions $\frac{-3}{2}$, $\frac{-6}{4}$, and $\frac{-9}{6}$ are related. In Table I we see that the numerators and denominators of any two of these fractions are related in an interesting way.

TABLE I

Pair of Fractions	Relationship
$\frac{-3}{2}, \frac{-6}{4}$	$^-3 \times 4 = 2 \times {}^-6$
$\frac{-3}{2}, \frac{-9}{6}$	$^-3 \times 6 = 2 \times {}^-9$
$\frac{-6}{4}, \frac{-9}{6}$	$^-6 \times 6 = 4 \times {}^-9$

For each pair of fractions the "cross product" of the numerator of the first fraction and the denominator of the second fraction is equal to the product of the denominator of the first fraction and the numerator of the second fraction. Thus $\frac{-3}{2}$ and $\frac{-6}{4}$ are equivalent to each other because $^-3 \times 4 = {}^-12$ and $2 \times {}^-6 = {}^-12$. Also $\frac{5}{9}$ and $\frac{20}{36}$ are equivalent to each other because $5 \times 36 = 180$ and $9 \times 20 = 180$.

More generally, fractions $\frac{a}{b}$ and $\frac{c}{d}$, where a and c represent integers and b and d represent positive integers, are equivalent to each other if and only if $a \times d = b \times c$. To see why this is so, notice that $\frac{a}{b}$ and $\frac{a \times d}{b \times d}$ correspond to the same point on the number line, say P, and that $\frac{c}{d}$ and $\frac{c \times b}{d \times b}$ correspond to the same point, say Q. In the latter designations for P and Q, unit segments have been separated into $b \times d$ congruent parts. Then points P and Q are the same point if and only if they lie the same number of these congruent parts to the right or to the left of the origin—that is, if and only if the numerators $a \times d$ and $c \times b$ are equal.

If two fractions are each equivalent to a third fraction, they are equivalent to each other. Thus, as soon as we see that each of the fractions $\frac{-14}{21}$ and $\frac{-20}{30}$ is equivalent to the fraction $\frac{-2}{3}$, we know that they are equivalent to each other. It should be noted, too, that every fraction is equivalent to itself; the fraction $\frac{-3}{4}$, for example, is equivalent to the fraction $\frac{-3}{4}$ because $^-3 \times 4 = 4 \times\ ^-3$.

Negative Denominators

We have already shown that any fraction of the form $\frac{-3 \times n}{2 \times n}$, where n is a natural number, can be used to designate the same point R on the number line (Fig. 12). Thus R can be designated by each fraction in the set

$$\left\{ \frac{^-3}{2}, \frac{^-6}{4}, \frac{^-9}{6}, \frac{^-12}{8}, \frac{^-15}{10}, \ \ldots \right\}.$$

We call this a set of equivalent fractions because each fraction in the set is equivalent to each of the others.

Can we extend our set of equivalent fractions still further? Are there other fractions equivalent to $\frac{-3}{2}$? What about such fractions as $\frac{3}{-2}, \frac{6}{-4}, \frac{9}{-6},$ etc.? These fractions are of the form $\frac{-3 \times n}{2 \times n}$, where n is a *negative* integer. Except for the fact that they have negative denominators, each of these fractions would seem to be equivalent to $\frac{-3}{2}$. If you check the cross products of $\frac{3}{-2}$ and $\frac{-3}{2}$, for example, you get $3 \times 2 =\ ^-2 \times\ ^-3$. Do we want to allow fractions to have negative denominators? We can use such a fraction to designate a point on the number line if we introduce the notion of a *negative* unit segment, or unit segment *directed to the left*, say from 0 to $^-1$. Thus, $\frac{3}{-2}$, for example, indicates that we have separated negative unit segments into halves and have taken three of these. You can see that the point designated by $\frac{3}{-2}$ is the same as the point designated by $\frac{-3}{2}$. Thus the introduction of fractions with negative denominators makes it possible for us to enlarge the set of fractions that are equivalent to the fraction $\frac{-3}{2}$.

Fractions have many uses, as we shall see later, and for some of these uses negative denominators will serve us well. Let us agree, then, that fractions can have negative integers as denominators. Thus not only are the symbols $\frac{3}{4}, \frac{0}{5}, \frac{-7}{1}$, and $\frac{10}{10}$ fractions, but so are the symbols $\frac{-4}{-2}, \frac{0}{-3}, \frac{5}{-2}$, and $\frac{-1}{-1}$. The fraction $\frac{-4}{-2}$ is read "negative four over negative two." We restate our test for the equivalence of fractions as follows:

Two fractions $\frac{a}{b}$ and $\frac{c}{d}$, where a, c, b, and d are integers, $b \neq 0$ and $d \neq 0$, are equivalent to each other if and only if $a \times d = b \times c$.

The fractions $\frac{-4}{-1}$ and $\frac{4}{-1}$ are equivalent to each other because $^-4 \times\ ^-1 = 4$ and $1 \times 4 = 4$. Also, $\frac{16}{-12}$ is equivalent to $\frac{-4}{3}$, since $16 \times 3 =\ ^-12 \times\ ^-4$, each product being equal to 48. For what integer a is the fraction $\frac{a}{-12}$

equivalent to the fraction $\frac{-6}{9}$? We form the products $a \times 9$ and $^-12 \times ^-6$. The second product is 72. For what value of a is $a \times 9$ equal to 72? The answer is 8. Thus the fraction $\frac{a}{-12}$ is equivalent to the fraction $\frac{-6}{9}$ if $a = 8$.

Exercise Set 2

1. Which of the following pairs of fractions are equivalent?

a. $\dfrac{4}{5}, \dfrac{4}{-5}$ **d.** $\dfrac{^-105}{99}, \dfrac{^-175}{165}$

b. $\dfrac{9}{16}, \dfrac{18}{32}$ **e.** $\dfrac{38}{65}, \dfrac{114}{185}$

c. $\dfrac{8}{2}, \dfrac{^-4}{^-1}$ **f.** $\dfrac{^-14}{195}, \dfrac{^-15}{196}$

2. The fraction $\frac{6}{25}$ is equivalent to the fraction $\frac{18}{75}$ because $6 \times 75 = 25 \times 18$. Check that these two products are equal by finding the prime factors of 6×75 and 25×18, instead of computing the products.

3. a. Draw a number line and separate each unit segment from $^-2$ to 2 into three congruent parts. Locate the points A, B, and C corresponding to $\frac{5}{3}$, $^-(\frac{4}{3})$, and $^-(\frac{2}{3})$, respectively, and label these points.

   b. Now separate each of the resulting segments of length $\frac{1}{3}$ into two congruent parts, and find new fraction labels for A, B, and C.

4. What fraction in this set is *not* equivalent to the others?

$$\left\{ \frac{150}{400}, \frac{^-6}{^-16}, \frac{51}{136}, \frac{^-21}{^-56}, \frac{48}{145}, \frac{^-9}{^-24} \right\}$$

Rational Numbers and Sets of Equivalent Fractions

We have enlarged the set

$$\left\{ \frac{^-3}{2}, \frac{^-6}{4}, \frac{^-9}{6}, \frac{^-12}{8}, \frac{^-15}{10}, \cdots \right\}$$

of fractions with positive denominators which are equivalent to the fraction $\frac{-3}{2}$ to include the fractions $\frac{3}{-2}, \frac{6}{-4}, \frac{9}{-6}$, and, indeed, any fraction of the form $\frac{3 \times n}{-2 \times n}$, where n is a natural number. For example, the fraction $\frac{3 \times 11}{-2 \times 11}$, or $\frac{33}{-22}$, is equivalent to the fraction $\frac{-3}{2}$, since $33 \times 2 = ^-22 \times ^-3$. Thus we arrive at the following set of fractions equivalent to the fraction $\frac{-3}{2}$:

$$\left\{ \cdots, \frac{9}{^-6}, \frac{6}{^-4}, \frac{3}{^-2}, \frac{^-3}{2}, \frac{^-6}{4}, \frac{^-9}{6}, \cdots \right\}$$

The three dots at each end indicate that the listing could be continued indefinitely in both directions. The set is the entire set of fractions, with integers as numerators and denominators, which are equivalent to the fraction $\frac{-3}{2}$. Each fraction in the set is of the form $\frac{^-3 \times n}{2 \times n}$, where n is a nonzero integer, and each is associated with the same point on the number line. Thus we have associated with a single point on the number line an infinite set of equivalent fractions in the sense that each fraction can be used to designate that point.

Now we have come to a very important point in our discussion. We associate with the above set of equivalent fractions one single number, which is associated with a definite point on the number line. We call it a *rational number*. Just as the fractions in the above set of equivalent fractions can all be used to designate this point, we now say that each of these fractions is a name for the same rational number.

Now let us briefly look at the notation used for rational numbers. You recall that the point labeled $\frac{3}{2}$ on the number line was located by separating the unit segment into two congruent parts and counting off three of them to the right of the origin, while the point labeled $\frac{-3}{2}$ was obtained by counting off three of these parts to the left of the origin. This second point is, of course, the reflection of the first point, when the positive half of the number line is reflected into the negative half, as discussed in an earlier section. The symbol that was assigned to the reflection point in that earlier discussion was $^-(\frac{3}{2})$. Thus we see that the fraction $\frac{-3}{2}$ is assigned to the same point as $^-(\frac{3}{2})$. The fraction $\frac{-3}{2}$ may still be read "negative three over two," but it names the same number as the symbol $^-(\frac{3}{2})$, which is read "negative three-halves." When we refer to the rational number itself with no particular emphasis on any of its names, we ordinarily use the phrase "negative three-halves."

The following is another set of equivalent fractions:

$$\left\{ \cdots , \frac{-3}{-6} , \frac{-2}{-4} , \frac{-1}{-2} , \frac{1}{2} , \frac{2}{4} , \frac{3}{6} , \cdots \right\}$$

Pick out a few pairs of these fractions and test them for equivalence. For the pair $\frac{-3}{-6}$, $\frac{2}{4}$, examine the products $^-3 \times 4$ and $^-6 \times 2$. You will see that these products are equal, and so $\frac{-3}{-6}$ and $\frac{2}{4}$ are equivalent fractions. This set of fractions is also associated with a single rational number, one-half.

If you examine the two sets we have studied,

$$\left\{ \cdots , \frac{-3}{-6} , \frac{-2}{-4} , \frac{-1}{-2} , \frac{1}{2} , \frac{2}{4} , \frac{3}{6} , \cdots \right\} ,$$

and

$$\left\{ \cdots , \frac{9}{-6} , \frac{6}{-4} , \frac{3}{-2} , \frac{-3}{2} , \frac{-6}{4} , \frac{-9}{6} , \cdots \right\} ,$$

you will notice that these sets have no fraction as a common element, that is, the two sets are disjoint. In fact, every fraction $\frac{a}{b}$ belongs to exactly one set of equivalent fractions (it will henceforth always be assumed in this booklet that a and b are integers and that b is not 0) and hence names exactly one rational number. If $\frac{a}{b}$ and $\frac{c}{d}$ are two fractions, then either they belong to the same set of equivalent fractions or they belong separately to two sets of equivalent fractions which have no fraction in common. In the first case the two fractions name the same rational number; in the second case they name two distinct rational numbers. The fractions $\frac{^-10}{5}$ and $\frac{^-2}{1}$ belong to the same set of equivalent fractions, and they name the same rational number. The fractions $\frac{9}{6}$ and $\frac{4}{3}$, however, belong to two disjoint sets of equivalent fractions (since $9 \times 3 \neq 6 \times 4$), and so they name two different rational numbers.

Of special interest are the rational number *zero* and the rational number *one.* Zero is named by each of the fractions in the set

$$\left\{ \cdots , \frac{0}{^-3} , \frac{0}{^-2} , \frac{0}{^-1} , \frac{0}{1} , \frac{0}{2} , \frac{0}{3} , \cdots \right\}.$$

Do you see that this is a set of equivalent fractions? The fractions $\frac{0}{^-3}$ and $\frac{0}{2}$, for example, are equivalent because $0 \times 2 = {}^-3 \times 0$, both products being 0. The rational number one is associated with the following set of equivalent fractions:

$$\left\{ \cdots , \frac{^-3}{^-3} , \frac{^-2}{^-2} , \frac{^-1}{^-1} , \frac{1}{1} , \frac{2}{2} , \frac{3}{3} , \cdots \right\}$$

We shall see that the rational numbers zero and one play the same roles in the system of rational numbers as do the integers zero and one in the system of integers.

Exercise Set 3

1. **a.** On a horizontal number line, separate each unit segment from $^-2$ to 2 into 4 congruent parts. Locate and label the point corresponding to the fraction $\frac{^-5}{4}$.

   b. Which of the following fractions are correct labels for the same point as $\frac{^-5}{4}$?

   $$\frac{5}{^-4} , \frac{5}{4} , \frac{^-5}{^-4} , \frac{^-10}{8} , \frac{10}{^-8} , \frac{^-10}{^-8} , \frac{^-500}{400} , \frac{500}{^-400}$$

   c. What number must replace a if the fraction $\frac{^-15}{a}$ names the same rational number as $\frac{^-5}{4}$?

   d. What number must replace a if the fraction $\frac{a}{20}$ names the same rational number as $\frac{^-5}{4}$?

2. Every fraction of the form $\frac{^-5 \times n}{4 \times n}$, where n is an integer other than zero, is a name for the rational number negative five-fourths. Write the fraction that names negative five-fourths and has:

   a. $^-15$ as its numerator.   **c.** 36 as its denominator.

   b. 25 as its numerator.   **d.** $^-40$ as its denominator.

3. a. Which of the fractions

$$\frac{^-5}{2}, \frac{3}{1}, \frac{^-19}{^-2}, \frac{0}{^-5}, \frac{3 \times {}^-6}{5 \times {}^-6}, \frac{4 \times 3}{^-7 \times 3}, \frac{7}{^-3}$$

name positive rational numbers?

b. Which of these fractions name negative rational numbers?

c. Which of these fractions name zero?

4. Write six different fraction names for the number represented by $\frac{-8}{1}$.

Simplest Fraction Name for a Rational Number

In dealing with fraction names for positive rational numbers, in Booklet No. 6, we defined the *simplest* fraction name as the one in which the numerator and the denominator have no common factors other than 1. For example, for the rational number associated with the set of equivalent fractions $\{\frac{21}{35}, \frac{6}{10}, \frac{30}{50}, \frac{18}{30}, \cdots\}$ the simplest fraction name is $\frac{3}{5}$, because 3 and 5 have no common factor other than 1.

We now have fractions for which the numerator or denominator or both may be negative. Which is a simplest name—

(a) $\frac{3}{5}$ or $\frac{^-3}{^-5}$?

(b) $\frac{^-3}{5}$ or $\frac{3}{^-5}$?

(c) $\frac{^-6}{10}$ or $\frac{3}{^-5}$?

This question is settled by *definition*:

> *The simplest fraction name for a rational number named by a fraction $\frac{a}{b}$, where a and b are nonzero integers, is the equivalent fraction $\frac{c}{d}$, where d is a positive integer and the integers c and d have no common positive factors except 1. The simplest fraction name for $\frac{0}{b}$, where $b \neq 0$, is $\frac{0}{1}$.*

If we test the example above by the definition, we see that $\frac{3}{5}$ and $\frac{^-3}{5}$ are simplest fraction names of rational numbers, but neither $\frac{^-6}{10}$ nor $\frac{3}{^-5}$ is a simplest fraction name. The fraction $\frac{^-6}{10}$ is not a simplest name, since the numerator and denominator have the common positive factor 2. To find the simplest fraction name of the rational number named by $\frac{^-6}{10}$, we can write

$$\frac{^-6}{10} = \frac{^-3 \times 2}{5 \times 2}$$

$$= \frac{^-3}{5}.$$

(When we write "$\frac{^-6}{10} = \frac{^-3}{5}$," we do not mean that the two fractions are the same, but rather that they name the same rational number. You are already familiar with this idea; for example, when you write "5 + 3 = 8" you mean that the numerals "5 + 3" and "8" name the same number.) The fraction $\frac{3}{-5}$ is not a simplest name, since it has a negative denominator. We can multiply the numerator and denominator by $^-1$ to obtain

$$\frac{3}{^-5} = \frac{3 \times ^-1}{^-5 \times ^-1} = \frac{^-3}{5}.$$

The process of prime factorization is useful in finding the simplest fraction name for a rational number.[1] Consider the fraction $\frac{56}{^-420}$. To express the number by a fraction with a positive denominator, first multiply numerator and denominator by $^-1$:

$$\frac{56 \times ^-1}{^-420 \times ^-1} = \frac{^-56}{420}.$$

Now express the numerator and denominator in prime-factored form, first expressing $^-56$ as $^-1 \times 56$:

$$\frac{^-56}{420} = \frac{^-1 \times 56}{420} = \frac{^-1 \times 2 \times 2 \times 2 \times 7}{2 \times 2 \times 3 \times 5 \times 7}$$

$$= \frac{^-1 \times 2 \times (2 \times 2 \times 7)}{3 \times 5 \times (2 \times 2 \times 7)} \qquad \text{(The factors have been rearranged.)}$$

$$= \frac{^-1 \times 2}{3 \times 5} \qquad \begin{array}{l}\text{(Numerator and denominator have} \\ \text{been divided by } 2 \times 2 \times 7.)\end{array}$$

$$= \frac{^-2}{15}. \qquad \begin{array}{l}\text{(This is the simplest fraction name} \\ \text{for the number.)}\end{array}$$

Integers as Rational Numbers

In a previous section we displayed a number line labeled as shown in Figure 13. Each of the heavy dots has a fraction label and an integer label

FIGURE 13

representing a rational number and an integer, respectively. Are these the same number? Is the rational number $\frac{2}{1}$ the same as the integer 2? In an exact sense, no. The rational number $\frac{2}{1}$ is identified with the infinite set of fractions

$$\left\{ \ldots, \frac{^-4}{^-2}, \frac{^-2}{^-1}, \frac{2}{1}, \frac{4}{2}, \ldots \right\}.$$

This is not the case with the integer 2; fractions do not enter into the

[1] See Booklet No. 5: *Numbers and Their Factors.*

development of the system of integers. In spite of this we would like to treat the two sets of numbers

$$\left\{ \cdots, \frac{^-4}{1}, \frac{^-3}{1}, \frac{^-2}{1}, \frac{^-1}{1}, \frac{0}{1}, \frac{1}{1}, \frac{2}{1}, \frac{3}{1}, \frac{4}{1}, \cdots \right\}$$

and

$$\{ \cdots, {}^-4, {}^-3, {}^-2, {}^-1, 0, 1, 2, 3, 4, \cdots \}$$

as though they were the same. For all practical purposes we can do this. First of all, there is the natural one-to-one matching between the two sets of numbers indicated below:

$$\{ \cdots, {}^-4, {}^-3, {}^-2, {}^-1, 0, 1, 2, 3, 4, \cdots \}$$
$$\updownarrow \quad \updownarrow \quad \updownarrow \quad \updownarrow \quad \updownarrow \quad \updownarrow \quad \updownarrow \quad \updownarrow \quad \updownarrow$$
$$\left\{ \cdots, \frac{^-4}{1}, \frac{^-3}{1}, \frac{^-2}{1}, \frac{^-1}{1}, \frac{0}{1}, \frac{1}{1}, \frac{2}{1}, \frac{3}{1}, \frac{4}{1}, \cdots \right\}$$

This matching scheme can be denoted more briefly as follows:

$$\frac{n}{1} \leftrightarrow n \text{ for every integer } n.$$

Furthermore, in later sections we shall define addition and multiplication of rational numbers in such a way that the subset of rational numbers

$$\left\{ \cdots, \frac{^-4}{1}, \frac{^-3}{1}, \frac{^-2}{1}, \frac{^-1}{1}, \frac{0}{1}, \frac{1}{1}, \frac{2}{1}, \frac{3}{1}, \frac{4}{1}, \cdots \right\}$$

behaves in exactly the same way under addition and multiplication as the set of integers, $\{ \cdots, {}^-4, {}^-3, {}^-2, {}^-1, 0, 1, 2, 3, 4, \cdots \}$. The sum $\frac{4}{1} + \frac{3}{1}$, for example, will by definition be $\frac{7}{1}$. This corresponds to the addition fact for integers, $4 + 3 = 7$. The sum $\frac{^-3}{1} + \frac{9}{1}$ will by definition be $\frac{6}{1}$. This corresponds to $^-3 + 9 = 6$ for integers. Similarly, by the definition of multiplication of rational numbers, we shall have

$$\frac{7}{1} \times \frac{3}{1} = \frac{21}{1} \quad \text{and} \quad \frac{^-4}{1} \times \frac{5}{1} = \frac{^-20}{1},$$

corresponding to

$$7 \times 3 = 21 \quad \text{and} \quad {}^-4 \times 5 = {}^-20$$

for integers.

We say that the system of integers, and the particular subsystem of the rational numbers whose elements are

$$\left\{ \cdots, \frac{^-3}{1}, \frac{^-2}{1}, \frac{^-1}{1}, \frac{0}{1}, \frac{1}{1}, \frac{2}{1}, \frac{3}{1}, \cdots \right\},$$

are *isomorphic*. Because of this strong correlation between them, we usually do not make a distinction between the two systems or between their corresponding elements. Accordingly, we shall regard the integers 5 and $^-3$, for example, as rational numbers, not merely integers corresponding to rational numbers.

By the definition given on page 85 the simplest fraction names for the rational numbers five and negative three are $\frac{5}{1}$ and $\frac{-3}{1}$, respectively. Regarded as integers, these numbers can be expressed even more simply as 5 and ⁻3, respectively. We call the latter symbols the *common names* for these numbers.

Exercise Set 4

1. Which of the fractions

$$\frac{5}{6} \, , \, \frac{^-6}{9} \, , \, \frac{0}{2} \, , \, \frac{1}{^-6} \, , \, \frac{15}{1} \, , \, \frac{^-31}{73} \, , \, \frac{^-4}{^-11} \, , \, \frac{^-31}{93}$$

are simplest fraction names of rational numbers?

2. Write the simplest fraction name for the rational number named by each of the following:

   a. $\dfrac{24}{36}$ e. $\dfrac{^-32}{^-80}$

   b. $\dfrac{24}{^-36}$ f. $\dfrac{165}{^-5}$

   c. $\dfrac{^-7 \times 14}{8 \times 14}$ g. $\dfrac{^-64}{^-64}$

   d. $\dfrac{0}{^-19}$

3. Write the common name for the integer expressed by each of the following fraction names.

   a. $\dfrac{^-27}{3}$ d. $\dfrac{0}{5}$

   b. $\dfrac{16}{^-1}$ e. $\dfrac{^-84}{^-21}$

   c. $\dfrac{6}{6}$ f. $\dfrac{^-14 \times 19}{1 \times 19}$

4. The prime-factored form of 490 is $2 \times 5 \times 7 \times 7$, because the product is equal to 490 and each factor is a prime number.

   a. Express the numbers 126 and 60 in prime-factored form.

   b. Use the prime-factored forms you wrote in part a of this exercise to find the simplest fraction name for the rational number named by:

   i. $\dfrac{126}{60}$ ii. $\dfrac{^-126}{60}$ iii. $\dfrac{^-60}{^-126}$

5. Find the simplest fraction name for the rational number named by:

   a. $\dfrac{2 \times 2 \times 3 \times 19}{5 \times 2 \times 3 \times 19}$

b. $\dfrac{3 \times 11 \times 23}{^-1 \times 3 \times 23 \times 29}$

c. $\dfrac{^-1 \times 7 \times 11 \times 17}{2 \times 3 \times 7 \times 11 \times 13 \times 17}$

ADDITION AND SUBTRACTION OF RATIONAL NUMBERS

The Sum of Two Rational Numbers

Let us recall, from our discussion in Booklet No. 6, how positive rational numbers are added. For example,

$$\frac{2}{3} + \frac{5}{3} = \frac{2 + 5}{3} = \frac{7}{3}.$$

On the number line, this means that we use unit segments divided into three congruent parts and count off two of these, then count off five more, or seven in all.

In general terms, if a and c are nonnegative integers and b is a positive integer, then

$$\frac{a}{b} + \frac{c}{b} = \frac{a + c}{b}.$$

Will the same relation hold if b is positive, but if a or c or both are negative? Is it true that $\frac{2}{3} + \frac{^-5}{3} = \frac{(2 + ^-5)}{3}$? On the number line the denominator 3 indicates that we are to use unit segments separated into three congruent parts. Following the pattern for the "arrow addition" of integers, let us agree that the expression "$\frac{2}{3} + \frac{^-5}{3}$" indicates that we should count two

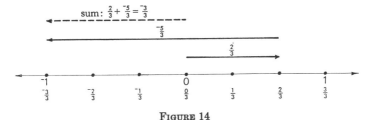

FIGURE 14

parts in the positive direction, then five parts in the negative direction (Fig. 14). The arrow diagram indicates that

$$\frac{2}{3} + \frac{^-5}{3} = \frac{2 + ^-5}{3} = \frac{^-3}{3}.$$

As further exercises, you might use arrow addition to show that

$$\frac{^-2}{3} + \frac{^-5}{3} = \frac{^-2 + ^-5}{3} = \frac{^-7}{3}$$

and that

$$\frac{^-2}{3} + \frac{5}{3} = \frac{^-2 + 5}{3} = \frac{3}{3}.$$

If two rational numbers are represented by fractions with different denominators, we can rename them by fractions with the same denominator. For example, $\frac{2}{3}$ and $\frac{^-1}{2}$ can be renamed $\frac{4}{6}$ and $\frac{^-3}{6}$, respectively. Now we

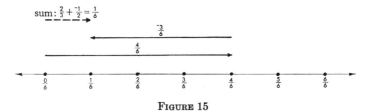

FIGURE 15

can use arrow addition (Fig. 15) as in the previous examples to obtain

$$\frac{4}{6} + \frac{^-3}{6} = \frac{4 + ^-3}{6} = \frac{1}{6}.$$

These examples suggest that if we have two rational numbers represented by fractions $\frac{a}{b}$ and $\frac{c}{b}$, where a and c are integers and b is a positive integer, then

$$\frac{a}{b} + \frac{c}{b} = \frac{a + c}{b}.$$

Now let us see what happens when we add two rational numbers that are represented by fractions having a negative common denominator. Take, for example, $\frac{5}{^-3}$ and $\frac{6}{^-3}$. We can rename the rational numbers as follows:

$$\frac{5}{^-3} = \frac{^-5}{3} \quad \text{and} \quad \frac{6}{^-3} = \frac{^-6}{3}.$$

Then

$$\frac{5}{^-3} + \frac{6}{^-3} = \frac{^-5}{3} + \frac{^-6}{3}$$

$$= \frac{^-5 + ^-6}{3}$$

$$= \frac{^-11}{3}.$$

Do we get the same answer if we apply the "formula" $\frac{a}{b} + \frac{c}{b} = \frac{a+c}{b}$ directly to $\frac{5}{^-3} + \frac{6}{^-3}$? We do, since in this case $\frac{a+c}{b}$ is $\frac{5+6}{^-3}$, or $\frac{11}{^-3}$, and $\frac{11}{^-3}$ is equivalent to $\frac{^-11}{3}$. This indicates that the sentence

$$\frac{a}{b} + \frac{c}{b} = \frac{a + c}{b}$$

is valid not only when b is a positive integer but also when it is a negative integer.

Now let us see how this formula can be used to add two rational numbers that are represented by fractions having different denominators (positive or negative). The same renaming property may be applied.

EXAMPLE: Find the sum $\dfrac{-5}{6} + \dfrac{7}{-10}$.

Solution: $\dfrac{-5}{6} + \dfrac{7}{-10} = \dfrac{-5}{6} + \dfrac{-7}{10}$ $\left(\dfrac{7}{-10} \text{ and } \dfrac{-7}{10} \text{ are equivalent.}\right)$

$\qquad\qquad = \dfrac{-5 \times 5}{6 \times 5} + \dfrac{-7 \times 3}{10 \times 3}$ (Renaming, using fractions with the same denominator.)

$\qquad\qquad = \dfrac{-25}{30} + \dfrac{-21}{30}$

$\qquad\qquad = \dfrac{-46}{30}$

$\qquad\qquad = \dfrac{-23}{15}.$

Let us formalize what we have done thus far as regards addition of rational numbers:

The sum of the rational numbers $\dfrac{a}{b}$ and $\dfrac{c}{b}$, where a and c are integers and b is an integer other than 0, is

$$\frac{a}{b} + \frac{c}{b} = \frac{a + c}{b}.$$

This definition can be used to add any two rational numbers, because it is always possible to express two rational numbers as fractions having a common denominator.

In adding two rational numbers represented by fractions having different denominators, we can use the product of the denominators as a common denominator. Thus, in the example on this page we could have used $6 \times {}^-10$ or $^-60$ as the common denominator, instead of 30. Then the solution would have looked like this:

$$\frac{-5}{6} + \frac{7}{-10} = \frac{-5 \times {}^-10}{6 \times {}^-10} + \frac{7 \times 6}{-10 \times 6}$$

$$= \frac{50}{-60} + \frac{42}{-60}$$

$$= \frac{50 + 42}{-60}$$

$$= \frac{92}{-60}$$

$$= \frac{-23}{15}.$$

Thus we obtain the same answer as before.

This raises an important question. Our definition of addition of rational numbers is given in terms of fractions that represent the rational numbers. The sentence $\frac{a}{b} + \frac{c}{b} = \frac{a+c}{b}$ gives a way of manipulating two symbols $\frac{a}{b}$ and $\frac{c}{b}$ to get the symbol $\frac{a+c}{b}$. Now, our main concern is with the rational numbers represented by the fractions, and not with the fractions themselves. Each of these rational numbers has many fraction names, and before applying the formula $\frac{a}{b} + \frac{c}{b} = \frac{a+c}{b}$, we have to choose fraction names for the addends. The question we raise is this: Does it make any difference which fraction names we use for the rational numbers we are adding? The answer, fortunately, is "no." When adding two rational numbers, we may use any fraction representatives of these two numbers. The previous examples illustrate this fact. We first added the rational numbers $\frac{-5}{6}$ and $\frac{7}{-10}$, using the fractions $\frac{-25}{30}$ and $\frac{-21}{30}$ as names for these numbers, and obtained the sum $\frac{-23}{15}$. We then added the same numbers, using the fractions $\frac{50}{-60}$ and $\frac{42}{-60}$, and obtained the same sum, $\frac{-23}{15}$.

Now let the fractions $\frac{a}{b}$ and $\frac{c}{d}$ represent any two rational numbers, where a and c represent integers and b and d represent integers other than zero. The sum of the two rational numbers can be found by using the product of the denominators as the common denominator, as follows:

$$\frac{a}{b} + \frac{c}{d} = \frac{a \times d}{b \times d} + \frac{b \times c}{b \times d} \qquad \text{(Renaming.)}$$

$$= \frac{(a \times d) + (b \times c)}{b \times d}. \qquad \begin{array}{l}\text{(Using the definition of}\\ \text{addition for fractions with}\\ \text{the same denominators.)}\end{array}$$

We see, then, that our definition of addition can be used to find the sum of *any* two rational numbers. This "general" example also shows a quick way of obtaining a fraction for the sum of any two rational numbers. You can follow the pattern $(a \times d) + (b \times c)$ to find the numerator and use the product of the denominators $(b \times d)$ for the denominator. Let us illustrate this convenient pattern to find the sum of the rational numbers $\frac{3}{5}$ and $\frac{2}{7}$. The numerator is $(3 \times 7) + (5 \times 2)$ and the denominator is 5×7, thus:

$$\frac{3}{5} + \frac{2}{7} = \frac{(3 \times 7) + (5 \times 2)}{5 \times 7}$$

$$= \frac{21 + 10}{35}$$

$$= \frac{31}{35}.$$

It is not necessary, however, to use the product of the two denominators as common denominator in adding rational numbers. Any common integer multiple will do. For example, we have

$$\frac{1}{6} + \frac{^-1}{9} = \frac{3}{18} + \frac{^-2}{18}$$

$$= \frac{3 + ^-2}{18}$$

$$= \frac{1}{18}.$$

We comment, finally, on the fact that our definition of addition of rational numbers is consistent with the addition of integers, in the sense that the sum of the rational numbers $\frac{a}{1}$ and $\frac{b}{1}$, where a and b represent integers, is given by $\frac{a+b}{1}$. This corresponds to the integer $a + b$, the sum of the integers a and b.

Exercise Set 5

1. Make an arrow diagram to show each of the following sums:

   a. $\dfrac{^-7}{3} + \dfrac{^-4}{3}$

   b. $\dfrac{^-7}{3} + \dfrac{4}{3}$

   c. $\dfrac{7}{3} + \dfrac{4}{3}$

   d. $\dfrac{7}{3} + \dfrac{^-4}{3}$

2. Solve for n:

   a. $\left|\dfrac{^-7}{3}\right| = n.$ e. $\left|\dfrac{3}{3}\right| = n.$

   b. $\left|\dfrac{4}{3}\right| = n.$ f. $\left|\dfrac{^-3}{3}\right| = n.$

   c. $\left|\dfrac{^-4}{3}\right| = n.$ g. $\left|\dfrac{^-11}{3}\right| = n.$

   d. $\left|\dfrac{7}{3}\right| = n.$ h. $\left|\dfrac{11}{3}\right| = n.$

3. Find the simplest fraction name or the common name for each of the following.

   a. $\dfrac{^-7}{9} + \dfrac{5}{6}$ d. $\left(\dfrac{13}{20} + \dfrac{5}{6}\right) + \dfrac{^-7}{12}$

   b. $\left(\dfrac{^-5}{12} + \dfrac{7}{6}\right) + \dfrac{^-3}{4}$ e. $\dfrac{13}{20} + \left(\dfrac{5}{6} + \dfrac{^-7}{12}\right)$

   c. $\dfrac{^-5}{12} + \left(\dfrac{7}{6} + \dfrac{^-3}{4}\right)$ f. $\dfrac{^-17}{10} + \dfrac{13}{6}$

4. Find n to make each sentence true.

a. $\dfrac{5}{8} + n = \dfrac{1}{8}.$ Think: $\dfrac{5}{8} + \dfrac{x}{8} = \dfrac{1}{8}$,

$$\dfrac{5 + x}{8} = \dfrac{1}{8}, \text{ so}$$

$$5 + x = 1,$$

$$5 + {}^-4 = 1,$$

$$x = {}^-4,$$

$$n = \dfrac{{}^-4}{8}.$$

b. $n + \dfrac{{}^-2}{3} = \dfrac{5}{3}.$ **e.** $\dfrac{{}^-5}{8} + n = \dfrac{{}^-1}{8}.$

c. $n + \dfrac{{}^-2}{3} = \dfrac{{}^-5}{3}.$ **f.** $\dfrac{{}^-5}{16} + n = \dfrac{3}{4}.$

d. $\dfrac{{}^-5}{8} + n = \dfrac{1}{8}.$ **g.** $\dfrac{7}{22} + n = \dfrac{{}^-3}{2}.$

Properties of Addition

In Booklet No. 9: *The System of Integers* we noted that the operation of *addition* in the set of integers has the following properties:

CLOSURE
If a and b are integers, then $a + b$ is an integer.

COMMUTATIVITY
For any two integers a and b, $a + b = b + a$.

ASSOCIATIVITY
For any three integers a, b, and c, $(a + b) + c = a + (b + c)$.

ADDITIVE IDENTITY
There is an integer, 0, such that for every integer a, $a + 0 = 0 + a = a$.

ADDITIVE-INVERSE ELEMENT
For every integer a, there is an integer ${}^\circ a$ such that $a + {}^\circ a = 0$.

We have found that it is reasonable to define the sum of two rational numbers, $\frac{a}{b}$ and $\frac{c}{d}$, where a and c represent integers and b and d represent nonzero integers, as

$$\frac{a}{b} + \frac{c}{d} = \frac{(a \times d) + (b \times c)}{b \times d}.$$

Will all of these properties then be true for the addition of rational numbers? Let us see whether this is the case.

1. *Closure Property of Addition*: If $\frac{a}{b}$ and $\frac{c}{d}$ represent rational numbers, does

$$\frac{(a \times d) + (b \times c)}{b \times d}$$

represent a rational number?

Let us look at the sum

$$\frac{^-2}{3} + \frac{5}{^-6} = \frac{(^-2 \times ^-6) + (3 \times 5)}{3 \times ^-6}.$$

Is $^-2 \times ^-6$ an integer? Is 3×5 an integer? Is $(^-2 \times ^-6) + (3 \times 5)$ an integer? The correct answer to each question is "yes." Thus, the numerator of the fraction above is a specified integer. The denominator $3 \times ^-6$ is also a specified integer, different from zero. So we see that

$$\frac{(^-2 \times ^-6) + (3 \times 5)}{3 \times ^-6}$$

does specify a rational number because the numerator is a specified integer and the denominator is a specified nonzero integer. In a similar way it can be shown that if $\frac{a}{b}$ and $\frac{c}{d}$ are rational numbers, then $\frac{a}{b} + \frac{c}{d}$ is a rational number.

2. *Commutative Property of Addition*: If $\frac{a}{b}$ and $\frac{c}{d}$ are rational numbers, is it true that

$$\frac{a}{b} + \frac{c}{d} = \frac{c}{d} + \frac{a}{b} ?$$

An example should help us see that the correct answer again is "yes." Is

$$\frac{^-2}{3} + \frac{5}{^-6} = \frac{5}{^-6} + \frac{2}{^-3}$$

a true sentence? Now

$$\frac{^-2}{3} + \frac{5}{^-6} = \frac{(^-2 \times ^-6) + (3 \times 5)}{3 \times ^-6}$$

and

$$\frac{5}{^-6} + \frac{^-2}{3} = \frac{(5 \times 3) + (^-6 \times ^-2)}{^-6 \times 3}.$$

Is it true that

$$\frac{(^-2 \times ^-6) + (3 \times 5)}{3 \times ^-6} = \frac{(5 \times 3) + (^-6 \times ^-2)}{^-6 \times 3} ?$$

Is it true that

$$^-2 \times ^-6 = ^-6 \times ^-2,$$
$$3 \times 5 = 5 \times 3,$$

and

$$3 \times ^-6 = ^-6 \times 3 ?$$

These statements are all true because multiplication is commutative in the

set of integers. Also
$$(^-2 \times {}^-6) + (3 \times 5) = (3 \times 5) + (^-2 \times {}^-6),$$
because addition is commutative in the set of integers, and
$$(^-2 \times {}^-6) + (3 \times 5) = (5 \times 3) + (^-6 \times {}^-2)$$
because multiplication is commutative in the set of integers. Hence
$$\frac{^-2}{3} + \frac{5}{^-6} = \frac{5}{^-6} + \frac{^-2}{3}.$$
The same kind of argument can be applied to the sum of any two rational numbers to give
$$\frac{a}{b} + \frac{c}{d} = \frac{c}{d} + \frac{a}{b} \text{ for any rational numbers } \frac{a}{b} \text{ and } \frac{c}{d}.$$

3. *Associative Property of Addition*: Is it true, for any rational numbers $\frac{a}{b}, \frac{c}{d},$ and $\frac{e}{f},$ that
$$\left(\frac{a}{b} + \frac{c}{d}\right) + \frac{e}{f} = \frac{a}{b} + \left(\frac{c}{d} + \frac{e}{f}\right)?$$
For example, is it true that
$$\left(\frac{^-2}{3} + \frac{5}{^-6}\right) + \frac{3}{4} = \frac{^-2}{3} + \left(\frac{5}{^-6} + \frac{3}{4}\right)?$$

The left-hand member gives us	The right-hand member gives us
$\left(\dfrac{^-2}{3} + \dfrac{5}{^-6}\right) + \dfrac{3}{4}$	$\dfrac{^-2}{3} + \left(\dfrac{5}{^-6} + \dfrac{3}{4}\right)$
$= \dfrac{(^-2 \times {}^-6) + (3 \times 5)}{(3 \times {}^-6)} + \dfrac{3}{4}$	$= \dfrac{^-2}{3} + \dfrac{(5 \times 4) + (^-6 \times 3)}{(^-6 \times 4)}$
$= \dfrac{12 + 15}{^-18} + \dfrac{3}{4}$	$= \dfrac{^-2}{3} + \dfrac{20 + {}^-18}{^-24}$
$= \dfrac{27}{^-18} + \dfrac{3}{4}$	$= \dfrac{^-2}{3} + \dfrac{2}{^-24}$
$= \dfrac{(27 \times 4) + (^-18 \times 3)}{^-18 \times 4}$	$= \dfrac{(^-2 \times {}^-24) + (3 \times 2)}{(3 \times {}^-24)}$
$= \dfrac{108 + {}^-54}{^-72}$	$= \dfrac{48 + 6}{^-72}$
$= \dfrac{54}{^-72}$	$= \dfrac{54}{^-72}$
$= \dfrac{^-3}{4}.$	$= \dfrac{^-3}{4}.$

Thus we see that
$$\left(\frac{^-2}{3} + \frac{5}{^-6}\right) + \frac{3}{4} = \frac{^-2}{3} + \left(\frac{5}{^-6} + \frac{3}{4}\right).$$
This example suggests that the addition of rational numbers has the associative property, and this is in fact true: For all rational numbers $\frac{a}{b}, \frac{c}{d},$ and $\frac{e}{f},$

$$\left(\frac{a}{b} + \frac{c}{d}\right) + \frac{e}{f} = \frac{a}{b} + \left(\frac{c}{d} + \frac{e}{f}\right).$$

4. *Identity Element for Addition*: Is there a rational number $\frac{c}{d}$ such that for all rational numbers $\frac{a}{b}$ we have

$$\frac{a}{b} + \frac{c}{d} = \frac{a}{b}\,?$$

We know that 0 is the identity element for addition of integers. This suggests that 0, regarded as a member of the set of rational numbers, might be the identity element for addition of rational numbers. Now 0 can be named by $\frac{0}{1}$ or $\frac{0}{2}$ or $\frac{-0}{7}$ or $\frac{0}{b}$, where $b \neq 0$. Finding the sum of $\frac{a}{b}$ and $\frac{0}{b}$, we get

$$\frac{a}{b} + \frac{0}{b} = \frac{a+0}{b} = \frac{a}{b}.$$

Thus we have $\frac{a}{b} + \frac{0}{b} = \frac{a}{b}$, or equivalently $\frac{a}{b} + 0 = \frac{a}{b}$, and zero is an identity element for addition of rational numbers. It is, in fact, the *only* identity element for addition, since for any such elements 0 and 0' we would have $0 + 0' = 0$ and $0 + 0' = 0'$, and hence $0 = 0'$.

5. *Additive-Inverse Element*: Recall that the additive inverse of an integer is an integer such that the sum of the two integers is 0. For example, 5 is the additive inverse of ⁻5, because ⁻5 + 5 = 0. Also ⁻5 is the additive inverse of 5.

This suggests that the additive inverse of a rational number might be its opposite. We expect the additive inverse of $\frac{3}{4}$, for example, to be $°(\frac{3}{4})$, the opposite of $\frac{3}{4}$. Let us see if this is true. Recall that $°(\frac{3}{4}) = {}^-(\frac{3}{4})$ and also that $^-(\frac{3}{4}) = \frac{-3}{4}$. Then

$$\frac{3}{4} + °\left(\frac{3}{4}\right) = \frac{3}{4} + \frac{-3}{4}$$

$$= \frac{3 + {}^-3}{4} = \frac{0}{4}$$

$$= 0.$$

So the additive inverse of $\frac{3}{4}$ is $°(\frac{3}{4})$, or $\frac{-3}{4}$. Also $\frac{3}{4}$ is the additive inverse of $\frac{-3}{4}$. Similarly, $\frac{11}{7}$ and $\frac{-11}{7}$ are additive inverses of each other. Every rational number has an additive inverse. The additive inverse of $\frac{a}{b}$ is $°(\frac{a}{b})$, which can also be written $\overset{\bullet}{\frac{a}{b}}$. Notice that, as with the integers, the additive inverse of zero is zero, since $0 + 0 = 0$.

Exercise Set 6

1. What property of addition is illustrated by each of the following:

a. $\dfrac{-5}{8} + \dfrac{3}{4} = \dfrac{3}{4} + \dfrac{-5}{8}.$

b. $\dfrac{^-5}{8} + \dfrac{5}{8} = 0.$

c. $\dfrac{^-5}{8} + 0 = \dfrac{^-5}{8}.$

d. $\dfrac{^-7}{6} + \left(\dfrac{^-5}{8} + \dfrac{3}{4}\right) = \left(\dfrac{^-7}{6} + \dfrac{^-5}{8}\right) + \dfrac{3}{4}.$

2. If n is a rational number such that $n + \frac{^-2}{5} = \frac{7}{8}$, we can show that $n = \frac{7}{8} + \frac{2}{5}$. What properties are illustrated in steps **b** through **e** of the argument below?

a. $n + \dfrac{^-2}{5} = \dfrac{7}{8}.$ (Given.)

b. $\left(n + \dfrac{^-2}{5}\right) + \dfrac{2}{5} = \dfrac{7}{8} + \dfrac{2}{5}.$

c. $n + \left(\dfrac{^-2}{5} + \dfrac{2}{5}\right) = \dfrac{7}{8} + \dfrac{2}{5}.$

d. $n + 0 = \dfrac{7}{8} + \dfrac{2}{5}.$

e. $n = \dfrac{7}{8} + \dfrac{2}{5}.$

Subtraction of Rational Numbers

Recall that in the system of whole numbers and in the system of integers, to subtract a number b from a number a means to find a number c such that $b + c = a$. The number $6 - 2$ is 4, because $2 + 4 = 6$, and the number $3 - (^-5)$ is 8, because $^-5 + 8 = 3$. Recall also from Booklet No. 9: *The System of Integers* that subtraction of an integer b from an integer a is accomplished by *adding* to a the additive inverse, or opposite, of b. In symbolic form, this is written

$$a - b = a + {}^\circ b.$$

In the system of whole numbers, subtraction is not always possible. For example, there is no whole number x such that $2 - 7 = x$. In the system of integers, however, subtraction is always possible. The reason for this is that every integer has an additive inverse.

What about subtraction in the system of rational numbers? Is it possible to subtract $\frac{5}{12}$ from $\frac{1}{4}$? We write $\frac{1}{4} - \frac{5}{12}$ for the number we seek. Let us denote $\frac{1}{4} - \frac{5}{12}$ by x. Then x is the rational number (if there is one) such that

$$x + \frac{5}{12} = \frac{1}{4},$$

because this is what we mean by subtraction. The additive inverse (or

THE SYSTEM OF RATIONAL NUMBERS

opposite) of $\frac{5}{12}$, denoted by $°(\frac{5}{12})$, is $\frac{-5}{12}$. Adding this number to both sides of the sentence $x + \frac{5}{12} = \frac{1}{4}$, we get

$$\left(x + \frac{5}{12}\right) + \frac{-5}{12} = \frac{1}{4} + \frac{-5}{12}.^2$$

Then

$$x + \left(\frac{5}{12} + \frac{-5}{12}\right) = \frac{1}{4} + \frac{-5}{12},$$

by the associative property of addition. Since $\frac{5}{12} + \frac{-5}{12} = 0$, we have

$$x + 0 = \frac{1}{4} + \frac{-5}{12},$$

and

$$x = \frac{1}{4} + \frac{-5}{12}.$$

You can check that this value does indeed satisfy the equation $x + \frac{5}{12} = \frac{1}{4}$. Thus, just as for integers, the subtraction of $\frac{5}{12}$ from $\frac{1}{4}$ is accomplished by adding to $\frac{1}{4}$ the additive inverse, $\frac{-5}{12}$, of $\frac{5}{12}$.

Thus we see that to subtract a rational number $\frac{c}{d}$ from a rational number $\frac{a}{b}$, we add to $\frac{a}{b}$ the additive inverse of $\frac{c}{d}$. In symbolic form, this is written

$$\frac{a}{b} - \frac{c}{d} = \frac{a}{b} + °\left(\frac{c}{d}\right).$$

Since every rational number has an additive inverse (or opposite), subtraction is always possible in the rational number system.

The operation of subtraction is the inverse operation of addition: the two operations "undo" each other. Thus

$$\left(\frac{a}{b} - \frac{c}{d}\right) + \frac{c}{d} = \frac{a}{b}$$

and

$$\left(\frac{a}{b} + \frac{c}{d}\right) - \frac{c}{d} = \frac{a}{b}.$$

Opposite of a Sum

We have seen that the associative property of addition justifies the omission of parentheses in an expression such as $\frac{-4}{9} + (\frac{5}{6} + \frac{2}{3})$, because for all rational numbers a, b, and c, $a + (b + c) = (a + b) + c$.

Does the associative property apply to an expression that involves subtraction, such as $\frac{-4}{9} - (\frac{5}{6} + \frac{2}{3})$? That is, is it true that

---

² Note that $x + \frac{5}{12}$ and $\frac{1}{4}$ are names for the same number. Thus adding $\frac{-5}{12}$ to that number yields exactly one number as sum, regardless of the numerals used. This is implied by the closure property for addition but is sometimes formalized by the statement that if $a = b$, then $a + c = b + c$.

$$\frac{^-4}{9} - \left(\frac{5}{6} + \frac{2}{3}\right) = \left(\frac{^-4}{9} - \frac{5}{6}\right) + \frac{2}{3} ?$$

The left-hand expression gives us	The right-hand expression gives us
$\frac{^-4}{9} - \left(\frac{5}{6} + \frac{2}{3}\right) = \frac{^-4}{9} - \left(\frac{5}{6} + \frac{4}{6}\right)$	$\left(\frac{^-4}{9} - \frac{5}{6}\right) + \frac{2}{3} = \left(\frac{^-4}{9} + \frac{^-5}{6}\right) + \frac{2}{3}$
$= \frac{^-4}{9} - \left(\frac{9}{6}\right)$	$= \left(\frac{^-8}{18} + \frac{^-15}{18}\right) + \frac{2}{3}$
$= \frac{^-4}{9} + \frac{^-9}{6}$	$= \frac{^-23}{18} + \frac{2}{3}$
$= \frac{^-8}{18} + \frac{^-27}{18}$	$= \frac{^-23}{18} + \frac{12}{18}$
$= \frac{^-35}{18}.$	$= \frac{^-11}{18}.$

It is clear that the associative property does *not* apply in this example. The definition of subtraction implies that

$$\frac{^-4}{9} - \left(\frac{5}{6} + \frac{2}{3}\right) = \frac{^-4}{9} + {}^\circ\!\left(\frac{5}{6} + \frac{2}{3}\right).$$

But how do we find the opposite of a sum?

Perhaps you guess that the opposite of a sum is the sum of the opposites. For $(\frac{5}{6} + \frac{2}{3})$ that would be saying that

$${}^\circ\!\left(\frac{5}{6} + \frac{2}{3}\right) = {}^\circ\!\left(\frac{5}{6}\right) + {}^\circ\!\left(\frac{2}{3}\right).$$

Is this true? Yes it is, because

$${}^\circ\!\left(\frac{5}{6} + \frac{2}{3}\right) = {}^\circ\!\left(\frac{5}{6} + \frac{4}{6}\right)$$

$$= {}^\circ\!\left(\frac{5 + 4}{6}\right)$$

$$= {}^\circ\!\left(\frac{9}{6}\right)$$

$$= \frac{^-9}{6},$$

and also

$${}^\circ\!\left(\frac{5}{6}\right) + {}^\circ\!\left(\frac{2}{3}\right) = {}^\circ\!\left(\frac{5}{6}\right) + {}^\circ\!\left(\frac{4}{6}\right)$$

$$= \frac{^-5}{6} + \frac{^-4}{6}$$

$$= \frac{^-5 + {}^-4}{6}$$

$$= \frac{^-9}{6}.$$

In general terms, if $\frac{a}{b}$ and $\frac{c}{d}$ are any two rationals, then

$$^\circ\left(\frac{a}{b} + \frac{c}{d}\right) = {}^\circ\left(\frac{a}{b}\right) + {}^\circ\left(\frac{c}{d}\right).$$

We can now compute $\frac{-4}{9} - [(\frac{5}{6}) + (\frac{2}{3})]$ as follows:

$$\frac{-4}{9} - \left(\frac{5}{6} + \frac{2}{3}\right)$$

$$= \frac{-4}{9} + {}^\circ\left(\frac{5}{6} + \frac{2}{3}\right) \qquad \text{(Definition of subtraction.)}$$

$$= \frac{-4}{9} + \left[{}^\circ\left(\frac{5}{6}\right) + {}^\circ\left(\frac{2}{3}\right)\right] \qquad \left[{}^\circ\left(\frac{a}{b} + \frac{c}{d}\right) = {}^\circ\left(\frac{a}{b}\right) + {}^\circ\left(\frac{c}{d}\right).\right]$$

$$= \frac{-4}{9} + \left(\frac{-5}{6} + \frac{-2}{3}\right) \qquad \left[{}^\circ\left(\frac{5}{6}\right) = \frac{-5}{6} \text{ and } {}^\circ\left(\frac{2}{3}\right) = \frac{-2}{3}.\right]$$

$$= \frac{-4}{9} + \frac{-9}{6}$$

$$= \frac{-8}{18} + \frac{-27}{18}$$

$$= \frac{-35}{18}.$$

Notice that this result agrees with the earlier computation of $\frac{-4}{9} - (\frac{5}{6} + \frac{2}{3})$ on page 100, where we first found the sum $\frac{5}{6} + \frac{2}{3}$ and then subtracted this sum from $\frac{-4}{9}$.

Mixed Forms

Consider the fractions $\frac{3}{4}$, $\frac{4}{4}$, $\frac{7}{4}$, and $\frac{11}{4}$. The number named by $\frac{4}{4}$ can be renamed more simply as $\frac{1}{1}$ or 1. The fractions $\frac{3}{4}$, $\frac{7}{4}$, and $\frac{11}{4}$ are in simplest form. Positive numbers such as $\frac{7}{4}$ and $\frac{11}{4}$, however, are frequently named in a different way, as the sum of an integer and a positive rational number less than one. Thus,

$$\frac{7}{4} = \frac{4+3}{4} = \frac{4}{4} + \frac{3}{4} = 1 + \frac{3}{4}.$$

This sum is usually written without the symbol "$+$," as $1\frac{3}{4}$. Similarly we write

$$\frac{11}{4} = \frac{8+3}{4} = \frac{8}{4} + \frac{3}{4} = 2 + \frac{3}{4} = 2\frac{3}{4}.$$

A numeral of this kind is often called a "mixed form," or "mixed number."

Negative rationals may be renamed in a similar way as negatives of positive mixed numbers. Thus $\frac{-7}{4}$ can be renamed as follows:

$$\frac{^-7}{4} = {}^-\!\left(\frac{7}{4}\right) = {}^-\!\left(1\,\frac{3}{4}\right), \quad \text{or often} \quad {}^-1\,\frac{3}{4}.$$

If we are given a "mixed form," such as $^-2\frac{5}{8}$, we can find an equivalent fraction name by reversing the process. Thus we have

$$^-2\,\frac{5}{8} = {}^-\!\left(2\,\frac{5}{8}\right) = {}^-\!\left(2 + \frac{5}{8}\right)$$
$$= {}^-\!\left(\frac{16}{8} + \frac{5}{8}\right)$$
$$= {}^-\!\left(\frac{16 + 5}{8}\right)$$
$$= {}^-\!\left(\frac{21}{8}\right), \quad \text{or} \quad \frac{^-21}{8}.$$

Mixed forms are frequently used to record measurements. For example, if a person's height is 5 feet $6\frac{1}{2}$ inches, he would hardly say, "I am 5 feet $\frac{13}{2}$ inches tall," nor would a baseball announcer say, "Now $\frac{11}{2}$ innings of the game are history."

Mixed forms are often used to find sums of rational numbers. The associative and commutative properties assure us, for example, that

$$2\,\frac{1}{2} + 8\,\frac{1}{3} = \left(2 + \frac{1}{2}\right) + \left(8 + \frac{1}{3}\right)$$
$$= 2 + \left(\frac{1}{2} + 8\right) + \frac{1}{3}$$
$$= 2 + \left(8 + \frac{1}{2}\right) + \frac{1}{3}$$
$$= (2 + 8) + \left(\frac{1}{2} + \frac{1}{3}\right)$$
$$= 10 + \left(\frac{1}{2} + \frac{1}{3}\right)$$
$$= 10 + \left(\frac{3}{6} + \frac{2}{6}\right)$$
$$= 10\,\frac{5}{6}.$$

As an example of subtraction of rational numbers named by mixed forms, consider

$$2\,\frac{1}{2} - 8\,\frac{1}{3}, \quad \text{or} \quad \left(2 + \frac{1}{2}\right) - \left(8 + \frac{1}{3}\right).$$

Subtraction does not have the associative and commutative properties; so we use the definition of subtraction and the fact that the opposite of a sum is the sum of the opposites. Thus we have

$$\left(2 + \frac{1}{2}\right) - \left(8 + \frac{1}{3}\right) = \left(2 + \frac{1}{2}\right) + {}^{\circ}\left(8 + \frac{1}{3}\right)$$

$$= 2 + \frac{1}{2} + {}^{-}8 + \frac{{}^{-}1}{3}$$

$$= (2 + {}^{-}8) + \left(\frac{1}{2} + \frac{{}^{-}1}{3}\right)$$

$$= {}^{-}6 + \frac{1}{6}$$

$$= {}^{-}5\frac{5}{6}.$$

In the last three steps we use the familiar properties of addition of rational numbers.

Exercise Set 7

1. Use the fact that $\frac{a}{b} - \frac{c}{d} = \frac{x}{y}$ means that $\frac{a}{b} = \frac{c}{d} + \frac{x}{y}$ to write an addition sentence equivalent to each subtraction sentence and a subtraction sentence equivalent to each addition sentence.

a. $\dfrac{9}{10} + \dfrac{{}^{-}7}{8} = \dfrac{1}{40}.$

d. $n - \dfrac{17}{3} = \dfrac{5}{6}.$

b. $\dfrac{7}{12} - \dfrac{{}^{-}3}{4} = \dfrac{4}{3}.$

e. $7\dfrac{1}{8} - n = {}^{-}1\dfrac{1}{4}.$

c. ${}^{-}1\dfrac{3}{4} + 2\dfrac{1}{6} = \dfrac{5}{12}.$

f. $\dfrac{{}^{-}14}{7} + \dfrac{{}^{-}5}{14} = n.$

2. Which of the following sentences are true?

a. ${}^{\circ}\left(\dfrac{7}{8} + \dfrac{{}^{-}3}{4}\right) = \dfrac{{}^{-}7}{8} + \dfrac{{}^{-}3}{4}.$

c. ${}^{\circ}\left(\dfrac{7}{8} + \dfrac{{}^{-}3}{4}\right) = \dfrac{{}^{-}7}{8} + \dfrac{3}{4}.$

b. ${}^{\circ}\left(\dfrac{7}{8} - \dfrac{{}^{-}3}{4}\right) = \dfrac{{}^{-}7}{8} + \dfrac{3}{4}.$

d. ${}^{\circ}\left(\dfrac{7}{8} + \dfrac{{}^{-}3}{4}\right) = \dfrac{7}{8} + \dfrac{3}{4}.$

3. Show why each sentence is true.

a. ${}^{-}7\dfrac{3}{8} = \dfrac{{}^{-}59}{8}.$

c. $\dfrac{{}^{-}13}{7} = {}^{-}1\dfrac{6}{7}.$

b. $\dfrac{64}{11} = 5\dfrac{9}{11}.$

d. $\dfrac{37}{18} = 2\dfrac{1}{18}.$

4. Find the value of n that makes each sentence true.

a. $\dfrac{7}{15} - \dfrac{19}{30} = n.$

c. ${}^{-}3\dfrac{1}{8} - 12\dfrac{1}{16} = n.$

b. $\dfrac{{}^{-}17}{12} - \dfrac{{}^{-}11}{6} = n.$

d. $9\dfrac{3}{4} + {}^{-}2\dfrac{7}{8} = n.$

MULTIPLICATION AND DIVISION OF RATIONAL NUMBERS

The Product of Two Rational Numbers

How shall the product of any two rational numbers be defined? Recall the definitions of multiplication of numbers in the following two subsets of the set of rational numbers:

1. Those rational numbers named by fractions whose numerators are whole numbers and whose denominators are natural numbers

   This includes numbers such as $\frac{0}{2}$, $\frac{5}{1}$, $\frac{4}{7}$, and $\frac{13}{125}$. The product of $\frac{4}{7}$ and $\frac{13}{125}$, for example, is

$$\frac{4}{7} \times \frac{13}{125} = \frac{4 \times 13}{7 \times 125} = \frac{52}{875}.$$

For rational numbers $\frac{a}{b}$ and $\frac{c}{d}$ in this set, we have

$$\frac{a}{b} \times \frac{c}{d} = \frac{a \times c}{b \times d}.$$

2. The integers, that is, the set $\{ \cdots, {}^-2, {}^-1, 0, 1, 2, \cdots \}$

   Multiplication in this set is illustrated by the following examples:

$${}^-3 \times 2 = {}^-6, \quad 3 \times {}^-2 = {}^-6, \quad {}^-3 \times {}^-2 = 6, \quad \text{and } 3 \times 2 = 6.$$

The general definition of multiplication of rational numbers should preferably be consistent with the definition of multiplication for these subsets. The following definition accomplishes this.

If $\frac{a}{b}$ and $\frac{c}{d}$ are any two rational numbers, where a, b, c, and d are integers and b and d are not 0, then

$$\frac{a}{b} \times \frac{c}{d} = \frac{a \times c}{b \times d}.$$

Since the positive rational numbers correspond to the members of the first subset mentioned above, this definition is consistent with the definition of multiplication for that subset. The product of the rational numbers $\frac{5}{1}$ and $\frac{-6}{1}$, according to this definition, is $\frac{5 \times {}^-6}{1 \times 1}$, or $\frac{{}^-30}{1}$, which corresponds to the product of the integers 5 and ${}^-6$: $5 \times {}^-6$, or ${}^-30$. This illustrates that consistency with multiplication of integers has also been achieved.

It is essential that no matter which representative fractions are chosen as names for the rational numbers, the product yielded by the definition should be the same. This is the case with our definition, a fact that is illustrated by the following example. Let us find the product of the rational numbers *two-thirds* and *negative four-fifths*, using first the fractions $\frac{2}{3}$ and $\frac{-4}{5}$, then $\frac{4}{6}$ and $\frac{4}{=5}$, and then $\frac{-2}{=3}$ and $\frac{-8}{10}$ for the two rational numbers:

$$\frac{2}{3} \times \frac{^-4}{5} = \frac{2 \times ^-4}{3 \times 5}$$
$$= \frac{^-8}{15}.$$

$$\frac{4}{6} \times \frac{4}{^-5} = \frac{4 \times 4}{6 \times ^-5}$$
$$= \frac{16}{^-30} = \frac{^-16}{30}$$
$$= \frac{^-8 \times 2}{15 \times 2}$$
$$= \frac{^-8}{15}.$$

$$\frac{^-2}{^-3} \times \frac{^-8}{10} = \frac{^-2 \times ^-8}{^-3 \times 10}$$
$$= \frac{16}{^-30} = \frac{^-16}{30}$$
$$= \frac{^-8}{15}.$$

Thus the product in each case is the same.

Recall that in each of the two subsets mentioned, the identity element for multiplication is the number 1. For example, $1 \times \frac{6}{5} = \frac{6}{5} \times 1 = \frac{6}{5}$ and $1 \times ^-7 = ^-7 \times 1 = ^-7$. What happens when we multiply *any* rational number $\frac{a}{b}$ by the rational number *one*, $\frac{1}{1}$? From our definition of multiplication,

$$\frac{a}{b} \times \frac{1}{1} = \frac{a \times 1}{b \times 1}$$
$$= \frac{a}{b}. \quad (a \times 1 = a \text{ is known to be true for integers.})$$

Similarly, $\frac{1}{1} \times \frac{a}{b} = \frac{a}{b}$. For this reason the rational number 1 is called the *multiplicative identity element* for the set of rational numbers. Again, this property of 1 does not depend on the fractional form that is used to represent it. Thus, for example,

$$\frac{a}{b} \times \frac{4}{4} = \frac{a \times 4}{b \times 4}$$
$$= \frac{a}{b}, \quad \text{because } \frac{a \times 4}{b \times 4} \text{ is equivalent to } \frac{a}{b}.$$

Now we come to an important property of rational numbers, a property that is shared by the first subset, the set of nonnegative rational numbers, but that is not shared by the second, the set of integers. Corresponding to any rational number other than zero, there is a unique rational number such that the product of the two numbers is 1. Thus, corresponding to $\frac{4}{5}$ there is $\frac{5}{4}$, where $\frac{4}{5} \times \frac{5}{4} = \frac{4 \times 5}{5 \times 4} = \frac{1}{1}$. We say that $\frac{5}{4}$ is the *multiplicative inverse* of $\frac{4}{5}$ and that $\frac{4}{5}$ is the multiplicative inverse of $\frac{5}{4}$.

What is the multiplicative inverse of $\frac{^-2}{3}$? What rational number, paired with $\frac{^-2}{3}$, yields the product 1? The answer is $\frac{3}{^-2}$ because

$$\frac{^-2}{3} \times \frac{3}{^-2} = \frac{^-2 \times 3}{3 \times ^-2}$$
$$= \frac{^-6}{^-6} = \frac{1}{1}.$$

To summarize, the multiplicative inverse of the rational number denoted by the fraction $\frac{a}{b}$, where the integer a is not zero (and, of course, the integer b is not zero either), is $\frac{b}{a}$ because

$$\frac{a}{b} \times \frac{b}{a} = \frac{a \times b}{b \times a}$$

$$= \frac{a \times b}{a \times b} \qquad \text{(Multiplication of integers is commutative.)}$$

$$= \frac{1}{1}. \qquad \left(\frac{a \times b}{a \times b} \text{ is equivalent to } \frac{1}{1}. \right)$$

Thus $\frac{b}{a}$, the *reciprocal* of $\frac{a}{b}$, is the multiplicative inverse of the nonzero rational number denoted by the fraction $\frac{a}{b}$.

The number zero, $\frac{0}{1}$, has no multiplicative inverse. There is no rational number $\frac{a}{b}$ such that $\frac{0}{1} \times \frac{a}{b} = \frac{1}{1}$ because for any rational number $\frac{a}{b}$

$$\frac{0}{1} \times \frac{a}{b} = \frac{0 \times a}{1 \times b}$$

$$= \frac{0}{1}, \qquad \text{which is not equal to} \quad \frac{1}{1}.$$

The result of multiplying by 0 is the same for rational numbers as it is in each of the subsets. If $\frac{a}{b}$ is any rational number, then

$$\frac{a}{b} \times \frac{0}{1} = \frac{a \times 0}{b \times 1} \qquad \text{(From definition of multiplication.)}$$

$$= \frac{0}{b} \qquad (a \times 0 = 0 \text{ and } b \times 1 = b \text{ for integers.})$$

$$= \frac{0}{1}. \qquad \left(\frac{0}{b} \text{ and } \frac{0}{1} \text{ are equivalent.} \right)$$

Similarly, $\frac{0}{1} \times \frac{a}{b} = \frac{0}{1}$. *The product of any rational number and zero is zero.* Furthermore, *if the product of two rational numbers is 0, at least one of the numbers is 0.*

Exercise Set 8

1. Consider the two pairs of equivalent fractions

$$\frac{^-5}{9}, \frac{15}{^-27} \quad \text{and} \quad \frac{7}{10}, \frac{14}{20}.$$

Form four products, each involving one fraction from the first pair and one fraction from the second pair, to illustrate the fact that the product of two rational numbers is not affected by the fractions used to name the numbers.

2. Using the rational number $\frac{^-25}{^-17}$, illustrate that $\frac{1}{1}$ is the identity element for multiplication of rational numbers.

3. Consider the numerals

$$\left(\frac{2}{3} \times \frac{^-4}{5}\right) + \left(\frac{2}{3} \times \frac{3}{8}\right) \quad \text{and} \quad \frac{2}{3} \times \left(\frac{^-4}{5} + \frac{3}{8}\right).$$

a. Express each as a single fraction in simplest form.

b. This example should suggest that a familiar property of other sets of numbers is shared by the rationals. Which property?

4. What is the multiplicative inverse of each of the following numbers?

a. $\frac{^-7}{3}$ **b.** $\frac{18}{^-13}$ **c.** $\frac{485}{1}$ **d.** $\frac{3}{97}$

Show that your answer is correct.

5. What is the reciprocal of each number in exercise 4?

6. Consider the numerals

$$\left(\frac{^-12}{5} \times \frac{15}{4}\right) \times \frac{2}{3} \quad \text{and} \quad \frac{^-12}{5} \times \left(\frac{15}{4} \times \frac{2}{3}\right).$$

a. Find a fraction in simplest form for each.

b. What property do the results suggest?

Properties of Multiplication

Recall that in the systems with which you are familiar, multiplication was found to have the properties of closure, commutativity, and associativity, and an identity element. The multiplicative-inverse property was also observed for the positive rationals, but not for the integers. Also, each set was found to have the distributive property of multiplication over addition. Additionally, there is a special multiplicative property of 0. We find that our general definition of multiplication of rational numbers is such that all of these properties continue to be true. Demonstrations that this is the case (mostly omitted here) depend heavily on the properties of integers, because a rational number is defined in terms of an ordered pair of integers (the numerator and denominator of a fraction naming the rational number).

1. *Closure Property of Multiplication*: If $\frac{a}{b}$ and $\frac{c}{d}$ are rational numbers, then the product $\frac{a}{b} \times \frac{c}{d}$ is a rational number.

2. *Commutative Property of Multiplication*: If $\frac{a}{b}$ and $\frac{c}{d}$ are rational numbers, then

$$\frac{a}{b} \times \frac{c}{d} = \frac{c}{d} \times \frac{a}{b}.$$

3. *Associative Property of Multiplication*: If $\frac{a}{b}$, $\frac{c}{d}$, and $\frac{e}{f}$ are rational numbers, then

$$\left(\frac{a}{b} \times \frac{c}{d}\right) \times \frac{e}{f} = \frac{a}{b} \times \left(\frac{c}{d} \times \frac{e}{f}\right).$$

4. *Identity Element for Multiplication*: The rational number one, $\frac{1}{1}$, is the identity element for multiplication; that is, if $\frac{a}{b}$ is any rational number, then

$$\frac{a}{b} \times \frac{1}{1} = \frac{1}{1} \times \frac{a}{b} = \frac{a}{b}.$$

5. *Multiplicative-Inverse Property*: Corresponding to every rational number $\frac{a}{b}$, other than zero, there is a unique rational number $\frac{z}{y}$ such that $\frac{a}{b} \times \frac{z}{y} = 1$. The number $\frac{z}{y}$ is called the multiplicative inverse of the number $\frac{a}{b}$, and $\frac{a}{b}$ is called the multiplicative inverse of $\frac{z}{y}$. The number 0 does not have a multiplicative inverse.

It is worth repeating that the integers do not have the multiplicative-inverse property. As a member of the system of integers, 5 does not have a multiplicative inverse, for there is no integer n such that $5 \times n = 1$. As a member of the system of rational numbers, $\frac{5}{1}$ (which corresponds to 5) does have a multiplicative inverse, $\frac{1}{5}$.

The multiplicative-inverse property makes it possible to solve equations like the following:

$$\frac{^-2}{3} \times n = \frac{1}{5}, \quad \text{and} \quad \frac{4}{7} \times n = \frac{^-3}{8}.$$

Each of these has a rational-number solution. Let us show how the first one can be solved. Multiply both sides by the multiplicative inverse of $\frac{^-2}{3}$, which is $\frac{3}{^-2}$. We have

$$\frac{^-2}{3} \times n = \frac{1}{5},$$

$$\frac{3}{^-2} \times \left(\frac{^-2}{3} \times n\right) = \frac{3}{^-2} \times \frac{1}{5},$$

since $\frac{^-2}{3} \times n$ and $\frac{1}{5}$ name the same rational number. By the associative property we have

$$\left(\frac{3}{^-2} \times \frac{^-2}{3}\right) \times n = \frac{3}{^-2} \times \frac{1}{5},$$

and by the multiplication of multiplicative inverses

$$\frac{1}{1} \times n = \frac{3}{^-2} \times \frac{1}{5}.$$

Finally, since $\frac{1}{1} \times n$ is n, we can write

$$n = \frac{3 \times 1}{^-2 \times 5} = \frac{3}{^-10} = \frac{^-3}{10}.$$

We see that $\frac{^-3}{10}$ is indeed the solution of the equation

$$\frac{^-2}{3} \times n = \frac{1}{5}$$

because the sentence

$$\frac{^-2}{3} \times \frac{^-3}{10} = \frac{6}{30} = \frac{1}{5} \text{ is true.}$$

You can follow a similar process to show that if $\frac{4}{7} \times n = \frac{^-3}{8}$, then $n = \frac{^-21}{32}$, and the converse (see Booklet No. 12: *Logic*, p. 223).

6. *Distributive Property of Multiplication over Addition*: If $\frac{a}{b}$, $\frac{c}{d}$, and $\frac{e}{f}$ are rational numbers, then

$$\frac{a}{b} \times \left(\frac{c}{d} + \frac{e}{f}\right) = \left(\frac{a}{b} \times \frac{c}{d}\right) + \left(\frac{a}{b} \times \frac{e}{f}\right).$$

The justification of this property in general terms is somewhat tedious, though not difficult. Let us content ourselves with an illustration. We show that

$$\frac{3}{4} \times \left(\frac{^-5}{6} + \frac{1}{2}\right) = \left(\frac{3}{4} \times \frac{^-5}{6}\right) + \left(\frac{3}{4} \times \frac{1}{2}\right).$$

On the left side, we first find the sum $\frac{^-5}{6} + \frac{1}{2}$, then multiply it by $\frac{3}{4}$:

$$\frac{3}{4} \times \frac{(^-5 \times 2) + (6 \times 1)}{6 \times 2}$$

$$= \frac{3}{4} \times \frac{^-10 + 6}{12}$$

$$= \frac{3}{4} \times \frac{^-4}{12}$$

$$= \frac{3 \times ^-4}{4 \times 12}$$

$$= \frac{^-12}{48}$$

$$= \frac{^-1}{4}.$$

On the right, we first calculate the products $\frac{3}{4} \times \frac{^-5}{6}$ and $\frac{3}{4} \times \frac{1}{2}$, then find their sum:

$$\frac{3 \times ^-5}{4 \times 6} + \frac{3 \times 1}{4 \times 2}$$

$$= \frac{^-15}{24} + \frac{3}{8}$$

$$= \frac{(^-15 \times 8) + (24 \times 3)}{24 \times 8}$$

$$= \frac{^-120 + 72}{192}$$

$$= \frac{^-48}{192}$$

$$= \frac{^-1}{4}.$$

Thus the two calculations yield the same answer.

7. *Multiplication by Zero*: The product of any rational number and zero is zero; that is, if $\frac{a}{b}$ is any rational number, then

$$\frac{a}{b} \times \frac{0}{1} = \frac{0}{1} \times \frac{a}{b} = \frac{0}{1}.$$

Conversely, if the product of two rational numbers is zero, then at least one of the two factors is zero.

Exercise Set 9

1. List the properties of the operations in the set of rational numbers discussed in the preceding section.

2. Use fractions from the set $\{\frac{-1}{9}, \frac{3}{7}, \frac{-4}{5}\}$ to make an example illustrating each property discussed in the preceding section.

3. Use the fact that $\frac{a}{b} = \frac{a}{1} \times \frac{1}{b} = a \times \frac{1}{b}$ to show how the distributive property can be used to find the following sums.

EXAMPLE: $\dfrac{5}{6} + \dfrac{7}{6} = \left(5 \times \dfrac{1}{6}\right) + \left(7 \times \dfrac{1}{6}\right)$

$= (5 + 7) \times \dfrac{1}{6}$ \qquad (Distributive property.)

$= 12 \times \dfrac{1}{6}$

$= \dfrac{12}{6}$

$= 2.$

a. $\dfrac{4}{11} + \dfrac{13}{11}$ \qquad c. $\dfrac{5}{6} + \dfrac{^-4}{6}$

b. $\dfrac{^-3}{4} + \dfrac{9}{4}$ \qquad d. $\dfrac{1}{13} + \dfrac{^-2}{13} + \dfrac{7}{13}$

Division of Rational Numbers

In the systems of numbers with which you are familiar, the operation of division was defined as the inverse operation of multiplication.[3] Thus in the system of whole numbers,

$$15 \div 3 = 5 \quad \text{because} \quad 3 \times 5 = 15.$$

In the system of nonnegative rationals,

$$\frac{3}{4} \div \frac{1}{2} = \frac{3}{2} \quad \text{because} \quad \frac{1}{2} \times \frac{3}{2} = \frac{3}{4}.$$

In the system of integers,

$$^-15 \div 3 = ^-5 \quad \text{because} \quad 3 \times ^-5 = ^-15.$$

In the system of whole numbers and in the system of integers, division is not always possible. There is no whole number n such that $2 \times n = 5$, and there is no integer n such that $4 \times n = ^-9$. In the second system, that of the nonnegative rationals, division is always possible except for division by zero.

In the system of rational numbers, division is once again defined in terms of multiplication:

[3] See Booklet No. 2: *The Whole Numbers;* Booklet No. 6: *The Rational Numbers;* Booklet No. 9: *The System of Integers.*

If $\frac{a}{b}$ and $\frac{c}{d}$ are any two rational numbers, with $\frac{c}{d} \neq 0$, then $\frac{a}{b} \div \frac{c}{d} = \frac{x}{y}$ means that $\frac{c}{d} \times \frac{x}{y} = \frac{a}{b}$.

We cannot divide by the rational number zero. There is no rational number $\frac{x}{y}$ that corresponds to $\frac{^-4}{3} \div \frac{0}{1}$, since the statement $\frac{^-4}{3} \div \frac{0}{1} = \frac{x}{y}$ would mean that $\frac{^-4}{3} = \frac{0}{1} \times \frac{x}{y}$. This is impossible, because $\frac{0}{1} \times \frac{x}{y} = \frac{0}{y}$, or $\frac{0}{1}$ (the product of zero and any rational number is zero), which is not equal to $\frac{^-4}{3}$. On the other hand, the number zero can be divided by any rational number other than zero, the quotient being zero. For example, $\frac{0}{1} \div \frac{^-4}{15} = \frac{0}{1}$, because

$$\frac{^-4}{15} \times \frac{0}{1} = \frac{0}{15}, \qquad \text{or} \qquad \frac{0}{1}.$$

Now let us use the definition of division in an example.

EXAMPLE: Divide $\frac{^-6}{7}$ by $\frac{2}{3}$.

Solution: If we denote $\left(\frac{^-6}{7}\right) \div \left(\frac{2}{3}\right)$ by $\frac{x}{y}$,

then:

$$\frac{2}{3} \times \frac{x}{y} = \frac{^-6}{7},$$
(Definition of division.)

$$\frac{3}{2} \times \left(\frac{2}{3} \times \frac{x}{y}\right) = \frac{3}{2} \times \frac{^-6}{7},$$
(Multiplying both sides by $\frac{3}{2}$; $\frac{3}{2}$ was chosen because it is the multiplicative inverse of $\frac{2}{3}$.)

$$\left(\frac{3}{2} \times \frac{2}{3}\right) \times \frac{x}{y} = \frac{^-6}{7} \times \frac{3}{2},$$
(Associative property of multiplication, commutative property of multiplication.)

$$1 \times \frac{x}{y} = \frac{^-6}{7} \times \frac{3}{2}, \qquad \left(\frac{3}{2} \times \frac{2}{3} = 1.\right)$$

$$\frac{x}{y} = \frac{^-6}{7} \times \frac{3}{2}. \qquad \left(1 \times \frac{x}{y} = \frac{x}{y}\right)$$

Thus

$$\frac{^-6}{7} \div \frac{2}{3} = \frac{^-6}{7} \times \frac{3}{2}. \qquad \left(\text{Since } \frac{^-6}{7} \div \frac{2}{3} = \frac{x}{y} \text{ and } \frac{x}{y} = \frac{^-6}{7} \times \frac{3}{2}.\right)$$

This example illustrates the fact that dividing by a rational number (other than zero) gives exactly the same result as multiplying by its multiplicative inverse. We can state this fact in the following form:

If $\frac{a}{b}$ and $\frac{c}{d}$ are two rational numbers and $\frac{c}{d} \neq \frac{0}{1}$, then $\frac{a}{b} \div \frac{c}{d} = \frac{a}{b} \times \frac{d}{c}$.

Since every rational number except zero has a multiplicative inverse, division of a rational number by a rational number other than zero is always possible, and the quotient is itself a rational number. Thus, the system of rational numbers is *closed* under division, excluding division by zero.

The operation of division is the inverse operation of multiplication, just as the operation of subtraction is the inverse operation of addition; that is, multiplication and division undo each other just as addition and subtraction undo each other (p. 99). For example,

$$\left(\frac{4}{5} \div \frac{^-6}{7}\right) \times \frac{^-6}{7} = \frac{4}{5}$$

and

$$\left(\frac{4}{5} \times \frac{^-6}{7}\right) \div \frac{^-6}{7} = \frac{4}{5}.$$

If this is not immediately clear, replace "$\div \frac{^-6}{7}$" in each sentence by "$\times \frac{7}{^-6}$," and compute the products

$$\left(\frac{4}{5} \times \frac{7}{^-6}\right) \times \frac{^-6}{7}$$

and

$$\left(\frac{4}{5} \times \frac{^-6}{7}\right) \times \frac{7}{^-6}.$$

Fractions as Symbols for Division

In an earlier section, we indicated that since the subset

$$\left\{ \cdots, \frac{^-3}{1}, \frac{^-2}{1}, \frac{^-1}{1}, \frac{0}{1}, \frac{1}{1}, \frac{2}{1}, \frac{3}{1}, \cdots \right\}$$

of rational numbers behaves exactly like the entire set of integers,

$$\{ \cdots, ^-3, ^-2, ^-1, 0, 1, 2, 3, \cdots \},$$

we would regard the two sets as being the same and hence consider the set of integers to be a subset of the set of rational numbers. With this agreement we shall now see that any fraction $\frac{a}{b}$ can be looked upon as a quotient of the integers a and b.

In the system of integers the division of $^-8$ by 3 is not possible. In the system of rational numbers the division *is* possible. The rational number $^-8$ (regarded to be the same as $\frac{^-8}{1}$) divided by the rational number 3 yields a quotient that is a rational number:

$$^-8 \div 3 = \frac{^-8}{1} \div \frac{3}{1}$$

$$= \frac{^-8}{1} \times \frac{1}{3} \qquad \text{(Division by } \frac{3}{1} \text{ gives the same result as multiplication by } \frac{1}{3}\text{.)}$$

$$= \frac{^-8 \times 1}{1 \times 3} \qquad \text{(Multiplication of rational numbers.)}$$

$$= \frac{^-8}{3}.$$

Thus, the symbols $^-8 \div 3$, $^-8 \times \frac{1}{3}$, and $\frac{^-8}{3}$ are names for the same rational number. More generally, if a is any integer and b is any integer other than zero, then

$$a \div b = \frac{a}{1} \div \frac{b}{1}$$
$$= \frac{a}{1} \times \frac{1}{b}$$
$$= \frac{a \times 1}{1 \times b}$$
$$= \frac{a}{b},$$

and $a \div b$, $a \times \frac{1}{b}$, and $\frac{a}{b}$ name the same rational number.

Complex Fractions

The fact that the quotient of two integers, such as $^-8 \div 3$, can be represented by a fraction raises a question: Can the quotient of two rationals, such as $\frac{^-1}{2} \div \frac{3}{4}$, be written as the "fraction" $\frac{^-1/2}{3/4}$? The fact is that fractions of this kind are often used. The question here is this: If the concept of fractions is extended to include symbols such as $\frac{^-1/2}{3/4}$ and more generally $\frac{a/b}{c/d}$, where a, b, c, and d are integers, $b \neq 0$, $c \neq 0$, $d \neq 0$, will these new fractions name rational numbers, and will they have the same properties as the fractions with which we are familiar?

We shall regard $\frac{a/b}{c/d}$ as a symbol for a quotient; then it is clear that $\frac{a/b}{c/d}$ names a rational number, because it has been shown that the operation of division of rationals has the closure property, except for division by zero. What is the simplest name for the rational number $\frac{^-1/2}{3/4}$? We have

$$\frac{^-1/2}{3/4} = \frac{^-1}{2} \div \frac{3}{4} = \frac{^-1}{2} \times \frac{4}{3} = \frac{^-4}{6} = \frac{^-2}{3}.$$

Thus

$$\frac{^-1/2}{3/4} = \frac{^-2}{3}.$$

How can one compute sums and products when rational numbers are named by these new fractions (called "complex fractions")? Is it possible to use the "renaming" property that was found convenient for the familiar fractions? We have used the property that

$$\frac{a}{b} = \frac{a \times n}{b \times n},$$

where a, b, and n are integers and $b \neq 0$, $n \neq 0$. Will this property hold if a, b, and n are rational numbers and $b \neq 0$, $n \neq 0$? Consider the fraction $\frac{2/3}{^-4/5}$ and let $n = \frac{^-3}{4}$. Is

$$\frac{2/3}{^-4/5} = \frac{2/3 \times ^-3/4}{^-4/5 \times ^-3/4}$$

a true sentence? The right-hand fraction can be written $\frac{^-6/12}{12/20}$, which is equivalent to $\frac{^-1/2}{3/5}$. Is it true that $\frac{2/3}{^-4/5} = \frac{^-1/2}{3/5}$? Let us carry out the two divisions:

$$\frac{2/3}{^-4/5} = \frac{2}{3} \div \frac{^-4}{5} \qquad\qquad \frac{^-1/2}{3/5} = \frac{^-1}{2} \div \frac{3}{5}$$

$$= \frac{2}{3} \times \frac{5}{^-4} \qquad\qquad\qquad = \frac{^-1}{2} \times \frac{5}{3}$$

$$= \frac{10}{^-12} \qquad\qquad\qquad\qquad = \frac{^-5}{6}.$$

$$= \frac{^-5}{6}.$$

So we see that in this case the "renaming property" has provided a fraction naming the same rational number as the original fraction, and it can be proved that if a, b, and n are rational and

$$b \neq 0, \qquad n \neq 0,$$

then

$$\frac{a}{b} = \frac{a \times n}{b \times n}.$$

In the previous example it was found that the two complex fractions $\frac{2/3}{^-4/5}$ and $\frac{^-1/2}{3/5}$ are equal. However, both are "complex," and they do not give the simplest name for the rational number they represent. To find such a name, we carried out the division. A judicious choice for n, in applying the renaming property, leads at once to a simpler fraction. Suppose that in renaming $\frac{2/3}{^-4/5}$ we choose $n = \frac{5}{^-4}$. (Note that $\frac{5}{^-4}$ is the reciprocal of $\frac{^-4}{5}$.) Then

$$\frac{2/3}{^-4/5} = \frac{2/3 \times 5/^-4}{^-4/5 \times 5/^-4}$$

$$= \frac{10/^-12}{1}$$

$$= \frac{10}{^-12}$$

$$= \frac{^-5}{6}.$$

Thus, by choosing for n the multiplicative inverse of the denominator of the complex fraction, operating with complex fractions is made easier.

We have seen that a complex fraction may name a rational number. We have also seen that one property of fractions of the form $\frac{a}{b}$, where a and b are integers and $b \neq 0$, also holds for complex fractions of the form $\frac{a/b}{c/d}$, where $\frac{a}{b}$ and $\frac{c}{d}$ are rational numbers and $\frac{c}{d} \neq 0$—namely, the "renaming" property. Will other properties hold also? In particular, do the expressions given earlier for the sum and product of rational numbers hold for rational numbers named by complex fractions? That is, if $\frac{a}{b}$, $\frac{c}{d}$, $\frac{e}{f}$, and $\frac{g}{h}$ are all rational numbers and $\frac{c}{d} \neq 0$ and $\frac{g}{h} \neq 0$, is it true that

$$\frac{a/b}{c/d} + \frac{e/f}{g/h} = \frac{(a/b \times g/h) + (c/d \times e/f)}{c/d \times g/h} \text{ and } \frac{a/b}{c/d} \times \frac{e/f}{g/h} = \frac{a/b \times e/f}{c/d \times g/h} ?$$

The answer is "yes." In exercise 3d of the following Exercise Set, you will have the opportunity to illustrate by example that the definition of multiplication holds for complex fractions.

Exercise Set 10

1. Find the simplest fraction equivalent to the following complex fractions:

   a. $\dfrac{1/2}{^-3/4}$ b. $\dfrac{^-7/16}{^-7/8}$ c. $\dfrac{4/3}{8/9}$

2. On each of the number lines below are arrows to represent the numerator and denominator of a complex fraction in exercise 1. Give the ratio of the length of the arrows in each drawing and state whether the arrows are in the same or opposite directions, using your answers for exercise 1.

a.

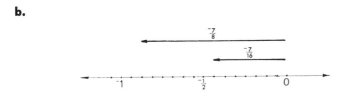

b.

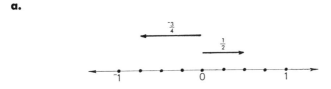

c.

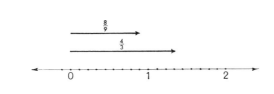

3. a. The two fractions $\frac{7/3}{7/2}$ and $\frac{5/2}{15/4}$ name the same rational number. Find its simplest fraction name.

b. The equivalence property of fractions states that if a, b, c, and d are integers, $b \neq 0$, $d \neq 0$, then $\frac{a}{b} = \frac{c}{d}$ if and only if $a \times d = b \times c$. Apply this property to the complex fractions in exercise 3a. Is the property true for these two fractions?

c. Show that the "renaming" property $\frac{a}{b} = \frac{a \times n}{b \times n}$ holds for the complex fraction $\frac{7/3}{7/2}$. Let $n = \frac{-6}{7}$.

d. If a, b, c, and d are integers, $b \neq 0$ and $d \neq 0$, then $\frac{a}{b} \times \frac{c}{d}$ has been defined to be $\frac{a \times c}{b \times d}$. Does this definition hold for rational numbers named by complex fractions? Is it true that $\frac{1/2}{3/8} \times \frac{7/9}{5/6} = \frac{1/2 \times 7/9}{3/8 \times 5/6}$? You will be able to answer this question after you complete the following example:

   i. If $\frac{a}{b} \times \frac{c}{d} = \frac{a \times c}{b \times d}$ is true for complex fractions, then

$$\frac{1/2}{3/8} \times \frac{7/9}{5/6} = \frac{1/2 \times 7/9}{3/8 \times 5/6} = \underline{\qquad}.$$

   ii. The simplest fraction name for your answer in 4d-i. is_____.

   iii. The simplest fraction name for $\frac{1/2}{3/8}$ is_____.
       The simplest fraction name for $\frac{7/9}{5/6}$ is_____.

   iv. Find the product of your two answers for exercise 4d-iii.

   v. Compare your answers for exercises 4d-ii and 4d-iv.

   vi. Does the definition for multiplication seem to hold when complex fractions are used?

COMPARISON OF RATIONAL NUMBERS

Order Property of the Rational Numbers

An important property of the system of integers (and also of the system of whole numbers) is the property of order. In each system a relation, denoted by "$<$," is defined, such that if a and b are any numbers in that system, exactly one of the following sentences is true and the others are false:

$$a < b, \qquad a = b, \qquad b < a.$$

For the numbers $^-8$ and 3 in the system of integers, of the three sentences

$$^-8 < 3, \qquad ^-8 = 3, \qquad 3 < {}^-8,$$

the first one is true and the second and third are false. What does it mean to say that $^-8 < 3$? It means that there is a positive integer n such that $^-8 + n = 3$. In this case $n = 11$ because $^-8 + 11 = 3$.

In general terms, if a and b are integers, then "$a < b$" means that there is a positive integer n such that $a + n = b$.

We can define a relation $<$ for the system of rational numbers such that for any two rational numbers $\frac{a}{b}$ and $\frac{c}{d}$, exactly one of the following sentences is true and other two are false:

$$\frac{a}{b} < \frac{c}{d}, \qquad \frac{a}{b} = \frac{c}{d}, \qquad \frac{c}{d} < \frac{a}{b}.$$

In fact, we define the relation in the same way as it was defined for the integers:

If $\frac{a}{b}$ and $\frac{c}{d}$ are rational numbers, then the statement $\frac{a}{b} < \frac{c}{d}$ means that there is a positive rational number $\frac{x}{y}$ such that

$$\frac{a}{b} + \frac{x}{y} = \frac{c}{d}.$$

Since adding a positive number is represented by "moving to the right" on the number line, the statement $\frac{a}{b} < \frac{c}{d}$ is equivalent to the statement that the point corresponding to $\frac{a}{b}$ is to the left of the point corresponding to $\frac{c}{d}$.

The statement $\frac{a}{b} < \frac{c}{d}$ can also be written equivalently as $\frac{c}{d} > \frac{a}{b}$, where "$>$" is read "is greater than."

Consider the rational numbers $\frac{3}{8}$ and $\frac{^-3}{4}$. Which one of the following sentences is true,

$$\frac{3}{8} < \frac{^-3}{4}, \qquad \frac{3}{8} = \frac{^-3}{4}, \qquad \frac{^-3}{4} < \frac{3}{8} \, ?$$

We can easily rule out the second sentence by using the condition for equivalence of fractions. Since $3 \times 4 \neq 8 \times {^-3}$, we know that $\frac{3}{8} \neq \frac{^-3}{4}$. Is $\frac{3}{8} < \frac{^-3}{4}$? If we add a positive number to $\frac{3}{8}$, can we possibly get $\frac{^-3}{4}$? Thinking about arrow addition on the number line will convince you that the correct answer is "no." This leaves just one question, which accordingly must have an affirmative answer: Is $\frac{^-3}{4} < \frac{3}{8}$? Is there a positive rational number which, added to $\frac{^-3}{4}$, yields $\frac{3}{8}$? Yes, that number is $\frac{9}{8}$, for

$$\frac{^-3}{4} + \frac{9}{8} = \frac{^-6}{8} + \frac{9}{8} = \frac{3}{8}.$$

The statement that, given any rational number $\frac{a}{b}$ and any rational number $\frac{c}{d}$, exactly one of the following is true,

$$\frac{a}{b} < \frac{c}{d}, \qquad \frac{a}{b} = \frac{c}{d}, \qquad \frac{c}{d} < \frac{a}{b},$$

is called the *principle of trichotomy*.

One way of testing how two rational numbers are related to each other is to express them by fractions having the same positive denominator. Consider the numbers $\frac{^-2}{3}$ and $\frac{^-4}{5}$. These can be renamed as follows:

$$\frac{^-2}{3} = \frac{^-10}{15}, \qquad \frac{^-4}{5} = \frac{^-12}{15}.$$

Now we can see that $\frac{^-12}{15} < \frac{^-10}{15}$ because

$$\frac{^-12}{15} + \frac{2}{15} = \frac{^-10}{15},$$

and $\frac{2}{15}$ is positive. Thus $\frac{^-4}{5} < \frac{^-2}{3}$. Notice that when we had renamed the numbers $\frac{^-10}{15}$ and $\frac{^-12}{15}$, we needed only to notice that $^-12 < ^-10$, to decide that $\frac{^-12}{15} < \frac{^-10}{15}$. It is true that if $\frac{a}{c}$ and $\frac{b}{c}$ are rational numbers and c is a positive integer, then $\frac{a}{c} < \frac{b}{c}$ if and only if $a < b$.

Suppose that r, s, and t are rational numbers and that it is known that $r < s$ and $s < t$. Can we conclude that $r < t$?

Let $r = \frac{^-12}{15}$, $s = \frac{^-10}{15}$, and $t = \frac{^-9}{15}$. Then $\frac{^-12}{15} < \frac{^-10}{15}$, because $\frac{^-12}{15} + \frac{2}{15} = \frac{^-10}{15}$; also $\frac{^-10}{15} < \frac{^-9}{15}$, because $\frac{^-10}{15} + \frac{1}{15} = \frac{^-9}{15}$. Is $\frac{^-12}{15}$, then, less than $\frac{^-9}{15}$? Consider the two sentences

$$\frac{^-12}{15} + \frac{2}{15} = \frac{^-10}{15},$$

$$\frac{^-10}{15} + \frac{1}{15} = \frac{^-9}{15}.$$

Now replace $\frac{^-10}{15}$ in the second sentence by $(\frac{^-12}{15} + \frac{2}{15})$. We then have

$$\left(\frac{^-12}{15} + \frac{2}{15}\right) + \frac{1}{15} = \frac{^-9}{15},$$

or

$$\frac{^-12}{15} + \left(\frac{2}{15} + \frac{1}{15}\right) = \frac{^-9}{15}, \qquad \text{(Associative property of addition.)}$$

or

$$\frac{^-12}{15} + \frac{3}{15} = \frac{^-9}{15}.$$

From this we see that $\frac{^-12}{15} < \frac{^-9}{15}$ because a positive rational, $\frac{3}{15}$, is added to $\frac{^-12}{15}$ to get $\frac{^-9}{15}$. The kind of reasoning we have used here can be used to show that if r, s, and t are any rational numbers such that $r < s$ and $s < t$, then $r < t$. This important property is called the *transitive property of order*.

On the number line, we observe that if $r < s$, then the point corresponding to r is to the left of the point corresponding to s. If $s < t$, then the point corresponding to s is to the left of the point corresponding to t. Hence, the point corresponding to r is to the left of the point corresponding to t. (See Fig. 16.) This again illustrates the transitive property of order.

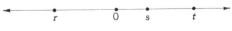

FIGURE 16

In particular, it is true that any negative rational number is less than zero, zero is less than any positive rational number, and thus any negative rational number is less than any positive rational number.

Addition Principle for Inequalities

Certain laws for operating with inequalities (we consider here sentences in which the verb phrase is denoted by "$<$" or "$>$") follow easily from the definition of the order relation.

Suppose we have two rational numbers, and to each we add the same rational number. What will be the order of the sums?

Relative ages are a good illustration. If you have a brother two years older than you, then each of you becomes a year older with each passing year, but the order of your ages does not change.

To generalize, if a, b, and c are rational numbers, and $a < b$, then

$$a + c < b + c.$$

It is helpful first to visualize what this means on the number line, as shown in Figure 17. The statement "$a < b$" means that the point for b is to the right of the point for a. Adding c means moving to the right if c is positive, or to the left if c is negative. Figure 17 shows the situation for

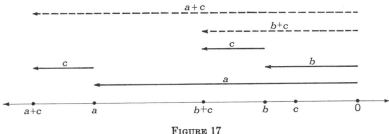

FIGURE 17

the case in which a, b, and c are negative. Notice that the point for $b + c$ is to the right of the point for $a + c$, just as the point for b is to the right of the point for a.

Looking at the same question from the numerical point of view,

$$a < b$$

means that there is a positive number n such that

$$a + n = b.$$

Adding c to both sides, we get

$$(a + n) + c = b + c.$$

The associative and commutative properties give us

$$(a + c) + n = b + c,$$

and since n is positive, by the definition of "$<$" we have

$$a + c < b + c.$$

Exercise Set 11

1. Complete the following sentences:
   a. $^-7 < {}^-4$, because, $^-7 + \underline{\hspace{2em}} = {}^-4$, and $\underline{\hspace{2em}}$ is a $\underline{\hspace{2em}}$ number.
   b. $587 < 625$, because $\underline{\hspace{2em}}$.
   c. $\dfrac{^-257}{2} < \dfrac{423}{4}$, because $\underline{\hspace{2em}}$.
   d. $0 < \dfrac{93}{7}$, because $\underline{\hspace{2em}}$.

2. Make an arrow diagram for the sentence you completed in exercise 1a.

3. Use the addition property for inequality to find the solution set for each of the following sentences.
   a. $n + {}^-2 < 9$.   (Hint: Add the additive inverse of $^-2$ to both sides.)
   b. $\dfrac{^-3}{4} + n < \dfrac{7}{8}$.
   c. $\dfrac{^-7}{10} < \dfrac{3}{10} + n$.

Multiplication Principle for Inequalities

We have seen that if a, b, and c are rational numbers and $a < b$, then $a + c < b + c$. We sometimes say that "adding the same number to both sides of an inequality preserves the inequality in the same direction." Let us now see the effect of multiplying both sides of an inequality by the same rational number.

First consider an inequality between specific rational numbers:

$$\frac{^-3}{4} < \frac{5}{2} \quad \text{because} \quad \frac{^-3}{4} + \frac{13}{4} = \frac{5}{2}, \quad \text{and} \quad \frac{13}{4} \text{ is positive.}$$

Now multiply both numbers by the positive rational number $\frac{8}{3}$:

$$\frac{8}{3} \times \frac{^-3}{4} = {}^-2 \quad \text{and} \quad \frac{8}{3} \times \frac{5}{2} = \frac{20}{3}.$$

Surely $^-2 < \frac{20}{3}$, because $^-2$ is negative and $\frac{20}{3}$ is positive. Thus $\frac{8}{3} \times \frac{^-3}{4} < \frac{8}{3} \times \frac{5}{2}$, and so we see that multiplication by $\frac{8}{3}$ preserved the inequality in the same direction.

But suppose we had multiplied by the rational number zero. Since multiplying any rational number by 0 yields 0 as product, we have

$$0 \times \frac{^-3}{4} = 0 \quad \text{and} \quad 0 \times \frac{5}{2} = 0.$$

Thus $0 \times \frac{-3}{4} = 0 \times \frac{5}{2}$, and we see that multiplication by zero replaced the inequality by an equality; the inequality was not preserved.

Now try multiplication by a negative number. We have

$$\frac{-3}{4} < \frac{5}{2}.$$

Multiply both numbers by $\frac{-8}{3}$:

$$\frac{-8}{3} \times \frac{-3}{4} = \frac{24}{12} = 2, \quad \text{and} \quad \frac{-8}{3} \times \frac{5}{2} = \frac{-40}{6} = \frac{-20}{3}.$$

Clearly, $\frac{-20}{3} < 2$, because $\frac{-20}{3}$ is negative and 2 is positive. So

$$\frac{-3}{4} < \frac{5}{2},$$

but

$$\frac{-8}{3} \times \frac{5}{2} < \frac{-8}{3} \times \frac{-3}{4},$$

or

$$\frac{-8}{3} \times \frac{-3}{4} > \frac{-8}{3} \times \frac{5}{2}.$$

We see that multiplication by $\frac{-8}{3}$ resulted in an inequality *in the opposite direction*. Thus, for multiplication we have observed three different results depending on our choice of the number by which we multiplied the members of the inequality,

$$\frac{-3}{4} < \frac{5}{2}.$$

When we multiplied both members by a positive number, $\frac{8}{3}$, the inequality was preserved. When we multiplied by 0, the inequality was replaced by equality. When we multiplied by a negative number, $\frac{-8}{3}$, the inequality was reversed in direction.

In Figure 18 the effect of multiplying both members of inequality $a < b$ by a positive number, by 0, and by a negative number is pictured by means of arrows. Here we use the numbers 2, 0, and $^-2$ as multipliers. With a negative number chosen for a and a positive number for b, the effect of multiplication by a positive number was to place the point for $2 \times a$ to the left of the point for a, and the point for $2 \times b$ farther to the right than the point for b. Thus, if

$$a < b, \quad \text{then} \quad 2 \times a < 2 \times b.$$

The effect of multiplication by 0 was to "shrink" each arrow to the same point, 0. Thus, if

$$a < b, \quad \text{then} \quad 0 \times a = 0 \times b.$$

The effect of multiplication by $^-2$ was to double the lengths of the arrows and then reflect them at 0. The reflection puts $^-2 \times a$ to the right of 0 and $^-2 \times b$ to the left of 0. So if

$$a < b, \quad \text{then} \quad {}^-2 \times a > {}^-2 \times b.$$

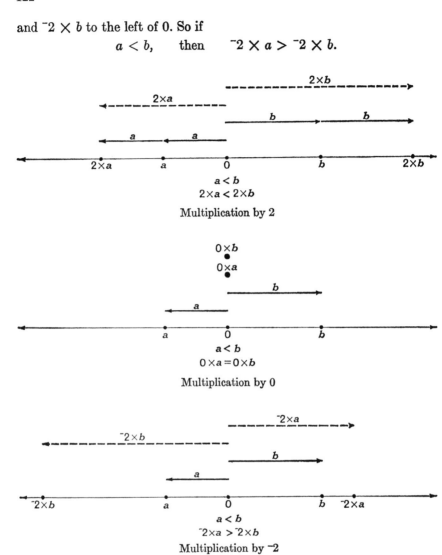

a < b
2×a < 2×b

Multiplication by 2

a < b
0 × a = 0 × b

Multiplication by 0

a < b
$^-2 \times a > {}^-2 \times b$

Multiplication by $^-2$

FIGURE 18

By choosing an inequality in which both members are positive, and one in which both are negative, you can convince yourself that the same relations hold, and that if a, b, and c are rational numbers and $a < b$, then

$$c \times a < c \times b \quad \text{if} \quad c > 0,$$
$$c \times a = c \times b \quad \text{if} \quad c = 0,$$
$$c \times a > c \times b \quad \text{if} \quad c < 0.$$

Exercise Set 12

1. Given the inequality

$$\frac{^{-}9}{10} < \frac{^{-}9}{100},$$

illustrate the multiplication principle for inequalities by multiplying by:

a. $\dfrac{10}{3}$ **b.** 0 **c.** $\dfrac{^{-}10}{3}$

2. Find the solution set of each of the following inequalities.

a. $\dfrac{2}{3} \times n < 5$ **c.** $\dfrac{8}{5} \times n < 25$

(Hint: Multiply by $\frac{3}{2}$.)

b. $\dfrac{^{-}2}{3} \times n < 5$ **d.** $\dfrac{^{-}8}{5} \times n < 25$

3. Here is a proof that if $r < s$, then $2 \times r < 2 \times s$. Give a reason for each step from **b** through **f**.

a. $r < s$. (Given.)

b. There is a positive number n such that $r + n = s$.

c. $2 \times (r + n) = 2 \times s$.

d. $(2 \times r) + (2 \times n) = 2 \times s$.

e. $2 \times n$ is positive.

f. $2 \times r < 2 \times s$.

Density

We say that the rational number $\frac{7}{8}$ is *between* the rational numbers $\frac{3}{4}$ and $\frac{9}{8}$ because $\frac{3}{4} < \frac{7}{8}$ and $\frac{7}{8} < \frac{9}{8}$, which is usually written $\frac{3}{4} < \frac{7}{8} < \frac{9}{8}$. On the number line this means that the point corresponding to $\frac{7}{8}$ is between the points corresponding to $\frac{3}{4}$ and $\frac{9}{8}$. Is there a rational number between $\frac{3}{4}$ and $\frac{7}{8}$? Rename these two numbers as follows:

$$\frac{3}{4} = \frac{12}{16}, \qquad \frac{7}{8} = \frac{14}{16}.$$

It is easy to see that $\frac{12}{16} < \frac{13}{16} < \frac{14}{16}$, so that $\frac{13}{16}$ is between $\frac{12}{16}$ and $\frac{14}{16}$, that is, between $\frac{3}{4}$ and $\frac{7}{8}$. Is there a rational number between $\frac{12}{16}$ (or $\frac{3}{4}$) and $\frac{13}{16}$? If you rename these two numbers $\frac{24}{32}$ and $\frac{26}{32}$, you see that $\frac{24}{32} < \frac{25}{32} < \frac{26}{32}$, so that $\frac{25}{32}$ is between $\frac{24}{32}$ and $\frac{26}{32}$; that is, $\frac{25}{32}$ is between $\frac{12}{16}$ (or $\frac{3}{4}$) and $\frac{13}{16}$.

Perhaps these examples suggest to you that between any two rational numbers there is another rational number. This is, in fact, true. Indeed, there is a straightforward way of finding such a number. In the preceding paragraph, we found $\frac{13}{16}$ to be between $\frac{12}{16}$ and $\frac{14}{16}$. The following example will show how $\frac{13}{16}$ might be obtained from $\frac{12}{16}$ and $\frac{14}{16}$:

$$\frac{\dfrac{12}{16} + \dfrac{14}{16}}{2} = \frac{\dfrac{12 + 14}{16}}{2}$$

$$= \frac{\dfrac{26}{16}}{\dfrac{2}{1}}$$

$$= \frac{26}{16} \times \frac{1}{2} = \frac{26}{32}$$

$$= \frac{13}{16}.$$

You see that $\frac{13}{16}$ was obtained by adding the numbers $\frac{12}{16}$ and $\frac{14}{16}$ and then dividing the sum by 2. In other words, $\frac{13}{16}$ is the average of $\frac{12}{16}$ and $\frac{14}{16}$.

Will the average of two rational numbers always yield a rational number that is between the original two rational numbers? Let us see if it works out that way with $\frac{-5}{6}$ and $\frac{-6}{7}$. Note that $\frac{-6}{7} < \frac{-5}{6}$, since $\frac{-6}{7} = \frac{-36}{42}$, $\frac{-5}{6} = \frac{-35}{42}$, and $\frac{-36}{42} < \frac{-35}{42}$. We have

$$\frac{\dfrac{-5}{6} + \dfrac{-6}{7}}{2} = \frac{\dfrac{(-5 \times 7) + (6 \times -6)}{6 \times 7}}{2}$$

$$= \frac{\dfrac{-35 + -36}{42}}{2}$$

$$= \frac{\dfrac{-71}{42}}{\dfrac{2}{1}}$$

$$= \frac{-71}{42} \times \frac{1}{2} = \frac{-71}{84}.$$

Is $\frac{-71}{84}$ between $\frac{-5}{6}$ and $\frac{-6}{7}$? To see that it is, rename the numbers $\frac{-5}{6}$ and $\frac{-6}{7}$ by fractions having denominator 84. Thus,

$$\frac{-5}{6} = \frac{-5 \times 14}{6 \times 14} = \frac{-70}{84},$$

$$\frac{-6}{7} = \frac{-6 \times 12}{7 \times 12} = \frac{-72}{84}.$$

Now we see that $\frac{-72}{84} < \frac{-71}{84} < \frac{-70}{84}$, since $-72 < -71 < -70$. Thus $\frac{-71}{84}$ is between $\frac{-72}{84}$ and $\frac{-70}{84}$.

In a similar way it can be shown that if r and s are any two rational numbers, then $\frac{r+s}{2}$ is a rational number between r and s. If $r < s$, then

$$r < \frac{r + s}{2} < s.$$

It should be remarked that the process of averaging is only one way of producing a rational number that is between two given rational numbers. The chief significance of the process lies in the fact that it presents a precise way of showing the existence of a rational number between two given rational numbers by actually exhibiting such a number.

The fact that between two rational numbers there is another rational number (and therefore many) is of great inportance to us. We call it the *density property* of the rational number system. It is common also to say that the rational numbers are *dense*. (See Booklet No. 11: *The System of Real Numbers.*)

The system of integers does not have this property. There is no integer, for example, between 2 and 3, nor is there an integer between ⁻3 and ⁻2.

What is the geometrical significance of the density property of the rationals? It is this: Between any two points (no matter how close together they are) that correspond to rational numbers, there is another point (in fact, infinitely many points) that corresponds to a rational number. This is true even if there seems intuitively to be no room between the given two points. There may not be any room for the dots we use to represent points; but points are abstractions, and between any two of them there is always another.

Exercise Set 13

1. Order each pair of numbers and justify your answer by writing an addition sentence.

   a. $\dfrac{3}{7}, \dfrac{4}{8}$ c. $\dfrac{3}{5}, \dfrac{11}{14}$

   b. $\dfrac{^-9}{10}, \dfrac{^-8}{9}$ d. $\dfrac{^-6}{13}, \dfrac{1}{26}$

2. For each pair of rational numbers in exercise 1 find a third rational number that is between the two numbers.

3. Arrange the following numbers in order from least to greatest:

$$0, \frac{^-528}{3}, \frac{200}{^-3}, \frac{^-4}{^-2}, \frac{75}{3}, \frac{1}{2}.$$

4. In Booklet No. 6: *The Rational Numbers* it was shown that

$$\frac{a}{b} < \frac{c}{d} \quad \text{if and only if} \quad a \times d < b \times c,$$

where a and c are whole numbers and b and d are natural numbers. Does this test apply to any pair of rational numbers, and does it apply when fractions with negative denominators are used to name these rational numbers? For each of the following true inequalities, compute and order $a \times d$ and $b \times c$ and see if this ordering agrees with that of the rational numbers.

a. $\dfrac{^-7}{4} < \dfrac{^-5}{4}.$ e. $\dfrac{7}{^-4} < \dfrac{^-5}{^-4}.$

b. $\dfrac{^-7}{4} < \dfrac{5}{4}.$ f. $\dfrac{5}{4} < \dfrac{\iota}{4}.$

c. $\dfrac{7}{^-4} < \dfrac{5}{4}.$ g. $\dfrac{^-5}{4} < \dfrac{7}{4}.$

d. $\dfrac{^-7}{4} < \dfrac{^-5}{^-4}.$ h. $\dfrac{^-5}{4} < \dfrac{^-7}{^-4}.$

5. From your results for exercise 4 can you draw a conclusion about the form in which rational fractions must be written so that the inequality test will apply?

6. Write the following as inequalities:

a. $\frac{5}{8}$ is between $\frac{8}{9}$ and $\frac{1}{3}$.

b. $\frac{7}{100}$ is between 0.7 and 0.007.

c. 999.5 is between 946 and 1002.

d. $223\frac{1}{10}$ is between $223\frac{1}{20}$ and $223\frac{3}{20}$.

SUMMARY

In Booklet No. 9: *The System of Integers* it was shown that the integers have all of the properties of the whole numbers, as well as an additional one: each integer has a unique additive inverse. An important consequence of this property is that the system of integers has closure for subtraction, as well as for addition and multiplication.

The system of rational numbers, as we have shown in this booklet, has all of the properties of the system of integers, as well as two additional properties:

1. Every rational number other than zero has a unique multiplicative inverse, or reciprocal.

   This property has an important consequence, namely, that the rational numbers have closure for division, except for division by zero.

2. The rational numbers have the property of *density*; that is, between

any two rational numbers there is another rational number (hence there are infinitely many rational numbers). This property of density is not shared by the system of whole numbers or the system of integers, although they do have the order relation. However, density *is* a property of the system of nonnegative rationals and of the real number system, of which the entire system of rational numbers is a subsystem. The real number system will be discussed in Booklet No. 11.

For Further Reading

Among the various helpful references that deal with the subject here introduced are the following books:

COURANT, RICHARD, and ROBBINS, HERBERT E. *What Is Mathematics?* London and New York: Oxford University Press, 1941. (Reprinted 1958.) Pp. 521. Available from the Oxford University Press, Inc., 200 Madison Ave., New York, N.Y. 10016.

FEHR, HOWARD F., and HILL, THOMAS J. *Contemporary Mathematics for Elementary Teachers.* Boston: D. C. Heath & Co., 1966. Pp. 394. Available from D. C. Heath & Co., 285 Columbus Ave., Boston, Mass. 02116.

VAN ENGEN, HENRY; HARTUNG, MAURICE L.; and STOCHL, JAMES E. *Foundations of Elementary School Arithmetic.* Chicago: Scott, Foresman & Co., 1965. Pp. 450. Available from Scott, Foresman & Co., 1900 E. Lake Ave., Glenview, Ill. 60025.

ANSWERS TO EXERCISES

Exercise Set 1

1. a.

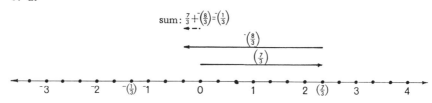

$$\text{sum}: \tfrac{7}{3} + {}^-\!\left(\tfrac{8}{3}\right) = {}^-\!\left(\tfrac{1}{3}\right)$$

b.

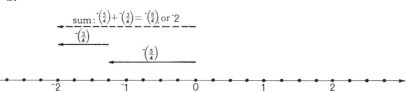

$$\text{sum}: {}^-\!\left(\tfrac{5}{4}\right) + {}^-\!\left(\tfrac{3}{4}\right) = {}^-\!\left(\tfrac{8}{4}\right), \text{ or } {}^-2$$

c.

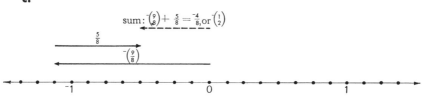

$$\text{sum}: {}^-\!\left(\tfrac{9}{8}\right) + \tfrac{5}{8} = \tfrac{{}^-4}{8}, \text{ or } {}^-\!\left(\tfrac{1}{2}\right)$$

d.

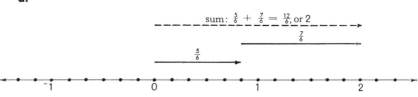

$$\text{sum}: \tfrac{5}{6} + \tfrac{7}{6} = \tfrac{12}{6}, \text{ or } 2$$

2.

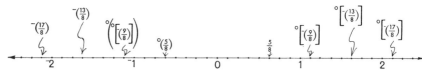

3. Any rational number may be used. Here is shown the diagram for $\frac{4}{3}$ and its opposite.

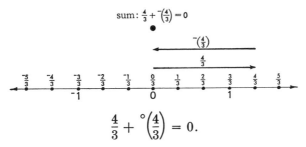

$$\frac{4}{3} + {}^{\circ}\!\left(\frac{4}{3}\right) = 0.$$

4. a. $\dfrac{21}{50}$ **c.** $\dfrac{35}{36}$

  b. $^-\!\left(\dfrac{21}{50}\right)$ **d.** $^-\!\left(\dfrac{143}{20}\right)$

5. a. $^-\!\left(\dfrac{12}{5}\right)$ **e.** 0

  b. $^-\!\left(\dfrac{9}{5}\right)$ **f.** $\dfrac{3}{5}$

  c. $^-\!\left(\dfrac{6}{5}\right)$ **g.** $\dfrac{6}{5}$

  d. $^-\!\left(\dfrac{3}{5}\right)$ **h.** $\dfrac{9}{5}$

Exercise Set 2

1. The pairs in **b**, **c**, and **d**

2. $6 = 2 \times 3.$
  $75 = 3 \times 5 \times 5.$
  $6 \times 75 = 2 \times 3 \times 3 \times 5 \times 5.$
  $25 = 5 \times 5.$
  $18 = 2 \times 3 \times 3.$
  $25 \times 18 = 2 \times 3 \times 3 \times 5 \times 5.$

3. a.

  b.

4. $\dfrac{48}{145}$

Exercise Set 3

1. a.

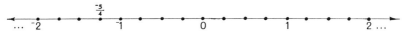

b. $\dfrac{5}{^-4}$, $\dfrac{^-10}{8}$, $\dfrac{10}{^-8}$, $\dfrac{^-500}{400}$, $\dfrac{500}{^-400}$.

c. 12

d. 25

2. a. $\dfrac{^-5}{4} = \dfrac{^-15}{12}$. **c.** $\dfrac{^-5}{4} = \dfrac{^-45}{36}$.

b. $\dfrac{^-5}{4} = \dfrac{25}{^-20}$. **d.** $\dfrac{^-5}{4} = \dfrac{50}{^-40}$.

3. a. $\dfrac{3}{1}$, $\dfrac{^-19}{^-2}$, and $\dfrac{3 \times ^-6}{5 \times ^-6}$.

b. $\dfrac{^-5}{2}$, $\dfrac{4 \times 3}{^-7 \times 3}$, and $\dfrac{7}{^-3}$.

c. $\dfrac{0}{^-5}$

4. Answers may vary. Some correct names are

$$\dfrac{^-16}{2}, \quad \dfrac{^-24}{3}, \quad \dfrac{32}{^-4}, \quad \dfrac{^-40}{5}, \quad \dfrac{48}{^-6}, \quad \dfrac{^-800}{100}.$$

Exercise Set 4

1. $\dfrac{5}{6}$, $\dfrac{15}{1}$, and $\dfrac{^-31}{73}$.

($\dfrac{1}{^-6}$ is not a simplest name because the denominator is negative.)

2. a. $\dfrac{2}{3}$ **d.** $\dfrac{0}{1}$ **g.** $\dfrac{1}{1}$

b. $\dfrac{^-2}{3}$ **e.** $\dfrac{2}{5}$

c. $\dfrac{^-7}{8}$ **f.** $\dfrac{^-33}{1}$

3. a. ⁻9   **d.** 0

   b. ⁻16   **e.** 4

   c. 1   **f.** ⁻14

4. a. $126 = 2 \times 3 \times 3 \times 7$.

   $60 = 2 \times 2 \times 3 \times 5$.

   b. i. $\dfrac{21}{10}$ **ii.** $\dfrac{^-21}{10}$ **iii.** $\dfrac{10}{21}$

5. a. $\dfrac{2}{5}$ **b.** $\dfrac{^-11}{29}$ **c.** $\dfrac{^-1}{78}$

Exercise Set 5

1. a.

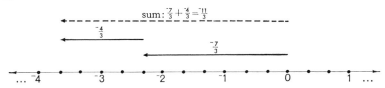

b.

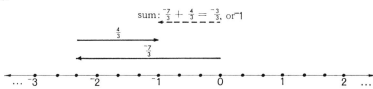

c

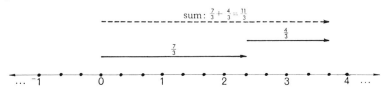

d.

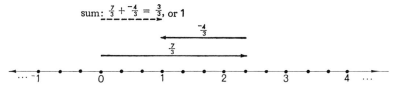

2. a. $\dfrac{7}{3}$ **e.** $\dfrac{3}{3}$, or 1

 b. $\dfrac{4}{3}$ **f.** $\dfrac{3}{3}$, or 1

 c. $\dfrac{4}{3}$ **g.** $\dfrac{11}{3}$

 d. $\dfrac{7}{3}$ **h.** $\dfrac{11}{3}$

3. a. $\dfrac{1}{18}$ **d.** $\dfrac{9}{10}$

 b. 0   **e.** $\dfrac{9}{10}$

 c. 0   **f.** $\dfrac{7}{15}$

4. a. $\dfrac{^-4}{8}$, or $\dfrac{^-1}{2}$ **e.** $\dfrac{4}{8}$, or $\dfrac{1}{2}$

 b. $\dfrac{7}{3}$ **f.** $\dfrac{17}{16}$

 c. $\dfrac{^-3}{3}$, or $^-1$ **g.** $\dfrac{^-40}{22}$, or $\dfrac{^-20}{11}$

 d. $\dfrac{6}{8}$, or $\dfrac{3}{4}$

Exercise Set 6

1. a. Commutative property
 b. Additive-inverse property
 c. Zero as identity element
 d. Associative property
2. b. $n + \frac{^-2}{5}$ and $\frac{7}{8}$ name the same number; hence, the two sums are equal.
 c. Associative property of addition
 d. Additive-inverse property
 e. Zero is the additive identity element.

Exercise Set 7

1. a. $\dfrac{1}{40} - \dfrac{^-7}{8} = \dfrac{9}{10}$ or $\dfrac{1}{40} - \dfrac{9}{10} = \dfrac{^-7}{8}$.

b. $\dfrac{4}{3} + \dfrac{^-3}{4} = \dfrac{7}{12}.$

c. $\dfrac{5}{12} - 2\dfrac{1}{6} = {}^-1\dfrac{3}{4}$ or $\dfrac{5}{12} - {}^-1\dfrac{3}{4} = 2\dfrac{1}{6}.$

d. $\dfrac{5}{6} + \dfrac{17}{3} = n.$

e. ${}^-1\dfrac{1}{4} + n = 7\dfrac{1}{8}.$

f. $n - \dfrac{^-14}{7} = \dfrac{^-5}{14}$ or $n - \dfrac{^-5}{14} = \dfrac{^-14}{7}.$

2. b, c

3. a. ${}^-\left(7\dfrac{3}{8}\right) = {}^-\left(7 + \dfrac{3}{8}\right) = {}^-\left(\dfrac{56}{8} + \dfrac{3}{8}\right) = \dfrac{^-59}{8}.$

b. $\dfrac{64}{11} = \dfrac{55 + 9}{11} = \dfrac{55}{11} + \dfrac{9}{11} = 5 + \dfrac{9}{11} = 5\dfrac{9}{11}.$

c. $\dfrac{^-13}{7} = {}^-\left(\dfrac{7 + 6}{7}\right) = {}^-\left(\dfrac{7}{7} + \dfrac{6}{7}\right) = {}^-\left(1 + \dfrac{6}{7}\right) = {}^-1\dfrac{6}{7}.$

d. $\dfrac{37}{18} = \dfrac{36 + 1}{18} = \dfrac{36}{18} + \dfrac{1}{18} = 2 + \dfrac{1}{18} = 2\dfrac{1}{18}.$

4. a. $\dfrac{^-5}{30},$ or $\dfrac{^-1}{6}$ **c.** $\dfrac{^-243}{16},$ or ${}^-15\dfrac{3}{16}$

b. $\dfrac{5}{12}$ **d.** $\dfrac{55}{8},$ or $6\dfrac{7}{8}$

Exercise Set 8

1. $\dfrac{^-5}{9} \times \dfrac{7}{10} = \dfrac{^-35}{90} = \dfrac{^-7}{18}.$

$\dfrac{15}{^-27} \times \dfrac{7}{10} = \dfrac{105}{^-270} = \dfrac{7}{^-18} = \dfrac{^-7}{18}.$

$\dfrac{^-5}{9} \times \dfrac{14}{20} = \dfrac{^-70}{180} = \dfrac{^-7}{18}.$

$\dfrac{15}{^-27} \times \dfrac{14}{20} = \dfrac{210}{^-540} = \dfrac{7}{^-18} = \dfrac{^-7}{18}.$

2. $\dfrac{25}{^-17} \times \dfrac{1}{1} = \dfrac{25 \times 1}{^-17 \times 1} = \dfrac{25}{^-17}.$

3. a. Each can be expressed as $\frac{^-17}{60}$.
  b. Distributive property

4. a. $\frac{3}{^-7}$, or $\frac{^-3}{7}$ $\qquad \frac{^-7}{3} \times \frac{3}{^-7} = \frac{^-21}{^-21} = 1.$

  b. $\frac{^-13}{18}$ $\qquad \frac{18}{^-13} \times \frac{^-13}{18} = \frac{^-234}{^-234} = 1.$

  c. $\frac{1}{485}$ $\qquad \frac{485}{1} \times \frac{1}{485} = \frac{485}{485} = 1.$

  d. $\frac{97}{3}$ $\qquad \frac{3}{97} \times \frac{97}{3} = \frac{291}{291} = 1.$

5. a. $\frac{^-3}{7}$

  b. $\frac{^-13}{18}$

  c. $\frac{1}{485}$

  d. $\frac{97}{3}$

6. a. $\frac{^-6}{1}$

  b. Associative property of multiplication

Exercise Set 9

1. Closure property of multiplication
  Commutative property of multiplication
  Associative property of multiplication
  Identity element for multiplication
  Multiplication property of zero
  Multiplicative-inverse property
  Distributive property of multiplication over addition

2. Answers may vary. Examples are suggested below.
  Closure: $\frac{^-1}{9} \times \frac{3}{7} = \frac{^-3}{63}$, or $\frac{^-1}{21}$. ($\frac{^-1}{21}$ names a rational number.)
  Commutativity: $\frac{^-1}{9} \times \frac{3}{7} = \frac{3}{7} \times \frac{^-1}{9}$.
  Associativity: $(\frac{^-1}{9} \times \frac{3}{7}) \times \frac{^-4}{5} = \frac{^-1}{9} \times (\frac{3}{7} \times \frac{^-4}{5})$.
  Identity element: $\frac{^-1}{9} \times \frac{1}{1} = \frac{^-1}{9}$.
  Multiplication property of zero: $\frac{^-1}{9} \times \frac{0}{1} = \frac{0}{9} = \frac{0}{1}$, or 0.

Multiplicative-inverse property: $\frac{-1}{9} \times \frac{-9}{-1} = \frac{-9}{-9} = 1$.

Distributive property: $\frac{-1}{9} \times (\frac{3}{7} + \frac{-4}{5}) = (\frac{-1}{9} \times \frac{3}{7}) + (\frac{-1}{9} \times \frac{-4}{5})$.

3. a. $\frac{4}{11} + \frac{13}{11} = \left(4 \times \frac{1}{11}\right) + \left(13 \times \frac{1}{11}\right)$

$= (4 + 13) \times \frac{1}{11}$

$= 17 \times \frac{1}{11} = \frac{17}{11}$.

b. $\left(^-3 \times \frac{1}{4}\right) + \left(9 \times \frac{1}{4}\right) = (^-3 + 9) \times \frac{1}{4} = 6 \times \frac{1}{4} = \frac{6}{4}$, or $\frac{3}{2}$.

c. $\frac{5}{6} + \frac{^-4}{6} = \left(5 \times \frac{1}{6}\right) + \left(^-4 \times \frac{1}{6}\right) = (5 + ^-4) \times \frac{1}{6} = 1 \times \frac{1}{6} = \frac{1}{6}$.

d. $\left(1 \times \frac{1}{13}\right) + \left(^-2 \times \frac{1}{13}\right) + \left(7 \times \frac{1}{13}\right)$

$= (1 + ^-2 + 7) \times \frac{1}{13} = 6 \times \frac{1}{13} = \frac{6}{13}$.

Exercise Set 10

1. a. $\frac{^-2}{3}$ **b.** $\frac{1}{2}$ **c.** $\frac{3}{2}$

2. a. The length of the arrow for $\frac{1}{2}$ is $\frac{2}{3}$ the length of the arrow for $\frac{^-3}{4}$, and the arrows are in opposite directions. The ratio is two to three.

b. The length of the arrow for $\frac{7}{16}$ is $\frac{1}{2}$ the length of the arrow for $\frac{7}{8}$, and the arrows are in the same direction. The ratio is one to two.

c. The length of the arrow for $\frac{4}{3}$ is $\frac{3}{2}$ times the length of the arrow for $\frac{8}{9}$, and the arrows are in the same direction. The ratio is three to two.

3. a. $\frac{2}{3}$

b. $\frac{7}{3} \times \frac{15}{4} = \frac{105}{12} = \frac{35}{4}$.

$\frac{7}{2} \times \frac{5}{2} = \frac{35}{4}$.

The equivalence property of fractions *does* apply to the complex fractions in exercise 3a.

c. $\dfrac{\frac{7}{3}}{\frac{7}{2}} = \dfrac{\frac{7}{3} \times \frac{^-6}{7}}{\frac{7}{2} \times \frac{^-6}{7}} = \dfrac{\frac{^-42}{21}}{\frac{^-42}{14}} = \frac{^-42}{21} \times \frac{14}{^-42} = \frac{14}{21} = \frac{2}{3}$.

d. **i.** $\dfrac{\dfrac{1}{2} \times \dfrac{7}{9}}{\dfrac{3}{8} \times \dfrac{5}{6}} = \dfrac{\dfrac{7}{18}}{\dfrac{15}{48}}$. **iv.** $\dfrac{56}{45}$

ii. $\dfrac{56}{45}$ **v.** The answers are the same.

iii. $\dfrac{1/2}{3/8} = \dfrac{4}{3}$, $\dfrac{7/9}{5/6} = \dfrac{14}{15}$. **vi.** Yes.

Exercise Set 11

1. a. $^-7 < 4$ because $^-7 + 3 = {}^-4$ and 3
   is a positive number.

b. $587 < 625$ because $587 + 38 = 625$ and 38
   is a positive number.

c. $\dfrac{^-257}{2} < \dfrac{423}{4}$ because $\dfrac{^-257}{2} + \dfrac{937}{4} = \dfrac{423}{4}$ and $\dfrac{937}{4}$
   is a positive number.

d. $0 < \dfrac{93}{7}$ because $0 + \dfrac{93}{7} = \dfrac{93}{7}$ and $\dfrac{93}{7}$
   is a positive number.

2.

3. a. $(n + {}^-2) + 2 < 9 + 2,$
   $n + ({}^-2 + 2) < 9 + 2,$
   $n + 0 < 9 + 2,$
   $n < 11.$
   The solution set consists of all rational numbers less than 11.

b. $\dfrac{^-3}{4} + \left(\dfrac{3}{4} + n\right) < \dfrac{3}{4} + \dfrac{7}{8},$

   $\left(\dfrac{^-3}{4} + \dfrac{3}{4}\right) + n < \dfrac{3}{4} + \dfrac{7}{8},$

   $0 + n < \dfrac{13}{8},$

   $n < \dfrac{13}{8}.$

The solution set consists of all rational numbers less than $\frac{13}{8}$. (Note that if n is replaced by any number less than $\frac{13}{8}$, the sentence will be true.)

c. $\dfrac{^-3}{10} + \dfrac{^-7}{10} < \dfrac{^-3}{10} + \left(\dfrac{3}{10} + n\right),$

$\dfrac{^-3}{10} + \dfrac{^-7}{10} < \left(\dfrac{^-3}{10} + \dfrac{3}{10}\right) + n,$

$\dfrac{^-10}{10} < 0 + n,$

$^-1 < n.$

The solution set consists of all rational numbers greater than $^-1$.

Exercise Set 12

1. a. $\dfrac{^-9}{10} \times \dfrac{10}{3} = \dfrac{^-90}{30} = ^-3,$

$\dfrac{^-9}{100} \times \dfrac{10}{3} = \dfrac{^-90}{300} = \dfrac{^-3}{10},$

$^-3 < \dfrac{^-3}{10}.$

The equivalence is preserved in the same direction.

b. $\dfrac{^-9}{10} \times 0 = 0; \qquad \dfrac{^-9}{100} \times 0 = 0.$

The inequality is replaced by equality.

c. $\dfrac{^-9}{10} \times \dfrac{^-10}{3} = \dfrac{90}{30} = 3,$

$\dfrac{^-9}{100} \times \dfrac{^-10}{3} = \dfrac{90}{300} = \dfrac{3}{10},$

$\dfrac{3}{10} < 3.$

The inequality is reversed in direction.

2. a. $\dfrac{3}{2} \times \dfrac{2}{3} \times n < \dfrac{3}{2} \times 5,$

$1 \times n < \dfrac{15}{2},$

$n < \dfrac{15}{2}.$

The solution set consists of all rationals less than $\frac{15}{2}$.

b. $\dfrac{^-3}{2} \times \dfrac{^-2}{3} \times n > \dfrac{^-3}{2} \times 5,$

$$1 \times n > \dfrac{^-15}{2},$$

$$n > \dfrac{^-15}{2}.$$

The solution set consists of all rationals greater than $\frac{^-15}{2}$.

c. $\dfrac{5}{8} \times \dfrac{8}{5} \times n < \dfrac{5}{8} \times 25,$

$$1 \times n < \dfrac{125}{8}, \qquad \text{or} \qquad 15\dfrac{5}{8},$$

$$n < 15\dfrac{5}{8}.$$

The solution set consists of all rationals less than $15\frac{5}{8}$.

d. $\dfrac{^-5}{8} \times \dfrac{^-8}{5} \times n > \dfrac{^-5}{8} \times 25,$

$$1 \times n > \dfrac{^-125}{8}, \qquad \text{or} \qquad ^-15\dfrac{5}{8},$$

$$n > {}^-15\dfrac{5}{8}.$$

The solution set consists of all rationals greater than $^-15\frac{5}{8}$.

3. b. Definition of order

   c. $r + n$ and s name the same number.

   d. Distributive property

   e. Product of two positive numbers

   f. Definition of order

Exercise Set 13

1. a. $\dfrac{3}{7} < \dfrac{4}{8},$

$$\dfrac{24}{56} + n = \dfrac{28}{56},$$

$$\dfrac{24}{56} + \dfrac{4}{56} = \dfrac{28}{56}.$$

Thus $\dfrac{3}{7} + \dfrac{4}{56} = \dfrac{4}{8}$, and $\dfrac{4}{56} > 0.$

b. $\dfrac{^-9}{10} < \dfrac{^-8}{9}$,

$$\dfrac{^-81}{90} + n = \dfrac{^-80}{90},$$

$$\dfrac{^-81}{90} + \dfrac{1}{90} = \dfrac{^-80}{90}.$$

Thus $\dfrac{^-9}{10} + \dfrac{1}{90} = \dfrac{^-8}{9}$, and $\dfrac{1}{90} > 0$.

c. $\dfrac{3}{5} < \dfrac{11}{14}$,

$$\dfrac{42}{70} + n = \dfrac{55}{70},$$

$$\dfrac{42}{70} + \dfrac{13}{70} = \dfrac{55}{70}.$$

Thus $\dfrac{3}{5} + \dfrac{13}{70} = \dfrac{11}{14}$, and $\dfrac{13}{70} > 0$.

d. $\dfrac{^-6}{13} < \dfrac{1}{26}$,

$$\dfrac{^-12}{26} + n = \dfrac{1}{26},$$

$$\dfrac{^-12}{26} + \dfrac{13}{26} = \dfrac{1}{26}.$$

Thus $\dfrac{^-6}{13} + \dfrac{13}{26} = \dfrac{1}{26}$, and $\dfrac{13}{26} > 0$.

2. a. $\dfrac{3}{7} < \dfrac{4}{8}$,

$$\dfrac{\dfrac{3}{7} + \dfrac{4}{8}}{2} = \dfrac{26}{56},$$

$$\dfrac{24}{56} < \dfrac{26}{56} < \dfrac{28}{56}, \qquad \text{or} \qquad \dfrac{3}{7} < \dfrac{26}{56} < \dfrac{4}{8}.$$

b. $\dfrac{^-9}{10} < \dfrac{^-8}{9}$,

$$\dfrac{\dfrac{^-9}{10} + \dfrac{^-8}{9}}{2} = \dfrac{^-161}{180},$$

$$\dfrac{^-162}{180} < \dfrac{^-161}{180} < \dfrac{^-160}{180}, \qquad \text{or} \qquad \dfrac{^-9}{10} < \dfrac{^-161}{180} < \dfrac{^-8}{9}.$$

c. $\dfrac{3}{5} < \dfrac{11}{14}$,

$\dfrac{\frac{3}{5} + \frac{11}{14}}{2} = \dfrac{97}{140}$,

$\dfrac{84}{140} < \dfrac{97}{140} < \dfrac{110}{140}$, or $\dfrac{3}{5} < \dfrac{97}{140} < \dfrac{11}{14}$.

d. $\dfrac{^-6}{13} < \dfrac{1}{26}$,

$\dfrac{\frac{^-6}{13} + \frac{1}{26}}{2} = \dfrac{^-11}{52}$,

$\dfrac{^-24}{52} < \dfrac{^-11}{52} < \dfrac{2}{52}$, or $\dfrac{^-6}{13} < \dfrac{^-11}{52} < \dfrac{1}{26}$.

(A much easier way to solve this problem is to notice that the number 0 is between $\frac{^-6}{13}$ and $\frac{1}{26}$.)

3. $\dfrac{^-528}{3}$, $\dfrac{200}{^-3}$, 0, $\dfrac{1}{2}$, $\dfrac{^-4}{^-2}$, $\dfrac{75}{3}$.

(Express each as a fraction having 6 as a denominator.)

4. a. $^-28 < {}^-20$; agrees.

   b. $^-28 < 20$; agrees.

   c. $28 > {}^-20$; does not agree.

   d. $28 > {}^-20$; does not agree.

   e. $^-28 < 20$; agrees.

   f. $20 < 28$; agrees.

   g. $^-20 < 28$; agrees.

   h. $20 > {}^-28$; does not agree.

5. The test applies to any pair of rational numbers, provided they are expressed by fractions both having positive denominators or both having negative denominators.

6. a. $\dfrac{1}{3} < \dfrac{5}{8} < \dfrac{8}{9}$.

   b. $0.007 < \dfrac{7}{100} < 0.7$.

   c. $946 < 999.5 < 1002$.

   d. $223\dfrac{1}{20} < 223\dfrac{1}{10} < 223\dfrac{3}{20}$.

●●

BOOKLET NUMBER ELEVEN:

THE SYSTEM
OF REAL NUMBERS

INTRODUCTION

In Booklet No. 10 of this series, the system of *rational numbers* was discussed. This system includes certain number systems previously investigated: the system of *whole numbers* (Booklet No. 2), the system of *nonnegative rational numbers* (Booklets No. 6 and 7), and the system of *integers* (Booklet No. 9). Now we are going to study a still more extended system, the system of *real numbers.*

We should first give special attention to some characteristics of the rational number system that will be of particular importance to the development of our study. One is the matter of notation. Rational numbers are most commonly denoted by *fractions,* such as 3/2, 5/4, and 6/8. In the fraction 3/2, for example, the number 3 is the *numerator* and the number 2 is the *denominator.* Another common representation is the *decimal* notation, in which the position of a digit has a place value that is used to convey the idea that the denominator is a power of ten. Thus we write 0.25 for 25/100 or 1/4. Remember that 2/8, 1/4, and the decimal numeral 0.25 are all names for the same rational number. (It will often be convenient to use simply the term "decimal" in place of the longer term, "decimal numeral.")

In Booklet No. 7: *Numeration Systems for the Rational Numbers,* an extended type of decimal representation was mentioned. This is the repeating infinite-decimal notation. Here the word "infinite," which we shall use repeatedly in this booklet, reminds us that these decimals, unlike 0.25, do not have a last digit. The whole idea is of such importance that it will be covered in detail later. For the present, let us look at an illustration or two that will remind us of some facts: For example, among the notations

141

for the rational number denoted by 1/3 is 0.333 ⋯ , where the dots indicate an infinite extension of the pattern of the repeated digit 3. Or again, 1/11 can be written as 0.090909 ⋯ and 2/9 as 0.222 ⋯ .

Another important property of the rational numbers is quite difficult to phrase carefully without further development of our study. This is the property of *betweenness*, which permits us to use rational numbers to express measurement or calculation with greater and greater precision. In fact, all computations, all measurements, all practical uses of numbers, are made with rational numbers alone.

Why, then, extend the system of rational numbers? We must carry out an extension in order to avoid clumsy and inexact use of language and to gain a clear picture of the relationship between numbers and the number line. When we have performed the extension, it will be much easier to talk about the unlimited possibility of conceptual accuracy to which we alluded in the last paragraph. We are going to develop a new property called *completeness*, which the system of rational numbers lacks.

Without attempting at the moment to define this concept of completeness, let us look at an example or two. First, consider a "positive number" that when multiplied by itself, or squared, is 2. We want a number, which we shall designate by $\sqrt{2}$ and call the positive square root of 2, such that $\sqrt{2} \times \sqrt{2} = 2$ and $\sqrt{2} > 0$. Sometimes we see inexact expressions, such as 1.414, for $\sqrt{2}$. But 1.414 is not a square root of 2; it is a square root of 1.999396, as you can determine by multiplying 1.414 by 1.414. We shall see later that *there is no rational number that is the positive square root of 2.*

Shall we give up and say there is no number that is the positive square root of 2? Or shall we invent a new number system such that 2 will have a positive square root among the numbers of the system? The ancient Greeks followed the first course and turned aside from arithmetic because it was incomplete in this way. Modern mathematicians have chosen the second course.

It would be possible to invent a system barely sufficient to provide 2 with a positive square root and to satisfy the basic rules of arithmetic. In such a system, it would turn out that 3 did not have a square root. Then we should have to start all over again to remedy this situation. Actually, it would be possible to formulate a system in which every positive number in the system has a positive square root, but in which there would not exist any number representing the ratio of the circumference of a circle to its diameter.

We shall, however, find it quite possible to do a *complete* job in the sense that all ratios of geometrical quantities—all values that could be the result of conceptual measurements—will be in the system we construct.

The procedure we shall use will be formulated in the next section. It may be thought of as "filling the number line."

As we create the new numbers, we should also create definitions for arithmetical operations on them—addition, subtraction, multiplication, and division—that will preserve the basic properties of these operations as they apply to the rational numbers. We want the new system to include the rational numbers not only as a subset but also as a *subsystem*, just as the system of rational numbers may be considered to include the system of integers. (See Booklet No. 10: *The System of Rational Numbers.*) This goal will be accomplished by defining the operations on the new numbers in terms of operations on rational numbers.

THE NUMBER LINE AND INFINITE DECIMALS

The Rolling Circle

Let us make a number line in the following way. We draw a horizontal line, which we assume to be perfectly straight and entirely immune from all imperfections of the real world. It is not disturbed by lumps in the paper; it has no gaps due to spaces between molecules. This line exists only in our imagination, of course, but drawing parts of it will aid our thought and help us to communicate information.

On the line, we choose an arbitrary point and mark it 0. To the right of this point, we choose a second arbitrary point and mark it 1. (See Fig. 1.) Using the distance between these two points as a basic unit, we mark additional points to the right as 2, 3, $\cdots$. Then we reflect to the left as in a mirror held at 0, marking the reflections ⁻1, ⁻2, $\cdots$. (See Booklet No. 9: *The System of Integers.*)

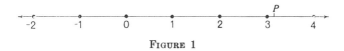

FIGURE 1

One further point, P, has been put on the line between the points marked 3 and 4, in order to illustrate our next concept, the idea of a *decimal expansion*. The point was obtained, at least theoretically, in this way: We made a mark on the circumference of a circle whose diameter measures the same as the distance between the points 0 and 1 marked on our line. Matching that mark to the zero point of the line, we rolled the circle on the line (without slipping) until the mark again met the line. This point of contact was then called P, as indicated in Figures 1 and 2.

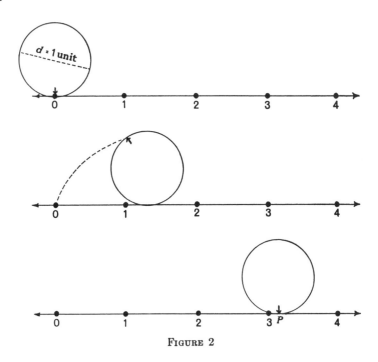

FIGURE 2

Suppose that we subdivide *each* of the intervals between the points marked with integers into *ten congruent smaller intervals*. In order to pursue our example more directly, we shall draw the result only for the segment between the points marked 3 and 4, as shown in Figure 3. As the work progresses we shall continue to concentrate on intervals containing the illustrating point *P*. For convenience, such phrases as "the point marked 3" will be replaced by "point 3." Although the numeral names both a number and a point, the context will tell us which meaning is intended. This should not prove confusing; the same names are used for different types of things in many other areas of our experience. Consider the sentence "Rose picked a rose," for example.

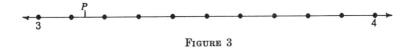

FIGURE 3

Denote now the end points of the intervals from left to right by 3.1, 3.2, and so on, to 3.9. To keep our notations consistent, replace 3 and 4 by 3.0 and 4.0, respectively. These points named by decimals with *one* digit after the decimal point will be called *marking points of the first stage*.

The corresponding numbers, of course, are rational numbers. Now P is between 3.1 and 3.2. (See Fig. 4.)

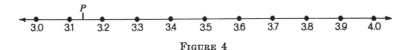

FIGURE 4

Let us continue the process of subdivision. For each successive step a drawing will show the relevant part of the previous line segment magnified by a factor of ten. It will be as if we looked at the part of the line containing P under a succession of microscopic lenses, each lens ten times as powerful as the one before.

In the next stage we see a magnification of the interval between 3.1 and 3.2. It has, in turn, been subdivided into ten congruent smaller intervals, as shown in Figure 5. We adjoin decimal digits as before, to

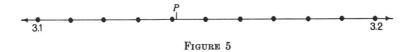

FIGURE 5

name the subdividing points. (See Fig. 6.) Now, however, there are *two* digits after the decimal point, and the points so marked are called *marking points of the second stage*. Again, they correspond to rational numbers. Note that marking points of the first stage are also marking points of the second stage. They get a new name by the adjunction of a 0 at the right; but it also is not unusual for an object, whether mathematical or other, to have several different names. For example, Dad is Mr. Brown or Gregory or Uncle Greg, depending on who is speaking about him. P is now to be seen (Fig. 6) between 3.14 and 3.15.

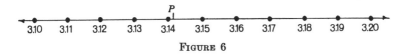

FIGURE 6

Let us magnify this second-stage segment. Now, however, we shall show it only after we have finished naming the appropriate *marking points*

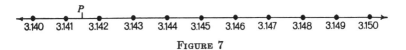

FIGURE 7

of the third stage. (See Fig. 7.) This time the higher magnification shows us that P is between 3.141 and 3.142.

Try another magnification; again we illustrate only the segment containing P. In Figure 8 it appears after the *marking points of the fourth*

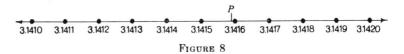

P

3.1410 3.1411 3.1412 3.1413 3.1414 3.1415 3.1416 3.1417 3.1418 3.1419 3.1420

FIGURE 8

stage have been indicated and named. We see that P is most of the way from 3.1415 to 3.1416. Still another magnification would indicate P between 3.14159 and 3.14160.

To obtain an overview of the whole process thus far, we combine four magnifications in the single representation of Figure 9.

We can simplify the descriptions of the location of P by a simple convention. At any given stage, instead of describing the location of a point as being in the segment between two marking points of that stage, we shall simply name the marking point immediately to the left of the point. (Of course, if a point is a marking point in its own right, we name that point according to its appropriate stage.) Thus, P would be indicated by 3.1 at the first stage, 3.14 at the second, and then successively by 3.141, 3.1415, and 3.14159. The standard way of saying this is to indicate the stage by the number of decimal digits and to use constructions such as "The decimal expansion of P to two decimal digits is 3.14," or simply "P is given to two decimals by 3.14."

Remember that this is an imaginary experiment. We are rolling a "perfect" circle on a "perfect" line. If we actually tried the experiment, our accuracy would be limited by imperfections in the circle and in the line, by the circle's slipping as it rolled, and by our inability to mark and measure with exact precision. Already we are at or beyond the limits of careful machining for sizes of things that we customarily handle. Industrial standards, for example, require that the pistons and piston rings of precision engines be accurate to better than one ten-thousandth of an inch (0.0001 in.), whereas we are already talking about intervals whose length is a hundred-thousandth (0.00001) of our original unit. Fortunately, mathematical calculation is not limited by such mundane considerations. By the use of electronic calculators, others have carried our theoretical experiment through ten thousand stages, working with trigonometrical formulas, which do not require any real circle or real line.

But our imagination is not limited by the cost or the time required for computation on a modern computing machine. We can imagine the process continuing literally forever, as decimal digit follows decimal digit

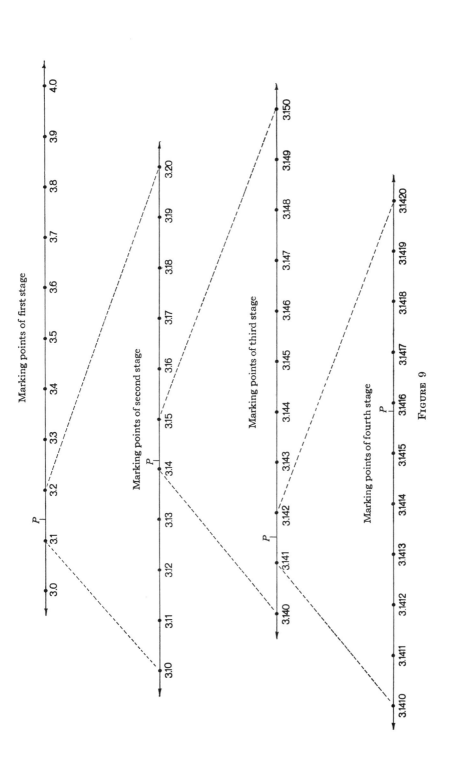

Marking points of first stage

Marking points of second stage

Marking points of third stage

Marking points of fourth stage

FIGURE 9

in the designation of *P*. It is this limitless, or infinite, decimal numeral that we think of as the name for *P*. All the finite preliminary numerals are merely initial stages.

The Real Numbers

We want to consider two other ideas that are related to the process we have been discussing.

The first idea is this: Each marking point has been given a decimal numeral. This decimal, as we have said, also denotes a *number*. Thus, *every marking point has an associated rational number*. This number specifies the length, in terms of our unit, of the segment bounded by zero and the marking point. We now invent a "number," designated by the numeral for *P*, that describes the distance from 0 to *P*. Note that this is perfectly in accord with our previous use of infinite decimals. The point one-third of the distance from 0 to 1 is denoted by 0.333 $\cdots$, and the numeral 0.333 $\cdots$ is associated with the rational number 1/3.

The second idea we have already suggested by implication. While our attention was fixed on the specific part of the line that contained *P*, we were aware of the possibility of performing the subdivisions at each stage on the *whole line*. At the first stage, *every* integer interval is divided into ten parts. At the second, there are one hundred subdivisions between *any two successive* integers, and so on. For example, at the second stage the marking point just to the right of 1.00 is 1.01; the point just to the left of 2.00 is 1.99. What comes just to the right of 0.50? Just to the left? The points 0.51 and 0.49, of course.

We should pay particular attention to that part of the line to the left of 0, because it may not be sufficiently clear merely to say that we reflect the right-hand side and use negative signs. At the first stage, the segment from ‾1.0 to 0.0 would have the appearance shown in Figure 10.

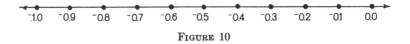

FIGURE 10

If our circle had rolled to the left, where would we have marked the resulting point? Between ‾3.1 and ‾3.2. Call the point *Q* instead of *P*, to distinguish between the experiments. (See Fig. 11.)

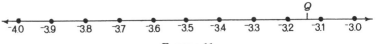

FIGURE 11

What decimal names Q at this stage? Remember the reflection idea. Think of a mirror mounted at 0. The "negative" part of the line is the image in the mirror of the "positive" part. When we chose 3.1 to represent P at the first stage, we chose the marking point between P and 0. Q is the reflection of P; and ‾3.1, between Q and 0, is the reflection of 3.1. So we associate Q and ‾3.1.

Now let us reconsider the number line in Figure 10. At the second stage, what are the marking points just left and right of ‾1.00? They are ‾1.01 and ‾0.99, respectively, as shown in Figure 12.

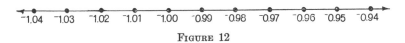

‾1.04   ‾1.03   ‾1.02   ‾1.01   ‾1.00   ‾0.99   ‾0.98   ‾0.97   ‾0.96   ‾0.95   ‾0.94

FIGURE 12

Now think of the whole line as we go from one stage to the next. The subdivisions increase in number; the intervals become shorter and shorter. Our intuition suggests that the intervals ultimately narrow to a point.

This concept turns out to be very difficult to examine rigorously in full logical detail, and almost as difficult to think about clearly in an intuitive manner. Some sources of our difficulties are the following:

1. *The problem of imagining the infinite.*—Infinite subdivisions and infinite decimals are far beyond our day-to-day experience.

2. *Our use of inexact images.*—We draw blobs of ink, pencil, or chalk and call those blobs points and lines. If we say, for example, "No matter how close distinct points are, eventually some marking point will come between them," we may get an answer like this: "But I'll mark two points here so close that they touch. You'll never get another point between them." The answer really implies, "If I make two *blobs* that touch, you can't put a *blob* between them." But blobs are not the same as points, because points have no dimension and cannot touch without being identical.

3. *Logical difficulties with infinite sets and infinite processes.*—These very real difficulties have occupied mathematicians for thousands of years. Only within the last hundred years has there been developed a method of handling infinite sets and infinite processes that is acceptable to the vast majority of modern mathematicians.

To return to our construction of the real numbers: At each step, every point is assigned to a nearby marking point named by a decimal numeral. At each successive step, the decimal numerals contain one more digit. As we subdivide the intervals without limit, we assign to each point its infinite decimal. In turn, each of the finite decimal numerals for the marking points names a particular rational number that indicates more and more closely the distance and direction of the point from the origin, or zero point. The infinite decimal, then, names this latter distance, or "real number."

For every point on the number line, there is an associated infinite decimal that names a real number. The converse of this statement, that for every infinite decimal there is an associated point, is a hypothesis of our development. In a way this is just what was meant when we required that the number line be free from gaps or imperfections.

What we want are the following one-to-one correspondences:

> Real Numbers ↔ Infinite Decimals ↔ Points on the Number Line.
> (Read "↔" as "correspond[s] to.")

We have given intuitive reasons why there is at least one infinite decimal for each real number and each point. We have also, by definition, made a one-to-one correspondence between real numbers and points by regarding a real number as expressing the length of a segment, with an appropriate sign adjoined to indicate the direction from the origin. We have not discussed the possibility that a point might have more than one infinite decimal associated with it. As a matter of fact, this happens in some special cases, and we must discuss these before going on.

When we were assigning marking points to points in the intervals, we said that if a point *is* a marking point, then it is assigned to itself. Otherwise, at each stage we take the nearest marking point to the left for points on the positive side of the origin and the nearest marking point to the right for points on the negative side of the origin.

What would happen if we always used just one rule, say the following? "At every stage, assign to any point on the positive side of the origin the nearest marking point to its left; and to any point on the negative side assign the nearest marking point to its right." This would of course mean that a marking point could no longer be assigned to itself.

For one thing, we should have to make a special definition for 0, which is on *neither* the positive *nor* the negative side. But other undesirable things would happen. Take, for example, the point originally marked 1. At the first stage, what is the nearest marking point on its left? Clearly, 0.9. What at the second stage? It is 0.99. Continue the process—at the tenth stage it is 0.9999999999. It becomes obvious that the resulting infinite decimal for the point is just "0." followed by an infinite string of 9's. Hence $1.000\cdots$ and $0.999\ \cdots$ name the same point.

We can see this duplication of names in another way. We know that the point 1/3 of the way from 0 to 1 has the infinite decimal $0.333\ \cdots$, an infinite string of 3's. This implies that the point 2/3 of the way from 0 to 1 has the decimal $0.666\ \cdots$, which can be expressed as "$2 \times 0.333\cdots$." Now, how about the point 3/3 of the way? We have

$$3 \times 0.333 \cdots = 0.999 \cdots = \frac{3}{3} = 1.000 \cdots .$$

A similar duplication happens at *every* nonzero marking point of *every* stage. Thus 0.249999 ⋯ names the same point as 0.250000 ⋯ , and ⁻1.73219999 ⋯ names the same point as ⁻1.7322000 ⋯ .

We are going to rule out of our consideration all infinite decimals that trail off in an infinite string of 9's. It will turn out that this takes care of all duplication difficulties. Our rule of assigning marking points to themselves takes care of this problem.

Order

In our discussion of the rational number system in Booklet No. 10, it was noted that the rational numbers are ordered; that is, for any two different rational numbers, one is less than the other. An ordering of the real numbers should correspond to the relationship between decimals and points on the number line. We try to make this precise with the following rules.

A. Grouping the infinite decimals into three classes (trichotomy)

    1. Zero: 0.000 ⋯ . If desired, it may be prefaced with either a negative or a positive sign; the number named is unchanged.

    2. Positive decimals: At least one digit is not 0 (for example, 0.0001000 ⋯), and the decimal is unsigned or prefaced with a positive sign.

    3. Negative decimals: At least one digit is a nonzero digit (for example, ⁻5.000 ⋯), and the decimal is prefaced with a negative sign.

B. Comparing the numbers

    1. If one of the decimals to be compared is zero—

        a) Zero is *less* than any real number represented by a positive decimal.

        b) Zero is *greater* than any real number represented by a negative decimal.

    2. If the decimals have opposite signs, any real number represented by a negative decimal is less than any real number represented by a positive decimal.

    3. If both decimals are positive, find the first digit at which the decimal representations differ. The number whose representation has the *lesser* digit at this point is the lesser:

$$0.45739876 \cdots < 0.45741245 \cdots .$$

$$07.352 \cdots < 21.352 \cdots .$$

If the difference is to the left of the decimal sign, we can still apply the rule strictly if we remember that zeros can fill in the empty places of the numeral. Thus, in the second example above, we can replace 7.352 $\cdots$ with 07.352, to balance the beginning points of the two numerals.[1]

4. If both decimals are negative, find the first digit at which the representations differ. The number whose representation has the *greater* digit at this point is the lesser number:

$$^-44.\underline{3}72 \cdots < {}^-43.\underline{3}72 \cdots .$$

Density

Between any two points with different decimal numerals there is a marking point.

We shall not try to give a formal proof but shall just indicate ways that a marking point can be found. There are in fact an infinite number of choices.

We use the following steps:

1. If the numbers have opposite signs, we know that zero is between them.

2. If the numbers have the same sign, we try "rounding off" the one representing the point further from the origin. Rounding off is the process of replacing with zeros all digits to the right of some particular chosen digit. This can be done at any digit after the first difference between the numerals appears. The process of rounding off is also called "cutting short."

   a) $R \leftrightarrow 0.45739876 \cdots$.
      $S \leftrightarrow 0.45741245 \cdots$.
      Marking points between R and S: $0.45740000 \cdots$,
      $0.45741000 \cdots$, $0.457412000 \cdots$, etc.

   b) $R \leftrightarrow {}^-0.0321981 \cdots$.
      $S \leftrightarrow {}^-0.0322012 \cdots$.
      Marking points between R and S: $^-0.0322000 \cdots$,
      $^-0.32201000 \cdots$, etc.

3. If this does not seem to work, we try the other point and another process:

   a) $R \leftrightarrow 0.4730000 \cdots$.
      $S \leftrightarrow 0.4712000 \cdots$.

---

[1] Notice that we originally reserved the dot notation at the end of a numeral to imply the projection of an established and readily visible pattern. Now we are dealing with general real numbers that may not have any pattern, but that we cannot write out in full. So we need to use the dot notation just to indicate continuation of real numbers: if no pattern is apparent before the dots begin, assume that none exists. Thus, for the examples in rules 3 and 4 no pattern is implied.

Cutting short $0.4730000\cdots$ will not work because it *is* cut short. Instead, we try "rounding up" $0.4712000\cdots$. The process used here is to increase by 1 a digit in the numeral representing the point nearer the origin and then to cut short. Rounding up can be done as soon as a different digit occurs that *can* be increased, that is, a digit that is not 9.

Marking points between R and S: $0.4720000\cdots$, $0.471300\cdots$, etc.

Note how all these suggestions would fail to put a point between those represented by $0.249999\cdots$ and $0.25000\cdots$. The former cannot be increased without exceeding the latter. In turn, we cannot decrease $0.25000\cdots$ and stay above $0.24999\cdots$. This is another way of seeing that these two decimals denote the same real number. You should recall that we have ruled out the one with the infinite string of nines.

We can put a number associated with a marking point between any two different real numbers. We can approximate any real number as closely as we wish by a number associated with a marking point. That is, given any distance, no matter how small, from a particular point on the number line, we can find a marking point within that distance.

For example, let us find a marking point within 0.00001 unit of the point P in the example of the rolling circle. Recall that P was located between the points denoted by 3.14159 and 3.14160. These are only 0.00001 units apart, and P is *between* them. Consequently, P must be nearer to each of them than 0.00001. Hence, both 3.14159 and 3.14160 are marking points within 0.00001 unit of P.

In the "Introduction" we mentioned two properties of the rational number system, "betweenness" and "completeness." These properties enable us to find a marking point between any two points denoted by different decimals and to approximate any real number as closely as we wish by using a number associated with a marking point. Thus we can use rational numbers in general, and numbers represented by decimal fractions ending in zeros (called terminating decimals) in particular, to approximate all real numbers and measurements.

In Booklet No. 6: *The Rational Numbers*, a similar property of the rational numbers was discussed: the rational numbers are *dense*. That is, between any two rational numbers there is another rational number. Here we are dealing with a generalization. Between every two *real* numbers there is a *rational* number—in fact, one that is denoted by a terminating decimal.

The mathematical usage is as follows. Suppose we have one set S of numbers and another set T that is a subset of S; then $T \subset S$, with the property that, given any two numbers of S, there is a number of T between them; *then T is said to be dense in S.*[2]

For example, the rational numbers are dense in themselves (between every two rational numbers there is a rational number). The rational numbers are dense in the real numbers. (Actually, the irrational numbers also are dense in the real numbers.) The integers are *not* dense in the rational numbers, since, for example, there is no integer between 1/2 and 2/3. Are the integers dense in themselves? Is there an integer between 2 and 3? Certainly not; so the integers are not dense in themselves. Are the numbers with terminating decimals dense in the rational numbers? Yes; it is easy, for example, to find a number with a terminating decimal between $0.72000\cdots$ and $0.73000\cdots$. One such terminating decimal is $0.725000\cdots$.

It is indeed fortunate that this possibility of approximation exists, since direct calculations using real numbers expressed in their infinite-decimal form are generally impossible. If the decimals have a special form, however, then the operation may often be carried out. We have already written

$$3 \times 0.3333\cdots = 0.999\cdots ,$$

but the right-hand side is not allowed; so, in permissible notation, we have

$$3 \times 0.3333\cdots = 1.000\cdots .$$

Again, we can write equations like

$$0.333\cdots - 0.111\cdots = 0.222\cdots ;$$

but we recognize this as just a cumbersome way of writing $1/3 - 1/9 = 2/9$, as we can check through expanding the fractions into decimals by the division algorithm.

Exercise Set 1

1. At the third stage as defined on page 6 in the text, name the marking point that is—
   a. Just to the left of 1.000.
   b. Just to the right of ⁻1.000.

2. Find a marking point between the points named by ⁻0.20134$\cdots$ and ⁻0.20245$\cdots$.

---

[2] This definition is usually replaced in modern advanced mathematics by

T is dense in S if, for each member a of S, there is a member of T as close as we please to a.

The two definitions are not strictly equivalent, but the definition given in the text is better adapted to our discussion of approximation, since we wish to emphasize the choice involved.

3. Arrange the following real numbers in increasing order: ⁻0.01234···, ⁻0.1234···, 1.234···, ⁻4.2310···, 12.345···, ⁻100.00···.

4. Replace the following decimal expressions by the correct decimal form (that is, without the infinite string of 9's) designating the same value:

a. 0.20999···

b. ⁻1.12999···

c. 2.134999···

RATIONAL NUMBERS AND REPEATING DECIMALS

Repeating Decimals

In Booklet No. 7: *Numeration Systems for the Rational Numbers*, a connection was established between rational numbers and repeating decimals. We are now going to treat this material again from a slightly different viewpoint. We wish to show that the set of rational numbers is identified with a very special subset of the set of real numbers—namely, the subset of real numbers for which the decimals have an infinite repeating pattern. Here are some repeating decimals:

$$0.333 \cdots$$
$$20.202020 \cdots$$
$$⁻5.73012012012 \cdots$$
$$13.25000 \cdots$$

In all cases, after perhaps a certain amount of initial hesitation, which may extend to the right of the decimal point, there occurs a digital pattern that continues indefinitely and consists of a fixed number of consecutive digits that repeat in the same order.

In the first example the pattern begins at the decimal point and consists of a single digit, 3.

In the second, the pattern begins two digits to the left of the decimal point and consists of two consecutive digits, 20.

In the third, the pattern does not start until the third digit to the right of the decimal point. It consists of three digits, 012.

The fourth pattern also begins three digits to the right of the decimal point but consists of a single digit, 0.

It is frequently convenient to use bars rather than dots to denote repetitions. Bars are placed over the digits of a pattern, or "block." Bars are never placed to the left of the decimal point. Thus, the four examples could be rewritten

$$0.\overline{3}$$
$$20.\overline{20}$$
$$^{-}5.73\overline{012}$$
$$13.25\overline{0}$$

Sometimes we may not wish to put bars as far to the left as we can. For example, in the equations $1/11 = 0.\overline{09}$ and $10/11 = 0.\overline{90}$ it might be desirable for computational purposes to use bars to show that the patterns are the same:

$$\frac{1}{11} = 0.\overline{09}, \qquad \frac{10}{11} = 0.9\overline{09};$$

or

$$\frac{1}{11} = 0.0\overline{90}, \qquad \frac{10}{11} = 0.\overline{90}.$$

We have two basic points to make in this section:

1. Every repeating decimal is a decimal expression of a rational number.
2. Every rational number has a repeating decimal expansion.

You should be careful to analyze the difference between the two statements. It is conceivable that one might be true and the other false, as is the case with the statements "Every cat is a mammal" and "Every mammal is a cat."

We shall see, however, that statements 1 and 2 are both true; together they establish the result that repeating decimals and fractions are just different representations of the same rational numbers.

Making a Fraction from a Repeating Decimal

To convince ourselves that statement 1 is true, we need a prescription showing how to find an equivalent fraction, given a repeating decimal. We shall choose as a first illustration of the prescription the decimal $0.272727\cdots$, which may be expressed as $0.\overline{27}$.

The method relies on the effect of multiplying by a power of ten a number that is represented by a decimal. Let us begin with the number $a = 0.272727$, which is like our example except that it terminates after six digits:

$$
\begin{aligned}
a &= 0.272727.\\
10 \times a &= 2.72727.\\
100 \times a &= 27.2727.\\
1{,}000 \times a &= 272.727.\\
10{,}000 \times a &= 2{,}727.27.
\end{aligned}
$$

The effect of each successive multiplication by a higher power of ten is to move the decimal point one place to the right in the decimal representation.

Now consider our nonterminating example:

$$b = 0.272727 \cdots = 0.\overline{27}.$$
$$10 \times b = 2.727272 \cdots = 2.\overline{72} = 2.7\overline{27}.$$
$$100 \times b = 27.272727 \cdots = 27.\overline{27}.$$

If we subtract the original value of b from $100 \times b$, we have

$$
\begin{array}{ll}
100 \times b & \text{or, in this case,} \quad 27.272727 \cdots \\
\underline{\quad -b \quad} & \quad\quad\quad\quad\quad\quad \underline{-0.272727 \cdots} \\
99 \times b & \quad\quad\quad\quad\quad\quad 27.000000 \cdots \; ;
\end{array}
$$

so

$$99 \times b = 27, \quad \text{or} \quad b = \frac{27}{99} = \frac{3 \times 9}{11 \times 9} = \frac{3}{11}.$$

Notice how b differs from a. As we multiply a by successive powers of ten the last digit is moved to the left in forming each resulting decimal. There are fewer digits after the decimal point. But for b there is no *last* digit; the decimals for b, $10 \times b$, and $100 \times b$ repeat their blocks indefinitely.

Why did we pick 100 for a multiple? Because it brought the repeating pattern into line with the original. If we had used

$$10 \times b = 2.\overline{72} = 2.7\overline{27},$$

the pattern would not have lined up with $0.\overline{27}$. Of course, 10,000 would work as well as 100:

$$10,000 \times b = 2,727.\overline{27}.$$

$$
\begin{array}{ll}
10,000 \times b & \text{or, in this case,} \quad 2,727.\overline{27} \\
\underline{\quad -b \quad} & \quad\quad\quad\quad\quad\quad \underline{-0.\overline{27}} \\
9,999 \times b & \quad\quad\quad\quad\quad\quad 2,727.\overline{00}
\end{array}
$$

Thus,

$$9,999 \times b = 2,727.$$

So

$$b = \frac{2,727}{9,999} = \frac{3 \times 909}{11 \times 909} = \frac{3}{11}.$$

But why do more work than we must? We choose the least multiple that will do the job.

Let us try another example: $0.\overline{148} = 0.148148 \cdots$. This time we need a shift of three places. Therefore, multiply by 1,000:

$$1,000 \times 0.\overline{148} = 148.\overline{148} \quad \text{(why?)};$$

subtract the original:

$$148.\overline{148}$$
$$-0.\overline{148}$$
$$\overline{148.\overline{0}}$$

We had 1,000 times the original number and subtracted the original number; 999 times the original is left and is equal to 148. So the original number has the value

$$\frac{148}{999} = \frac{4 \times 37}{27 \times 37} = \frac{4}{27}.$$

Here is a general procedure for carrying out the program:

1. Find the pattern length—that is, the number of digits in the pattern.
2. Multiply by the power of ten that will shift one complete pattern to the left.
3. Subtract the original decimal.
4. Form a fraction from the result.
5. Calculate what multiple of the original value resulted from steps 2 and 3.
6. Divide by the result of step 5. The result of the division is a fraction whose value is the same as that of the original decimal.
7. Simplify the fraction.

As a final example, we shall illustrate the method on a decimal whose pattern is slow to establish itself. Take

$$0.4135135\cdots = 0.4\overline{135}.$$

A little more work will be necessary, beginning at step 4, than was needed for the previous examples.

1. Pattern length:　　　　$0.4\overline{135}$ (three digits).
2. Multiply by 1,000:　　$413.\overline{513} = 413.5\overline{135}$.
   (It may be easier to see this without the bars:
   $1,000 \times 0.4135135135\cdots = 413.513513513\cdots = 413.5\overline{135}.$)

3. Subtract:
$$413.5\overline{135} = 1,000 \times n$$
$$-0.4\overline{135} = -1 \times n$$
$$\overline{413.1\overline{0} = 999 \times n}$$

4. Make a fraction:　　$413.1 = \dfrac{4{,}131}{10}.$

5. Find the multiple:　　$1,000 - 1 = 999.$

6. Divide:　　$\dfrac{4{,}131}{10} \div 999 = \dfrac{4{,}131}{9{,}990} = n.$

7. Simplify: $n = \dfrac{4{,}131}{9{,}990} = \dfrac{153 \times 27}{390 \times 27} = \dfrac{153}{370}.$

The process will always work because at step 3 it yields a terminating decimal that can be converted to a fraction at step 4.

Making a Repeating Decimal from a Fraction

To find a decimal expression for a rational number, when its fraction name is known, we use the division algorithm. We want to see why the resulting decimal necessarily repeats. This is essentially due to the repetitive nature of the algorithm itself. In performing the calculations we find ourselves eventually repeating the following three steps over and over:

1. Bring down a zero.
2. Divide by the denominator of the original fraction.
3. Get a new remainder.

But how many *different* new remainders can we get? Let us try an example, making a special point of keeping track of the remainders as we go, as in Example 1.

EXAMPLE 1: $12/7 = 1.\overline{714285}.$

```
        1.71428571
7 | 12.00000000              Remainder
    7
   ---------
    5 0                         5
    4 9
    ----
      10                        1
       7
     ----
       30                       3
       28
      ----
       20                       2
       14
      ----
       60                       6
       56
      ----
       40                       4
       35
      ----
       50                       5
       49
      ----
       10                       1
        7
      ----
        3                       3
```

After six steps of the algorithm, the remainder 5 repeats. As soon as it shows up again, the whole calculation repeats because each set of three steps is exactly the same when the remainders are the same. The blocks marked by the dotted lines are identical and will occur over and over. Thus,

$$\frac{12}{7} = 1.\overline{714285}.$$

Now, how do we know that some remainder must repeat? This is so because the number of possible remainders is limited.

If we get a remainder of zero, the decimal terminates; that is, it repeats in one-digit blocks consisting of zeros only.

If a zero remainder does not occur, the possible remainders range from 1 to one less than the divisor, inclusive. (In our example, 1, 2, 3, 4, 5, and 6 were possible remainders.) As soon as all possibilities have occurred, something has to repeat.

Of course, not all possible remainders have to occur; we may get a repeat long before all possibilities are exhausted.

EXAMPLE 2: $23/101 = 0.\overline{2277}$.

```
              0.22772
101 | 23.00000                        Remainder
      20 2
       2 80                               28
       2 02
         780                              78
         707
         730                              73
         707
         230                              23
         202
          28                              ‾2‾8‾
```

In Example 2 only four out of the one hundred possible nonzero remainders ever appear. In fact, because the three steps mentioned in the algorithm begin at once, since only 0 is ever brought down in this case, the problem repeats itself as soon as a remainder of 23 is obtained. The original problem was to divide 23 by 101, and when 23 occurs as a remainder, this is the situation again. Thus the digits in the answer start to repeat the established pattern at this point.

Whichever way it is, sooner or later the repetition of remainders must occur; and then we have finished a pattern, and start all over again.

Exercise Set 2

1. Expand as repeating decimals:

    a. $\dfrac{2}{13}$ **b.** $\dfrac{5}{37}$ **c.** $\dfrac{17}{35}$ **d.** $\dfrac{4}{13}$

2. Find a fraction (in simplest form) equivalent to

a. $0.20\overline{20}\cdots$　　**b.** $1.2\overline{36}$　　**c.** $0.\overline{384615}$　　**d.** $0.\overline{12345}$

3. Write the repeating decimals for 1/7, 2/7, 3/7, 4/7, 5/7, and 6/7. Show that if an appropriate starting point is selected, the same pattern occurs every time.

4. Show, by the method developed in this section, that $0.999\cdots = 1.000$.

IRRATIONAL NUMBERS

The Positive Square Root of 2

Real numbers whose decimal expansions do not have the form of an infinite repeated pattern are called "irrational numbers." It is easy to find the decimals for as many irrational numbers as we want. All we have to do is to avoid successively repeating patterns. Patterns are all right as long as they do not repeat. For example, an irrational number is represented by the decimal $0.101001000100001\cdots$, where there is an additional 0 in each block of 0's between successive 1's. Can you find the pattern in the following decimal?

$$0.12345678910111213141516171819202\cdots$$

(When you get to $\cdots 1011$, you may say "ten, eleven" or "one, zero, one, one.")

Although these numbers are interesting, it is natural to ask whether or not there are any irrational numbers more commonly useful. Here we run into complications. In the "Introduction" we mentioned $\sqrt{2}$. How can we *prove* that it is irrational? A computing machine can quickly give us thousands of decimal digits of its numeral, and we can see that no repeating pattern has emerged. But perhaps $\sqrt{2}$ is a rational number whose simplest fraction has a very great numerator and a very great denominator. It might easily require millions of digits, instead of thousands, before a repeat begins. We can never *prove* the number is irrational by looking at digits, no matter how many of them we produce.

Actually, the history of the problem is quite interesting. The Pythagoreans in ancient Greece wanted an expression for the length of a diagonal of a square in terms of the length of one of its sides. They sought the ratio of the length of a diagonal to the length of a side and expected to compute it as the ratio of two counting numbers. It is this idea of ratio that leads to the use of the term "rational" in the sense of "having a ratio."

The Pythagoreans knew that in a right triangle the square of the length of the long side is equal to the sum of the squares of the lengths of the shorter sides. The square of a number is the product when that number is multiplied by itself. The superscript 2 is used to indicate that a number is squared; for example, 3^2 means 3×3, or 9. For a right triangle with sides measuring 3 units, 4 units, and 5 units, as in Figure 13, we have the equation $3^2 + 4^2 = 5^2$; that is, $9 + 16 = 25$.

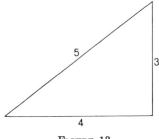

FIGURE 13   FIGURE 14

Now, if each side of a square figure measures 1 unit, then the square of the length of the diagonal is $1^2 + 1^2 = 1 + 1 = 2$. Therefore, the length of the diagonal is $\sqrt{2}$, as indicated in Figure 14, since $(\sqrt{2})^2 = 2$.

The Pythagoreans wished to write $\sqrt{2}$ as a ratio of integers—that is, as a "fraction." To understand what happened next, we need to review some facts:

A. All whole numbers are either even or odd. No number is both even and odd. (The even whole numbers are 0, 2, 4, 6, $\cdots$; the odd ones are 1, 3, 5, 7, $\cdots$.)

B. Any even whole number can be written as two times another whole number. For example,
$$10 = 2 \times 5,$$
$$12 = 2 \times 6.$$
Any number that is twice a whole number is even.

C. The square of an even number is even. The square of an odd number is odd. (Try some examples to convince yourself.)

D. Any fraction is equivalent to the fraction changed to its simplest form— that is, the form whose numerator and denominator have 1 as their greatest common divisor. For example, 30/42 is equivalent to 5/7, which is in simplest form.

E. If a fraction is in simplest form, then its numerator and denominator are not both even. (For then, according to statement B, we could divide numerator and denominator by 2.) At least one of them is odd.

Now let us try to write $\sqrt{2}$ as a fraction. This fraction (if there is

one) can be in simplest form, by statement D. The denominator is some
counting number, q, and the numerator is a whole number, p.

Then we have

$$\frac{p}{q} = \sqrt{2},$$

or

$$\frac{p}{q} \times \frac{p}{q} = \sqrt{2} \times \sqrt{2},$$

or

$$\frac{p^2}{q^2} = 2, \quad \text{by the definition of } \sqrt{2}.$$

Now, multiplying both sides of the equation by q^2, we get

$$\frac{p^2}{q^2} \times q^2 = 2 \times q^2,$$

or

$$p^2 = 2 \times q^2.$$

Thus p^2 is even, by statement B; and statement C implies that p is even.

Then q is odd, by statement E. Further, using the result that p is even
and applying fact B again, we see that there is some whole number r
such that $p = 2 \times r$. Therefore, we can substitute $2 \times r$ for p, in the
equation $p^2 = 2 \times q^2$, so that

$$(2 \times r)^2 = 2 \times q^2, \quad \text{or} \quad (2 \times r) \times (2 \times r) = 2 \times q^2.$$

Now the associative and commutative properties of multiplication
permit us to regroup the expression on the left as follows:

$$(2 \times 2) \times (r \times r) = 2 \times q^2,$$

or

$$4 \times r^2 = 2 \times q^2,$$

or, when we divide both sides by 2,

$$2 \times r^2 = q^2.$$

Now statements B and C imply that q^2 and q are even.

Hence, q is both even and odd. But, by fact A, this is impossible; q does
not exist and there is *no* fraction for $\sqrt{2}$. This completes the proof—but
if you have found it difficult, then perhaps you should start again on
page 162 to appreciate its subtleties.[3]

This discovery greatly amazed the Greeks. Here was length without
an acceptable number to go with it. They stated the fact by saying:
"The diagonal of a square and its side are incommensurable." That is, they

---

[3] See also Edwin F. Beckenbach, "Geometric Proofs of the Irrationality of $\sqrt{2}$," *Arithmetic Teacher*,
XV (1968), 244–50.

cannot be measured in terms of each other in the sense that if we repeatedly marked off diagonals and also sides on the same line, starting from the same point, the end points would never match. The length of seven sides is *close* to that of five diagonals, but the two lengths are not *equal*. (If the length of seven sides were equal to the length of five diagonals, then one-fifth the length of a side or one-seventh the length of a diagonal would be a common measure.) From this time on, the Greeks turned their attention almost exclusively to geometry, since arithmetic had proved to be incomplete. The result was that portions of mathematics depending on arithmetical calculations—algebra and trigonometry, for example—were neglected for centuries.

Today we are not so shocked by this proof as was Pythagoras. (Legend says that he swore his associates to secrecy and slaughtered one hundred oxen as a sacrifice!) We know how to approximate $\sqrt{2}$ with numbers represented by finite decimals. One way to do this is to make successive approximations by "bracketing."

To bracket, we begin by getting the value between successive integers; 1 is too small because $1 \times 1 = 1$, which is less than 2; 2 is too large because $2 \times 2 = 4$, which is greater than 2. Now we know that $\sqrt{2}$ is between 1 and 2, and therefore the decimal for $\sqrt{2}$ begins with 1.

Next we try for tenths. We successively multiply 1.1, 1.2, etc., by themselves until we get a product that is greater than 2:

$$1.1 \times 1.1 = 1.21 \text{ (too small)};$$
$$1.2 \times 1.2 = 1.44 \text{ (too small)};$$
$$1.3 \times 1.3 = 1.69 \text{ (too small)};$$
$$1.4 \times 1.4 = 1.96 \text{ (too small, but close)};$$
$$1.5 \times 1.5 = 2.25 \text{ (too large)}.$$

So the decimal for $\sqrt{2}$ begins with 1.4.

Next we go to hundredths and start with 1.41:

$$1.41 \times 1.41 = 1.9881 \text{ (too small)};$$
$$1.42 \times 1.42 = 2.0164 \text{ (too large)}.$$

Now we know that the expansion starts with 1.41.

The next step would be to get the third-stage digit. If we try 1.411, 1.412, 1.413, 1.414, and 1.415, we find that 1.415 is the first to be too large; hence, we know that $\sqrt{2}$ has a decimal approximation, at this stage, of 1.414. The process can obviously be continued as long as our interest or our patience lasts.

Other Irrational Numbers

There are many other interesting irrational numbers—for example, $\sqrt{3}$, $\sqrt{5}$, $\sqrt{6}$, $\sqrt{7}$, $\sqrt{8}$, $\sqrt{10}$. In general, any square root of a counting number is either a counting number or an irrational number. There is an interesting way of viewing lengths of segments corresponding to these square roots. Start with two perpendicular segments AB and BC, each of length 1. Draw the segment AC (Fig. 15). We have seen that this segment has length $\sqrt{2}$. Starting at C as shown, draw a segment of length 1 perpendicular to the segment of length $\sqrt{2}$ and join its end point D to end point A. What is the length of the new segment, AD? Its square is $1^2 + (\sqrt{2})^2 = 1 + 2 = 3$. Continue in this way. Each new segment from A will have length equal to the square root of the next greater counting number. A spiral will be formed.

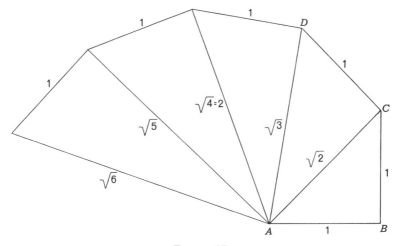

FIGURE 15

Proofs similar to the one given to show that $\sqrt{2}$ is irrational will work for $\sqrt{3}$, $\sqrt{5}$, etc.; but there are other, and more general, methods available to show this. Also, we can define and use higher roots; for example, the positive cube root of 2, written $\sqrt[3]{2}$, is the positive real number having the property that $\sqrt[3]{2} \times \sqrt[3]{2} \times \sqrt[3]{2} = 2$. Again this is irrational, as are most other numbers of this form (except, of course, particular ones like $\sqrt[3]{8}$, which equals 2, since $2 \times 2 \times 2 = 8$).

An especially interesting irrational number is π, the ratio of the circumference of a circle to the length of its diameter. That this ratio is a universal constant, the same for all circles regardless of size, seems to be a matter of very ancient knowledge. The oldest known approximation to π is 3. This appears in the Bible, where it is stated that Solomon, furnishing the temple in Jerusalem, provided a bronze bowl "nine cubits around and three cubits across." This approximation was also used by the Egyptians and the Babylonians.

It does not seem to be very clear when the approximation 22/7 (now so commonly used by school children) first came into use. It was certainly known by the time of the Renaissance. Meanwhile, Archimedes had shown by a geometric proof how to get as close a value as was desired by approximating the circle with polygons.

In 1761 the German mathematician Lambert first proved that π is irrational. No easy proof is known. For practical computation, the values of 3.1416 or 3.14159 are usually sufficiently accurate; but most books of mathematical tables list the value to at least ten digits after the decimal sign (eleven digits in all) for computations that require special precision. Here are the first twenty-five digits in the decimal for π:

$$3.141592653589793238462643.$$

Computation of π to greater and greater accuracy was a favorite mathematical hobby for many years. The coming of the electronic computer put an end to it, and the expansion to ten thousand digits was done merely as a sort of advertising device to show the power of modern computers.

Exercise Set 3

1. Find, by bracketing, to three digits after the decimal sign:
   a. $\sqrt{3}$ **b.** $\sqrt{6}$

2. Find $\sqrt[3]{2}$ to two digits after the decimal sign.

3. Decide which of the following sorts of numbers *cannot* be rational numbers:
   a. Reciprocals of irrational numbers (Hint: If $1/x = a/b$, then you would want to have $x = b/a$.)
   b. Halves of irrational numbers (Hint: If $x/2 = a/b$, then you would want to have $x = 2a/b$.)
   c. Products of irrational numbers by irrational numbers

APPROXIMATIONS AND OPERATIONS

How to Define Operations on the Real Numbers

So far, we have a set of real numbers denoted by infinite decimals and a definition of order on this set. We want to be able to talk about sums, differences, products, and quotients of real numbers. But how? We cannot even imagine the process of multiplying two numbers denoted by infinite decimals.

If the real numbers happen to have some shorter names like $\sqrt{2}$, and if we *assume* the basic laws of arithmetic apply also to the real numbers, then things look a little better. For example, suppose we think about combinations of $\sqrt{2}$ and $\sqrt{3}$. Is $\sqrt{2} \times \sqrt{3} = \sqrt{2 \times 3} = \sqrt{6}$? Is $\sqrt{2} + \sqrt{3} = \sqrt{2 + 3} = \sqrt{5}$?

We might first try similar questions on numbers we know to be rational. Is

$$\sqrt{4} \times \sqrt{9} = \sqrt{4 \times 9} = \sqrt{36}?$$

Yes, since

$$\sqrt{4} = 2, \quad \sqrt{9} = 3, \quad \sqrt{36} = 6, \quad \text{and} \quad 2 \times 3 = 6.$$

Is

$$\sqrt{4} + \sqrt{9} = \sqrt{4 + 9} = \sqrt{13}?$$

No!

$$\sqrt{4} + \sqrt{9} = 2 + 3 = 5; \quad \text{and} \quad 5 = \sqrt{25}, \quad \text{not} \quad \sqrt{13}.$$

Again,

$$\sqrt{9} + \sqrt{16} = 3 + 4 = 7,$$

but

$$\sqrt{9 + 16} = \sqrt{25} = 5.$$

Therefore, there seems no reason to suspect that $\sqrt{2} + \sqrt{3} = \sqrt{5}$ but good reason to believe that $\sqrt{2} \times \sqrt{3} = \sqrt{6}$.

To decide such questions, we must return to the definition of square root:

The square root of a given number is a number whose square is the given number.

If a real number is the square root of 6, then the result of multiplying it by itself will be 6; thus, we must have $\sqrt{6} \times \sqrt{6} = 6$.

Let us see what happens to $(\sqrt{2} \times \sqrt{3})$ when we multiply it by itself:

$$(\sqrt{2} \times \sqrt{3}) \times (\sqrt{2} \times \sqrt{3}).$$

The associative law provides that we can drop or rearrange parentheses in multiplication, at our convenience. If we can use this law, we may drop the parentheses temporarily and write as follows:

$$\sqrt{2} \times \sqrt{3} \times \sqrt{2} \times \sqrt{3}.$$

The commutative law will let us reorder terms in a product. Interchange the second and third terms:

$$\sqrt{2} \times \sqrt{2} \times \sqrt{3} \times \sqrt{3}.$$

Now put back the parentheses in a convenient way:

$$(\sqrt{2} \times \sqrt{2}) \times (\sqrt{3} \times \sqrt{3}).$$

But the very definition of $\sqrt{2}$ and $\sqrt{3}$ lets us know that $\sqrt{2} \times \sqrt{2} = 2$ and $\sqrt{3} \times \sqrt{3} = 3$, so we have

$$(\sqrt{2} \times \sqrt{2}) \times (\sqrt{3} \times \sqrt{3}) = 2 \times 3$$

and

$$2 \times 3 = 6.$$

Thus $(\sqrt{2} \times \sqrt{3})$ multiplied by itself is 6, and $\sqrt{2} \times \sqrt{3} = \sqrt{6}$, if we assume the associative and commutative laws of multiplication. If we perform a similar calculation with $(\sqrt{2} + \sqrt{3})$, we obtain

$$(\sqrt{2} + \sqrt{3}) \times (\sqrt{2} + \sqrt{3}) = (\sqrt{2})^2 + 2 \times (\sqrt{2} \times \sqrt{3}) + (\sqrt{3})^2$$
$$= 2 + (2 \times \sqrt{6}) + 3$$
$$= 5 + (2 \times \sqrt{6}),$$

which is certainly not 5. The expression $5 + (2 \times \sqrt{6})$ is a *name* for a real number, not an order to do something. We cannot proceed any further unless we actually get a decimal representation for $(2 \times \sqrt{6})$. Forms like $(2 + \sqrt{3})$ and $(\sqrt{2} + \sqrt{3})$, which are compound names, are frequently encountered. They are useful; they give a far more precise idea of the quantity named than does any partial decimal representation. Therefore, we use them as they are. A form like $(\sqrt{2} \times \sqrt{3})$ is a name, too, but there is a simpler name for the same number: $\sqrt{6}$. The situation is somewhat analogous to that of the fractions 6/8 and 3/4. In dealing with expressions like $\sqrt{2}$, however, we sometimes do not have any form that is clearly the *simplest*. For example, $\sqrt{1/2}$, $1/\sqrt{2}$, and $\sqrt{2}/2$ all actually name the same real number. Which form is the simplest?

After all this we can still ask: What gives us the right to *assume* all the laws of ordinary arithmetic? The answer is that we *construct* definitions of operations in such a way that we can be certain the laws are valid.

Approximate Calculation

In exercise 1, page 166, we asked for values of $\sqrt{3}$ and $\sqrt{6}$. Here is a table, in case you did not keep your answers. We also include $\sqrt{2}$ for reference:

$$\sqrt{2} = 1.414 \cdots .$$
$$\sqrt{3} = 1.732 \cdots .$$
$$\sqrt{6} = 2.449 \cdots .$$

We are going to try to check the statement that $\sqrt{2} \times \sqrt{3} = \sqrt{6}$. We shall use a method similar to the bracketing scheme used to calculate square roots. Take bracketing approximations to $\sqrt{2}$ and $\sqrt{3}$:

$$1.4 < \sqrt{2} < 1.5.$$
$$1.7 < \sqrt{3} < 1.8.$$

Now if we multiply 1.4 by 1.7, are we sure that the answer will be less than $\sqrt{2} \times \sqrt{3}$? Is 1.5×1.8 necessarily greater than $\sqrt{2} \times \sqrt{3}$?

One difficulty in answering these questions is that we still have not carefully defined $\sqrt{2} \times \sqrt{3}$.

A diagram will give a clearer picture. In Figure 16, $\overline{AB}$ is a segment of length $\sqrt{2}$ units, $\overline{AC}$ is of length 1.4, and $\overline{AD}$, 1.5. Similarly, $\overline{AE}$ is $\sqrt{3}$ units long while $\overline{AF}$ and $\overline{AG}$ are 1.7 and 1.8, respectively.

If we multiply 1.4 by 1.7, we calculate the area of the rectangle $ACPF$. If we compute 1.5×1.8, the area of $ADRG$ is obtained. By $\sqrt{2} \times \sqrt{3}$ we mean the area of $ABQE$. Clearly, the area of the rectangle $ABQE$ should be greater than that of the rectangle $ACPF$ and less than that of the rectangle $ADRG$.

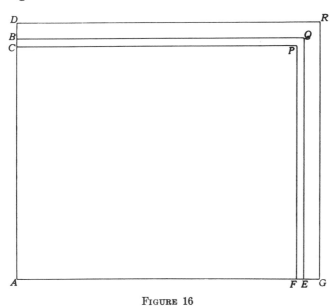

FIGURE 16

The upside-down and backward L-shaped region bounded by $CDRGFPC$ can be thought of as a region of fuzziness whose area represents our uncertainty about the exact answer.

Now, what happens if we make better approximations? Suppose C moves up toward B, and D down toward B. Similarly, let F move outward and G inward toward E. The widths of the bands of uncertainty shrink; the possible errors diminish. Let us look at Table I to see what happens.

What was the answer we expected? Look back at the value of $\sqrt{6} = 2.449\cdots$, which you computed in exercise 1, page 166. Everything is coming out as we expected.

The final position is that we define the product of two real numbers as the real number that results from the process of using, without limitations,

TABLE I

BRACKETING FOR MULTIPLICATION

Too Small	Too Large	Difference
1.4 × 1.7 = 2.38	1.5 × 1.8 = 2.70	0.32
1.41 × 1.73 = 2.4393	1.42 × 1.74 = 2.4708	0.0315
1.414 × 1.732 = 2.449048	1.415 × 1.733 = 2.452195	0.003147

the products of better and better approximations to the two numbers. That there is essentially one and only one such real number becomes intuitively clear when we think of the L-shaped region shrinking to a pair of perpendicular segments as the uncertainty decreases without limit.

Note that we do not have to approximate by bracketing. Whenever we take better approximations, we get better answers.

Incidentally, we are frequently able to improve our accuracy by taking one factor too large and one too small. For example, suppose we used 1.4 and 1.8 as approximations to $\sqrt{2}$ and $\sqrt{3}$, respectively. The result, $1.4 \times 1.8 = 2.52$, is much closer to the "right" answer, $2.449\cdots$, than 2.38 and 2.70, the products of 1.4×1.7 and 1.5×1.8, respectively.

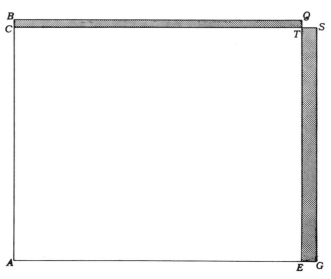

FIGURE 17

We can show the reason for this improvement by redrawing the rectangles just for this example (see Fig. 17). The same letters will be used to designate the segments retained from Figure 16; that is, $\overline{AB}$ is our segment of length $\sqrt{2}$ units, $\overline{AC}$ has length 1.4, $\overline{AE}$ is $\sqrt{3}$ units long, and $\overline{AG}$ is 1.8 units long. The new letters, T and S, designate new points located by extending segment CP to cross segments EQ and GR of the original drawing.

The "correct" rectangle is $ABQE$. Our product gave the area of $ACSG$. This is too small by the area of the upper shaded portion, which lies inside the correct rectangle but was missed, and is too large by the shaded area on the right, which is outside the exact rectangle and was included. Thus the errors partially cancel out.

What about addition? The ideas are very similar. If we want to know part of the decimal numeral for $\sqrt{2} + \sqrt{3}$, we can make a bracketing table. (See Table II.)

TABLE II
BRACKETING FOR ADDITION

Too Small	Too Large	Difference
1.4 $+ 1.7$ $= 3.1$	1.5 $+ 1.8$ $= 3.3$	0.2
1.41 $+ 1.73$ $= 3.14$	1.42 $+ 1.74$ $= 3.16$	0.02
1.414 $+ 1.732$ $= 3.146$	1.415 $+ 1.733$ $= 3.148$	0.002

The same idea works, but you can observe from the tables that for addition the comparative uncertainty (difference) at each step is rather less than for multiplication.

What about subtraction? Watch out! The bracketing table must be made up in a different way. As an example, we shall use $\sqrt{3} - \sqrt{2}$. If we want a resulting approximation that is definitely less than the right answer, we subtract a too-large approximation for $\sqrt{2}$ from a too-small approximation for $\sqrt{3}$. (Why?) To get a result that is definitely greater than the right answer, we subtract a too-small approximation for our larger number, $\sqrt{3}$, from a too-large approximation for $\sqrt{2}$. (See Table III.)

TABLE III
BRACKETING FOR SUBTRACTION

APPROXIMATIONS FOR TOO-SMALL ANSWER			APPROXIMATIONS FOR TOO-LARGE ANSWER			
Too Small for $\sqrt{3}$	Too Large for $\sqrt{2}$	RESULT	Too Large for $\sqrt{3}$	Too Small for $\sqrt{2}$	RESULT	DIFFERENCE
1.7 $- 1.5$		$= 0.2$	1.8 $- 1.4$		$= 0.4$	0.2
1.73 $- 1.42$		$= 0.31$	1.74 $- 1.41$		$= 0.33$	0.02
1.732 $- 1.415$		$= 0.317$	1.733 $- 1.414$		$= 0.319$	0.002

For division, the situation is similar to that of subtraction. To get an answer that we are certain is too small, we must divide an approximation that is too small for the dividend by one that is too large for the divisor. (The greater the divisor, the less the answer.)

So far, all our examples and illustrative calculations have been done with positive real numbers. What about operations involving negative numbers? No new problem arises that was not already present in defining operations with negative rational numbers. (See Booklet No. 10: *The System of Rational Numbers.*) The definitions of operations are given in terms of the same operations on rational numbers, and we simply follow those same rules. For example, if we wish to compute $(\sqrt{2} \times {}^{-}\sqrt{3})$, the value is ${}^{-}\sqrt{6}$ because the rule $a \times {}^{-}b = {}^{-}(a \times b)$ for rational numbers also applies in the extended system.

Whatever operation we are trying to perform, the basic result always is that *if we approximate close enough to the operands (the original real numbers), then we will get a result as close to a fixed real number as we wish. The real number thus approached is designated the result of the operation.*

Since all operations on real numbers are defined in terms of the operations on rational numbers and agree, to as close an approximation as we please, with the corresponding rational operations, the basic algebraic properties of the rational number system are, indeed, carried over to the real number system. For convenience, we shall summarize the whole structure by listing each of its essential properties.

Before doing so, let us remind ourselves of certain basic inclusion properties that are features of the systems constructed in mathematics. The integers are included in the real numbers. In the course of our construction, the integer usually named 2 got the rather unwieldy name 2.0000⋯ , but we now feel free to simplify this and all other cumbersome decimals so that our terminating decimals really terminate.

Here is a more general statement:

SYSTEM INCLUSION

{Counting Numbers} ⊂ {Whole Numbers} ⊂ {Integers}
                              ⊂ {Rational Numbers} ⊂ {Real Numbers}.

CLOSURE

Addition: The sum of any two real numbers is a unique real number.
Subtraction: The difference of any two real numbers is a unique real number.
Multiplication: The product of any two real numbers is a unique real number.
Division: The quotient of any two real numbers, when the divisor is not zero, is a unique real number.

COMMUTATIVITY

Addition: If a and b are real numbers, then $a + b = b + a$.
Multiplication: If a and b are real numbers, then $a \times b = b \times a$.

ASSOCIATIVITY
Addition: If a, b, and c are real numbers, then $(a + b) + c = a + (b + c)$.
Multiplication: If a, b, and c are real numbers, then $(a \times b) \times c = a \times (b \times c)$.

IDENTITIES
Addition: There is a real number, 0, such that if a is a real number, then $a + 0 = 0 + a = a$.
Multiplication: There is a real number, 1, such that if a is a real number, then $a \times 1 = 1 \times a = a$.

INVERSES
Addition: If a is a real number, then there is a real number ^-a such that $a + {}^-a = 0$.
Multiplication: If a is a real number not equal to zero, then there is a real number $1/a$ such that $a \times 1/a = 1$.

ORDER
Trichotomy: If a is a real number and b is a real number, then either $a = b$, $a < b$, or $b < a$, and only one of these holds.
Addition: If a and b are real numbers such that $a < b$, and c is any real number, then $a + c < b + c$.
Multiplication: If a and b are real numbers such that $a < b$, and c is a real number such that $c > 0$, then $ac < bc$.

DENSITY
If a and b are real numbers such that $a < b$, then there is a real number c such that $a < c < b$. (In fact, c may always be selected so that it is rational.)

COMPLETENESS
To each point on the number line there corresponds a real number, and to each real number there corresponds a point on the number line.

It is the last-named property—the property of completeness—that *really* distinguishes the real number system from the rational number system.

Exercise Set 4

1. In a city park, paths were arranged as follows: A square 100 yards on each side was bounded by a circular path circumscribed around it.

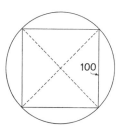

FIGURE 18

Notice that it requires a walk of 400 yards to go around the park, following the sides of the square. The question arose as to how much farther it was to walk around the circle. Is the circular path more or less than a quarter of a mile around? Note that its diameter is $100 \times \sqrt{2}$ yards. A quarter of a mile is 440 yards.

2.a. Take each of the systems mentioned, page 172, and the list of laws on pages 172–73 and check each to see how many laws are not satisfied when the words "real number" are replaced throughout by "counting number." For example, the counting numbers do not satisfy the identity property for addition because the statement would read "There is a counting number, 0, such that if a is a counting number, then $a + 0 = 0 + a = a$." But 0 is not a counting number.

Pay particular attention to closure for subtraction and division, to inverses for addition and multiplication, to density, and to completeness.

b. Repeat exercise 2a, replacing the words "real number" by "whole number."

c. Repeat exercise 2a, replacing the words "real number" by "integer."

d. Repeat exercise 2a, replacing the words "real number" by "rational number."

HOW MANY?

We have seen that a rational number is in essence a very special kind of real number. In this section we are going to try to answer, at least partly, the question "How special?" Our trouble lies with a general fuzziness that involves all such questions when we deal with infinite sets.

It is easy to maintain that half of the squares on a checkerboard are black. You can prove it by counting them, and any way of counting that is not obviously wrong will always give 32 black squares and 64 squares in all. Counting, you will recall, is the process in which we put a set into one-to-one correspondence with a set of ordered counting numbers, where the latter set must have the property that if it contains any counting number it must also contain all the previous counting numbers. That is, we are not allowed to count at random (for example, "2, 7, 4, 11"); we must count in order, "1, 2, 3, 4." Then the last counting number used is called the "cardinal number" of the set counted, or simply the number of things in the set.

Now what happens if there is no last counting number used? In this case (if the set has any members at all) we say that it is "infinite." With infinite sets we at once run into problems. Think of this entirely reasonable-seeming assertion: "Half of the counting numbers are even." Suppose someone argues about it. You proceed to "count" all the counting numbers and then all the even ones, but it takes *all* the counting numbers to count just the even ones.

Even numbers: 2 4 6 8 10 $\cdots$

$\updownarrow$ $\updownarrow$ $\updownarrow$ $\updownarrow$ $\updownarrow$

Counting numbers: 1 2 3 4 5 $\cdots$

So there are just as many even counting numbers as counting numbers!

You can, of course, maintain your original assertion in some such manner as this: "Suppose I take the counting numbers up to some large number; then, depending on where I stop, either exactly half or half of just one less than the stopping number are even. In either case, the *proportion* of even ones is very close to one-half and differs from one-half by as little as I want. For example, if I stop at 1,000,000, it is exactly half; if I stop at 1,000,001, it is $\dfrac{500,000}{1,000,001}$, which equals 0.4999995 $\cdots$."

In the case of the even counting numbers, we saw a subset that could be put into one-to-one correspondence with the entire set of counting numbers. It should not be any further surprise to discover that the counting numbers can be used to count sets that contain the counting numbers as proper subsets.

For example, let us think of the set of all counting numbers and all halves of counting numbers:

$$H = \{\tfrac{1}{2}, 1, 1\tfrac{1}{2}, 2, 2\tfrac{1}{2}, 3, 3\tfrac{1}{2}, 4, \cdots\}.$$

Write the elements all with denominator 2:

$$H = \{\tfrac{1}{2}, \tfrac{2}{2}, \tfrac{3}{2}, \tfrac{4}{2}, \tfrac{5}{2}, \tfrac{6}{2}, \tfrac{7}{2}, \tfrac{8}{2}, \cdots\}.$$

Now make the correspondence with the numerators:

H: $\tfrac{1}{2}$ $\tfrac{2}{2}$ $\tfrac{3}{2}$ $\tfrac{4}{2}$ $\cdots$

$\updownarrow$ $\updownarrow$ $\updownarrow$ $\updownarrow$

Counting numbers: 1 2 3 4 $\cdots$

Every member of H is counted.

A slightly harder problem is to count all the integers:

$$I = \{\cdots, {}^-3, {}^-2, {}^-1, 0, 1, 2, 3, \cdots\}.$$

You can make a correspondence like that in Figure 19. Here the even

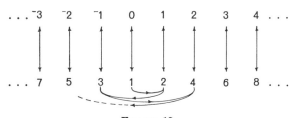

FIGURE 19

counting numbers count the positive integers, and the odd counting numbers count zero and the negative integers.

It is time to stop and remind ourselves of what we mean by "counting" a set. We are merely establishing a one-to-one correspondence between the given set and a set of counting numbers, beginning with 1 and not jumping or skipping any counting number. Then if there is a last counting number used, it is the cardinal number of the set. When, as in the cases we have shown, every member of the set has a counting number but there is no last one used, the cardinality of the set is called aleph-zero ($\aleph_0$), a name given by Georg Cantor about a hundred years ago. In spite of writing and printing difficulties, the name has remained.

So far, we have produced the following sets with cardinality aleph-zero:

{The counting numbers}
{The even counting numbers}
{Halves of counting numbers}
{The integers}

The reader is invited to produce (and to count) other such sets. Here are some for counting practice:

1. The set of counting numbers greater than 5, that is, $\{6, 7, 8, \cdots\}$
2. The set of counting numbers whose last three digits are 573, that is, $\{573, 1573, 2573, \cdots\}$
3. The set of integers not divisible by 3
4. The set of fractions, in simplest form, whose denominators are 1, 2, 3, or 6

A question now arises. Can *every* nonempty set be counted? Obviously, by the very definition a finite set can be counted because the property of being finite and nonempty simply consists of having a counting set with a last counting number. So what we really want to know is this: "Can every infinite set be counted?" In our new terminology we ask: "Does every finite set have cardinality aleph-zero; or are there larger sets that just cannot be covered by the counting numbers, no matter how clever we are?"

Note that sometimes we do have to be clever. There are many profligate ways to use all the counting numbers without counting all the integers, for example. If we were careless enough, we could use the entire set just on the positive even integers. It takes some cunning to decide to pick up the positive and the negative ones more or less simultaneously.

What about the set of rational numbers? This seems to be a much larger set than we have tried to count so far. No trick anywhere near so simple as any we have used up to now will work this time. Recall that the set of points representing rational numbers is dense on the number line!

Let us write fractions for the positive rational numbers, in a table thought of as being infinite in two directions. In the first row we write those with denominator 1; in the second, those with denominator 2, and so on. In the first column are all fractions with numerator 1; in the second column are those with numerator 2, and so on. (See Fig. 20.)

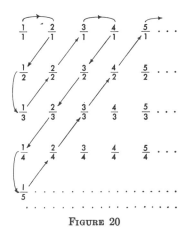

FIGURE 20

The rows are infinite and the columns are infinite, but the right-up, left-down diagonals are *finite*. Follow the arrows and number the fractions as you go. First, number 1/1 with 1; this is the only fraction whose numerator and denominator add up to 2. Now number the fractions (two of them) whose numerator and denominator add up to 3; next, the three fractions that give a sum of 4, and so on.

$$\frac{1}{1} \quad \frac{2}{1} \quad \frac{1}{2} \quad \frac{1}{3} \quad \frac{2}{2} \quad \frac{3}{1} \quad \frac{4}{1} \quad \frac{3}{2} \quad \frac{2}{3} \quad \frac{1}{4} \cdots$$
$$\updownarrow \quad \updownarrow \quad \updownarrow \quad \updownarrow \quad \updownarrow \quad \updownarrow \quad \updownarrow \quad \updownarrow \quad \updownarrow \quad \updownarrow$$
$$1 \quad 2 \quad 3 \quad 4 \quad 5 \quad 6 \quad 7 \quad 8 \quad 9 \quad 10 \cdots$$

Does every fraction get a counting number? Yes! Just add the numerator and denominator of a fraction, and you know which diagonal it is in. Further, since there are only a finite number of fractions in each diagonal (one less than the sum of the numerator and denominator for that diagonal), we shall have expended only a finite number of counting numbers before we get there. A finite number of finite numbers is finite. Think about this argument until you are sure that you are convinced.

In fact, if we do a bit of algebra, we can make a rough approximation of the counting number that will go with any given fraction.

We mentioned that first we counted one fraction in the first diagonal, then two in the next diagonal, then three in the next, then four, and so on. Each diagonal has one more fraction in it than the one before. Now, how many were there altogether when we finished each diagonal? There was one after the first diagonal; there were three after the second (we added two), six after the third (we added three), ten after the fourth, and so on. (See Table IV.)

TABLE IV

Sum of Numerator and Denominator	Fractions with This Particular Sum	Fractions with This or Smaller Sum
2	1	1
3	2	3 = 1 + 2
4	3	6 = 3 + 3
5	4	10 = 6 + 4
6	5	15 = 10 + 5

Now suppose we consider the following formula:[4] Take one-half the sum of numerator and denominator multiplied by one less than this sum— that is,

$$\frac{\text{Sum} \times (\text{Sum} - 1)}{2}.$$

For a sum of 2: $\dfrac{2 \times 1}{2} = 1.$

For a sum of 3: $\dfrac{3 \times 2}{2} = 3.$

For a sum of 4: $\dfrac{4 \times 3}{2} = 6.$

For a sum of 5: $\dfrac{5 \times 4}{2} = 10.$

For a sum of 6: $\dfrac{6 \times 5}{2} = 15.$

Working out the formula for each sum gives us the numbers in the third column of Table IV. We shall not prove this formula here, but you can check it until you are reasonably convinced that it works.

What number counts the fraction 1/5? It is the first fraction in the diagonal where the sum is 1 + 5 = 6. How many fractions had smaller sums? Referring to Table IV, look at the fourth line of the third column, opposite the "5" in the first column; or compute $(5 \times 4)/2 = 10$. So for each of ten fractions the sum of numerator and denominator was

---

[4] This can be compared with the section titled "Unusual Problem Solving," in Booklet No. 17: *Hints for Problem Solving.*

less than or equal to 5. Then 1/5 is the eleventh fraction counted, or 1/5 ↔ 11.

What counting number will go with 7/9? The numerator and denominator add up to 16. It took us $(15 \times 14)/2 = 210/2$, or 105, numbers to finish those that add up to 15. To complete those that add up to 16 will take $(16 \times 15)/2 = 240/2 = 120$. So the number will be somewhere between 106 and 120, inclusive.

We can do even better; our arrows swing up when the totals are even, down when they are odd. (Look at the diagram; notice the arrows for totals 2, 3, 4, 5, and 6.) Our total is 16, and 7/9 is the seventh fraction numbered in this diagonal. (Why?) The first fraction is numbered 106; the second, 107; so the seventh will be numbered 112. If you do not believe this, finish the diagram through fifteen diagonals and count for yourself; then go back through the mathematical argument.

In any case, every fraction gets numbered. You may complain that we started talking about numbering *rational numbers* and ended up counting *fractions*. We have numbered 1/1 differently from 2/2 and 3/3, $\cdots$. Each rational number has been assigned an infinite number of different counting numbers. Can we fix this? Sure! Just leave out of each row any fraction that is equivalent to a fraction in an earlier row, but keep the pattern, as shown in Figure 21.

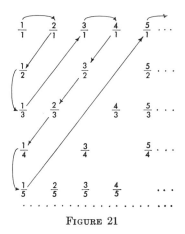

FIGURE 21

Now, number again:

$$\frac{1}{1} \quad \frac{2}{1} \quad \frac{1}{2} \quad \frac{1}{3} \quad \frac{3}{1} \quad \frac{4}{1} \quad \frac{3}{2} \quad \frac{2}{3} \quad \frac{1}{4} \quad \frac{1}{5} \quad \frac{5}{1} \cdots$$
$$\updownarrow \quad \updownarrow \quad \updownarrow \quad \updownarrow \quad \updownarrow \quad \updownarrow \quad \updownarrow \quad \updownarrow \quad \updownarrow \quad \updownarrow \quad \updownarrow$$
$$1 \quad 2 \quad 3 \quad 4 \quad 5 \quad 6 \quad 7 \quad 8 \quad 9 \quad 10 \quad 11 \cdots$$

Some of our diagonals may have only a few elements; but this just saves time and counting numbers. Of course, the formulas do not work any more; but they still give a *maximum*. We know that a rational number will be numbered at or before the former number of any of its equivalent fractions. How about all rationals, or all fractions—positive, negative, and zero? We can make up a pattern, as in Figure 22, that will give a counting method! The arrows go around in spirals, starting at 0/1.

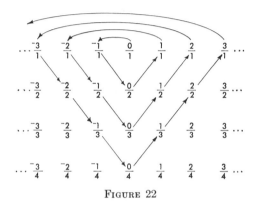

FIGURE 22

Probably you will have already phrased the next question: How about the real numbers? In 1874 Georg Cantor proved that we *cannot* count them. There is no way to stretch the counting numbers this far.

Before we begin the actual proof, it might be well to carry on some discussion of mathematical impossibility. All too often a statement in mathematical terms that something or other is impossible is understood to mean "I can't do it" or "Nobody has done it yet." This misunderstanding has caused tremendous wastes of time, both to the people who did not understand and promptly tried to do the impossible, and to the people who had to find the inevitable errors that resulted from these attempts.

Practically every mathematical statement can be converted to a statement of impossibility. Even "2 + 2 = 4" can be read as, "It is impossible, under the standard rules of arithmetic and numerical notation, that the sum of two and two should differ from four."

The statement "It is impossible to give a straightedge and compass construction for trisecting an arbitrary angle" is essentially no different from the preceding statement. It could be expressed positively: "Tools other than a straightedge and compass are needed to make a construction that will trisect an arbitrary angle."

Our situation is similar. We must show that no one, regardless of his genius or cunning, can ever succeed in putting the set of real numbers into one-to-one correspondence with the counting numbers. In fact, it is a logical contradiction to imply such a correspondence.

The way we are going to demonstrate this is to assume that someone claims to have made the correspondence and presents us with the result. Then we shall look at his list and point out a real number that is not in the list. Indeed, there will be infinitely many real numbers not in the list, but we need only point out *one* to defeat his claim. It is important to note that our method will work no matter how often our friend with the list goes "back to the old drawing board." In theory we can always glance at any list he produces and write down a real number that he has left out.

We shall work only with the real numbers greater than zero and less than one and shall show that not even these can be counted. These numbers will be represented, for convenience of discussion, by infinite decimals without the customary 0 to the left of the decimal point. Some examples are

$$.1000000000 \cdots ,$$
$$.1010010001 \cdots ,$$
$$.1212121212 \cdots .$$

Now imagine the correspondence like this:

Counting Number	Infinite Decimal
1 ↔	._____ ⋯
2 ↔	._____ ⋯
3 ↔	._____ ⋯
⋯	⋯

where some digit stands above each underline and the table consists of infinite decimals and extends infinitely far down.

In the following manner we specify an infinite decimal A that is *not* in this list: Look at the first digit of the first numeral listed. If it is not 5, then the first digit of A will be 5; if the first digit of the first numeral is 5, then the first digit of A will be 4. Thus, A starts with either .4 or .5; and we are sure that, whatever A is going to be, it is not going to be the first numeral in the table, because it starts off differently.

Next, look at the second digit of the second numeral (the one corresponding to 2). If this digit is not 5, make the second digit of A equal to 5; if it is 5, use 4 as the second digit of A. So A starts in one of the four ways: .55, .54, .45, or .44. Now we know that A is not going to be equal to either the first or the second numeral in the table.

Let us go on. We look at the third digit of the third numeral and pick either 4 or 5 as a third digit for A, just as before. By so doing we guarantee that A is different from the first, second, and third numerals.

Let us continue. If the list actually began

$$
\begin{aligned}
1 &\leftrightarrow .\underline{1}4372956 \cdots \\
2 &\leftrightarrow .3\underline{5}219784 \cdots \\
3 &\leftrightarrow .71\underline{9}85132 \cdots \\
4 &\leftrightarrow .312\underline{9}6540 \cdots \\
5 &\leftrightarrow .1200\underline{0}000 \cdots \\
6 &\leftrightarrow .90763\underline{8}41 \cdots \\
7 &\leftrightarrow .132041\underline{5}2 \cdots \\
8 &\leftrightarrow .5555555\underline{5} \cdots ,
\end{aligned}
$$

then A would begin

.54555544...

because of the successive values of the underscored digits.

Continue this process and then think about the result. We get an infinite decimal for A. It is not *any* of the decimals in the list because it differs from *every* member of the list. So A wasn't in the list at all.

There is nothing special about our rule that picked 4 or 5. Any rule will do as long as it guarantees that A is different from each member of the list and that A neither equals 0 nor trails off in an infinity of 9's, both of which choices are barred. (We use only positive reals in our list, and earlier in this booklet we specified that those decimals ending in an infinite string of 9's were not acceptable.) Another perfectly good system would be to work with numbers 1 and 7, instead of 4 and 5. Try making up your own rules, choosing your own pairs of numbers.

This proof has been named the "diagonal proof" because we go down the diagonal of the table from left to right, making up A, digit by digit, by changing the digits in this diagonal.

What do we know now? We see, by a convincing demonstration, that there are more real numbers than rationals. The counting numbers could be stretched to count the rational numbers; they cannot count the real numbers. The cardinal number of the reals—that is, the number that is associated with each of the sets that *can* be put into one-to-one correspondence with these reals—is called C. Is C the greatest cardinal? No. It can be shown that there is no limit to the cardinality of sets that can be created, but the proof is too long and complicated to give here.

Exercise Set 5

1. Suppose the correspondence began

$$
\begin{aligned}
1 &\leftrightarrow .12345678 \cdots \\
2 &\leftrightarrow .11111111 \cdots \\
3 &\leftrightarrow .55544444 \cdots \\
4 &\leftrightarrow .55455555 \cdots \\
5 &\leftrightarrow .10000000 \cdots \\
6 &\leftrightarrow .01010101 \cdots
\end{aligned}
$$

How would A appear, explicitly to six digits, if you followed the rule given first to construct it?

2. Given: $A = .554544 \cdots$.
Give the first six decimal digits of six different infinite decimals in which the first member differs from A only by its first digit, the second member differs from A only by its second digit, and so on.

SUMMARY

The system of real numbers has been constructed to remedy a defect, an incompleteness, in the system of rational numbers: the fact that there are ratios of lengths of segments that cannot be evaluated in terms of ratios of whole numbers.

We have represented the real numbers by infinite decimal numerals, and we have seen which of these numerals corresponded to the rational numbers as a subset of the real numbers.

Operations corresponding to the arithmetical operations on the rational numbers have been defined for the real numbers; and methods have been given to approximate, as closely as we wish, calculations with real numbers.

Finally, we have seen that the extension of the rational number system to the real number system involves a very great extension indeed. In fact, it requires a completely new order of infinity, a new infinite cardinal number.

For Further Reading

Among the various helpful references that deal with the subject here introduced are the following:

BIRKHOFF, GARRETT, and MACLANE, SAUNDERS. *A Survey of Modern Algebra* (2d ed.). New York: Macmillan Co., 1966.

NIVEN, IVAN MORTON. *Numbers: Rational and Irrational.* ("New Mathematical Library," Vol. I.) New York and Toronto: Random House, 1961.

SCHOOL MATHEMATICS STUDY GROUP. *Number Systems.* ("Studies in Mathematics," Vol. VI.) Pasadena, Calif.: A. C. Vroman, 1961.

ANSWERS TO EXERCISES

Exercise Set 1

1. a. 0.999   **b.** ⁻0.999

2. ⁻0.202400···   (or ⁻0.20135 ···, ⁻0.20200 ···, etc.)

3. ⁻100.00 ···,   ⁻4.2310 ···,   ⁻0.1234 ···,   ⁻0.01234 ···,   1.234 ···,   12.345 ···

4. a. 0.21000 ···   **b.** ⁻1.13000 ···   **c.** 2.135000 ···

Exercise Set 2

1. a. $0.\overline{153846}$ **b.** $0.1\overline{35}$ **c.** $0.\overline{4857142}$ **d.** $0.\overline{307692}$

2. a. $\dfrac{20}{99}$ **b.** $\dfrac{68}{55}$ **c.** $\dfrac{5}{13}$ **d.** $\dfrac{4115}{33333}$

3. $0.\overline{142857}$, $0.2\overline{857142857}$, $0.42\overline{857142857}$, $0.\overline{571428 57}$, $0.7\overline{142857}$. $0.\overline{857142857}$

4. $x = 0.\overline{9}$, $10x = 9.\overline{9}$. Subtract $9x = 9$, $x = 1$.

Exercise Set 3

1. a. 1.732 (Try squaring 1.732 and 1.733.)   **b.** 2.449

2. 1.25 (Notice that 1.25 × 1.25 × 1.25 = 1.953125; 1.26 × 1.26 × 1.26 = 2.000376.)

3. The types of numbers named in exercises 3a and 3b cannot be rational numbers. But $\sqrt{2} \times \sqrt{2} = 2$, so products of irrational numbers *can* be rational numbers.

Exercise Set 4

1. The circular path is more than 444 yards long, since

$$100\sqrt{2} > 141.4 \quad \text{and} \quad \pi > 3.14.$$

2. a. Laws not satisfied by substitution of "counting number": closure for subtraction closure for division additive identity additive inverse multiplicative inverse density completeness

b. Same as exercise 2a except additive identity

c. Same as exercise 2b except additive inverse

d. Completeness

Exercise Set 5

1. .554455 ⋯

2. There are many correct answers. Here is one:

$$1 \leftrightarrow .454544 \cdots$$
$$2 \leftrightarrow .544544 \cdots$$
$$3 \leftrightarrow .555544 \cdots$$
$$4 \leftrightarrow .554444 \cdots$$
$$5 \leftrightarrow .554554 \cdots$$
$$6 \leftrightarrow .554545 \cdots$$

BOOKLET NUMBER TWELVE:

LOGIC

INTRODUCTION

Logic in general, and symbolic logic in particular, is the systematic study of the process of precise reasoning. It is not, however, a *substitute* for precise reasoning; manipulating symbols, which is one of the procedures of logic, is not the same thing as thinking. What the methods of logic can do for us is to clarify our patterns of thought, guide us to correct reasoning processes, and help us avoid errors.

The aim of symbolic logic is to reduce complicated verbal procedures to simple patterns of letters and signs. This can be roughly compared to using the numerals and signs of arithmetic to help simplify what would otherwise be long and involved verbal statements about numbers. To experience the advantage of symbols in arithmetic, you might try to put the number concepts expressed by $(3 + 4) + 5 = 12$ into words.

Just as numbers are the basic elements of arithmetic, simple declarative sentences are the elements of logic. We start our arithmetical experiences with a simple set of counting numbers, $\{1, 2, 3, \cdots\}$, and build more complicated structures, such as the system of rational numbers. Similarly, we begin in logic with simple sentences, and we then use these to form more complicated ones. In arithmetic we learn rules for operating with numbers. In logic we learn rules for manipulating sentences.

SENTENCES

Simple Sentences

A simple sentence, often called an atomic sentence, is very much the same thing in logic as it is in standard English grammar. To ensure greater precision in logic, some restrictions that do not apply to grammar are placed on sentences to make them qualify as acceptable.

First let us look at some simple English and mathematical sentences.

T 1. Lincoln was the sixteenth president of the United States.
  2. 3 < 5.
F 3. San Francisco is the capital of California.
  4. 6 > 7.
O 5. He is a teacher.
  6. $x > 9$.
N 7. Mary is in the third grade.
  8. The king of France has red hair.

In general, a simple sentence is declarative. It has a subject and a predicate. It has no compound clauses joined by connectives such as "and," "or," "if. . . then."

It does not pay to belabor the definition of simplicity too much. On the one hand, simple sentences and compound sentences often convey the same meanings: "Good men are generous" and "If a man is good, then he is generous"; "Mary and John are six years old" and "Mary is six years old, and so is John." On the other hand, simplicity is sometimes hard to be sure of. The sentence "He is taller than she is" has two verbs; but the conjunction "than" is not in the prohibited list ("and," "or," "if. . . then"), and the sentence is quite similar in form to "5 > 3."

There is one special restriction, which is illustrated by the grouping that has been made of the examples. The first two sentences are true (T). They state indisputable facts. The second two are false (F). They contradict indisputable facts. The next two are open (O). They contain a pronoun or a variable and depend for their truth or falsehood on what will be substituted for the pronoun or variable. The last two are meaningless (N) as they stand. "Mary," although a proper noun, is not sufficiently clear. The sentence could well become true or false if stated in context—for example, if it were part of a mother's answer to another woman's question, "What grades are your children in now?" The final sentence is utterly hopeless, unless there has been a sudden turn of events in French politics between the time this booklet was written and the time you read it. The subject of the sentence is not simply unclear, like "Mary," but just nonexistent.

We are going to require that all simple sentences used must be capable of being classified as true or false for every permissible replacement of variables or pronouns (if any) that is made. This requirement demands that we specify what nouns may be used to replace the pronouns or variables; the set of nouns is called the "replacement set." It must not contain nonappropriate terms. "President Johnson" cannot be in the replacement set for x in sentence 6. The subset of the replacement set that makes a sentence true is called the "truth set" of the sentence. For example, the replacement set for sentence 6 might be the set of counting numbers, and then the truth set is $\{10, 11, 12, \cdots\}$.

Let us clarify what we mean by "capable of being classified as true or false." Why not just be straightforward and demand that the sentence *be* true or false after any necessary replacement? We have seen an example that illustrates the answer: "Mary is in the third grade." Indeed, it is very difficult to classify almost any English sentence as true or false on its own merits without an established context. Take sentence 1, for example. How do you answer someone who says, "False; Lincoln is a city in England," or one who says, "Who is Lincoln?"

One of the major sources of disagreement between people is just that they do not have the same classification of truth or falsity for their simple sentences. All the precise logical manipulation in the world will not save us if our basic building blocks are faulty. In mathematics the context is usually clearer than it is in casual conversation, but we must be on guard to ensure clarity even there. Statements made while thinking about counting numbers (the set $\{1, 2, 3, \cdots\}$) become false in terms of the integers (the set $\{\cdots, {}^-3, {}^-2, {}^-1, 0, 1, 2, 3, \cdots\}$) and vice versa. "The product of two numbers is at least as great as either of the factors" is a statement that will be true of the counting numbers but not of the integers, since, for example, $0 \times 5 = 0$; and the resulting product is not as great as 5. The statement "When one number is subtracted from another, the result is a number" is true for the integers; but it is not true for the counting numbers because $1 - 5$ has no meaning in terms of counting numbers.

Further, both in mathematics and in literature we have sentences that are true just because we say they are. In mathematics these sentences are *definitions* and *axioms*. In literature they are the fundamental assumptions of a piece of fiction. If you found on a true-false test the statement "Huckleberry Finn was a friend of Tom Sawyer's," you would classify it as true because Mark Twain so conceived it.

Thus, without pushing the matter further, let us assume that we have a set of simple sentences meeting the conditions laid down for true or false classification. Frequently we shall use a capital letter to stand for a full sentence. For example, we may replace "Lincoln was the sixteenth president of the United States" with the letter "L."

Compound Sentences

Sentences can be built from other sentences and, basically, from simple, or atomic, sentences by connecting them with an agreed list of logical connectives. These connectives are "and," "or," and "if... then"; we also use "not," although strictly speaking it is not a connective, since it involves only one sentence at a time. In logic these connectives are provided precise meanings so that the result will be a compound sentence having a classification of true or false, depending on the classification of its components. Thus, once the classification of our simple (atomic) sentences is given, we never lose the possibility of definite classification, no matter how complex our sentences become.

NOT

We start with "not," which we abbreviate by using the symbol $\neg$. Then "$\neg$ L" stands for "Lincoln was *not* the sixteenth president of the United States." We agree that the use of "not" or "$\neg$" acts to reverse the classification of the statement with which it is used. We express this as "The negation of a true sentence is a false one, and the negation of a false sentence is a true one." Note that the negation of a negation brings back the original classification unchanged. The statement "It is not the case that Lincoln was not the sixteenth president of the United States" is the same as "$\neg$ $\neg$ L" and is a cumbersome way of expressing exactly the meaning already assigned to L itself.

In English, "not" is commonly put just after the first verbal element of the sentence; in mathematics, it is frequently indicated by drawing a bar through a symbol. From "$x = 3$" (read "x is equal to 3") we get "$x \neq 3$" (read "x is not equal to 3") by negating it.

AND

Next, consider the word "and." If we put "and" between two simple sentences, we are asserting both of the declarations involved. Suppose G stands for "$x > 5$" and E for "x is even," with the replacement set being the set of counting numbers. Then the sentence "$x > 5$ and x is even," which we abbreviate by "$G \& E$," is true just when G and E are simultaneously true—that is, whenever x names a number that is both greater than 5 and even. The truth set of G is $\{6, 7, 8, 9, 10, \cdots\}$, and that for E is $\{2, 4, 6, 8, 10, \cdots\}$. For $G \& E$ it is $\{6, 8, 10, \cdots\}$, which consists of the even counting numbers greater than 5. Although 7 is in the truth set for G ($7 > 5$), it is not in the truth set for $G \& E$ because 7 is not even. While 4 is in the truth set of E (x is even), it is not in the truth set for $G \& E$ because it is not greater than 5.

For sentences containing variables a diagram similar to a Venn or Euler diagram is frequently useful. (See Booklet No. 1: *Sets*.) You will recall that a Venn diagram is a diagram such as the one shown in Figure 1, in which a replacement, or universal, set U is represented by the interior of a rectangle and where one or more subsets are represented by the interiors

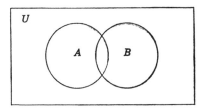

Fɪɢ. 1.—Venn diagram.

of other simple closed curves, such as the circles shown. By shading appropriate regions we can represent the union or intersection of subsets, as suggested in Figure 2, where the left-hand diagram represents the set whose members are those in both A and B, while the right-hand diagram represents the set whose members are those in either A or B or both.

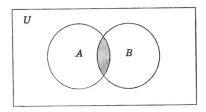 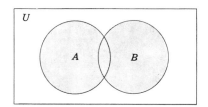

$A \cap B$ shaded $A \cup B$ shaded

Fɪɢᴜʀᴇ 2

The kind of diagram we wish to use is a little different in appearance but very similar in interpretation. First, let us agree to represent the replacement set for a variable in a simple sentence by the interior of a rectangle. (See Fig. 3.)

Replacement set
for
a simple sentence P

Fɪɢᴜʀᴇ 3

Since the replacement set for the sentence "$x > 5$" was assumed to be the set of all counting numbers, $\{1, 2, 3, \cdots\}$, the interior of the rectangle for this sentence is imagined to contain all of the members of this set.

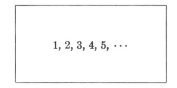

1, 2, 3, 4, 5, $\cdots$

Fig. 4.—Replacement set for x in "$x > 5$."

(See Fig. 4.) Next, by drawing a vertical segment across the interior of the rectangle, we can imagine separating the replacement set into two subsets, one of which is the truth set for $x > 5$, while the other is the subset of counting numbers not in this truth set. Let us agree in this case to use the right-hand region for the truth set, as suggested by Figure 5.

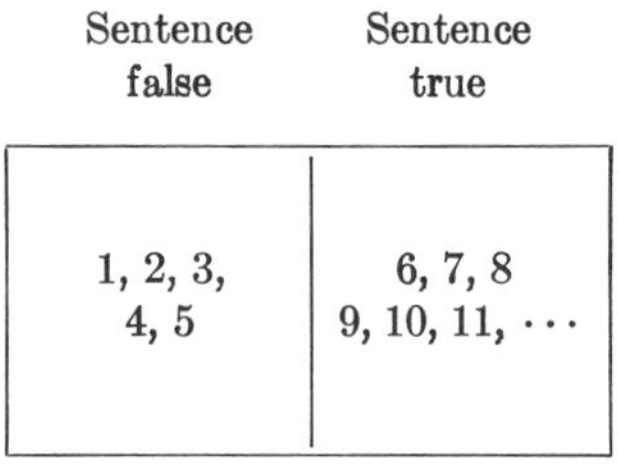

Sentence false	Sentence true
1, 2, 3, 4, 5	6, 7, 8 9, 10, 11, $\cdots$

Fig. 5.—Replacement set for x in "$x > 5$."

Alternatively, we might draw a dividing segment horizontally across the interior of a different rectangle to separate the replacement set into two sets, one of which is the truth set for another sentence. To illustrate this, let us use the sentence "x is even" and agree to use the upper region for the truth set, as shown in Figure 6.

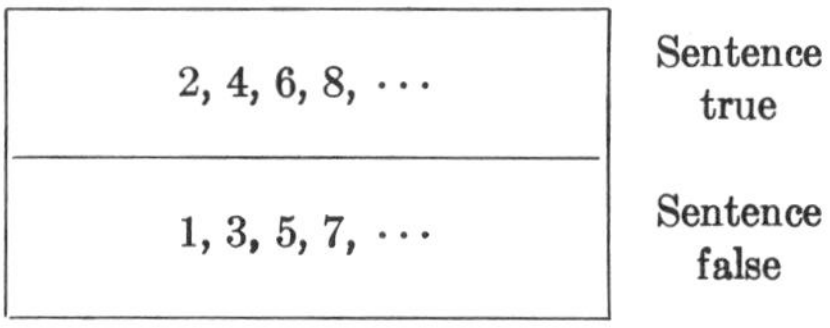

2, 4, 6, 8, $\cdots$	Sentence true
1, 3, 5, 7, $\cdots$	Sentence false

Fig. 6.—Replacement set for x in "x is even."

Since the interiors of the two rectangles in Figures 5 and 6 represent the same set, $\{1, 2, 3, \cdots\}$, let us superimpose one on the other to produce the rectangle shown in Figure 7.

	"x > 5" false	"x > 5" true	
	2, 4	6, 8, 10, ···	"x is even" true
	1, 3, 5	7, 9, 11, ···	"x is even" false

Fig. 7.—Replacement set for x in "$x > 5$, and x is even."

We now can picture the contents of the four regions into which this rectangle is divided, as in Figure 8. We can generalize the idea of rectangle

"x > 5" is false. "x is even" is true.	"x > 5" is true. "x is even" is true.
"x > 5" is false. "x is even" is false.	"x > 5" is true. "x is even" is false.

FIGURE 8

diagrams, developed using "$x > 5$" and "x is even," and apply it to any two simple sentences. To do this we shall have to represent the sentences in some way, so let us agree to call one of them P and the other one Q. Then the negation of P will be represented by $\neg P$ (read "not P"), and the negation of Q by $\neg Q$ (read "not Q"). Notice that P and $\neg P$ are never true for the same replacements of their variable. Thus, "$x > 5$" and "$x \not> 5$" are never simultaneously true. In fact, the truth of one implies the falsehood of the other. When x is equal to 2, for instance, $2 > 5$ is false but $2 \not> 5$ is true; whereas, when x is equal to 7, $7 > 5$ is true but $7 \not> 5$ is false.

Using the symbols P, $\neg P$, Q, and $\neg Q$, we can picture the truth sets of each, as suggested by the rectangles shown in Figure 9.

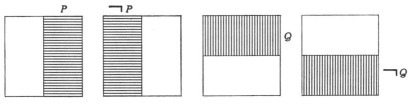

FIGURE 9

Then, when we superimpose one of these rectangles on the other, the truth sets of compound sentences appear as double-shadow regions. In Figure 10 the rectangle for P, superimposed upon the rectangle for Q, shows the truth set for the compound $P \& Q$. The truth set for $P \& Q$ is the *intersection* of the truth sets for P and Q. Compare this with the overlapping areas in a Venn diagram for the intersection of sets A and B (Fig. 11).

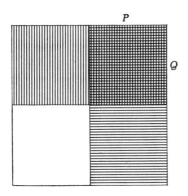

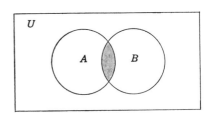

FIG. 10.—Compound sentence
$P \& Q$ doubly shaded.

FIG. 11.—Sentence $A \cap B$.

A diagram for the truth set of a compound sentence of the form $P \& \neg Q$ would appear as shown in Figure 12. As a specific example of this kind of

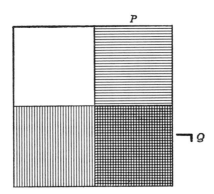

FIG. 12.—Compound sentence $P \& \neg Q$ doubly shaded.

compound sentence, let us again consider the simple sentences "$x > 5$" and "x is even," with the replacement set being the set of counting (natural) numbers. We let P play the role of "$x > 5$"; if Q plays the role of "x is even," then $\neg Q$ is the sentence "x is *not* even." The diagrams for the truth sets of P and $\neg\, Q$ would, before being superimposed one on the other, look like Figure 13.

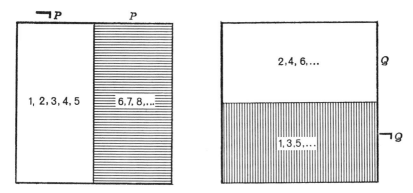

FIGURE 13

By superimposing one rectangle on the other, we then produce Figure 14. The lower right-hand region, which is doubly shaded, is the truth set of $P\,\&\,\neg\,Q$.

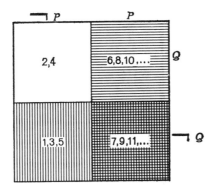

FIG. 14.—Compound sentence $P\,\&\,\neg\,Q$ doubly shaded.

In English there are many ways in which the conjunction that we abbreviate by "&" can be phrased. Sometimes we write, "Both P and Q." Or perhaps we write, "P but Q," which carries the same logical meaning as "P and Q" but a different mood. For example, if P stands for "It is raining" and Q for "I am going," we express a sense of reluctance or annoyance by saying, "It is raining, but I am going." This feeling is not apparent in "It is raining, and I am going," although, logically speaking, the same combination is asserted.

If the two simple statements being combined have the same subject, a relative or even adjectival construction may be used. For example, we can combine "x is an odd number" and "x is a multiple of 5" in either of the following ways: "x is an odd number that is a multiple of 5," or "x is an odd multiple of 5."

Note that P & Q and Q & P have the same classification of truth or falsity. In common speech there may again be a slight change of mood due to emphasis. "I'm going but it's raining" and "It's raining but I'm going" have a different ring to them; but there is no difference in their truth or falsity.

When two logical expressions always agree in their classification, regardless of special instances of substitution, they are called "logically equivalent." Thus, P & Q and Q & P are logically equivalent, as are P and $\neg \neg P$.

OR

The conjunction "or" has two meanings in English. One is called the "exclusive or" and is sometimes phrased "either one or the other but not both." The other is called the "inclusive or" and is sometimes expressed in legal documents by "and/or." In mathematics and in logic we *always* use the "inclusive or." The Romans had two different words for the two meanings: *aut* was an "exclusive or," and *vel* was the "inclusive or." In mathematics our abbreviation for "or" is $\vee$, which reminds us of *vel*. Thus, "$P \vee Q$" means "P and/or Q" but for convenience is read "P or Q."

The truth set of $P \vee Q$ is the *union* of the truth sets for P and Q. That is, we classify $P \vee Q$ as true whenever either P is true or Q is true or both are true. A rectangle diagram for the truth set of $P \vee Q$ is shown in Figure 15. The entire shaded region, comprising three-fourths of the

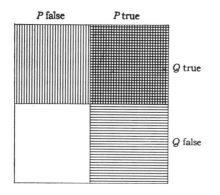

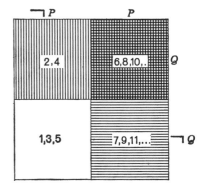

FIG. 15.—Compound sentence $P \vee Q$ shaded or doubly shaded.

FIG. 16.—Compound sentence "$x > 5$ or x is even" shaded or doubly shaded.

large rectangle, represents the truth set. You should compare this shaded area with the shaded area in the Venn diagram for the union of sets A and B, $A \cup B$, in Figure 2. As a specific example, let us again think of the simple sentences "$x > 5$" and "x is even," where the replacement set for x is the set of counting numbers. The resulting diagram, showing the members of the replacement set, would appear as shown in Figure 16. Since "$x > 5$, or x is even" is true *either* when $x > 5$ or when x is even, *or both*, the only numbers in the replacement set that are not also in the truth set are 1, 3, and 5.

Just as "$P \& Q$" and "$Q \& P$" are logically equivalent, so are "$P \lor Q$" and "$Q \lor P$." When one sentence is true, so is the other; and when one sentence is false, so is the other.

IF...THEN

The remaining basic connective uses the two words "if" and "then" in its usual form, although there are many ways of expressing the same idea. The connective is used with simple sentences P and Q to obtain compound sentences of the form "If P, then Q." Since the direct logical consequences of this connective are easier to explain than the verbal problems associated with it, let us start with the former.

The connective is symbolized by means of a single-headed arrow, $\rightarrow$. Thus $P \rightarrow Q$ is read "If P, then Q," or "P implies Q." The truth value assigned to $P \rightarrow Q$ is in some ways curious. The rectangle in Figure 17

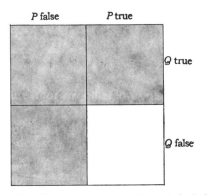

FIG. 17.—Compound sentence $P \rightarrow Q$ shaded.

shows this truth set. The picture shows that $P \rightarrow Q$ is true except when P is true and Q is false. For example, let P be the simple sentence "It is warm," and let Q be the simple sentence "I am going." The compound sentence $P \rightarrow Q$ would then be: "If it is warm, then I am going."

In an English sentence the word "then" is often omitted as superfluous, the sentence normally being worded "If it is warm, I am going."

When would the statement be false? Only if the weather was warm and the speaker did not go. What if the weather was cold? The speaker would have to decide again. He might go anyway. Does this mean that he told a falsehood originally when he said, "If it is warm, I am going"? Not at all. His condition was not met, so his statement did not bind him to any action either positive or negative. This renders slightly less curious the notion that $P \to Q$ is said to be true even though P itself is false.

To illustrate the rather confusing variety of designations for this connective which are used particularly in mathematics, we shall substitute number sentences for P and Q. For P, called the *antecedent of the implication*, let us use "$x > 5$"; for Q, called the *consequent*, let us use "$x > 4$." The replacement set may again be considered to be the counting numbers. Our standard rectangle diagram then looks like Figure 18. The truth

"x > 5" false	"x > 5" true	
5	6, 7, 8, ⋯	"x > 4" true
1, 2, 3, 4		"x > 4" false

Fig. 18.—Compound sentence $(x > 5) \to (x > 4)$.

set for $P \to Q$ is the whole set of counting numbers because the lower right-hand box is empty. There is no counting number for which "$x > 5$" is true and "$x > 4$" is false.

Here are a number of ways in which the idea of $P \to Q$, or "$x > 5$" → "$x > 4$," may be expressed:

1. If $x > 5$, then $x > 4$.
2. $x > 5$ implies $x > 4$.
3. $x > 4$ whenever $x > 5$.
4. $x > 5$ is a sufficient condition that $x > 4$.
5. $x > 4$ is a necessary condition for $x > 5$.
6. Given that $x > 5$, then it follows that $x > 4$.
7. $x > 4$ if $x > 5$.
8. $x > 5$ only if $x > 4$.
9. $x > 4$ provided that $x > 5$.

How many of these expressions make sense when the English sentence examples are used—that is, when P is "It is warm" and Q is "I am going"?

Certainly, one would never say: "It is warm only if I am going." Try the others. Wherever you see "$x > 5$," put in "It is warm." Where you see "$x > 4$," put in "I am going." Some will be good English, while others will be very strange.

Compounding Compounds

Once we have the building blocks of simple sentences and the mortar of connectives, there is no theoretical limit to the size of the edifice we can construct.

One very useful compounded compound is $(P \rightarrow Q)$ & $(Q \rightarrow P)$. This statement is so common that it has its own abbreviation, which is suggested by the two arrows in the formula. This abbreviation is the double-headed arrow: $P \leftrightarrow Q$ (read "P if and only if Q").

Let us consider the classification of this statement in terms of P and Q. The sentence $P \rightarrow Q$ is true unless P is true and Q is false; $Q \rightarrow P$ is true unless Q is true and P is false. (See Fig. 19.) The lower left-hand and

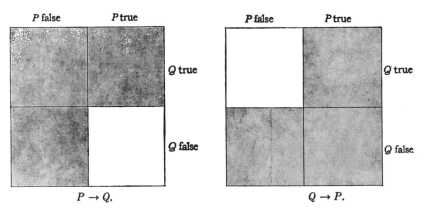

FIGURE 19

upper right-hand boxes are shaded in *both* diagrams. The diagram for $(P \rightarrow Q)$ & $(Q \rightarrow P)$ is shown in Figure 20.

The compound sentence turns out to be true precisely when the simple sentences P and Q are both true or both false. In mathematics this compound sentence is given various special names made up by running together some of the words used for $P \rightarrow Q$ and $Q \rightarrow P$. One of these, as mentioned earlier, is "P if and only if Q." Another is "P is a necessary and sufficient condition for Q."

Of course, $P \leftrightarrow Q$ is logically equivalent to $Q \leftrightarrow P$, so we could exchange the two.

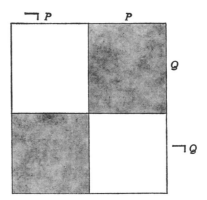

FIG. 20.—Compound sentence $P \leftrightarrow Q$.

In order to give some mathematical examples of the use of this connective, let us first recall a few definitions:

An *equilateral triangle* is a triangle in which all three sides are equal in length.

An *equiangular triangle* is a triangle in which all three angles are equal in measure.

A *square counting number* is a counting number that is equal to the product of some counting number with itself: $25 = 5 \times 5$; that is, 25 is the square of 5.

Here are two statements we can discuss using the preceding definitions.

A triangle is equiangular if and only if it is equilateral.

A necessary and sufficient condition for a number to be even is that its square be a multiple of 4.

The phase "if and only if" is not often used outside of mathematics. Few persons would ever say "I am going if and only if it is warm," whereas someone might say something like "I am going if it is warm, but only if it is warm."

Another serviceable compound is used when we have more than one hypothesis and thus have a compound antecedent to an implication. For instance, it is often convenient to have the replacement set named in the basic sentence: "If a and b are counting numbers and $a > 1$, then $(a \times b) > b$." We shall split the sentence into simple components.

A: a is a counting number.
B: b is a counting number.
C: $a > 1$.
D: $(a \times b) > b$.

We can then abbreviate the entire sentence in this way: $[(A \& B) \& C] \rightarrow$ D. This symbolism might be read "If A, B, and C are true, then so is D," or "A and B, together with C, imply D." Notice the double grouping symbols. These appear because none of our connectives apply to more than two sentences at a time, and the brackets and parentheses are strategically located to identify which two in each case. Thus, the parentheses in

$$(A \& B) \& C$$

show that we first form the compound sentence $A \& B$ and then form the compound sentences $(A \& B) \& C$ by connecting $A \& B$ with C. Next, the brackets in

$$[(A \& B) \& C] \rightarrow D$$

show that the sentence $(A \& B) \& C$ is connected with D by an "if. . . then" connective. As you look at

$$[(A \& B) \& C] \rightarrow D,$$

it may occur to you that as we write more and more complicated expressions, we can easily find ourselves in considerable trouble with parentheses and brackets. Let us agree to a few simple rules that will eliminate some of the problems.

1. A negation, $\neg$, is a weak symbol. Its influence covers only the symbol or parenthetical expression immediately to the right of it.

That is, $\neg A \& B$ can be used instead of $(\neg A) \& B$ because we understand that $\neg$ goes only with the A. Similarly, $[\neg (A \lor B)] \rightarrow C$ may be simplified to read $\neg (A \lor B) \rightarrow C$ because we cannot mistake the latter for $\neg [(A \lor B) \rightarrow C]$.

2. The symbols $\&$ and $\lor$ rank next and rank equally.
3. The symbols $\rightarrow$ and $\leftrightarrow$, which outweigh $\&$ and $\lor$, are equal to each other in rank.

$(A \& B) \rightarrow C$ can be replaced by $A \& B \rightarrow C$ because we should not mistake the latter for $A \& (B \rightarrow C)$. Let us try simplifying a few expressions that will occur, in simplified form, in the exercises:

$$R \& (\neg G)$$

No need for parentheses; the $\neg$ can only go with G: $R \& \neg G$.

$$[(\neg W) \& (\neg R)] \leftrightarrow C.$$

No need for parentheses around $\neg W$ and $\neg R$: $(\neg W \& \neg R) \leftrightarrow C$. No need for *any* parentheses; the double arrow will go all the way:

$\neg W \& \neg R \leftrightarrow C$. The form $(\neg W \& \neg R) \leftrightarrow C$, however, may be clearer. Do not overwork the conventions; they are supposed to help, not confuse.

Exercise Set 1

Given the following designated abbreviations for the simple sentences, write the ten compound sentences in colloquial English. Do *not* simply insert the standard connective translation unless it sounds natural.

> W: It is warm.
> R: It is raining.
> G: I am going.
> C: He is coming.

EXAMPLE: $R \to \neg G$. (English sentence: I am not going if it is raining.)

1. $R \& \neg G$.
2. $\neg C \to G$.
3. $W \to R$.
4. $W \lor R$.
5. $\neg (R \& \neg G)$.
6. $\neg (W \& R) \leftrightarrow C$.
7. $(\neg W \& \neg R) \leftrightarrow C$.
8. $(W \lor \neg R) \to G$.
9. $((W \& R) \& G) \& C$.
10. $(G \lor C) \& \neg (G \& C)$.

Substituting the letter abbreviation for each simple sentence and the correct symbol for the connectives, write symbolic equivalents of the compound statements:

> E: x is even.
> F: x is a multiple of 4.
> G: $x > 5$.
> H: $x < 3$.

EXAMPLE: x is a multiple of 4 but is not greater than 5. (Sentence in symbols: $F \& \neg G$.)

11. If x is a multiple of 4, it is not less than 3.
12. If x exceeds 5, it is not less than 3.
13. If x is even but not a multiple of 4, it is either greater than 5 or less than 3.
14. In order for x to be a multiple of 4, x must be even.
15. x is even or x is greater than 5.

16. If x is not even, then x is not a multiple of 4.

17. If x is not less than 3, then x is greater than 5 or x is even.

Translate each of the following symbolic expressions into English sentences.
EXAMPLE: $H \rightarrow \neg G$ (English sentence: If x is less than 3, then x does not exceed 5.)

18. $G \& E$.

19. $\neg (E \& H) \rightarrow F$.

20. $\neg H \vee F \rightarrow G$.

21. $\neg E \& H \rightarrow \neg F \vee G$.

22. $\neg (G \vee \neg E) \rightarrow H$.

23. $\neg H \& \neg F$.

24. $\neg (E \& G) \rightarrow \neg F$.

25. $F \rightarrow \neg (G \vee H)$.

26. $F \vee \neg E \rightarrow G \vee \neg H$.

Truth Values and Truth Tables

Although box diagrams are useful, they are rather cumbersome for analysis of compound-sentence structure. A more formal pattern, called a truth table, can be used for this purpose. If we let T stand for "true" and F for "false," then all possibilities for the two elements of a compound sentence are included in the set {TT, TF, FT, FF}. These four possibilities

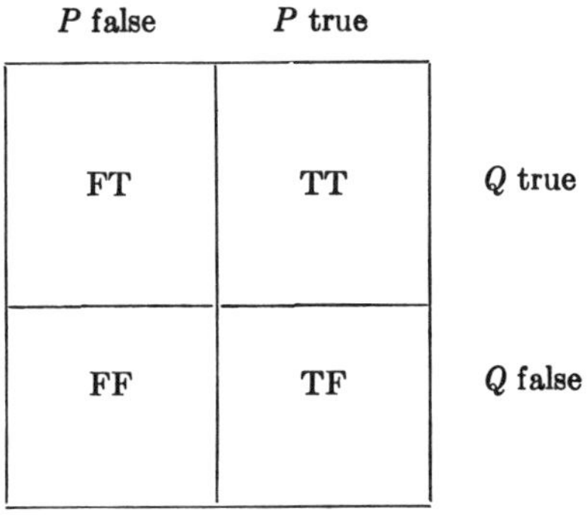

P false P true

FT	TT	Q true
FF	TF	Q false

FIGURE 21

correspond to the four boxes in the diagram. Instead of shading, we simply enter the corresponding combination of T and F that is the "truth value" of the compound. Thus, we might have the diagram seen in Figure 21.

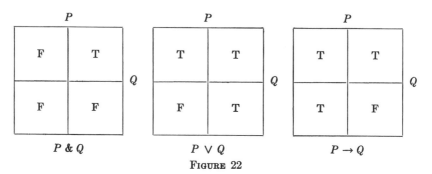

FIGURE 22

Then, to simplify this for the compound sentences P & Q, $P \lor Q$, and $P \to Q$ we could just show the diagrams as in Figure 22.

It is customary in making truth tables, however, to dispense with rectangles altogether and simply to use columnar arrangements. Tables I and II are the tables for the basic connectives. The tables are to be read

TABLE I	
P	$\neg P$
T	F
F	T

TABLE II

P	Q	P & Q	$P \lor Q$	$P \to Q$
T	T	T	T	T
T	F	F	T	F
F	T	F	T	T
F	F	F	F	T

across, line by line. The next-to-the-last line in the larger table tells us, for example, that when P is false and Q is true, then P & Q is false, but $P \lor Q$ and $P \to Q$ are true. As an example of an application of this table, we can let P be the simple sentence "Jack eats starchy food" and Q be "Jack eats too much." Then the truth of the following compound sentences can be determined from Table II, which has the various truth values of P and Q.

1. Jack eats starchy food and Jack eats too much.
2. Jack eats starchy food or Jack eats too much.
3. If Jack eats starchy food, then Jack eats too much.

Thus, if Jack does not eat starchy food but does indeed overeat, then from the third line of Table II with P false and Q true, we find that sentence 1 is false, 2 is true, and 3 is true.

If we keep these basic tables handy or memorize their content, we can analyze more complicated compounds. For example, what is the classification of $\neg P \lor Q$ for the various classifications of P and Q? We do the job one part at a time as in Table III.

TABLE III

P	Q	$\neg P$	Q	$\neg P \lor Q$
T	T	F	T	T
T	F	F	F	F
F	T	T	T	T
F	F	T	F	T

First, we write the basic columns for P and Q; then we write any parts of our sentence that can be immediately calculated from them, $\neg P$ in this case; Q has been rewritten to make it more available for the next step, which is $\neg P \lor Q$. To finish this step, we look at the various combinations for the two elements. They are, in order, FT, FF, TT, TF. Now we recall the meaning of "$\lor$." A compound with $\lor$ is true if at least one of the components is true. So we write T on all lines of the last column except the second line, which we mark F.

Compare the table for $\neg P \lor Q$ with the one for $P \to Q$. They are identical. That is, $P \to Q$ and $\neg P \lor Q$ are *logically equivalent*. This accounts for our sometimes saying, for example, "Either she doesn't come to the party or I won't" in place of "If she comes to the party, then I won't," when we mean that at least one of us is not going to be there, under any circumstances.

Let us try a slightly more difficult compound: $\neg (\neg P \lor \neg Q)$, by the process illustrated in Tables IV to VII.

1. Form the basic columns, as in Table IV:

TABLE IV

P	Q
T	T
T	F
F	T
F	F

2. Calculate the simplest elements of the sentence from the basic columns, as in Table V:

TABLE V

¬P	¬Q
F	F
F	T
T	F
T	T

3. From these columns we can compute ¬ P ∨ ¬ Q, in Table VI.

TABLE VI

¬P	¬Q	¬P ∨ ¬Q
F	F	F
F	T	T
T	F	T
T	T	T

4. Finally, we are ready to calculate the table for ¬ (¬ P ∨ ¬ Q), in Table VII. Just reverse the values of the last column in Table VI.

TABLE VII

¬P ∨ ¬Q	¬(¬P ∨ ¬Q)
F	T
T	F
T	F
T	F

This is the same as the column for P & Q. We shall have to dig a little deeper to find an example in English for this one, but it is conceivable (although improbable) that one might say "It is not true that I do not like John or I do not like Mary," instead of "I like John and I like Mary." The last two examples show that we really did not need *four* basic connectives. We could have started with "¬" and "∨" and *defined* sentence $P \to Q$ as ¬ P ∨ Q and sentence P & Q as ¬(¬ P ∨ ¬ Q). There is no real gain in such a procedure, however, since we all feel that "→" and "&" are just as basic as "∨." Indeed, it is possible to pick "¬" and any other one of the basic connectives and define the remaining two connectives in terms of our choice. (In fact, *all four* of the basic connectives, ¬, &, ∨, and →, can be defined in terms of the *single* connective "not both... and ... ," and all four can also be defined in terms of the *single* connective "neither... nor....") Let us try one more application of truth tables. Think of the following two sentences:

1. If it snows this week and my check comes, I am going skiing this weekend.
2. If it snows this week, then, if my check comes, I am going skiing this weekend.

Is there any difference in meaning? We shall check. Define P, Q, and R as follows:

> P: It snows this week.
> Q: My check comes.
> R: I am going skiing this weekend.

Then sentence 1 is $(P$ & $Q) \to R$, and 2 is $P \to (Q \to R)$. Now we have eight possible combinations of T and F for P, Q, R. The truth table for sentence 1 is seen in Table VIII. The only F in the last column is in the line where P & Q is true and R is false.

TABLE VIII

P	Q	R	P & Q	R	$(P$ & $Q) \to R$
T	T	T	T	T	T
T	T	F	T	F	F
T	F	T	F	T	T
T	F	F	F	F	T
F	T	T	F	T	T
F	T	F	F	F	T
F	F	T	F	T	T
F	F	F	F	F	T

Table IX is the truth table for sentence 2. Comparing the final columns

TABLE IX

P	Q	R	$Q \to R$	P	$(Q \to R)$	$P \to (Q \to R)$
T	T	T	T	T	T	T
T	T	F	F	T	F	F
T	F	T	T	T	T	T
T	F	F	T	T	T	T
F	T	T	T	F	T	T
F	T	F	F	F	F	T
F	F	T	T	F	T	T
F	F	F	T	F	T	T

in Tables VIII and IX, we find them identical and hence conclude that
the sentences are logically equivalent.

Exercise Set 2

Make a truth table for each sentence.

1. $P \& (Q \lor R)$.   **5.** $(P \& Q) \& R$.
2. $P \lor (Q \& R)$.   **6.** $P \& (Q \& R)$.
3. $P \lor (Q \lor R)$.   **7.** $(P \& Q) \lor (P \& R)$.
4. $(P \lor Q) \lor R$.   **8.** $(P \lor Q) \& (P \lor R)$.
         9. Which of the sentences 1 to 8 are logically equivalent?

Logical Equivalents; Tautologies

The logical symbols $\&$ and $\lor$ are closely related to the set symbols
$\cap$ and $\cup$, respectively. (See Booklet No. 1: *Sets*.) If P and Q are open
sentences in the variable x, with truth sets p and q, respectively, then we
see that

the truth set of $P \& Q$ is $p \cap q$,

and

the truth set of $P \lor Q$ is $p \cup q$.

It should not be surprising, then, that the algebra of & and $\lor$ is parallel to the algebra of $\cap$ and $\cup$, with which you are perhaps more familiar. In fact, you can verify by truth tables (and did, if you worked exercises 1 to 9 in Exercise Set 2) the following facts about certain logically equivalent sentences. We use the symbol $\equiv$ to mean "is logically equivalent to." (Corresponding statements from the theory of sets will result when three sentences such as P, Q, and R are replaced by their respective truth sets p, q, and r. Of course, & and $\lor$ would again be replaced by $\cap$ and $\cup$, respectively, and $\equiv$ would be interpreted as denoting set equality. For sets, the results can be understood best by drawing Venn diagrams.)

$$P \;\&\; Q \equiv Q \;\&\; P \left.\right\} \text{ commutative properties}$$
$$P \lor Q \equiv Q \lor P \left.\right\} \text{ of \& and } \lor$$

$$P \;\&\; (Q \;\&\; R) \equiv (P \;\&\; Q) \;\&\; R \left.\right\} \text{ associative properties}$$
$$P \lor (Q \lor R) \equiv (P \lor Q) \lor R \left.\right\} \text{ of \& and } \lor$$

With the latter equivalences in mind, we can drop more parentheses and equivalently write simply $P \;\&\; Q \;\&\; R$, $P \lor Q \lor R$.

Notice that in this algebra there are two distributive properties:

$$P \lor (Q \;\&\; R) \equiv (P \lor Q) \;\&\; (P \lor R) \left.\right\} \text{ distributive properties}$$
$$P \;\&\; (Q \lor R) \equiv (P \;\&\; Q) \lor (P \;\&\; R) \left.\right\} \text{ of } \lor \text{ and } \&$$

Two more useful equivalences have already been checked in the preceding section:

$$(P \;\&\; Q) \to R \equiv P \to (Q \to R);$$
$$P \to Q \equiv \neg P \lor Q.$$

For corresponding equalities in set theory, you should replace "$\to$" with the set-inclusion symbol "$\subseteq$," and "$\neg$" with the complement symbol "$^-$."

A type of sentence that is more useful than would seem apparent at first glance is the "tautology." A tautology is a sentence that is true for all possible truth-value assignments.

Here are two with a single basic component: $P \to P$ and $P \lor \neg P$. These are not unfamiliar in everyday usage, since one frequently hears such tautological gems as "If that's the way it is, then that's the way it is" and "Either it is or it isn't."

The tautology $P \lor \neg P$ has a special name. It is called "the law of the excluded middle," because it provides that a simple sentence must either be true or else be false. There is no middle ground in logic.

One way to make a tautology is to take two equivalent statements and connect them with a single or double arrow, as, for example, $(P \to Q) \leftrightarrow (\neg P \lor Q)$.

Here are two other useful tautologies:

$$Q \to (P \to Q)$$
$$\neg P \to (P \to Q).$$

They can be checked by the truth values in Tables X and XI. As you

TABLE X

P	Q	$P \to Q$	$Q \to (P \to Q)$
T	T	T	T
T	F	F	T
F	T	T	T
F	F	T	T

TABLE XI

P	Q	$\neg P$	$P \to Q$	$\neg P \to (P \to Q)$
T	T	F	T	T
T	F	F	F	T
F	T	T	T	T
F	F	T	T	T

can see, the final column in each table has only T's. This means that the compound sentences $Q \to (P \to Q)$ and $\neg P \to (P \to Q)$ are true, regardless of the truth values of the simple sentences P and Q.

Tautologies have a definite place in logical reasoning. They can be inserted at any point in an argument, with any logically admissible sentences whatever in place of the symbols. Whenever in the course of a discussion someone says, "Well, it's either this way or it isn't, you can't have it both ways," he is really using *two* tautologies: $P \lor \neg P$ and $\neg (P \& \neg P)$.

Exercise Set 3

Show that each sentence is a tautology.

1. $P \to (\neg P \to Q)$.   **3.** $\neg P \to \neg (P \& Q)$.
2. $(P \& Q) \to P$.   **4.** $(P \& Q) \to (P \lor Q)$.

RULES OF INFERENCE

We are ready now to put our symbolic apparatus to work, checking methods of deduction both in mathematics and in other fields. The typical situation is this: We are given some sentences, simple or compound. We assert these. They are to be assumed true. We want to get from the premises to a conclusion by logical argument. To do this, we may use our premises and tautologies, together with the rules of inference that we shall now study.

For the sake of simplicity we are going to limit our attention to strict *logical* deduction. For example, it will not be permissible in our work to infer from the premise $x = 5$ the conclusion that $x + 1 = 6$. This conclusion is *arithmetical* in nature and requires its own extensive logical development. If we need such results, we shall just have to toss them into the hopper as extra premises.

Modus Ponens

This argument goes also by the longer name of *modus ponendo ponens*, which is Latin for "the method of getting [the consequent] by asserting [the antecedent]." Here is a sample: "If it is raining, then I am staying home. It is raining. So, I am staying home." There are two premises: one is an implication; the other is the antecedent of the implication. The result, or conclusion, is the consequent of the implication. The argument is abbreviated as follows:

> Implication: $P \to Q$
> Antecedent: P
> Conclusion: Q

Notice that the *modus ponens* argument is associated with a tautology—namely, one having the logical form $[(P \to Q) \ \& \ P] \to Q$—and hence does not depend on the truth or falsity of P, Q, or $P \to Q$ for its validity.

Naturally, if something is wrong with the premises, we may get a false conclusion; but this does not invalidate the argument itself, which mechanically grinds out the consequent when fed the implication and its antecedent.

In a simple *modus ponens* argument the conclusion is at once evident when the premises are given. Let us try two more:

(a)   If $x > 5$, then $x^2 > 25$.
Given: $x > 5$.
Conclusion: $x^2 > 25$.

(b)   Swimming is poor if the surf is rough.
Given: The surf is rough.
Conclusion: Swimming is poor.

Be sure that one of your premises is the antecedent. Substituting the consequent and deriving the antecedent is a fallacious mode of reasoning. Do not say, for example, "Swimming is poor if the surf is rough. Swimming is poor. Therefore, the surf is rough." The truth of the matter may be that the surf is calm but there are a lot of sharks.

In practice the *modus ponens* argument is used in more complicated arguments, at one or more stages. Before going on, let us state some rules of argument:

1. Any premise may be used at any point in an argument. In sketching forms of argument we shall indicate the use of a premise by "Pr."

2. Any tautology may be used anywhere in an argument. We shall indicate the use of a tautology by "T."

3. A logical equivalent of any statement may be substituted for the statement in a derivation. If we are substituting a logical equivalent of a statement marked 5 in our derivation, we shall write "L 5."

4. When *modus ponens* is used, for example, on statements 2 and 3 (which of course must be in correct form), we shall write "MP 2, 3."

Table XII lists these symbols, together with their meaning. You should

TABLE XII

Symbol	What It Means
Pr	This statement is true because we assume it to be true.
T	This statement is true because it is a tautology, and tautologies are always true.
L 3	This statement is true because it is logically equivalent to statement 3.
MP 6, 8	This statement is true because we are applying *modus ponens* to statements 6 and 8.

not try to memorize all of this because if the meaning of one of these symbols is not clear, you can always refer to this table. To see why these symbols are used at all, let us look at a simple argument both with and without the symbols. Consider the assertion: "If it rains, I will stay home.

If I stay home, I will miss the concert. It is raining. Therefore, I will miss the concert."

Now, what we wish to do is to establish that if all of the things about rain and staying home are true, then it has to be true that I will miss the concert. We shall begin by listing those things that we assume to be true. First, let us have an agreement about names for statements.

R means "It is raining," or "It rains."
H means "I will stay home."
C means "I will miss the concert."

Next, let us get to the matter of missing the concert. We shall do this with a series of steps listing some true sentences and the reasons these sentences are true.

1. $R \rightarrow H$.   This statement is true because we assume it to be true.
2. $H \rightarrow C$.   This statement is true because we assume it to be true.
3. R.   This statement is true because we assume it to be true.
4. H.   This statement is true because we are applying *modus ponens* to statements 1 and 3.
5. C.   This statement is true because we are applying *modus ponens* to statements 2 and 4.

Now here is the same argument, using symbols from Table XII.

1. $R \rightarrow H$.   Pr
2. $H \rightarrow C$.   Pr
3. R.   Pr
4. H.   MP 1, 3
5. C.   MP 2, 4

In both forms the steps make it possible to develop a formal, logical derivation of the truth of C, given the truths of $R \rightarrow H$, $H \rightarrow C$, and R.

Here is another example, this one concerned with counting numbers. "If $x > 3$ and $x < 5$, then $x = 4$. Given that $x > 3$ is true, and that $x < 5$ is true, then $x = 4$ must be true."

In this case, we are assuming it to be true that *if* x is a counting number greater than 3 and less than 5, then x has to be 4. We are also assuming that x *is* greater than 3 and less than 5. We want to conclude that x is 4. Let us employ these symbols:

$A: x > 3.$
$B: x < 5.$
$C: x = 4.$

Here is the argument.

1. $(A \,\&\, B) \rightarrow C$.   Pr
2. A.   Pr

3. B.   Pr
4. $A \rightarrow (B \rightarrow C)$.   L   1 (Look this up in the table.)
5. $B \rightarrow C$.   MP 4, 2
6. C.   MP 5, 3

You should go over this example a few times to make sure you follow the argument. At step 4 we substituted the compound sentence $A \rightarrow (B \rightarrow C)$ for the compound sentence $(A \& B) \rightarrow C$ and justified the substitution on the grounds that these are logically equivalent sentences. If they are not logically equivalent, the argument goes to pieces right there, of course; but if you look back, page 213, you will find that we used truth tables to establish the logical equivalences. While none of our examples in this section has made use of rule 2 on tautologies, we shall get to its use at a later point. It was included here for completeness.

Exercise Set 4

State whether or not each given conclusion is valid by *modus ponens*.

1. If it snows, then I shall go skiing. It snows. Therefore I shall go skiing.
2. If it snows, then I shall go skiing. It doesn't snow. Therefore, I shall not go skiing.
3. If I fall from a ladder, I shall be injured. I am injured. Therefore, I fell from a ladder.
4. If I go shopping, I shall buy a hat. I shall buy a blue dress if I buy a hat. I go shopping. Therefore, I buy a blue dress.
5. Argue that the conclusion in exercise 1 is valid.
6. Argue that the conclusion in exercise 4 is valid.

Modus Tollens

The longer name for this rule is *modus tollendo tollens*, the method of denying [the antecedent] by denying [the consequent].

Let us imagine the following situation: A boy is watching television. He hears his father say, "If it rains, I'll stay home." Sometime later, when his program ends, he looks around and discovers that his father has gone out. Without looking out the window he says to himself, "So it didn't rain after all."

We might picture the situation using symbols as follows:

R: It rains.
H: I'll stay home.

Implication: $R \rightarrow H$
Observation: $\neg H$
Conclusion: $\neg R$

The formal chart, then, shows two premises. One is an implication. The other is the denial of the consequent of the implication. The conclusion is the denial of the antecedent. The argument is abbreviated as follows:

$$P \to Q$$
$$\underline{\neg Q}$$
therefore: $\quad \neg P$

The argument is quite closely related to *modus ponens*. In fact, consider the truth table for $\neg Q \to \neg P$. (See Table XIII.)

TABLE XIII

P	Q	$\neg Q$	$\neg P$	$\neg Q \to \neg P$
T	T	F	F	T
T	F	T	F	F
F	T	F	T	T
F	F	T	T	T

This is exactly the table for $P \to Q$ (p. 204). Hence, $P \to Q$ and $\neg Q \to \neg P$ are logically equivalent, and a formal derivation could proceed:

1. $P \to Q$.   Pr
2. $\neg Q$.   Pr
3. $\neg Q \to \neg P$.   L   1
4. $\neg P$.   MP 3, 2

One way to think about this is that the use of *modus tollens* saves us two steps at the price of having to remember another rule of inference. We shall adopt *modus tollens* as a rule of argument and represent it in formal derivations by "MT."

Let us try a slight variation of *modus tollens*. A teacher says, "If you don't get your project in, I'll give you a low grade." The student gets a good grade. We conclude that he got his project in. Using symbols, this comes out as follows:

P: Student gets his project in.
G: Teacher gives a low grade.

1. $\neg P \to G$.   Pr
2. $\neg G$.   Pr
3. $\neg \neg P$.   MT 1, 2
4. P.   L   3

The foregoing derivation shows us the result of having an antecedent that was already a negation. The first conclusion is a double negative. We replace this, by logical equivalence, with the direct statement.

Exercise Set 5

State whether or not each given conclusion is correct by *modus tollens*.

1. If I go to New York, then I shall travel by plane.
   I am traveling by train.
   Therefore, I am not going to New York.

2. If I do not get a haircut, then I shall stay home.
   I go to church.
   Therefore, I got a haircut.

3. If I am sick, then I do not go to work.
   I am not sick.
   Therefore, I am at work.

4. If I am not sick, then I shall not take my medicine.
   I take my medicine.
   Therefore, I am sick.

5. Argue the validity of the conclusion in exercise 1.

6. Argue the validity of the conclusion in exercise 2.

HOW TO MAKE YOUR OWN RULES OF INFERENCE

There are many other named rules. It would be burdensome to go through them all; and even if we did, you might well find an argument that seemed valid but apparently used another rule.

If an argument uses a rule you have not covered, try the following steps:

1. Check that the argument actually proceeds by working with sentences or propositions as units. Arithmetical manipulation is not under study here. Also, manipulations involving set membership or set inclusion have not yet been covered. (Socrates is a man; all men are mortal; hence Socrates is mortal. Formally this looks like: Socrates $\in$ men. Men $\subset$ mortals. Hence, Socrates $\in$ mortals).

2. Write down the formal inference pattern.

3. Check whether or not a logical equivalence will put the argument directly in MP or MT form.

4. Check whether or not a tautology can be introduced to give a more standard argument.

Let us take some examples. Suppose we have $P \& Q$ and want to use both P and Q as separate premises or just one of them, say P, by itself. We want this inference: $P \& Q$ is true, so P is true. In symbols,

$$\frac{P \& Q}{P}$$

Now we may say to ourselves, "Naturally, if we know both P and Q, then we certainly know P." The words "naturally" and "certainly" suggest a tautology on the rest of the statement: "If both P and Q, then P"; that is, $(P \& Q) \rightarrow P$. It is easy to check that this is indeed a tautology. Now we are ready:

1. $P \& Q$.   Pr
2. $(P \& Q) \rightarrow P$.   T
3. P.   MP 2, 1

This suffices to show what we mean when we say you can make your own rules of inference without making a formal argument about them. Here are two more examples.

  (a)   Today is either Friday or Saturday.
           It is not Saturday.
           Therefore it is Friday.

The pattern is

$$\frac{\begin{array}{c} P \vee Q \\ \neg Q \end{array}}{P}$$

  (b)   If it rains here, then it is snowing in the mountains.
           If it snows in the mountains, then I am going skiing.
           Therefore, if it rains here, then I am going skiing.

The pattern is

$$\frac{\begin{array}{c} P \rightarrow Q \\ Q \rightarrow R \end{array}}{P \rightarrow R}$$

Exercise Set 6

Write the pattern for each of the following:

1. If it rains, then I shall not go to the beach.
I am at the beach.
Therefore, it is not raining.

2. If you do not like dogs, then you do not like dachshunds.
You like dachshunds.
Therefore, you like dogs.

3. Is the conclusion in exercise 1 valid?

4. Is the conclusion in exercise 2 valid?

Conditional Proof

Here is a bit of deliberately complicated argument: If the committee adopts Plan A, then, if the Governor concurs, the law will be changed. Either the Highway Commission cannot function or Plan A must be adopted. The governor concurs. Therefore, if the Highway Commission can function, the law will be changed.

Let us get down to symbols:

A: The committee adopts Plan A.
G: The governor concurs.
L: The law will be changed.
H: The Highway Commission can function.

The argument goes as follows:

$$A \to (G \to L)$$
$$\neg H \lor A$$
$$\underline{G \qquad\qquad}$$
$$\text{therefore:} \quad H \to L$$

How are we to derive the conclusion from the premises? We seem to be stymied, because the only obvious thing is to replace $\neg H \lor A$ by the logically equivalent statement $H \to A$ (p. 205), and H appears nowhere in the premises. Suppose we just add H to the premises and, to save a formal step, go right ahead and replace $\neg H \lor A$ by $H \to A$.

1. H.	Pr
2. $A \to (G \to L)$.	Pr
3. $H \to A$.	Pr
4. G.	Pr
5. A.	MP 3, 1
6. $G \to L$.	MP 2, 5
7. L.	MP 6, 4

By adding H to the list of assumptions we proved L. That is, given our premises and assuming H as well, we deduce L. But what is the difference between the last statement and saying that, given the premises, H implies

L? Essentially none. When we make such a statement as "Either the Highway Commission cannot function or Plan A must be adopted," that is, ⌐ *H* ∨ *A*, the assumption that it is *possible* for the Highway Commission to function (*H*) is implicit. Were this not the case, the premise (⌐ *H* ∨ *A*) could simply be replaced with ⌐ *H*, since the truth or falsity of *A* would be irrelevant: The adoption of Plan A would then have no bearing on the matter of the Highway Commission functioning.

To formalize all this, let us adopt the following rule. (It can be proved from the previous rules, but this will not be carried out here.)

> *Rule of conditional proof*: *If a statement Q can be deduced from a set of premises and a particular premise P, then P → Q can be deduced from the other premises alone.*

Thus it is that if we want to prove an implication, it is standard practice to throw the antecedent of the implication in with the premises and then to try to deduce the consequent.

As a general rule, to make a formal proof verifying or correcting an argument, write down the premises. Transform them into the forms of implications, taking apart forms like *P* & *R* to list the components separately. If the result to be proved has the form of an implication, *add its antecedent to the premises*. Then try to derive the consequent by MP and MT.

Let us try another complex example: If the witness is telling the truth, Sam has an alibi. Either the witness is telling the truth or there is a conspiracy. If there is a conspiracy, John is involved. If Sam has an alibi, George is innocent. So, if John is not involved, George is innocent.

All clear? Perhaps not, so let us get the words out and the symbols in. Then we can see.

W: The witness is telling the truth.
S: Sam has an alibi.
C: There is a conspiracy.
J: John is involved.
G: George is innocent.

The form is as follows:

$$W \to S$$
$$W \lor C$$
$$C \to J$$
$$\frac{S \to G}{\neg J \to G}$$

Now, replace $W \lor C$ by $\neg W \to C$ according to our standard system, and adjoin $\neg J$ to the premises.

1. $\neg J$.   Pr
2. $W \to S$.   Pr
3. $\neg W \to C$.   Pr
4. $C \to J$.   Pr
5. $S \to G$.   Pr
6. $\neg C$.   MT 4, 1
7. $\neg \neg W$.   MT 3, 6
8. W.   L   7
9. S.   MP 2, 8
10. G.   MP 5, 9

We have derived the consequent G on the assumption of $\neg J$ and the other premises. This is what was wanted.

Exercise Set 7

1. Find the errors in the following derivation.

1. $A \to B$.   Pr   6. $\neg \neg D$.   MT 5, 4
2. $C \lor D$.   Pr   7. D.   L   6
3. $D \to \neg B$. Pr   8. $\neg B$.   MP 3, 7
4. $\neg C$.   Pr   9. $\neg A$.   MT 1, 8
5. $C \to \neg D$. L   2

2. Correct the errors in the derivation in exercise 1 and then reach the *same* conclusion.

Negations, Contrapositives, and Converses

Except in the course of making formal exchanges in proofs, we have not discussed in detail the problems involved in negating compound expressions, that is, expressions such as $P \& Q$, $P \lor Q$, and $P \to Q$. Let us start with "and" and "or." Consider the assertion

Peter will come, and Quincy will come.

We might think that negating this is simply a matter of negating both simple sentences:

Peter will not come, and Quincy will not come.

Upon subjecting these to truth-table evaluations, however, we obtain Table XIV.

TABLE XIV

P	Q	$P \& Q$	$\neg P$	$\neg Q$	$\neg P \& \neg Q$
T	T	T	F	F	F
T	F	F	F	T	F
F	T	F	T	F	F
F	F	F	T	T	T

$P:$ Peter will come. $\neg P:$ Peter will not come.
$Q:$ Quincy will come. $\neg Q:$ Quincy will not come.

Inspecting columns 3 and 6, we might be surprised to find that $P \& Q$ and $\neg P \& \neg Q$ are far from being negatives of each other. In order for $P \& Q$ to be true, P and Q must both be true. If either P or Q is false ($\neg P \vee \neg Q$), then $P \& Q$ will be false. This line of thinking leads us to test $P \& Q$ and $\neg P \vee \neg Q$ with truth tables. (See Table XV.)

TABLE XV

P	Q	$P \& Q$	$\neg P$	$\neg Q$	$\neg P \vee \neg Q$
T	T	T	F	F	F
T	F	F	F	T	T
F	T	F	T	F	T
F	F	F	T	T	T

By inspecting columns 3 and 6 as before, we now find F's for T's and T's for F's in all the right places, so that the logical equivalence of $\neg (P \& Q)$ and $\neg P \vee \neg Q$ is a fact.

This leads us to suspect that since

$$\neg (P \& Q) \equiv \neg P \vee \neg Q,$$

then it might be that the pattern is the same for negating an "or" compound. That is, it may be that

$$\neg (P \vee Q) \equiv \neg P \& \neg Q.$$

An example of this would be

It is not true that either Peter will come or Quincy will come,

and

Peter will not come, and Quincy will not come.

The truth table for these sentences is shown in Table XVI.

TABLE XVI

P	Q	$P \vee Q$	$\neg P$	$\neg Q$	$\neg P \& \neg Q$
T	T	T	F	F	F
T	F	T	F	T	F
F	T	T	T	F	F
F	F	F	T	T	T

Since in comparing columns 3 and 6 we find T's for F's and F's for T's in all cases, our suspicion was correct. The negation of $P \vee Q$ is $\neg P \& \neg Q$.

The statements of logical equivalence,

$$\neg (P \vee Q) \equiv \neg P \& \neg Q,$$

and

$$\neg (P \& Q) \equiv \neg P \vee \neg Q,$$

are called *De Morgan's laws*. The process of obtaining these equivalents may be summed up in this way:

> To negate an "and" or "or" expression, negate both components and change the connective; that is, negate both components, then replace "and" by "or," and "or" by "and."

Next, consider this sentence:

If Peter will come, then Quincy will come.

Which of the following is its correct negation?

1. If Peter will come, then Quincy will not come.
2. If Peter will not come, then Quincy will come.
3. If Peter will not come, then Quincy will not come.
4. If Quincy will come, then Peter will not come.
5. Peter will come, but Quincy will not come.

We want the negation of $P \to Q$. Recall that $P \to Q \equiv \neg P \vee Q$. Hence $\neg (P \to Q) \equiv \neg (\neg P \vee Q)$. Now apply De Morgan's law:

$$\neg (P \to Q) \equiv \neg (\neg P \vee Q) \equiv \neg \neg P \& \neg Q \equiv P \& \neg Q.$$

This is sentence 5.

What is wrong with sentence 1, $P \to \neg Q$? Look at Tables XVII and

XVIII, which have truth values for each sentence. The lines concerning what happens when Peter will *not* come produce different truth values in the final columns of the tables.

TABLE XVII			
P	Q	$P \rightarrow Q$	$\neg (P \rightarrow Q)$
T	T	T	F
T	F	F	T
F	T	T	F
F	F	T	F

TABLE XVIII				
P	Q	P	$\neg Q$	$P \rightarrow \neg Q$
T	T	T	F	F
T	F	T	T	T
F	T	F	F	T
F	F	F	T	T

Consider still another pair of sentences:

If Peter will come, then Quincy will come,

and

If Quincy will not come, then Peter will not come.

One has the form $P \rightarrow Q$; the other, $\neg Q \rightarrow \neg P$. How do they differ in value? Let us compare them by writing both in the "or" form:

$$P \rightarrow Q \equiv \neg P \vee Q.$$
$$\neg Q \rightarrow \neg P \equiv \neg \neg Q \vee \neg P \equiv Q \vee \neg P.$$

But $\vee$ is commutative, and $Q \vee \neg P \equiv \neg P \vee Q$, so

$$P \rightarrow Q \equiv \neg Q \rightarrow \neg P.$$

When convenient, we are permitted to turn any implication around if we negate each component. This equivalence was mentioned when MT was shown to be derivable from MP. It is of considerable importance in its own right, and $\neg Q \rightarrow \neg P$ is called the *contrapositive* of $P \rightarrow Q$. It is often the case that one of the two expressions will seem clearer or convey a thought better than the other, although they are logically equivalent. An extreme case of a different mood appears when we form the contrapositive of "If it rains, then I stay home." The *logically equivalent contrapositive* is "If I do not stay home, then it is not raining."

There is another sentence closely related to $P \rightarrow Q$. This is the *converse*, $Q \rightarrow P$. Note that $Q \rightarrow P$ is neither the negation nor the equivalent of $P \rightarrow Q$. Perhaps the box diagrams in Figure 23 can give the clearest picture.

There are two boxes in which the values do not match and two boxes in which they do.

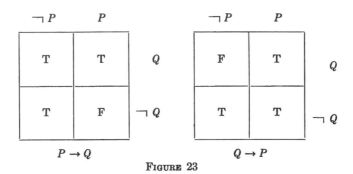

FIGURE 23

Form the converse of the following three statements:

1. If a number is a multiple of 4, then it is a multiple of 2.
2. If it rains, then I shall stay home.
3. If $x < y$, then $y > x$.

You have

1.* If a number is a multiple of 2, then it is a multiple of 4.
2.* If I stay home, then it will rain.
3.* If $y > x$, then $x < y$.

By noting that the truth values for sentences (1) and (1*) and for sentences (2) and (2*) are different [although the values for (3) and (3*) are the same], you should see that, in general, one must never mix up a statement and its converse, even though there are cases, such as statement (3), where it does not matter.

Let us sum up the situation:

Implication: $P \rightarrow Q$
Contrapositive: $\neg Q \rightarrow \neg P$ (logically equivalent to $P \rightarrow Q$)
Converse: $Q \rightarrow P$ (not logically equivalent to $P \rightarrow Q$)
Negation: $P \ \& \ \neg Q$

Exercise Set 8

State the negation of each of the following.

1. If I go downtown, then I shall buy a new hat.
2. I am going to dinner and to a show.
3. I am going to the beach or the mountains.
4. If I do not hurry, I shall be late.
5. John will go if I go.

State the converse of—

6. The implication in exercise 1.

7. The implication in exercise 4.
8. The implication in exercise 5.

PREDICATE LOGIC

Terms and Predicates

So far, we have used sentences as our basic building blocks. To go on, we must get inside sentences. Consider the following simple arguments:

> All natural numbers are greater than 0.
> The number 3 is a natural number.
> Therefore, 3 is greater than 0.

> No dogs have six legs.
> Rover is a dog.
> Therefore, Rover does not have six legs.

There is nothing we can do with these arguments from a symbolic standpoint because there are no "and," "or," or "if. . . then" connectives to be found. Therefore, we cannot formalize them. From a formal standpoint, each of the three-sentence statements in each argument is an atomic sentence. The sentences are related, but the relationship is within the sentences.

Up to this point it has been possible to explain the words and sentence structures in this study by comparing their uses with their similar uses in English grammar. But from now on we must sometimes use definitions that have meanings unique to symbolic logic. For the purposes of logic we define *term* to mean a proper name or other word specifying a definite, unique object. The terms in the above arguments are "Rover," "3," and "0."

The common way to describe a *predicate* is to say that it is anything that can be the rest of a simple sentence having a term as the subject. (Predicates occurring in the examples are "is a natural number"; "is greater than 0"; "does not have six legs"; and "is a dog." Notice that we have not included "are greater than 0" and "have six legs"; for these sentences have plural subjects, which are not "terms" as defined above.)

Note, however, that one of these predicates contains a term. When this happens, it is sometimes convenient to change our description to allow a predicate to be *the part of a sentence that becomes a simple sentence on insertion of one or more terms at correct points*: "Man [term] loves," "*x* [term] is greater than 5 [term]," and so forth.

We want to use predicates symbolically. We shall use a capital letter for a predicate. When we want to show how many terms may be involved, we shall put lowercase letters such as x or y to its right. If C stands for

"is a natural number," then we write Cx for "x is a natural number."
If G stands for "is greater than," then we write Gxy for "x is greater than
y." In Table XIX is a brief listing of some examples of this symbolism that
will be used in the pages that follow.

TABLE XIX

Predicate	Meaning	Predicate and Term	Meaning
C	is a natural number	Cx	x is a natural number.
G	is greater than	Gxy	x is greater than y.
R	runs fast	Rb	Bob runs fast.
Z	is greater than zero	Zy	y is greater than zero.
D	is a dog	Dx	x is a dog.
L	has six legs	Lx	x has six legs.

Note that common nouns and descriptions, as distinguished from proper
names, form parts of predicates. A predicate may or may not have such
common nouns. "Bob runs fast" has "runs fast" as its predicate.

In symbolizing sentences, we shall often use lowercase letters for terms.
For example, if R stands for "runs fast," we could let b stand for "Bob"
and abbreviate the sentence to Rb. We shall always keep x, y, and z for
general use, however, and never use them as particular terms. If we should
ever have a sentence like "Xerxes runs fast" we would find some letter
like e for "Xerxes": Re.

Exercise Set 9

Using appropriate capital letters for predicates, and lowercase letters for
terms, symbolize each of the following:

1. x is equal to y.

2. Rover has four legs.

3. Bossy gives milk.

4. Pussy drinks milk.

Quantifiers

We are still not quite ready to symbolize the arguments with which
we started. We need to do something about "All natural numbers are
greater than zero," and "No dog has six legs."

Let us go as far as we can with the following phrases and terms.

C: is a natural number
Z: is greater than zero
D: is a dog

L: has six legs
r: Rover
t: 3

What we need now is some way of saying "All counting numbers are greater than zero" and "No dog has six legs." In terms of our symbolic structure the neatest procedure is to turn these sentences into something like

For every x, if x is a counting number, then x is greater than zero.
For every y, if y is a dog, then y does not have six legs.

The reason for this apparently clumsy locution is that we need only one more symbol and we will be able to summarize the arguments symbolically. We let $(\forall x)$ stand for any of the following:

For every x
For each x
For all x
Every
Everything

Now reconsider our two arguments in symbolic forms:

$$(\forall x)(Cx \to Zx)$$
$$\frac{Ct}{Zt}$$

and

$$(\forall y)(Dy \to \neg Ly)$$
$$\frac{Dr}{\neg Lr}$$

These look, except for a minor detail, just like the familiar *modus ponens*. We shall fill in the details after a short discussion on the use of $(\forall x)$.

It must be clear how far the symbol $(\forall x)$, called a "universal quantifier," exercises influence over a compound sentence. This clarification can be accomplished by another pair of parentheses around the compound sentence. If we omitted parentheses and wrote $(\forall x)Cx \to Zx$, we should understand something like this: "If everything is a counting number, then x is greater than zero." Thus, to achieve our real meaning, we must enclose $Cx \to Zx$ in parentheses: $(\forall x)(Cx \to Zx)$.

We must never use confusing variables. One way to avoid this is to have in each situation a different letter for every different category, or type of objects, and for every term.

This brings us to another rule we shall need.

Rule of instantiation: *In any sentence preceded by a universal quantifier, the variable indicated by the quantifier may be replaced throughout the sentence by any term.*

We shall indicate the use of the rule of instantiation by "I."

1. $(\forall x)(Cx \rightarrow Zx)$.   Pr
2. Ct.   Pr
3. $Ct \rightarrow Zt$.   I   1
4. Zt.   MP 3, 2

1. $(\forall y)(Dy \rightarrow \neg Ly)$.   Pr
2. Dr.   Pr
3. $Dr \rightarrow \neg Lr$.   I   1
4. $\neg Lr$.   MP 3, 2

In other words, our new system is just our old system, once we get the universal quantifier out of the way by replacing the variable with a suitable term. Naturally, we have to select the suitable term with care; it would not help much to end up with a sentence such as this: "If 3 is a dog, then 3 does not have six legs."

Exercise Set 10

Write the symbolic form for each argument.

1. All cats have whiskers.
   Tabby is a cat.
   Therefore, Tabby has whiskers.
2. Every Saturday I sleep until noon.
   Today is Saturday.
   Therefore, I will sleep until noon today.
3. All sloops have sails.
   "Seafoam" is a sloop.
   Therefore, "Seafoam" has sails.
4. Each man was once a boy.
   Mr. Smith is a man.
   Therefore, Mr. Smith was once a boy.
5. Write a complete proof of the symbol form for exercise 1.
6. Write a complete proof of the symbol form for exercise 3.

Negation and Existence

We must be quite careful with the use of negatives in connection with quantifiers. For example, consider these statements:

(1)   Not all men are fools.
(2)   No man is a fool.

Sentence (1) is clearly the direct negation of the sentence "All men are fools." If someone says, "All men are fools," we expect to deny the statement by saying, "No, not all," or "No, some men aren't fools."

The other statement is different. Before we look for its negation we might first try to rewrite the sentence as "All men are not fools." This is confusing. If we saw the sentence standing alone, we would not know whether it was equivalent to sentence (1) or to sentence (2). This is one reason for being careful. Try it this way: "Every man is not a fool." For symbolic purposes, we write this as: "For every x, if x is a man, then x is not a fool." That is, we placed the negation in the consequent of an implication.

We might have put it in a different form having the same logical connotation: "For every x, it is not the case that x is both a man and a fool." In symbols: $(\forall x)(\neg (Mx \, \& \, Fx))$, as you can see from Table XX.

TABLE XX

Mx	Fx	$Mx \, \& \, Fx$	$\neg Fx$	$Mx \to \neg Fx$	$\neg (Mx \, \& \, Fx)$
T	T	T	F	F	F
T	F	F	T	T	T
F	T	F	F	T	T
F	F	F	T	T	T

What about $(\forall x)(\neg (Mx \to Fx))$? This will be more easily read by remembering the form for negating an implication: $\forall x(Mx \, \& \, \neg \, Fx)$. "Everything is a man but not a fool." This is not at all what we have in mind. How do we say "Some men are fools"? We deny the statement "No man is a fool":

$$\neg (\forall x)(Mx \to \neg Fx) \quad \text{or} \quad \neg (\forall x)(\neg (Mx \, \& \, Fx)).$$

The symbolic combination $\neg (\forall x) \neg$ is given a special designation $\exists (x)$ and read as any of the following:

> There is an x such that,
> There exists an x such that,
> For some x,

or an equivalent. For example,

$$(\exists x)(Mx \, \& \, Fx)$$

is read "There is an x that is both a man and a fool," or "For some x, x is both a man and a fool," or "Some men are fools."

Exercise Set 11

Write English sentences that are the negatives of the following:

1. All cats are white.
2. Some cats are white.
3. No cats are white.
4. No cats are not white.
5. Using convenient symbols, express each of the sentences above and its negative.

For Further Reading

Among the various helpful references that deal with the subject here introduced are the following:

MOORE, CHARLES G., and LITTLE, CHARLES E. *Basic Concepts of Mathematics*. New York: McGraw-Hill Book Co., 1967.

SUPPES, PATRICK, and HILL, SHIRLEY. *First Course in Mathematical Logic* (2d ed.). Boston: Ginn & Co., 1966.

SWAIN, ROBERT L. "Logic: For Teacher, for Pupil," in *Enrichment Mathematics for the Grades*. Twenty-seventh Yearbook of the National Council of Teachers of Mathematics. Washington, D.C.: The Council, 1963. Available from the National Council of Teachers of Mathematics, 1201 16th St., N.W., Washington, D.C. 20036.

WILLERDING, MARGARET F., and HAYWARD, RUTH A. *Mathematics—the Alphabet of Science*. New York: John Wiley & Sons, 1968.

ANSWERS TO EXERCISES

Exercise Set 1

1. It is raining, and I am not going.
2. If he doesn't come, I am going.
3. When it is warm, it rains.
4. Either it's warm or it's raining.
5. It is not the case that it is raining and I am not going. (Better: Either it isn't raining or I am going.)
6. He is coming if it is not both warm and raining and only in that case.
7. He is coming if it is both not warm and not raining and only in case of both.
8. I am going if it is warm or if it is not raining.
9. It is warm and raining; I am going, but he is coming.
10. I am going, or he is coming, but not both.
11. $F \to \neg H$.
12. $G \to \neg H$.
13. $(E \,\&\, \neg F) \to (G \lor H)$.
14. $F \to E$.
15. $E \lor G$.
16. $\neg E \to \neg F$.
17. $\neg H \to G \lor E$.
18. x is greater than 5 and x is even.
19. If it is not the case that x is even and x is less than 3, then x is a multiple of 4.
20. If x is not less than 3 or x is a multiple of 4, then x exceeds 5.
21. If x is not even and x is less than 3, then x is not a multiple of 4 or x exceeds 5.
22. If it is not the case that x exceeds 5 or x is not even, then x is less than 3.
23. x is not less than 3 and x is not a multiple of 4.
24. If it is not the case that x is even and x exceeds 5, then x is not a multiple of 4.
25. If x is a multiple of 4, then it is not the case that x exceeds 5 or x is less than 3.
26. If x is a multiple of 4 or x is not even, then x is greater than 5 or x is not less than 3.

Exercise Set 2

If the basic tables are arranged in the same manner as in the tables just preceding the exercise set, the results are:

P	Q	R	1.	2.	3.	4.	5.	6.	7.	8.
T	T	T	T	T	T	T	T	T	T	T
T	T	F	T	T	T	T	F	F	T	T
T	F	T	T	T	T	T	F	F	T	T
T	F	F	F	T	T	T	F	F	F	T
F	T	T	F	T	T	T	F	F	F	T
F	T	F	F	F	T	T	F	F	F	F
F	F	T	F	F	T	T	F	F	F	F
F	F	F	F	F	F	F	F	F	F	F

9. Sentences 1 and 7, 2 and 8, 3 and 4, 5 and 6.

Exercise Set 3

1.

P	Q	$\neg P$	Q	$\neg P \to Q$	$P \to (\neg P \to Q)$
T	T	F	T	T	T
T	F	F	F	T	T
F	T	T	T	T	T
F	F	T	F	F	T

2.

P	Q	$P \& Q$	$P \& Q \to P$
T	T	T	T
T	F	F	T
F	T	F	T
F	F	F	T

3.

P	Q	$\neg P$	$P \& Q$	$\neg (P \& Q)$	$P \to \neg (P \& Q)$
T	T	F	T	F	T
T	F	F	F	T	T
F	T	T	F	T	T
F	F	T	F	T	T

4.

P	Q	$P \& Q$	$[P \lor Q$	$(P \& Q) \to (P \lor Q)$
T	T	T	T	T
T	F	F	T	T
F	T	F	T	T
F	F	F	F	T

Exercise Set 4

1. Yes

2. No

3. No

4. Yes

5. S: It snows; G: I will go skiing.
   1. $S \to G$.   Pr
   2. S.   Pr
   3. G.   MP 1, 2

6. S: I go shopping; H: I will buy a hat; D: I will buy a blue dress.
   1. $S \to H$.   Pr
   2. $H \to D$.   Pr
   3. S.   Pr
   4. H.   MP 1, 3
   5. D.   MP 2, 4

Exercise Set 5

1. Yes

2. Yes

3. No   **4.** Yes

5. N: I go to New York; P: I travel by plane.

   1. $N \rightarrow P$.   Pr

   2. $\neg P$.   Pr

   3. $\neg N$.   MT

6. H: I get a hair cut; S: I stay home.

   1. $\neg H \rightarrow S$.   Pr

   2. $\neg S$.   Pr

   3. $\neg \neg H$.   MT 1, 2

   4. H.   L   3

Exercise Set 6

1. $P \rightarrow \neg Q$
$$\frac{\qquad\qquad Q}{\neg P}$$

2. $\neg P \rightarrow \neg Q$
$$\frac{\qquad\qquad Q}{P}$$

3. Yes

4. Yes

Exercise Set 7

1. Steps 5 and 6 are wrong.

2. The following is correct:

   1. $A \rightarrow B$.   Pr

   2. $C \vee D$.   Pr

   3. $D \rightarrow \neg B$.   Pr

   4. $\neg C$.   Pr

   5. $\neg C \rightarrow D$.   L   2

   6. D.   MP 5, 4

   7. $\neg B$.   MP 3, 6

   8. $\neg A$.   MT 1, 7

Exercise Set 8

1. I am going downtown, but I shall not buy a new hat.

2. Either I am not going to dinner, or I am not going to a show.

3. I am not going to the beach, and I am not going to the mountains.

4. I am not hurrying, but I shall not be late.

5. I am going, but John isn't.

6. If I buy a new hat, I shall go downtown.

7. If I shall be late, I shall not hurry.

8. If John goes, I shall go.

Exercise Set 9

1. E: is equal to; Exy.

2. F: has four legs; Fr.

3. M: gives milk; Mb.

4. D: drinks milk; Dp.

Exercise Set 10

1. C: is a cat; W: has whiskers; t: Tabby.

$$(\forall x)(Cx \rightarrow Wx,$$
$$\frac{Ct}{Wt}$$

2. S: is Saturday; N: is a day when I sleep till noon; t: today.

$$(\forall x)(Sx \rightarrow Nx)$$
$$\frac{St}{Nt}$$

3. S: is a sloop; H: has sails; s: Seafoam.

$$(\forall x)(Sx \rightarrow Hx)$$
$$\frac{Ss}{Hs}$$

4. M: is a man; B: was a boy; s: Mr. Smith.

$$(\forall x)(Mx \to Bx)$$
$$\underline{Ms}$$
$$Bs$$

5.

    1. $(\forall x)(Cx \to Wx)$.   Pr
    2. Ct.   Pr
    3. $Ct \to Wt$.   I   1
    4. Wt.   MP 3, 2

6.

    1. $(\forall x)(Sx \to Hx)$.   Pr
    2. Ss.   Pr
    3. $Ss \to Hs$.   I   1
    4. Hs.   MP 3, 2.

Exercise Set 11

1. Some cats are not white.

2. All cats are not white; or, no cats are white.

3. Some cats are white.

4. Some cats are not white.

5. Cx: x is a cat; Wx: x is white.

    (1) $(\forall x)(Cx \to Wx)$, $(\exists x)(Cx \;\&\; \neg\, Wx)$.
    (2) $(\exists x)(Cx \;\&\; Wx)$, $(\forall x)(Cx \to \neg\, Wx)$.
    (3) $(\forall x)(Cx \to \neg\, Wx)$, $(\exists x)(Cx \;\&\; Wx)$.
    (4) $(\forall x)(\neg\, Wx \to \neg\, Cx)$, $(\exists x)(Cx \;\&\; \neg\, Wx)$.

BOOKET NUMBER THIRTEEN:

GRAPHS, RELATIONS, AND FUNCTIONS

OPEN SENTENCES IN ONE VARIABLE

In this first section we shall discuss several ideas of considerable importance that will be used in the remainder of the booklet. The following section, "Open Sentences in Two Variables," should be valuable to teachers in the upper elementary grades. These two sections form a natural extension of the material in Booklet No. 8: *Number Sentences.* You may wish to read (or reread) that particular booklet first; but it is not essential to do so, since we shall begin by reviewing the pertinent ideas in it.

We assume some familiarity with the idea of the number line and a nodding acquaintance with some of the commonly used systems of numbers. The number sets we shall use, together with their standard names, are listed below for your convenience:

N = the set of natural or counting numbers = $\{1, 2, 3, \cdots\}$;
W = the set of whole numbers = $\{0, 1, 2, 3, \cdots\}$;
J = the set of integers = $\{\cdots, {}^{-}2, {}^{-}1, 0, 1, 2, \cdots\}$;
R = the set of real numbers. (See Booklet No. 11: *The System of Real Numbers.*)

We shall also use the familiar equality symbol, "$=$," the is-not-equal-to symbol, "$\neq$," and the order symbols, which are listed here with their meanings:

$<$ means "is less than,"
$>$ means "is greater than,"
$\leq$ means "is less than or equal to," and
$\geq$ means "is greater than or equal to."

Open English Sentences and Their Truth Values

The language of mathematics has a grammar, just as the English language has. It is true that symbols are often used instead of words, but these symbols are mathematical parts of speech (nouns, pronouns, verbs,

237

and so on), and we can use them to form sentences both simple and compound. In mathematics, as in English, the most important sentences are declarative ones. In this section, we classify meaningful declarative sentences into three types.

Let us look at some declarative sentences in English.

T $\begin{cases} \text{San Francisco is in California.} \\ \text{The earth is larger than the moon.} \end{cases}$

F $\begin{cases} \text{Abraham Lincoln was born in France.} \\ \text{Napoleon Bonaparte died in 1962.} \end{cases}$

O $\begin{cases} \text{He was a president of the United States.} \\ \text{She is the wife of Prince Philip.} \end{cases}$

Each of these six sentences makes an assertion about something and is therefore declarative. Those in group T are *true* sentences, while those in group F are *false*. Thus, given any one of the first four sentences, we can assign to it what logicians call a *truth value*; that is, we can decide whether it is true or false.

But what about the sentences in group O? Can we say that the sentence "She is the wife of Prince Philip" is true? Or that it is false? Of course, the name "Elizabeth II" comes to mind, and the sentence is indeed true if this name is used to replace "She." But what if the name "Brigitte Bardot" is used to replace "She"? The sentence again makes sense, but this time it is false. Two things now stand out. First, as soon as the name of any woman is used to replace "She," the sentence then has a truth value: that is, it is either true or false. Secondly, whether the sentence is true or false remains an open question until such a replacement has been made. Such a sentence is called an *open* sentence. Thus we have a classification of meaningful declarative sentences into three types: true, false, and open. Meaningless declarative sentences, such as "The king of France has red hair," will not be considered in this booklet. (See Booklet No. 12: *Logic*.)

Open Mathematical Sentences

The method used in English for classifying meaningful declarative sentences as true, false, or open is carried over into mathematical language, too. The idea of an open sentence turns out to be much more important in mathematics, however, than it is in English. In this section we shall discuss only *number sentences*—that is, sentences that make assertions about numbers. The following do just that:

T $\begin{cases} 3 \leq 7. \\ 2 \times 3 \neq 5. \end{cases}$

F $\begin{cases} \frac{1}{2} + \frac{2}{3} = \frac{3}{8}. \\ 5 - 2 > 4. \end{cases}$

Each of these four sentences has a definite truth value; that is, in each case we can say whether the sentence is true or false. Those in group T, of course, are true, and those in group F are false.

Now, what does an open sentence look like in mathematics? Here are some:

$$O \begin{cases} 2 + \square = 7. \\ 3 \times n < 12. \\ 6 - \triangle = 2. \\ x + 2 > 5. \end{cases}$$

We cannot tell in these cases whether the assertions made are true or false until we have replaced the symbols $\square$, n, $\triangle$, and x with numerals. For example, the sentence "$2 + \square = 7$" becomes a true sentence if $\square$ is replaced by 5; but it becomes a false sentence if $\square$ is replaced by 4, 7, or indeed the numeral for any number other than 5. (Henceforth, to avoid excessive verbiage, we shall often omit "numeral for a number." This popular usage seldom results in misunderstanding.) Similarly, the sentence "$3 \times n < 12$" becomes a true sentence if n is replaced by 2, because $3 \times 2 = 6$ and it *is* true that $6 < 12$. But it becomes false if n is replaced by 4 because $3 \times 4 = 12$, and it is false that $12 < 12$. (Of course, these are not the only numbers that make the sentence "$3 \times n < 12$" true or false. Can you find some others?)

Variables and Replacement Sets

The symbols $\square$, n, $\triangle$, and x, which appear in the above examples, play the same role that the pronouns "He" and "She" played in the English open sentences, page 238. In mathematics they are called *variables*. Thus we see that *open sentences are those that contain variables*.

Let us consider the open sentence "$3 \times n < 12$" in more detail. Answering the question "What replacements for n will make this a true sentence?" you soon observe that if the variable n is replaced by 1, 2, or 3, a true sentence results; but if n is replaced by 4 or any number greater than 4, the resulting sentence is false. May we therefore conclude that the sentence "$3 \times n < 12$" is true only if n is replaced by 1 or 2 or 3? This is indeed the case if the only allowable replacements for the variable n are natural numbers—that is, numbers from the set $N = \{1, 2, 3, 4, \cdots\}$. But suppose we said that n could be replaced by any integer— that is, any number from the set $J = \{\cdots, -2, -1, 0, 1, 2, \cdots\}$? In this case the open sentence "$3 \times n < 12$" then becomes a true sentence when the variable n is replaced by any integer less than 4. (For example, if n is replaced by -5, the sentence becomes "$3 \times -5 < 12$," or "$-15 < 12$," which is a true sentence.)

We see from this example that to be completely definite in discussing open sentences, we must do more than just state the sentence. We must also specify the set of permissible replacements for the variable in the sentence. This set is called the *replacement set* for the variable. Thus, if we are given an open sentence and the replacement set for its variable, then the only numbers that we are allowed to substitute for the variable are numbers from the replacement set. Ordinarily, some of these numbers will make the sentence true and others will make it false. Because we are usually more interested in the set of numbers that makes the sentence true, we give it a special name: the *truth set*. We say that the truth set (or *solution set*) of an open sentence is the set of all numbers in the replacement set that make the sentence a true statement.

We shall clarify these ideas by means of a number of examples; see Table I. (Recall the standard names for sets given on page 237.)

TABLE I

TRUTH SETS

Open Sentence	Replacement Set	Truth Set
$3 \times \square < 12$	W	$\{0, 1, 2, 3\}$
$3 \times n < 12$	W	$\{0, 1, 2, 3\}$
$3 \times \square < 12$	J	$\{\cdots, -2, -1, 0, 1, 2, 3\}$
$3 \times \square < 12$	R	$\{$real numbers less than 4$\}$
$3 \times \triangle = 12$	$N, W, J,$ or R	$\{4\}$
$x^2 < 5$	N	$\{1, 2\}$
$x^2 < 5$	J	$\{-2, -1, 0, 1, 2\}$
$2 + \triangle \leq 2$	W	$\{0\}$
$2 + \triangle \leq 2$	N	$\{\ \}$

Two remarks about these examples are in order. We note in the first two examples that the truth sets are the same, even though the variable in one of the sentences is called $\square$ and in the other it is called n. This is not surprising, because the two open sentences make the same assertion —namely, "Three times some number is less than twelve." We therefore regard two open sentences as being the same if the only difference between them is the symbol used for the variable. The sentence "$3 + \triangle = 10$" means the same as "$3 + x = 10$."

The other remark has to do with set notation. The truth sets in the last two examples are $\{0\}$ and $\{\ \}$. These are different sets, because set $\{0\}$ contains one member, namely the number 0, while $\{\ \}$ has no members at all. The latter is called the *empty set* and is usually denoted either by $\emptyset$ or by $\{\ \}$.

Compound Open Sentences

A compound open sentence in mathematics can be formed by taking two simple sentences of the type we have been considering and joining them with one or the other of the connective words "and" and "or." Thus if we connect the sentence " $^-2 < x$ " with the sentence " $x < 4$ " by using an "and," we get " $^-2 < x$ and $x < 4$," which is usually written " $^-2 < x < 4$ " for brevity. A number makes this sentence true if and only if it makes *both* of the simple sentences true. (See Booklet No. 12: *Logic*.) The truth sets of this sentence for various replacement sets are shown in Table II.

TABLE II
TRUTH SETS FOR DIFFERENT
REPLACEMENT SETS

Sentence	Replacement Set	Truth Set
$^-2 < x < 4$	N	$\{1, 2, 3\}$
	W	$\{0, 1, 2, 3\}$
	J	$\{^-1, 0, 1, 2, 3\}$

We might observe that the truth set for the compound sentence is the intersection of the truth sets of the two simple sentences. Recall that the *intersection* of two sets, A and B, consists of the set of all elements belonging to both of them—that is, the set of all elements A and B have in common. It is denoted by $A \cap B$. In this example, with replacement set J the truth set of " $^-2 < x$ " is

$$\{^-1, 0, 1, 2, 3, 4, 5, \cdots\},$$

the truth set of " $x < 4$ " is

$$\{\cdots, ^-3, ^-2, ^-1, 0, 1, 2, 3\},$$

and the intersection of these is indeed

$$\{^-1, 0, 1, 2, 3\}.$$

Let us see by an example what happens when we join two simple sentences with "or." When we combine " $6 < n$ " with " $n < 3$ " in this way, we get the compound sentence " $6 < n$ or $n < 3$." (We do not write this in the form " $6 < n < 3$ " because this abbreviated form has already been preempted for "and" sentences.) A number makes the sentence " $6 < n$ or $n < 3$ " true if and only if it makes either one or the other (or both) of the simple sentences true. Hence, for the replacement set N the truth set of this compound sentence is the union of the truth set of " $6 < n$," namely $\{7, 8, 9, \cdots\}$, and the truth set of " $n < 3$," namely $\{1, 2\}$. (Recall that the *union* of two sets A and B, denoted by $A \cup B$, is the set of all things belonging either to A or to B or to both.) Therefore, the truth set is $\{1, 2, 7, 8, 9, \cdots\}$.

Notice that in mathematics we use the word "or" in the inclusive sense "either one or the other or both." (The barbarism "and/or" is sometimes employed outside of mathematics for this purpose.) For example, if J is the replacement set for the variable x in the sentence "$2 < x$ or $x < 6$," then the truth set is J itself, because every number in J makes at least one of the two associated simple sentences true. Some numbers, such as $^-2$, 1, and 7, make just one of the sentences true; others, such as 3 and 5, make both true.

Notice also that a sentence such as $x \leq 3$ is an "or" sentence, for it is read, "x is less than or equal to 3." If the replacement set for this open sentence is N, then the solution set is $\{1, 2, 3\}$.

Exercise Set 1

1. Are the following sentences true, false, or open?
  a. He is prime minister of England.
  b. Lincoln was the first president of the United States.
  c. She is sitting in the first row.
  d. Austin is the capital of Texas.

2. Are the following mathematical sentences true, false, or open?
  a. $3 + 3 = 33$.
  b. $9 \times \square = 54$.
  c. $7 - 7 \leq 0$.
  d. $n + 13 > 27$.
  e. $^-4 < 1 < 3$.
  f. $2 < 1$ or $2 > 3$.
  g. $2 < 1$ or $2 > {}^-3$.
  h. $^-4 < \square < 3$.
  i. $\triangle > 2$ or $\triangle < {}^-2$.
  j. $2 \leq 2 < 4$.

3. Using the replacement set $W = \{0, 1, 2, \cdots\}$ for the variable in each of the open sentences below, find the truth set of each sentence.
  a. $n - 8 = 28$.
  b. $\triangle + 1 < 5$.
  c. $2 \times \square > 5$.
  d. $x + 1 < 2$.
  e. $z + 1 < 1$.

4. Using the replacement set $J = \{\cdots, {}^-2, {}^-1, 0, 1, 2, \cdots\}$ for the variable in each of the compound open sentences below, find the truth set of each sentence.
  a. $1 < \square < 5$
  b. $^-1 < x < 1$
  c. $1 < n < 2$
  d. $\triangle < {}^-2$ or $\triangle > 2$
  e. $\triangle < 2$ or $\triangle > {}^-2$
  f. $z \leq 3$

Set-Builder Notation

It is convenient to have a shorthand notation for the truth set of a given open sentence. As an example, let us take the sentence "$\triangle < 4$," with replacement set N. The notation we shall adopt to indicate the truth set of this sentence is

$$\{\triangle \mid \triangle \text{ is in } N, \text{ and } \triangle < 4\}.$$

Its translation into English is "The set of all 'triangle' such that 'triangle' is in N and 'triangle' is less than 4." Thus, in reading the notation, start with the phrase "The set of all"; then name the variable; then read the vertical bar as "such that"; and finally read the statement or statements following the bar.

Observe that although this notation looks cumbersome, it conveys all the pertinent information about the example. The fact that braces, { }, are used alerts us to the fact that the thing being described is a set. The first mention of $\triangle$, before the vertical bar, tells us what symbol is being used for the variable. (As we noted earlier, the particular symbol used is of little importance, but we must decide on *some* symbol before we can write the open sentence.) After the bar is the information telling us what the replacement set is and what the open sentence is. The bar is there as a sort of fence to keep things from getting mixed up; some people use a colon (:) instead.

Now a word about the "$\triangle$ is in N" part of the notation. We know that it is important to have the replacement set made specific. But sometimes the replacement set has been definitely established in advance. If we are sure that this has been done, then we may omit a phrase like "$\triangle$ is in N." Even if the phrase cannot safely be omitted, it can be shortened to "$\triangle \ \varepsilon \ N$" by using the standard symbol "ε," which means "is a member of," or "is an element of."

Let us consider some examples.

$\{\triangle \mid \triangle \ \varepsilon \ N \text{ and } \triangle < 4\}$ $= \{1, 2, 3\}.$
$\{\triangle \mid \triangle \ \varepsilon \ R \text{ and } \triangle < 4\}$ $= \{\text{all real numbers less than 4}\}.$
$\{n \mid n \ \varepsilon \ W \text{ and } ^-2 < n < 1\} = \{0\}.$
$\{n \mid n \ \varepsilon \ J \text{ and } ^-2 < n < 1\}$ $= \{^-1, 0\}.$
$\{x \mid x \ \varepsilon \ J \text{ and } ^-3 < x < 4\}$ $= \{^-2, ^-1, 0, 1, 2, 3\}.$
$\{\square \mid \square \text{ is one of the states in}$
     the United States$\}$ $= \{\text{Alabama, Alaska}, \cdots, \text{Wyoming}\}.$
$\{z \mid z \ \varepsilon \ J \text{ and } z \geq ^-2\}$ $= \{^-2, ^-1, 0, 1, 2, 3, \cdots\}.$
$\{\triangledown \mid \triangledown \ \varepsilon \ J \text{ and } \triangledown \geq ^-2\}$ $= \{^-2, ^-1, 0, 1, 2, 3, \cdots\}.$

The last two examples point up again the fact that it does not matter what symbol we use for the variable.

Since our notation seems, in a sense, to be a sort of "blueprint" for building a specific set, we call it *set-builder notation*.

We can use set-builder notation in a different way—backwards, as it were. We do this when we have a definite set in mind and wish to describe it with the notation. All we have to do is to make up an open sentence that has the given set as its truth set. For example, suppose we want to describe the set {0, 1, 2, 3}. We could reason as follows: all the members of the set are integers, the least is 0, the greatest is 3, and all of the integers between 0 and 3 are in the set; therefore

$$\{0, 1, 2, 3\} = \{\square \mid \square \; \varepsilon \; J \quad \text{and} \quad 0 \leq \square \leq 3\}.$$

Slightly different lines of reasoning might lead us to

$$\{0, 1, 2, 3\} = \{x \mid x \; \varepsilon \; J \quad \text{and} \quad {}^{-}1 < x < 4\},$$

or to

$$\{0, 1, 2, 3\} = \{n \mid n \; \varepsilon \; W \quad \text{and} \quad n \leq 3\}.$$

It is perfectly all right to use some words. For instance, to describe the set {1, 3, 5, . . . , 99} of all odd natural numbers less than 100, we could write $\{x \mid x \; \varepsilon \; N, x < 100, \text{and } x \text{ is odd}\}$.

Graphing Open Sentences in One Variable

We shall now turn to the problem of giving a pictorial representation of the truth set of an open sentence in one variable. For this purpose we shall require the number line shown in Figure 1. We have, of course,

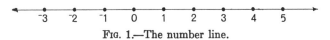

-3   -2   -1   0   1   2   3   4   5

FIG. 1.—The number line.

shown only part of the line and have labeled only a few of the points corresponding to integers. However, we know, that to each number in any of our commonly used sets, N, W, J, and R, there corresponds a unique point on the line. It therefore seems reasonable to try to portray on the line the truth sets of the kinds of open number sentences we have considered so far.

Indeed, all we need is some pictorial device for distinguishing a particular set of points. One way to do this is simply to enlarge the pictures of its members—that is, to make larger dots. (This should not imply that the points get any larger. Points, after all, are only hinted at by any picture: they have no real physical existence.) Or we may label the points of the set with letters.

We call the pictorial representation of the truth set of an open sentence the *graph* of the sentence. Now let us look at a few examples in Figure 2, where the description of each graph is given below it in convenient set-builder notation. Instead of being written out as "The truth set of the open sentence $\square \leq 4$, with replacement set N," the information is simply expressed as "$\{\square \mid \square \ \varepsilon \ N \text{ and } \square \leq 4\}$." In the first three examples the truth set is also given explicitly.

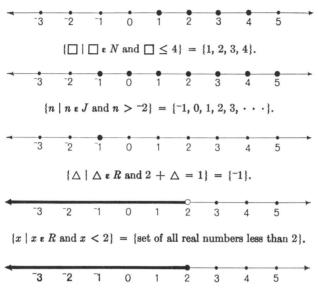

$\{\square \mid \square \ \varepsilon \ N \text{ and } \square \leq 4\} = \{1, 2, 3, 4\}.$

$\{n \mid n \ \varepsilon \ J \text{ and } n > {}^-2\} = \{{}^-1, 0, 1, 2, 3, \cdot \cdot \cdot\}.$

$\{\triangle \mid \triangle \ \varepsilon \ R \text{ and } 2 + \triangle = 1\} = \{{}^-1\}.$

$\{x \mid x \ \varepsilon \ R \text{ and } x < 2\} = \{\text{set of all real numbers less than 2}\}.$

$\{x \mid x \ \varepsilon \ R \text{ and } x \leq 2\} = \{\text{set of all real numbers less than or equal to 2}\}.$

FIG. 2.—Graphs of number sentences.

In the last two examples presented in Figure 2, we ran into a technical difficulty. How do we show that the point representing 2 is not included in the first graph but that it is clearly included in the second graph? There are various ways of solving this artistic problem. We have chosen to indicate inclusion by a solid dot, and noninclusion by a hollow one. In

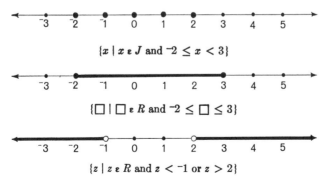

$\{x \mid x \ \varepsilon \ J \text{ and } {}^-2 \leq x < 3\}$

$\{\square \mid \square \ \varepsilon \ R \text{ and } {}^-2 \leq \square \leq 3\}$

$\{z \mid z \ \varepsilon \ R \text{ and } z < {}^-1 \text{ or } z > 2\}$

FIG. 3.—Graphs of compound number sentences.

order to indicate that all the points of a segment or ray are in the graph, we use a heavy mark as shown.

Let us look back at Figure 3, page 245, for a few more examples, this time using compound sentences.

Exercise Set 2

1. Write out in words each of the sets that are described below in set-builder notation.

   a. $\{\Box \mid \Box \ \varepsilon \ W \quad \text{and} \quad \Box < 3\}$

   b. $\{n \mid n \ \varepsilon \ J \quad \text{and} \quad {}^-2 < n < 3\}$

   c. $\{\triangle \mid \triangle \ \varepsilon \ N \quad \text{and} \ {}^-2 < \triangle < 3\}$

   d. $\{x \mid x \ \varepsilon \ R \quad \text{and} \quad x + 1 = 3\}$

   e. $\{\triangle \mid \triangle \ \varepsilon \ N, \ \triangle < 14, \quad \text{and} \quad \triangle \text{ is even}\}$

   f. $\{x \mid x \text{ is the name of a state in the United States that begins with "A"}\}$

2. Graph each of the following sets on a number line.

   a. The truth set of $\Box - 1 = 4$, replacement set N

   b. The truth set of $\triangle - 1 < 4$, replacement set N

   c. $\{\triangle \mid \triangle \ \varepsilon \ N \quad \text{and} \quad \triangle - 1 < 4\}$

   d. $\{x \mid x \ \varepsilon \ R \quad \text{and} \quad {}^-2 < x < 1\}$

   e. The truth set of ${}^-2 < \Box < 1$, replacement set R

   f. $\{\triangle \mid \triangle \ \varepsilon \ J \quad \text{and} \quad \triangle < 3\}$

OPEN SENTENCES IN TWO VARIABLES

Up to now we have considered open sentences that contain only one variable. We now turn to a discussion of those that contain two. Open sentences can occur in English in such forms as "This is larger than that" and "She is his wife." These are open if no previous discussion, pointing to objects, or other means of specifying has established antecedents of the pronouns. Since in English such vague statements rarely occur out of context, we shall not go any further into the matter. By contrast, open sentences that contain two variables are of frequent occurrence in mathematics and are of great importance.

Ordered Pairs

Let us look at the sentence

$$(2 \times \Box) + \triangle = 9.$$

This sentence is declarative in form, but we cannot tell whether the assertion it makes is true or false until both of the symbols, $\Box$ and $\triangle$, have been replaced by numbers. We call these symbols *variables*, just as we did in the open sentences considered earlier. If the variable □ is replaced by 2 and the variable △ is replaced by 5, the sentence becomes "$(2 \times 2) + 5 = 9$," which is true. If □ is replaced by 3 and △ by 4, the resulting sentence is "$(2 \times 3) + 4 = 9$," which is false. We see that we must substitute a *pair* of numbers, one for □ and one for △, in the sentence, before it has a truth value—that is, before it becomes true or false. We might wish to list many of these pairs. To be consistent, let us agree to call □ the *first* variable and △ the *second* variable. (This choice is perfectly arbitrary, but having made it, we must stick to it. When the variables are to be expressed by letters of the alphabet, we usually let alphabetical order dictate our choices for first and second variable.) Then, in listing a pair we shall write the □ replacement first and the △ replacement second. The two pairs we substituted above would be written (2, 5) and (3, 4). The order in which we write the numbers for each pair is very important. We saw that the pair (2, 5) makes the sentence true. But the pair (5, 2), which contains the same numbers but in the opposite order, causes the sentence to become "$(2 \times 5) + 2 = 9$," which is false. We must therefore distinguish between (2, 5) and (5, 2). This is the reason we use parentheses, ( ), rather than braces, { }, in writing such pairs: {2, 5} and {5, 2} would denote exactly the same set. To emphasize that order is important, we call (2, 5) and (5, 2) *ordered pairs*. We call the first of the two numbers to occur in an ordered pair the *first component* of the pair and the other the *second component*.

Before continuing this example let us recall that in considering one-variable sentences it is important to know the replacement set for the variable, that is, the set from which we are allowed to draw replacements for the variable. The situation is the same for the two-variable sentences, except that now we must have replacement sets for both variables.

We are given an open sentence that contains two variables, one of which is called the first variable and the other the second variable. We are also given a replacement set, say A, for the first variable and a replacement set B for the second. (The set B may or may not be the same as A.) An ordered pair belongs to the *truth set* of the given sentence if its first component is a member of A, its second component is a member of B, and it makes the sentence a true statement. The truth set of the sentence is the set of all such ordered pairs.

Finite Truth Sets

We shall illustrate the ideas introduced at the end of the previous section by continuing our discussion of the open sentence

$$(2 \times \square) + \triangle = 9.$$

Let us take the replacement set for each of the variables □ and △ to be $N = \{1, 2, 3, \cdots\}$. (Most of our examples will feature the particularly important type of sentence in which both variables have the same replacement set.) Now, the numbers 2 and 5 are in N, and we have seen that when we replace □ by 2 and △ by 5, the sentence becomes true. Therefore the ordered pair (2, 5) is in the truth set of the sentence. Let us look for some more members of the truth set. A systematic way of conducting the search would be to replace one of the variables, say □, by some number in N and then to see if there is any replacement for △ that will make the sentence true. For example, if we substitute 1 for □, the sentence becomes "(2 × 1) + △ = 9." This is still open; but since it has only one variable remaining, the problem has been made easier. We soon see that if △ is replaced by 7, the sentence becomes true. Thus we have found another ordered pair, (1, 7), in the truth set. If we substitute 2 for □, we get the ordered pair (2, 5). Try it for yourself. If we repeat this procedure, we get (3, 3) and (4, 1) as the result of substituting 3 and then 4 for □. If we substitute 5 for □, the sentence becomes "(2 × 5) + △ = 9." We see that if △ is then replaced by any member of N (remember that N is the replacement set for both variables), the left-hand side will be greater than 9; therefore, there can be no ordered pair with first component 5 in the truth set. In the same way, we see that if □ is replaced by any of the numbers 6, 7, 8, $\cdots$, △ can have no replacement from N that makes the sentence true. So we can conclude as follows:

The truth set of the sentence
$(2 \times □) + △ = 9$,
with N the replacement set for
both variables, is
$\{(1, 7), (2, 5), (3, 3), (4, 1)\}$.

This sentence can be expressed more succinctly in set-builder notation: $\{(□, △) \mid □ \,\epsilon\, N, △ \,\epsilon\, N, \text{and } (2 \times □) + △ = 9\} = \{(1, 7), (2, 5), (3, 3), (4, 1)\}$. The first part of this would be read, "The set of all ordered pairs (box, triangle) such that box is in N, triangle is in N, and two times box, plus triangle, equals nine." All this is in accord with the way we used set-builder notation in previous sections. However, we now have *two* variables to name in the space before the vertical bar, and these must be named in a specific order; hence we write the ordered pair (□, △) there.

Infinite Truth Sets

In the example we have been considering, the truth set turned out to be finite; that is, it contained only a finite number (four) of ordered pairs. Let us see what happens if we keep the same open sentence and the same replacement set, N, for the variable $\square$, but let the replacement set for $\triangle$ be J, the set of integers. That is, we want the set

$$\{(\square, \triangle) \mid \square \; \varepsilon \; N, \; \triangle \; \varepsilon \; J, \quad \text{and} \quad (2 \times \square) + \triangle = 9\}.$$

This set will contain all the ordered pairs we found earlier, because every member of N is also a member of J. But now if we replace $\square$ by 5, getting "$(2 \times 5) + \triangle = 9$," we can find for $\triangle$ a replacement in J that makes the sentence true, namely, $^-1$. Hence $(5, \; ^-1)$ is in our truth set. In the same way, we can find $(6, \; ^-3)$, $(7, \; ^-5)$, etc., to be in the truth set. Thus

$$\{(\square, \triangle) \mid \square \; \varepsilon \; N, \; \triangle \; \varepsilon \; J, \text{ and } (2 \times \square) + \triangle = 9\}$$
$$= \{(1, 7), (2, 5), (3, 3), (4, 1), (5, \; ^-1), (6, \; ^-3), \cdots\}.$$

This truth set contains infinitely many ordered pairs, and we observe that in the successive members the first component increases by 1, starting with 1, whereas the second component decreases by 2, starting with 7.

It is often more difficult to discern a pattern in the ordered pairs of the solution set, particularly if the sentence is complicated—if its verb is, let us say, $\leq$ instead of $=$ or if the replacement sets for the variables are very large sets, such as R.

As an example let us consider the open sentence "$m + n \leq 2$," where the replacement set for each of the variables m and n is J. We would like to describe its truth set:

$$\{(m, n) \mid m \; \varepsilon \; J, \; n \; \varepsilon \; J, \quad \text{and} \quad m + n \leq 2\}.$$

Of course, what we have just written does describe the set, but can we not do better? It is not hard to find a number of ordered pairs that belong to this truth set; for example:

$$(1, 1), (1, 0), (0, 0), (0, 2), (^-1, 2), (^-1, 3), (4, \; ^-3).$$

But listing them in such a way as to indicate some pattern is difficult. Is there any other way of describing this set? If only we could draw a picture of it!

Let us take the open sentence just considered, "$x + y \leq 2$" (remember, what we call the variables does not matter); but let the replacement set for both the variables be R, the set of real numbers. Now there are even more ordered pairs in the truth set—for example, $(\frac{1}{2}, 1\frac{1}{2})$, $(1\frac{1}{2}, \frac{1}{2})$, $(\pi, \; ^-2)$, $(^-\sqrt{2}, 3)$. The problem of indicating a complete list of these is insurmountable. Are we then reduced just to saying that the truth set is $\{(x, y) \mid x \; \varepsilon \; R,$ $y \; \varepsilon \; R, \text{and } x + y \leq 2\}$ and leaving it at that? This is an accurate description, to be sure, but it does not give us much of a feeling for what the truth set really is. Again, we feel that if we only had some way of picturing this set, things would become clearer. Fortunately, we do have such a way, and we shall discuss it after some preliminaries.

The Tabular Method

It is often convenient to use a tabular method of listing some of the ordered pairs in the truth set of an open sentence. Occasionally we can even tabulate them all, as in the following example. On page 246 we considered the open sentence "$(2 \times \square) + \triangle = 9$," with the replacement set for each variable being N. We found that the truth set

$$\{(\square, \triangle) \mid \square \ \varepsilon \ N, \ \triangle \ \varepsilon \ N, \ \text{and} \ (2 \times \square) + \triangle = 9\}$$

is $\{(1, 7), (2, 5), (3, 3), (4, 1)\}$. We can list these efficiently in a *table*, as shown in Figure 4. The entry 1 in the $\square$ column is to be paired with

$\square$	$\triangle$
1	7
2	5
3	3
4	1

Fig. 4.—$\{(2 \times \square) + \triangle = 9, \square \ \varepsilon \ N, \triangle \ \varepsilon \ N\}$.

the entry 7 in the $\triangle$ column to give the ordered pair $(1, 7)$. The entries on the next line stand for the ordered pair $(2, 5)$, and so on.

Of course, it is not always possible to tabulate the entire truth set. Figure 5 shows a partial tabulation of the truth set for the same open

$\square$	$\triangle$
1	7
2	5
3	3
4	1
5	⁻1
6	⁻3
.	.
.	.
.	.

Fig. 5.—$\{(2 \times \square) + \triangle = 9, \square \ \varepsilon \ N, \triangle \ \varepsilon \ J\}$.

sentence "$(2 \times \square) + \triangle = 9$," with N still the replacement set for $\square$ but with J as replacement set for $\triangle$. The columns of dots indicate that the table is incomplete.

Exercise Set 3

1. Write out completely the following sets of ordered pairs. In exercises 1a and 1c, the given replacement set is for both variables.

   a. The truth set of $\square + \triangle = 5$, replacement set N

b. $\{(x, y) \mid x \, \varepsilon \, N, y \, \varepsilon \, N, \text{ and } x + y = 5\}$

c. The truth set of $m + n < 2$, replacement set W

2. Find at least four members of each of the following sets. The replacement set, when given, is for both variables.

a. The truth set of $x = y$, replacement set R

b. The truth set of $\square + \triangle = 2$, replacement set J

c. $\{(m, n) \mid m \, \varepsilon \, J, n \, \varepsilon \, J, \text{ and } m + n = 2\}$

d. $\{(\square, \triangle) \mid \square \, \varepsilon \, R, \triangle \, \varepsilon \, R, \text{ and } \square < \triangle\}$

e. The truth set of $(2 \times \square) - \triangle < 0$, replacement set J

3. Write in tabular form your answers to exercises 1a and 2b.

Graphs of Ordered Pairs

You will recall that when we graphed one-variable open sentences (that is, graphed their truth sets), we used a number line. It seems reasonable that to graph the truth sets of two-variable sentences, we might employ two number lines to advantage. But how should we go about doing so? It was a great contribution to mathematics when René Descartes (1596–1650), a French philosopher-mathematician, conceived the idea of placing two number lines so that one is horizontal and the other vertical and so that they cross at the zero point of each, as shown in Figure 6.

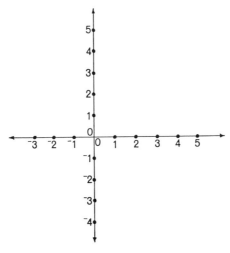

FIG. 6.—The coordinate plane.

It turns out that this *coordinate plane* is precisely what we need to picture ordered pairs of numbers and hence to picture the truth set of an open

sentence in two variables. The graph of an ordered pair of numbers
will be a point, represented by a dot, in the plane determined by the two
intersecting number lines (for example, the plane of the sheet of paper
or chalkboard on which the lines are drawn).

In describing how to locate the point that is the graph of a given
ordered pair, it will be convenient to have a name for the point where the
two number lines cross; it is called the *origin*. Let us now locate the point
that is the graph of the ordered pair (3, 2). We start at the origin and go
three units horizontally to the right. Then we go two units straight up,
and we are there. This is shown in both of the pictures in Figure 7.

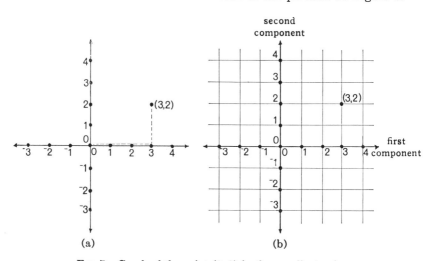

(a)   (b)

FIG. 7.—Graph of the point (3, 2) in the coordinate plane.

The dotted line in Figure 7(a) shows the route (right 3, up 2) we took
in getting to the graph of (3, 2) and should be ignored from now on.
Figure 7(b) differs from Figure 7(a) only in that horizontal and vertical
lines have been drawn through the "integer points" of the original two
number lines. All these lines form a grid that makes it easier for us to find
our way around. Paper already printed with a grid is called *graph paper*
or *quadrille paper*.

Why did we start by going three units horizontally from the origin,
instead of vertically? This is a convention, but a very strong one. We
almost always associate the *horizontal* direction with the *first* component
of the ordered pair and the *vertical* direction with the *second* component.
(Economists often do it the other way around.) But why did we go three
units to the right instead of to the left? This is because of another strong
convention: that the units to the right and up are taken to be positive, and

those to the left and down to be negative. Thus we measured three units to the right of the origin on the horizontal number line; had we gone to the left, we would be at ⁻3. Similarly, by going up two units (after going three to the right) we are opposite 2 on the vertical number line, rather than opposite ⁻2, which we would have reached had we gone down. There is nothing compelling in these conventions, however, and a mathematician would not hesitate to violate them if for any reason it seemed preferable for a particular problem.

The foregoing remarks suggest how we would locate a point corresponding to a number pair having at least one negative component. To locate (⁻3, 1)—by which we mean to locate the point corresponding to (⁻3, 1), or having *coordinates* ⁻3 and 1—we start at the origin, go three units to the left, then one unit up. To locate (⁻2, ⁻3), we go two units to the left from the origin, then three units down. To locate (1½, ⁻2⅓), we go one and one-half units to the right, then two and one-third units down. All these points are graphed in Figure 8.

What if one or both of the components of an ordered pair are 0? We need only interpret the instruction "go 0 units" to mean "stay where you are." This can cause some confusion, however, for two reasons. First, some people fight the fact that 0 *is* anything, although 0 is a perfectly good number. Secondly, and more confusing, when we follow the instructions to locate (⁻4, 0), say, by going four units to the left and then staying there, we find ourselves at the point marked ⁻4 on the horizontal number line. Now, ⁻4 is not the same as (⁻4, 0). What has happened is this: The label ⁻4 was left over from the time when we were considering

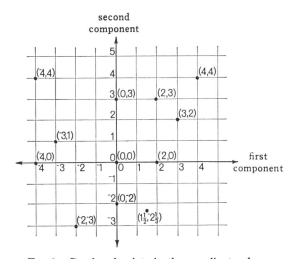

Fig. 8.—Graphs of points in the coordinate plane.

only the horizontal number line. We leave such labels on the number lines simply as a convenience for locating points in the plane. It is important to realize that every point in the plane, whether it is on one of the original number lines or not, has *two* coordinates. Figure 8 shows several points representing ordered pairs with a 0 component.

Notice in Figure 8 that the graphs of (3, 2) and (2, 3) are differently located in the plane. They should be, since the ordered pairs are different!

The grid pattern of Figure 8 suggests the street map of a city. Indeed, thinking of it in this way may help clarify the ideas that have been presented. You can think of the vertical lines as representing streets and the horizontal ones avenues. Then the "address" (⁻3, 1) is at the intersection of Negative Third Street and Positive First Avenue, while (2, 0) is at the intersection of Positive Second Street and Zero Avenue.

Graphing Open Sentences in Two Variables

Now that we can picture ordered pairs of numbers, it is an easy matter to picture sets of ordered pairs and therefore the truth sets of open sentences.

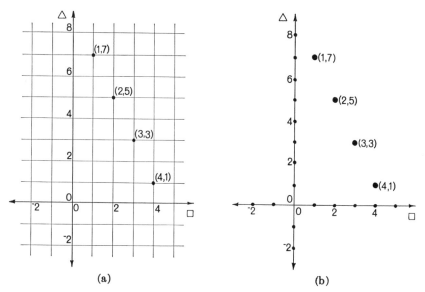

(a)   (b)

FIG. 9.—Graph of (2 × □) + △ = 9, □ ε N, △ ε N.

As an example, let us look once again at the open sentence "(2 × □) + △ = 9," with replacement set N for both variables. We found earlier that the truth set is { (1, 7), (2, 5), (3, 3), (4, 1) }.

Figures 9(a) and 9(b) show the pictorial representation of this truth set—that is, the *graph* of the open sentence. We label the two number lines "□" and "△" to make it clear that the replacements for □, that is, the first components of the ordered pairs, are associated with the horizontal direction and that the △ replacements are associated with the vertical direction. Because the grid seems to clutter up the picture somewhat, we shall hereafter omit it. (You may always draw in the grid if you wish.) The truth set in the case just considered was a relatively simple one.

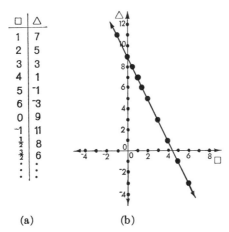

□	△
1	7
2	5
3	3
4	1
5	‾1
6	‾3
0	9
‾1	11
½	8
3/2	6
⁝	⁝

(a)   (b)

Fig. 10.—Graph of $(2 \times \Box) + \triangle = 9$, $\Box \; \varepsilon \; R$, $\triangle \; \varepsilon \; R$.

Suppose, however, that the replacement set for the variables in "$(2 \times \Box) + \triangle = 9$" is R, instead of N. Now the truth set $\{(\Box, \triangle) \mid \Box \; \varepsilon \; R, \triangle \; \varepsilon \; R$, and $(2 \times \Box) + \triangle = 9\}$ contains infinitely many ordered pairs. Let us list some of these in a table, Figure 10(a), and as we do so, locate the corresponding points, Figure 10(b). After a while we notice that there appears to be one straight line that contains all of these points. It seems reasonable to suppose that if *all* the points corresponding to ordered pairs in the truth set could be graphed, they would fill this line. We therefore draw in the whole line and say it is the graph of the open sentence. (This takes some faith on our part. A branch of mathematics called analytic geometry gives us the means to *prove* that the graph of this open sentence is indeed the line we have drawn.)

Let us consider the open sentence "$m + n \le 2$," with J as the replacement set for each variable. (This was considered briefly, page 239.) Perhaps the easiest way of graphing this sentence is to begin with the graph of $m + n = 2$, with replacement set J. This first step is shown in

Figure 11 as the diagonal set of enlarged dots. Note that the sum of the coordinates of the point represented by any one of these enlarged dots is exactly 2. Now, as you consider any one of these points, you can see that every point directly (that is, vertically) below it has the same first coordinate as this point but has a lesser second coordinate. Hence the sum of these coordinates is *less* than 2. Then every such point with coordinates that are integers is in the graph of $m + n \leq 2$ with J the replacement set for both m and n. To illustrate this, let us start with $(^-1, 3)$. As we go down unit distances we arrive successively at the points corresponding to $(^-1, 2)$, $(^-1, 1)$, $(^-1, 0)$, $(^-1, ^-1)$, and so on. In each case the sum of the components is less than or equal to 2, so all these points are in the graph of the set $\{(m, n) \mid m \; \varepsilon \; J, n \; \varepsilon \; J, \text{and } m + n \leq 2\}$. The graph of the given open sentence thus consists of a sort of "infinite triangle," a part of which is indicated in Figure 11. Such a graph is sometimes labeled "Incomplete graph," but ordinarily the label is omitted when the context implies that the graph is an infinite triangle.

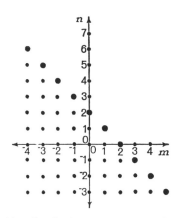

FIG. 11.—Graph of $m + n \leq 2$, $m \; \varepsilon \; J$, $n \; \varepsilon \; J$.
(Incomplete graph)

From Figure 11 we can construct the graph of $m + n < 2$ with J the replacement set for each variable. All we have to do is erase the top diagonal line of dots.

The graphs of the sentences "$x + y \leq 2$" and "$x + y < 2$," with R the replacement set for both variables in each sentence, can be constructed in a way similar to that just described. They are shown in Figures 12(a) and 12(b), respectively. Notice that we have chosen to indicate the *presence* in graph 12(a) of points on the line $x + y = 2$, such as $(3, ^-1)$

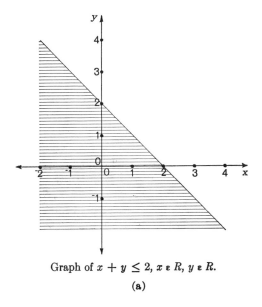

Graph of $x + y \leq 2$, $x \, \varepsilon \, R$, $y \, \varepsilon \, R$.

(a)

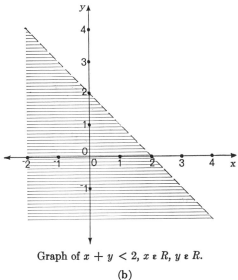

Graph of $x + y < 2$, $x \, \varepsilon \, R$, $y \, \varepsilon \, R$.

(b)

FIGURE 12

and $(\frac{1}{2}, 1\frac{1}{2})$, by a solid line and their *absence* in graph 12(b) by a dotted line. In each case all of the points below and to the left of the diagonal line are in the graph.

We have been using the symbol "$<$" quite freely in previous examples. One of the simplest open sentences that can be formed with this order symbol is

$$x < y.$$

In the next section we shall need the graph of this sentence. We show it in Figure 13 for the case in which the replacement set for each variable is R. A few points have been labeled for checking purposes; the point $(3, 1)$ is *not* in the graph, since $3 \not< 1$.

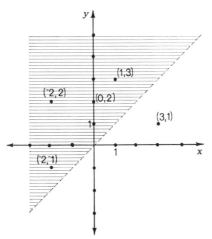

Fɪɢ. 13.—Graph of $x < y$, $x \, \varepsilon \, R$, $y \, \varepsilon \, R$

Compound Sentences in Two Variables

Throughout this section we shall let R, the set of real numbers, be the replacement set for all variables that occur.

Let us form a sentence by connecting the following simple sentences with the word "and":

$$(2 \times \square) + \triangle = 9;$$
$$\square = 4 \times \triangle.$$

We get the compound sentence

$$(2 \times \square) + \triangle = 9 \quad \text{and} \quad \square = 4 \times \triangle.$$

We would like to find the truth set of this sentence. We have already considered the first of the simple sentences at some length, pages 246–56. The sentence "$\square = 4 \times \triangle$" is easy to analyze; some of the ordered pairs in its truth set are $(8, 2)$, $(^-4, \, ^-1)$, $(2, \frac{1}{2})$, $(0, 0)$, $(4, 1)$, $(4 \sqrt{2}, \sqrt{2})$. (Remember that we have agreed on the replacement set R.) Now, an ordered pair makes the compound sentence true if and only if it makes both of the simple sentences true. We notice that the pair (4, 1) does this and is therefore in the truth set,

$$\{(\Box, \triangle) \mid (2 \times \Box) + \triangle = 9 \quad \text{and} \quad \Box = 4 \times \triangle\},$$

of the compound sentence. Are there any more ordered pairs in this truth set? After some investigation, perhaps involving the construction of a table for each of the two simple sentences, we begin to be convinced that (4, 1) is indeed the only one.

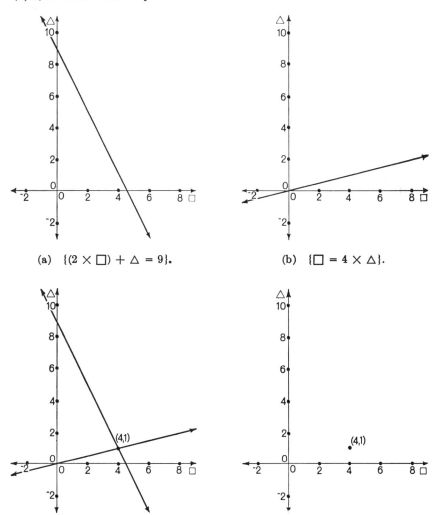

(a) $\{(2 \times \Box) + \triangle = 9\}$.   (b) $\{\Box = 4 \times \triangle\}$.

(c) $\{(2 \times \Box) + \triangle = 9\}$; $\{\Box = 4 \times \triangle\}$.   (d) $\{(2 \times \Box) + \triangle = 9$ and $\Box = 4 \times \triangle\}$.

FIG. 14.—Steps to graphing a compound sentence.

This conclusion will be reinforced as we look at the graphs. The truth set of this "and" type of compound sentence is the intersection of the truth sets of the two simple sentences. Therefore, the graph of the compound sentence is the intersection of the graphs of the simple sentences. The graph of "$(2 \times \square) + \triangle = 9$" was obtained in Figure 10; we reproduce it in Figure 14(a). The graph of "$\square = 4 \times \triangle$" is not hard to draw. It is a straight line, too, and is shown in Figure 14(b). In Figure 14(c) we have redrawn these two graphs in the same plane. It is quite clear now that their intersection is a single point, namely, the one associated with (4, 1). Figure 14(d) shows the graph of the compound sentence. We are now quite convinced that

$$\{(\square, \triangle) \mid (2 \times \square) + \triangle = 9 \quad \text{and} \quad \square = 4 \times \triangle\} = \{(4, 1)\};$$

that is, the truth set of the compound sentence

$$(2 \times \square) + \triangle = 9 \quad \text{and} \quad \square = 4 \times \triangle$$

is the set whose only member is the ordered pair (4, 1).

Now let us look at a compound sentence whose truth set has more members; for example,

$$x < y \quad \text{and} \quad x + y < 2.$$

These two associated simple sentences were considered in the preceding section. Again, we wish to find the truth set

$$\{(x, y) \mid x < y \quad \text{and} \quad x + y < 2\}$$

of the compound sentence. This set contains many ordered pairs: (0, 1), $(\frac{1}{2}, \frac{3}{4})$, ($^-3$, 2), and ($^-2$, $^-1$), to name just a few. (You should verify that these pairs actually are in the truth set of the compound sentence. Remember that each of them must make *both* simple sentences true.) It seems that probably the best way of describing the set in question is to picture it by drawing its graph. In order to do so, we begin by drawing the graphs of "$x < y$" (Fig. 15[a]) and of "$x + y < 2$" (Fig. 15[b]). Then we redraw them both in the same plane as shown in Figure 15(c). After some practice, steps (a) and (b) can be omitted. Now we use the fact that the truth set of a compound sentence of the "and" type is the intersection of the truth sets of the simple sentences that are joined to form it. By superimposing the graph of one truth set upon the other, we can see that the graph of the truth set of the compound sentence is the doubly-hatched part of Figure 15(c). In Figure 15(d) the drawing has been simplified so that the set we want stands out better.

Now, let us form a different type of compound sentence by connecting the same two simple sentences with "or":

$$x < y \quad \text{or} \quad x + y < 2.$$

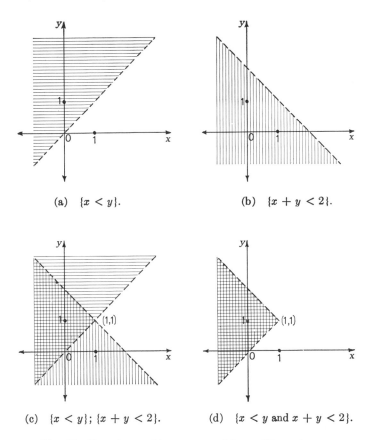

(a) $\{x < y\}$.

(b) $\{x + y < 2\}$.

(c) $\{x < y\}$; $\{x + y < 2\}$.

(d) $\{x < y \text{ and } x + y < 2\}$.

Fig. 15.—Steps to graphing compound inequality sentences.

The truth set

$$\{(x, y) \mid x < y \quad \text{or} \quad x + y < 2\}$$

of this "or" type of sentence consists of all ordered pairs that make either or both of the simple open sentences

$$x < y,$$
$$x + y < 2,$$

true statements. That is, the truth set of the compound sentence is the union of the truth sets of the two simple sentences. This fact makes it easy to draw the graph of the compound sentence; it is just the union of the graphs of the simple sentences. This set appears in Figure 15(c) as the entire shaded part of the picture. It is shown in Figure 16. Remember that a dotted line indicates that all points *up to the line* are included, but not the points located *on* the dotted line itself. Therefore the ordered pair (1, 1) doesn't make the compound sentence true.

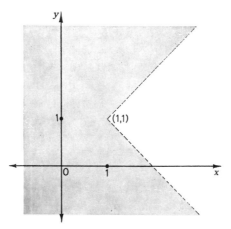

FIG. 16.—$\{x < y \text{ or } x + y < 2\}$.

In this connection we might note that the union of the two lines in Figure 14(c), page 259, is the graph of the compound sentence

$$(2 \times \square) + \triangle = 9 \quad \text{or} \quad \square = 4 \times \triangle.$$

Exercise Set 4

1. Graph the following sentences in the same picture. Take the replacement sets to be R, the set of real numbers.
   a. $y = x.$ **b.** $y = 2 \times x.$ **c.** $y = 3 \times x.$

2. Graph each of the following sentences in a separate picture, using $W = \{0, 1, 2, \cdots\}$ for the replacement sets.
   a. $\square + \triangle = 2.$ **b.** $\square + \triangle < 2.$ **c.** $\square + \triangle > 2.$

3. Graph each of the compound sentences, using R for the replacement sets.
   a. $x + y > 2$ and $y < 1.$ **b.** $x + y > 2$ or $y < 1.$

RELATIONS

In preceding sections we made use of the symbols "$<$" and "$\geq$," which stand for the phrases "is less than" and "is greater than or equal to," respectively. Now, each of these phrases can be thought of as the name of a *relation* (or relationship) that exists between the members of certain ordered pairs of numbers. For example, the relation is less than exists between 2 and 5 (in that order).

A few other phrases that seem to name relations between pairs of things are given below.

Name of the Relation	Things Being Related
is a multiple of	integers
has lighter hair than	persons
is parallel to	straight lines
is a brother of	persons
is a subset of	sets
is congruent to	triangles
gives more milk than	cows
is not equal to	numbers
is the square of	numbers

In the sections that follow we shall decide exactly what we want to mean by a relation, give a rather technical definition of the word "relation," and then study certain kinds of relations that are of particular importance in mathematics.

The Word "Relation" Defined

Almost everyone thinks he knows what is meant by a relation; but if challenged to say exactly what a relation is, he would probably be reduced to giving some examples. In mathematics we do not define things by giving examples of them, although examples certainly help anyone to understand what a definition means. What we require here, in terms as simple as possible, is a statement differentiating each entity that is a relation from all those entities that are not.

In trying to formulate such a definition it is perfectly all right to let specific examples guide us. What do all the phrases in the above list have in common? Each is part of a statement about a *pair* of things; for example, "12 is a multiple of 3," "Mary has lighter hair than John," and "Bossy gives more milk than Brownie." (If you are not sure about the phrase is a multiple of, you might go ahead to page 267 where it is discussed in some detail.) Moreover, the order of the members of the pair of things makes a difference. For instance, "12 is a multiple of 3" is a true sentence, while "3 is a multiple of 12" is false.

All this is reminiscent of our discussion of open sentences. Indeed, each of the phrases we have been talking about can be associated in a natural way with a simple open sentence in two variables: "□ is a multiple of △," "x has lighter hair than y," and so on. Now, just what do we want the relation named by is a multiple of to be? We could say that it *is* the open sentence "□ is a multiple of △," but we prefer to say that it is the *truth set* of this sentence. By this agreement, the relation **is a multiple of** is the set $\{(\square, \triangle) \mid \square$ is a multiple of $\triangle\}$, the relation **has lighter hair than** is the set $\{(x, y) \mid x$ has lighter hair than $y\}$, and so on. Of course, in each case the replacement sets must be specified. The advantage in taking the truth set to *be* the relation is that it tells us exactly what things are considered as being related to what other things. That is, if the ordered pair (a, b) is one of the members of a certain relation, then we know that a is related to b by this relation.

We have not quite finished. We now know what we mean by any specific relation like **is a multiple of**. But what is a *relation*, in general? That is, what things are relations and what things are not? To answer this question, let us see what all of our specific relations have in common. To begin with, they are all sets of ordered pairs. But this is also the end of it. What else do all sets like $\{(12, 3), (18, 3), (8, 2), \cdots\}$, $\{$(Mary, John), (John, Helen), $\cdots\}$, and so on, have in common? Nothing! We are therefore almost forced to the following definition:

A relation is a set of ordered pairs.

This definition has certain advantages. It uses only elementary terms, "set" and "ordered pair"; and it is completely discriminating. It leaves no doubt as to whether a thing is a relation or not. On the other hand, it does not seem to fit our intuitive ideas of what a relation is. Probably the reason for this is that we tend to think about specific relations: relations that have names or that can easily be described. As an illustration of this difficulty, let us consider $\{$(Timbuktu, Rome), (Rome, London), (Timbuktu, London)$\}$. By our definition, this set of ordered pairs is a relation. But what relation is it? What is its name? It might be **has a smaller population than**, or **is located south of**, or something else. We cannot tell. The fact remains, however, that the only thing common to all relations is that they are sets of ordered pairs.

One more word about terminology. In many important situations a given relation associates some members of a certain set with other members of the same set. (This is the case with all the relations listed, page 263.) We then say that the relation is *defined on* that set. In more technical terms, a relation is *defined on* a set A if both components of each ordered pair in the relation are members of A. We sometimes shorten this phraseology and simply say that a relation is *on* A. For example, the relation **is a multiple of** is defined on J, the integers; **gives more milk than** is defined on any herd of cows; and **is the square of** is on R, the set of real numbers. This does not mean that these relations cannot be defined on other sets. For example, **is a multiple of** is also defined on N, the set of natural numbers.

Not all relations are defined on a single set. For example, was born in the year (as "John was born in the year 1958") relates people to integers. We shall consider such relations later.

An Example of Relations

It may help to clarify the idea of a relation as a set of ordered pairs if we consider an example in which some relations can be written out completely. Let us consider the Smith family, which consists of a husband, a wife, two sons, and a daughter. Some of their vital statistics are given in Table III.

TABLE III

THE SMITH FAMILY

Name	Age	Weight	Height
Mr. Smith (Dad)	42	170	6'1"
Mrs. Smith (Mom)	40	125	5'6"
Tom	19	135	5'11"
Edwin	17	145	5'4"
Linda	15	105	5'0"

There are many relations defined on the Smith family. **Is a brother of** is one. According to the previous section, this relation, as a set of ordered pairs, is the truth set of the open sentence "X is a brother of Y," with the replacement set for each variable being the Smith family. That is, this relation on the Smith family *is* the set $\{(X, Y) \mid X \text{ is a brother of } Y\}$. This set is small enough to write out completely, and we find that the relation **is a brother of** is

$\{(\text{Tom, Edwin}), (\text{Edwin, Tom}), (\text{Tom, Linda}), (\text{Edwin, Linda})\}.$

You should satisfy yourself that each of these pairs belongs in the set by substituting a pair at a time in the open sentence. You should also be sure that no other pairs belong in the set. Try (Linda, Tom) in the open sentence.

Before we give more examples of relations on the Smith family, let us shorten things by abbreviating Mr. Smith's name to D (for Dad), Mrs. Smith's to M, Tom's to T, Edwin's to E, and Linda's to L. Then the result of working out the first relation defined on the Smith family becomes

is a brother of $= \{(T, E), (E, T), (T, L), (E, L)\}.$

Some other relations defined on the Smiths are

is a child of $= \{(T, D), (T, M), (E, D), (E, M), (L, D), (L, M)\}.$

was born within three years of

$$= \{(D, D), (D, M), (M, M), (M, D), (T, T), (T, E),$$
$$(E, E), (E, T), (E, L), (L, L), (L, E)\}.$$

Notice here that, for example, *Dad* was born within three years of *Dad*. If we arbitrarily decide that one person is bigger than another if and only if he is both taller and heavier than the other, then

is bigger than $= \{(D, M), (D, T), (D, E), (D, L), (M, L),$
$$(T, M), (T, L), (E, L)\}.$$

Try your hand at naming some other relations defined on the Smith family and then writing out the corresponding sets of ordered pairs. Some of these may get rather cumbersome. For example, **is of the same sex as** consists of 13 ordered pairs; it contains pairs like (D, D) and both (D, T) and (T, D).

Exercise Set 5

1. Write out completely, as sets of ordered pairs, the following relations defined on the Smith family of the preceding section:

a. is the sister of

b. is a sibling of (sibling = brother or sister)

c. is both older and taller than

2. Find at least four ordered pairs in each of the relations named below:

a. was born before, defined on the set {Columbus, Cleopatra, Eisenhower, Napoleon}

b. is located east of, defined on the set of all cities in the United States

3. Find two phrases that have different meanings but that name the following relation, defined on the set {Sphinx, Parthenon, Eiffel Tower}: {(Sphinx, Parthenon), (Parthenon, Eiffel Tower), (Sphinx, Eiffel Tower)}.

Graphs of Relations

There are two standard ways of picturing relations. One is by means of arrow diagrams, which we shall discuss in the next section; the other is by means of graphs.

Let us start by considering the graphs of numerical relations, that is, relations that are defined on sets of numbers. First, we shall look at the relation is less than ($<$), defined on R, the set of real numbers. By our definition this relation is precisely the truth set of the open sentence $x < y$ with replacement set R, and this truth set we have already graphed in Figure 13, page 258. The picture in Figure 13 *is* the graph of the relation is less than defined on R. The graph in Figure 17, like the one in Figure 13, is of course incomplete.

Suppose we look at the same relation is less than, but this time defined on J, the set of integers. (See Fig. 17.) It is not hard to see that the graph now consists of those points of the graph shown in Figure 13 corresponding to ordered pairs whose two components are integers.

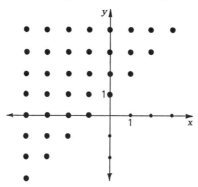

Fig. 17.—The relation is less than, defined on J.

At this time we might well pause to recall that the truth set of every open sentence with two variables is a set of ordered pairs and is therefore a relation. The second section of this booklet, "Open Sentences in Two Variables," therefore provides us with many examples of relations and their graphs. Some of these are a little hard to name verbally. For example, we discussed the open sentence "$m + n \leq 2$" for the replacement set J, the set of integers. If we try, we can concoct a phrase that names the corresponding relation, and the phrase

produces a sum not exceeding 2 when added to

will do. (Try putting a 3 in front of this phrase and a ⁻1 behind it.) This is a far cry from such simple phrases as is less than or is the sum of, but it does describe the relation in question. The important point, however, is that whether we can think up a name for it or not, $\{(m, n) \mid m \, \varepsilon \, J, n \, \varepsilon \, J,$ and $m + n \leq 2\}$ *is* a relation defined on J. Figure 11, page 256, shows its graph.

We see, then, that we have to learn nothing new in order to graph numerical relations because we already know how to graph sets of ordered number pairs. We shall, however, give one more example.

We have made frequent reference to the relation is a multiple of, defined on the set J of integers. Let us look at it in some detail and construct its graph. To fix the idea of multiple in our minds, let us ask what the multiples of 3 are. Certainly 1×3, 2×3, and 3×3 are some. But so are 0 × 3, ⁻1 × 3, ⁻2 × 3, ⋯ . So we see that all the numbers ⋯ , ⁻6, ⁻3, 0, 3, 6, 9, ⋯ are multiples of 3; and hence the ordered pairs ⋯ , (⁻6, 3), (⁻3, 3), (0, 3), (3, 3), (6, 3), (9, 3), ⋯ are in the relation is a multiple of. Similarly, the multiples of ⁻3 are

⋯ , ⁻2 × ⁻3, ⁻1 × ⁻3, 0 × ⁻3, 1 × ⁻3, 2 × ⁻3, ⋯

and therefore the ordered pairs

⋯ , (6, ⁻3), (3, ⁻3), (0, ⁻3), (⁻3, ⁻3), (⁻6, ⁻3), ⋯

are in the relation. (Notice that all the ordered pairs in the two lists are different.) If we graph the ordered pairs we have obtained so far, we will have two rows of dots, one three units above the horizontal number line, the other three units below it. Let us repeat the procedure for the multiples of 0, the multiples of 1 and ⁻1, of 2 and ⁻2, of 4 and ⁻4 (we have already graphed the multiples of 3 and ⁻3), of 5 and ⁻5, and so on. Notice that the only multiple of 0 is 0 itself, because the product of any number and 0 is 0. The multiples of 1 are all the integers and so are the multiples of ⁻1. When we have graphed a good many points, we will have obtained the butterfly-like picture shown in Figure 18.

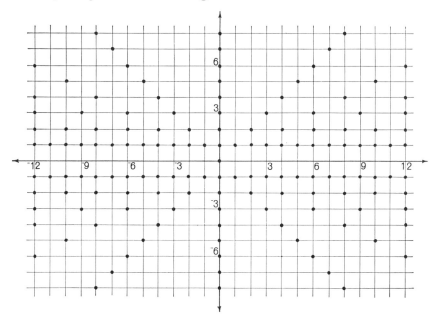

Fig. 18.—The relation **is a multiple of,** defined on *J.*

We could have approached this problem of graphing **is a multiple of** in a different way: For a given integer, such as 6, we could ask, What are the integers of which it is a multiple? Since 6 is equal to each of the products

1 × 6, 2 × 3, 3 × 2, 6 × 1, ⁻6 × ⁻1, ⁻3 × ⁻2, ⁻2 × ⁻3, and ⁻1 × ⁻6
but to no other products of integers, we find that 6 is a multiple of just
6, 3, 2, 1, ⁻1, ⁻2, ⁻3, ⁻6. Therefore the pairs (6, 6), (6, 3), (6, 2), (6, 1),
(6, ⁻1), (6, ⁻2), (6, ⁻3) and (6, ⁻6) are in the relation, but no other ordered
pairs with first-component 6 are. When we graph these ordered pairs, we
get all of the part of the graph that lies directly above and directly below
the point on the horizontal number line that is labeled 6.

You are urged to close this booklet and graph is a multiple of, defined
on *J*, for yourself (graph paper makes the job easier). Constructing this
graph is an excellent way of really getting to understand multiples of
integers.

Graphs of Nonnumerical Relations

How can we graph a relation that is defined on a set of things that are
not numbers but, for example, people or cows? Let us illustrate a technique
we can use.

Recall that on pages 265–66 we considered some relations defined
on the Smith family. The members of the family and the symbols we use

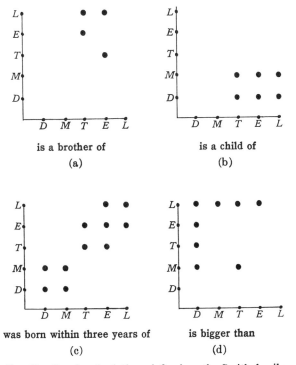

is a brother of   is a child of
(a)   (b)

was born within three years of is bigger than
(c)   (d)

FIG. 19.—Graphs of relations defined on the Smith family.

to denote them are the following: Mr. Smith, D; Mrs. Smith, M; their sons, Tom, T, and Edwin, E; and their daughter, Linda, L. One of the relations we considered, is a brother of, is the set of ordered pairs

$$\{(T, E), (E, T), (T, L), (E, L)\}.$$

To graph this relation, we can take the crossed number lines we have been using and on each line use the labels D, M, T, E, and L instead of 1, 2, 3, 4, and 5. Then we can picture the ordered pair (T, E) by a dot directly above the point labeled T and directly opposite the point labeled E. If we do this for all the pairs in the relation, we get the graph shown in Figure 19 (a).

Parts (b), (c), and (d) of Figure 19 show graphs of the other relations defined on the Smith family which were discussed earlier. To eliminate unnecessary clutter, we have shown only the parts of the number lines that we actually need.

Picturing Relations with Arrow Diagrams

A second method of picturing relations is most useful for relations containing relatively few ordered pairs. The idea is this: Suppose we have a relation defined on a set S. On paper or chalkboard we first put down a set of dots, one for each member of S, and label them with the names of the members of S. Then for each ordered pair (x, y) in the relation we draw an arrow pointing from the dot labeled x toward the dot labeled y. That is, if x is related to y, we draw an arrow from dot x to dot y. When we have finished, we have the *arrow diagram* picture of the relation.

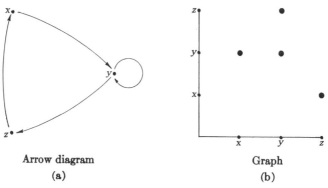

| Arrow diagram | Graph |
| (a) | (b) |

FIG. 20.—The relation $\{(x, y), (y, y), (y, z), (z, x)\}$.

As an example, in Figure 20(a) we have drawn the arrow diagram for the relation $\{(x, y), (y, y), (y, z), (z, x)\}$ defined on the set $\{x, y, z\}$. (Do not try to name this relation or find any particular meaning in it. We are just using it as an illustration.) For comparison we show in Figure 20(b) the graph of the same relation. Notice that the "ringlet" arrow pointing from y to y is necessary because we must somehow convey visually the information that y is related to itself—that is, that (y, y) is in the relation.

In Figure 21 we give more examples of the technique by showing the arrow diagrams of the same four relations on the Smith family that we graphed in Figure 19.

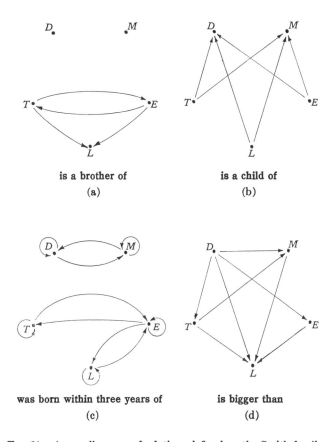

is a brother of
(a)

is a child of
(b)

was born within three years of
(c)

is bigger than
(d)

FIG. 21.—Arrow diagrams of relations defined on the Smith family.

In Figures 21(a) and (c), pairs of arrows, ·⟳·, appear. Such pairs are often replaced by double-headed arrows, ·↔·. Figure 22 shows what Figure 21(c) becomes when this device is used. The device simplifies the appearance of the diagram but makes it a little more difficult to see the individual relationship. For example, to find how many individual relationships there are (that is, how many ordered pairs are in the relation), we must count arrowheads instead of arrows.

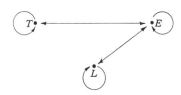

Fig. 22.—Double-headed arrow diagram.

In acquainting children with the concept of relations, the first and most important objective is to get across the idea of a set of ordered pairs. This is perhaps best done by using the arrow-diagram device. As an example of the procedure, we present a classroom discussion adapted from a demonstration given by Georges Papy:[1]

Do you know each other's first names and last names? Point to any of the other boys and girls whose *last* name begins with the same letter as your *first* name.

How can we show this on the board? We need a plan of the class. Would somebody come out and do that as simply as possible? Would you now show me where you are on the plan? Is he right? Anne, would you come out and show me where you are on this plan? Is she right?

(There is now a set of dots on the board indicating the positions of the children.) [See Fig. 23.]

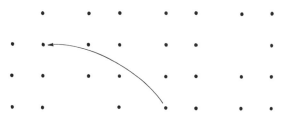

Fig. 23.—Classroom discussion.

Now will anyone who was pointing come out and show this on the board. Are those the right positions? How are we going to know that you were pointing at him? We must be clear about the direction in which we are pointing. An arrow is a good idea. (The arrow is drawn in.)

---

[1] *Some Lessons in Mathematics*, ed. Trevor J. Fletcher (London: Cambridge University Press, 1964), pp. 189–90. This excellent collection of articles, written by members of the Association of Teachers of Mathematics, presents relations and a number of other topics in a very interesting way.

Now will someone else come out and show who he was pointing at. Is that right? How do you know? Now someone else, please. Can any of you point to more than one other person? If you can, then put in *all* the arrows that are needed. All right; come and show us. We have several lines on the drawing now and we do not want to get them mixed up. So be careful where you draw your line. Is that arrow going the right way? Come and put it right.

(This situation can be developed as far as seems necessary. We may have an interesting discussion if it occurs to someone to point to himself. If the class does not provide a suitable example, the teacher can fabricate a class member, such as Charlie Chaplin or Brigitte Bardot, who will serve the purpose. How is this kind of pointing shown on the graph? An obvious way is to put a little ringlet joining the point to itself. Does a ringlet need an arrow-head? There may be other important ideas, or germs of ideas, such as two people pointing at each other. Why does this happen? Suppose George Grant and Grace Garvie join the class, how shall the arrows be drawn?)

When this project is completed, what Figure 23 will show is, of course, the arrow diagram for the relation

's first name has the same initial as the last name of.

Because the name of this particular relation is so awkward, it would probably not be advisable to emphasize it, or even mention it, in the classroom.

Exercise Set 6

1. Draw (a) the graph and (b) the arrow diagram of the relation $\{(L, E), (L, T), (L, M), (L, D), (E, T), (E, M), (E, D), (T, D), (M, D)\}$. (This is actually the relation **is younger and shorter than**, defined on the Smith family on page 265.)

2. Draw enough of the graph of the relation **is greater than**, defined on the set N of natural numbers, to make its pattern evident.

A Convention

We went to a good deal of trouble to arrive at our definition of a relation as a set of ordered pairs. Now that we have it we shall find that it leads us into some rather exotic situations.

Let us consider for a moment the relation **is less than**. This is such an important relation that we have a special symbol for it, namely, "$<$." Now, by our definition this relation *is* the set $\{(x, y) \mid x < y\}$. We are therefore forced to accept

$$< \ = \ \{(x, y) \mid x < y\}$$

and

$$\text{is less than} \ = \ \{(x, y) \mid x < y\}$$

as correct statements. Even stranger perhaps is the fact that since $2 < 5$, the following are correct statements:

$$(2, 5) \; \varepsilon \; <$$

and

$$(2, 5) \; \varepsilon \; \text{is less than.}$$

Although they may be correct, these are certainly peculiar looking, and we prefer to avoid them. We certainly would prefer to write $2 < 5$ rather than $(2, 5) \; \varepsilon \; <$.

Can we always do something like this? There is no trouble if the relation in question can be described by a simple phrase or a conventional symbol. We would always write, "Tom is a child of Mr. Smith," instead of (Tom, Mr. Smith) ε is a child of, especially if we wanted to be understood by our fellow man.

But sometimes we work with relations for which no conventional symbols exist and that may even be hard to describe in words. We must then devise a symbol of our own as the name of the relation. Suppose we find ourselves in this situation: Let us decide to name our relation $\mathbf{R}$. What do we know about $\mathbf{R}$? It is a set of ordered pairs. Now if the ordered pair (a, b) is in this set, we can write $(a, b) \; \varepsilon \; \mathbf{R}$. This corresponds to writing $(2, 5) \; \varepsilon \; <$. But because $(2, 5) \; \varepsilon \; <$ is usually written $2 < 5$, we decide to make the corresponding change in our case and write $a\mathbf{R}b$. In other words, we will adopt the following convention:

Let $\mathbf{R}$ be a relation. Then $a\mathbf{R}b$ means the same as $(a, b) \; \varepsilon \; \mathbf{R}$.

Let us illustrate this convention with the relation is a multiple of. Now, this relation already has a simple phrase that describes it. Nevertheless, we might decide to abbreviate this phrase is a multiple of and call it $\mathbf{M}$, say. If we do, then

$$\mathbf{M} = \{(\square, \triangle) \mid \square \quad \text{is a multiple of} \quad \triangle\}.$$

By our convention, "$(18, 3) \; \varepsilon \; \mathbf{M}$" and "$18\mathbf{M}3$" mean exactly the same thing, namely, that 18 is a multiple of 3.

Exercise Set 7

1. Let $\mathbf{R}$ be the name of the relation $\{(x, y), (y, z), (y, y), (z, x)\}$.

   a. Is $z\mathbf{R}y$ a true statement?

   b. Is $y\mathbf{R}z$ a true statement?

   c. Write out all the true statements.

2. Suppose we know about the relation $\mathbf{R}$ that only the following are true statements: $x\mathbf{R}y$, $x\mathbf{R}z$, $z\mathbf{R}y$, $y\mathbf{R}z$, and $z\mathbf{R}z$. Write out the relation $\mathbf{R}$ as a set of ordered pairs.

EQUIVALENCE RELATIONS

Some relations have special characteristics, or properties, that make them particularly useful in mathematics and elsewhere. Some general kinds of relations are so important that they have names of their own. Three of these are equivalence relations, order relations, and functions. You have probably heard the word "function" used almost in its mathematical sense in such commonplace sentences as "Your tax rate is a function of your income" and "One's discomfort is a function not only of the heat but also of the humidity." Functions are so useful in mathematics that we shall later on devote several sections to a discussion of them.

We have already used such order relations as $<$ and $\leq$ in earlier sections. We could analyze and generalize the concept of order as a relation, but lack of space in this booklet precludes our doing so.

In the following sections we shall study equivalence relations and certain important properties of relations.

Equivalence Relations Defined

Almost everyone has preconceived ideas about equivalence. For example, we feel that the fractions 2/6 and 3/9 are equivalent. Why? It is because they name the same number. We might be willing to agree, even at this early stage, that the relation **names the same number as**, defined on the set of fractions, is an "equivalence relation."[2] On the other hand, we probably feel that the relation **is less than** is not an equivalence relation. Why not? For one thing, we feel that equivalence implies some sort of reciprocity, and **is less than** does not have this feature. For example, 2 is related to 5 by **is less than**, but 5 is not so related to 2.

Our objective is to decide what characteristics, or properties, a relation must have before we would be willing to call it an "equivalence relation." We shall start on this project by looking at a nonmathematical relation, one which will turn out, however, to be an equivalence relation.

Let us consider the Shady Lawn Elementary School at some particular instant of time. The several hundred persons in the school building—teachers, pupils, the principal, and so on—are all happily at work in their various rooms. Now, the phrase **is in the same room** as names a specific relation defined on the set of people in the school building. We see that this relation has the following three simple properties:

1. Every person is in the same room as himself.
2. If one person is in the same room as a second, then the second is in the same room as the first.

---

[2] The idea of an equivalence relation is discussed at length in Booklet No. 10: *The System of Rational Numbers.*

3. If one person is in the same room as a second, and the second is in the same room as a third, then the first is in the same room as the third.

These three statements are so obvious that it appears almost silly to write them down. It does seem, however, that any relation we would want to call an equivalence relation should have properties analogous to these, and we can think of no other property that every such relation should have.

In order to study the anatomy of these three properties and, incidentally, to shorten their statements, let us use some symbols. We shall use symbols to stand for the members of the set on which our relation is defined—that is, for the people in the school building. We shall also use the letter **R** as the name of the relation itself; that is, **R** will mean **is in the same room as.** Then the symbolic statement "x**R**y" is an abbreviation for the statement "Person x is in the same room as person y." The three properties of the relation **is in the same room as** which were stated before (the three properties of the relation **R**) can now be written very concisely as follows:

1. For every x, we have x**R**x.
2. If x**R**y, then y**R**x.
3. If x**R**y and y**R**z, then x**R**z.

(You should convince yourself that these three symbolic statements do indeed mean the same as the corresponding statements above. Try reading them aloud, saying "Person x," instead of "x," and "is in the same room as," instead of "**R.**")

The three symbolic statements could be statements (not necessarily true) about *any* relation, not just the one we have been considering. Let us therefore consider *any* relation **R** whatsoever, defined on a set S. Remember that **R** is a set of ordered pairs of members of S. Remember also that by our convention we regard (x, y) ε **R** and x**R**y as meaning exactly the same thing. Now we are in a position to make the basic definition of *equivalence relation.*

> *A relation* **R,** *defined on a set* S *is an equivalence relation if and only if it has the following properties*:
>
> 1. *For every* x *in* S, *we have* x**R**x.
> 2. *If* x**R**y, *then* y**R**x.
> 3. *If* x**R**y *and* y**R**z, *then* x**R**z.

These conditions admittedly are stark, and perhaps even a little terrifying, in their abstractness and brevity. You will find that they are not so bad if you have a more down-to-earth way of reading them, either aloud or to yourself. A way of reading "x**R**y," for example, is to say or think, "x is **R**-related to y" or simply "x is related to y." (In the latter case you should have at the back of your mind that by "related" we mean "related by the relation **R**.") If this device is used, the properties appearing in the definition would read as follows:

1. For every x in S, x is related to x (that is, each member of S is related to itself).
2. If x is related to y, then y is related to x (that is, if one member of S is related to a second, then the second is related to the first).
3. If x is related to y and y is related to z, then x is related to z (that is, if one member of S is related to a second, and that second member is related to a third, then the first is related to the third).

In view of the definition given above and of our previous discussion, we see that the relation **is in the same room as**, defined on the set of people in the school building, is an example of an equivalence relation. We shall give some more examples presently.

Properties of Relations

First, however, let us discuss separately the three properties that appear in the definition of equivalence relation. Each of these is of such frequent occurrence in mathematics that it has been given a name. Property 1 is called *reflexivity*; and if a relation **R** on a set S is such that each thing in S is **R**-related to itself, then **R** is said to be a *reflexive* relation. Property 2 is called *symmetry*, and any relation that has this property is a *symmetric* relation. Property 3 is called *transitivity*, and any relation that has this property is a *transitive* relation. (It has been said that mathematics gives easy names to hard ideas; in this case the opposite is true.)

A given relation may satisfy all, some, or none of the conditions of reflexivity, symmetry, and transitivity. Only if it satisfies all three do we say it is an equivalence relation.

The relation $<$, **is less than**, defined on the set of integers, is not reflexive, since it is not true, for example, that $3 < 3$. (The symbol "$<$" is now playing the role of **R**.) Nor is it symmetric, because we have $2 < 5$ but *not* $5 < 2$. The relation $<$ is transitive, however, since if $x < y$ and $y < z$, then $x < z$. Because it does not satisfy all of the required conditions, $<$ is not an equivalence relation.

The relation $\leq$, **is less than or equal to**, is reflexive, since $x \leq x$ for every x. It is also transitive. But it is not symmetric. (Why not? Well, $2 \leq 5$, but ....) Therefore, $\leq$ is not an equivalence relation.

The relation **was born within three years of**, defined on the Smith family (p. 266), turns out to be reflexive and symmetric. (You should check this.) But it is not transitive, because although Linda was born within three years of Edwin and Edwin was born within three years of Tom, Linda was *not* born within three years of Tom. Therefore, was born within three years of is not an equivalence relation.

Let us look at the relation $R = \{(a, a), (c, c), (a, c), (c, a)\}$, defined on the set $S = \{a, b, c\}$. We can verify that this relation is symmetric and transitive by an exhaustive checking of cases. For example, since (a, c) and (c, a) are in R, we have aRc and cRa. Do we also have aRa, which is required for transitivity? Yes, because (a, a) is in R. But the relation R is not reflexive, because it does not contain (b, b). Therefore, we do not have bRb although $b \in S$.

In the last three paragraphs we have given examples of relations that have two of the three properties of reflexivity, symmetry, and transitivity, but not the third. Let us now look at a relation that has all three properties.

We say that two natural numbers have the *same parity* if they are both even or both odd. Thus 6 has the same parity as 14 because they are both even, and 7 has the same parity as 3 because they are both odd. But 5 does not have the same parity as 8. Now, has the same parity as names a relation defined on the set of natural numbers. You can check that this relation is reflexive, symmetric, and transitive; has the same parity as is therefore an equivalence relation.

We sometimes find ourselves working with some one fixed equivalence relation, R, over a long period of time. If the relation does not have an established name or short phrase to describe it, we often use the intuitively appealing phrase "x is equivalent to y" to describe the situation xRy or $(x, y) \in R$. We use such a phrase only when the relation involved is an *equivalence* relation. Also, because "x is equivalent to y" makes no reference to any particular relation, it must be clearly understood what the unmentioned relation is.

The phrase "equivalent to" is also occasionally used in a generic sense, as follows. One of Euclid's axioms states that "things that are equal to the same thing are equal to each other." To express the idea that equivalence relations are like equality in this respect, we might say that "things that are equivalent to the same thing are equivalent to each other." The precise meaning of this sentence is expressed in the following theorem.

Let R be an equivalence relation on a set S, and let x, y, and z be members of S. If xRz and yRz, then xRy.

The first sentence of this theorem sets the stage, so to speak, while the second describes in exact terms that property of equivalence relations with which we are concerned. The situation may seem a little confusing, because what we are to prove looks so much like the transitive property and we already know that the relation R is transitive. On close inspection, however, we see that there is a difference. Notice that the proof of the theorem, which we shall now give, uses *two* of the three properties of an equivalence relation: Since **R** is a symmetric relation and we are given that $y\mathbf{R}z$, we have also $z\mathbf{R}y$. We now have both $x\mathbf{R}z$ (given) and $z\mathbf{R}y$, and since **R** is transitive, we get $x\mathbf{R}y$.

Exercise Set 8

1. The condition that a relation **R** on a set S be reflexive can be expressed in terms of ordered pairs as follows: For every $x \;\varepsilon\; S$, we have $(x, x) \;\varepsilon\; \mathbf{R}$. Express the conditions of symmetry and transitivity in terms of ordered pairs.

2. Determine which of the following relations on the set $\{x, y, z\}$ is an equivalence relation and which is not.

  a. $\{(x, x), (y, y), (z, z), (x, z), (z, x)\}$

  b. $\{(x, x), (y, y), (z, z), (x, z), (z, x), (x, y), (y, x)\}$

3. Is the relation **is not equal to**, defined on the set J of integers, reflexive? symmetric? transitive?

4. The word "sibling" is used to mean "brother or sister." Is the relation **is a sibling of** an equivalence relation?

5. Is the relation **has the same mother as** an equivalence relation?

Examples of Equivalence Relations

We have already seen two examples of equivalence relations: **is in the same room as** and **has the same parity** as (pp. 276, 278). We list a few more below, together with the sets on which they are defined.

Relation	Set
is a citizen of the same country as	people of the world
has the same number of legs as	animals (mammals, birds, fish)
has the same number of letters as	words of the English language
has the same initial letter as	words of the English language
is parallel to	straight lines
is congruent to	triangles

It is quite easy to verify that each of these relations is reflexive, symmetric, and transitive and is therefore an equivalence relation.

Many equivalence relations occur in mathematics, and the most important of them have been given names like "is isomorphic to" and "is homeomorphic to." Unfortunately, a complete explanation of these terms would be so technical as to make it beyond the scope of this booklet.

We shall devote the rest of this section to a discussion of a simpler mathematical equivalence relation.

In this example we shall use $\sim$ instead of $\mathbf{R}$ to name our relation, because we want to reserve $\mathbf{R}$ for later use. The symbol "$\sim$" is sometimes read "wiggle."

Let us define a relation $\sim$ on the set J of integers by describing exactly when one integer is related to a second integer, as follows:

$m \sim n$ if and only if $m - n$ is a multiple of 3.

A completely equivalent way of saying this is

$(m, n) \; \varepsilon \sim$ if and only if $m - n$ is a multiple of 3.

We can read $m \sim n$ as "m is $\sim$-related to n" or, since we will be dealing only with the relation $\sim$ in this example, simply as "m is related to n." (We are not justified in saying "m is equivalent to n" because we do not yet know that $\sim$ is an equivalence relation.) The definition of our relation then says in words that one integer is related to a second if the first integer minus the second is a multiple of 3; that is, if this difference is one of the numbers $\cdots$, $^-9$, $^-6$, $^-3$, 0, 3, 6, 9, $\cdots$. (Recall our discussion of multiples of 3 on pages 267–68.)

We see, then, that $11 \sim 5$ because $11 - 5 = 6$, and 6 is a multiple of 3. Also $5 \sim {}^-4$ because $5 - {}^-4 = 9$, which is a multiple of 3; and $5 \sim 11$ because $5 - 11 = {}^-6$, which is a multiple of 3. But it is *not* true that $2 \sim 7$, because $2 - 7 = {}^-5$, which is not a multiple of 3. Observe that $4 \sim 4$ because $4 - 4 = 0$, which is a multiple of 3. Does this observation suggest any general statement? We shall get more pairs in the relation $\sim$ and draw its graph later on.

Is $\sim$ an equivalence relation? It is easy to prove that $\sim$ is reflexive: Let x be any member of J, that is, any integer. We know that $x - x = 0$ and that 0 is a multiple of 3 because $0 \times 3 = 0$. Therefore, by the definition of $\sim$ (with both m and n replaced by x) we see that $x \sim x$; that is, for every $x \; \varepsilon \; J$, we have $x \sim x$.

The proofs that $\sim$ is symmetric and that $\sim$ is transitive require more algebra—specifically, we need the facts that $^-(x - y) = y - x$ and that $(x - y) + (y - z) = x - z$—and we shall omit them. Consideration of some numerical cases, however, may be somewhat illuminating. Regarding symmetry (if $x \sim y$, then $y \sim x$), we notice that we have the true statement $11 \sim 5$, and we also have $5 \sim 11$; we have $6 \sim 21$, and also $21 \sim 6$; we have $5 \sim {}^-4$, and also $^-4 \sim 5$. (Some of these statements were verified two paragraphs back. You should check the others, using the definition of $\sim$.) Apropos of transitivity (if $x \sim y$ and $y \sim z$, then $x \sim z$), we see that we have the true statements $11 \sim 5$ and $5 \sim {}^-4$, and we also have $11 \sim {}^-4$; we have $6 \sim 21$ and $21 \sim {}^-3$, and we also have $6 \sim {}^-3$.

Once we are convinced that $\sim$ is an equivalence relation, we are justified in using "m is equivalent to n" instead of $m \sim n$, if we wish. Let us proceed systematically to find out what integers are equivalent to each other.

What integers are equivalent to 0? By the definition of our relation, an integer m is equivalent to 0 (that is, $m \sim 0$) if and only if $m - 0$ is a multiple of 3. Since $m - 0 = m$, this tells us that the integers equivalent to 0 are precisely the multiples of 3, that is, the integers in the set

$$A = \{\cdots, \ ^-9, \ ^-6, \ ^-3, \ 0, \ 3, \ 6, \ 9, \ \cdots\}.$$

Now, by the theorem, page 278, we see that any two integers that are equivalent to 0 are equivalent to each other. For example, since $^-9 \sim 0$ and $6 \sim 0$, we have $^-9 \sim 6$. We see, therefore, that every two integers in set A are equivalent to each other.

What integers are equivalent to 1? We know that m being equivalent to 1, that is, $m \sim 1$, means that $m - 1$ is a multiple of 3. Therefore, m itself must be exactly one more than some multiple of 3. Since set A contains all multiples of 3, we see that if we add 1 to any integer in that set, we get an integer that is equivalent to 1. Therefore, each member of the set

$$B = \{\cdots, \ ^-8, \ ^-5, \ ^-2, \ 1, \ 4, \ 7, \ 10, \ \cdots\}$$

is equivalent to 1. Just as before, an application of the theorem, page 278, shows that every two integers in set B are equivalent to each other.

The same reasoning yields the result that every two integers in the set

$$C = \{\cdots, \ ^-7, \ ^-4, \ ^-1, \ 2, \ 5, \ 8, \ 11, \ \cdots\}$$

are equivalent to each other.

We now know a large number of ordered pairs in the relation $\sim$. That is, if m and n are any two integers chosen from the *same* one of the sets A or B or C, then $m \sim n$, or (m, n) $\varepsilon \sim$. It can be shown that there are no ordered pairs in $\sim$ besides the ones we get in this way. In other words, no integer in any one of the sets A, B, and C is equivalent to an integer in either of the other two sets.

We are now in a position to graph the relation $\sim$. Let us see, for example, what points of the graph lie above and below the point labeled 5 on the horizontal number line. We have seen that all the integers to which 5 is equivalent are contained in the set C, and therefore the points we want are those corresponding to

$$\cdots, \ (5, \ ^-7), \ (5, \ ^-4), \ (5, \ ^-1), \ (5, 2), \ (5, 5), \ (5, 8), \ \cdots.$$

After we locate these and several other columns of dots, say above and below the points labeled 6 and 7 on the horizontal number line, we see a pattern developing and can quite easily get the picture in Figure 24.

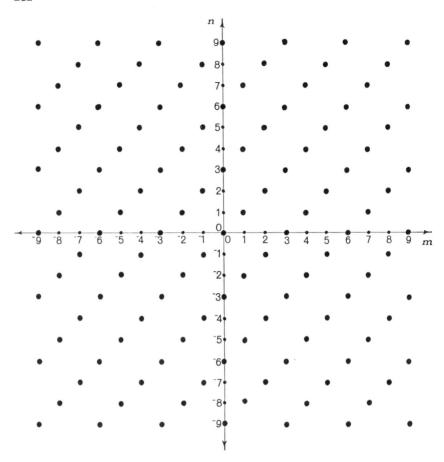

Fig. 24.—Graph of the relation $\sim$.

Equivalence Classes

When we were studying the equivalence relation $\sim$ on J in the preceding example (remember that "$m \sim n$" means "$m - n$ is a multiple of 3"), we found it convenient to introduce the subsets A, B, and C of J, where

$$A = \{ \cdots , ^-9, ^-6, ^-3, 0, 3, 6, \cdots \},$$
$$B = \{ \cdots , ^-8, ^-5, ^-2, 1, 4, 7, \cdots \},$$
$$C = \{ \cdots , ^-7, ^-4, ^-1, 2, 5, 8, \cdots \}.$$

We saw that the sets A, B, and C have the following property:

1. Each member of any one of the sets A or B or C is equivalent to every integer in *that* set, but to no other members of J.

We can also see without much difficulty that

2. Each member of J can be in only one of the sets A, B, or C.

Thus the equivalence relation $\sim$ seems to split up, or *partition*, the set J into subsets having properties 1 and 2.

It turns out that every equivalence relation partitions the set on which it is defined into subsets that have properties analogous to 1 and 2.

As another example of this partitioning phenomenon, consider the equivalence relation **has the same parity as**, defined on the set N of natural numbers (see p. 278). Let us look at the two subsets

$$H = \{1, 3, 5, \cdots\} \quad \text{and} \quad K = \{2, 4, 6, \cdots\}$$

of N, which consist, respectively, of the odd natural numbers and the even natural numbers. We see that these subsets of N have the following properties:

1a. Each member of either of the two sets H and K is equivalent to (that is, has the same parity as) every natural number in *that* set, but to no other members of N.

2a. Each member of N is in exactly one of the sets H or K.

These properties are the analogues of properties 1 and 2, so again we have this "natural" partitioning of a set by an equivalence relation defined on it.

As still another example, consider the equivalence relation **has the same initial letter as**, defined on the set of all words in the English language. This relation partitions the set on which it is defined into twenty-six subsets:

$$\{\text{aardvark, alone, acorn, } \cdots\},$$
$$\{\text{bicycle, baby, brown, } \cdots\},$$

.

.

.

$$\{\text{zebra, zither, zinc, } \cdots\}.$$

An unabridged dictionary gives the most nearly complete listing of the members of these twenty-six sets.

We have said that *any* equivalence relation partitions the set on which it is defined into subsets having properties analogous to 1 and 2. It will be convenient to have a name for these subsets. We therefore make the following definition:

Let **R** be any equivalence relation, defined on a set S; let u be any member of S:

The equivalence class of u is the set of all members of S that are **R**-*equivalent to u.*

The word "class" is used here as a synonym for the word "set." We could just as well use the phrase "equivalence set," but "equivalence class" has become traditional. If we use set-builder notation, we see that the definition given above expresses the fact that the equivalence class of a member u of S is $\{x \mid x \, \varepsilon \, S$ and $x\mathbf{R}u\}$, or, more simply, $\{x \mid x\mathbf{R}u\}$.

We were led to make this definition by what we did in the case of the equivalence relation $\sim$ on J. How did the sets A, B, and C first arise? We recall that A was defined as the set of all integers that are $\sim$-equivalent to 0; that is, $A = \{m \mid m \, \varepsilon \, J$ and $m \sim 0\}$, or simply $A = \{m \mid m \sim 0\}$. We see, therefore, that if we let $\sim$ play the role of $\mathbf{R}$, J play the role of S, and 0 play the role of u, the set A is precisely the equivalence class of 0. Similarly, since B is the set of all integers that are $\sim$-equivalent to 1, B is the equivalence class of 1. And since $C = \{m \mid m \sim 2\}$, the set C is the equivalence class of 2.

What are the equivalence classes of the other members of J? Let us take $^-5$ as an illustration. We find that $^-5$ is in B. Now, properties 1 and 2 (p. 282) tell us that each member of B is $\sim$-equivalent to $^-5$, and that no other members of J are $\sim$-equivalent to $^-5$. That is, B is the set of all members of J that are $\sim$-equivalent to $^-5$, and therefore B is the equivalence class of $^-5$. We see from this that it is quite possible for two different members of J to have the same set as their equivalence classes. It is not difficult to see that if two members of J are equivalent to each other, then their equivalence classes are the same. Thus, the equivalence class of each of the integers $\cdots$, $^-6$, $^-3$, 0, 3, 6, $\cdots$ is the set A, and C is the equivalence class of each of the integers $\cdots$, $^-7$, $^-4$, $^-1$, 2, 5, $\cdots$. We conclude that although each member of J has an equivalence class, there are only three *different* equivalence classes, namely A, B, and C.

Let us turn now to the equivalence relation **has the same parity as,** defined on the set N of natural numbers. We can see that the set $H = \{1, 3, 5, \cdots\}$ is the equivalence class of each odd natural number. And $K = \{2, 4, 6, \cdots\}$ is the equivalence class of each even natural number. In this example we have only two *different* equivalence classes.

In the case of the equivalence relation **has the same initial letter as** defined on the set of all words of the English language, there are twenty-six *different* equivalence classes. These twenty-six sets of words are, of course, those we mentioned on page 283.

After considering the foregoing examples, we gain confidence that the following may be true in general.

Let $\mathbf{R}$ be any equivalence relation, defined on a set S.

1b. Each member of a given equivalence class is equivalent to every member in *that* class but to no other member of S.

2b. Each member of S is in exactly one equivalence class.

These two properties are the analogues for the general case of properties 1 and 2, pages 282–83. We have merely used equivalence-class terminology in stating them. Properties 1*b* and 2*b* are indeed true of any equivalence relation. Their proofs, though not at all difficult, are somewhat abstract, and we shall not give them.

The fact that any equivalence relation partitions the set on which it is defined into equivalence classes will be used again.

Identification

Many times in mathematics we find it convenient to regard all the things in each equivalence class as being the same. We then say that we *identify* (that is, consider as being identical) the things in each equivalence class. Let us illustrate with two examples.

Let *A* be the set of all arrows that can be drawn from one integer point of the number line to another. (An "integer point" is the graph of an integer.) We show some of these arrows in Figure 25, where we have drawn them a little above the number line so that they show up better. It will be convenient to denote the arrow extending from the point *a* to the point *b* by $\overrightarrow{a, b}$. The dotted arrow in Figure 25 is $\overrightarrow{2, {}^{-}1}$. Now let us define a relation

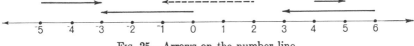

Fɪɢ. 25.—Arrows on the number line.

R on the set *A* of all these arrows by saying that one arrow is related to a second arrow if the first has the same length and same direction as the second. Thus $\overrightarrow{2, {}^{-}1}$ **R** $\overrightarrow{6, 3}$ because the first has length 3 and direction from right to left, and so does the second.

You can readily check that the relation **R** on *A* is an equivalence relation. Now, the equivalence class of $\overrightarrow{2, {}^{-}1}$ contains many arrows: $\overrightarrow{6, 3}$; $\overrightarrow{0, {}^{-}3}$; $\overrightarrow{{}^{-}1, {}^{-}4}$; and $\overrightarrow{1, {}^{-}2}$ are a few of them. For certain purposes, we might like to consider them all as being the same. For example, we could regard them as all representing the operation of adding $^{-}3$. In this case we would identify all the arrows in this equivalence class. We would do this identification in each of the equivalence classes. Thus, all the members of the equivalence class of $\overrightarrow{0, 2}$; $\overrightarrow{(1, 3}$; $\overrightarrow{{}^{-}4, {}^{-}2}$; $\overrightarrow{0, 2}$; $\overrightarrow{{}^{-}2, 0}$; and $\overrightarrow{{}^{-}1, 1}$ are some of them) would be considered the same because they represent the operation of adding 2. (The method just outlined is used in Booklet No. 9: *The System of Integers.*)

Our second example shows how the rational numbers can be developed from the integers. (The method we shall outline was used, rather informally, in Booklet No. 10: *The System of Rational Numbers.*) We shall now define a relation **R** that turns out to be names the same rational number as. Let us start by considering the set F of all ordered pairs of integers, with the restriction that 0 is not to be the second component of any ordered pair. Although F is a set of ordered pairs, it is not the relation we want. The relation **R** is to be defined *on* the set F. Thus a member of **R** will be an ordered pair of members of F, that is, an ordered pair of ordered pairs. To reduce the confusion, let as write the numbers of F in the form m/n rather than the usual form (m, n). Thus

$$F = \left\{ \frac{m}{n} \;\middle|\; m \;\varepsilon\; J, n \;\varepsilon\; J, \text{ and } n \neq 0 \right\}.$$

The members of F we call *fractions*.

Now we define the relation **R** on F by saying that $\frac{m}{n}$ **R** $\frac{p}{q}$ if and only if $m \times q = n \times p$. Thus $\frac{2}{4}$ **R** $\frac{5}{10}$ because $2 \times 10 = 4 \times 5$; and $\frac{12}{^-9}$ **R** $\frac{^-4}{3}$ because $12 \times 3 = {}^-9 \times {}^-4$.

With the help of some algebra it can be shown that **R** is an equivalence relation. Once we know this, we know also that **R** partitions F into equivalence classes. Some of these are

$$\left\{ \ldots, \frac{^-3}{^-6}, \frac{^-2}{^-4}, \frac{^-1}{^-2}, \frac{1}{2}, \frac{2}{4}, \frac{3}{6}, \ldots \right\};$$

$$\left\{ \ldots, \frac{^-9}{6}, \frac{^-6}{4}, \frac{^-3}{2}, \frac{3}{^-2}, \frac{6}{^-4}, \frac{9}{^-6}, \ldots \right\};$$

$$\left\{ \ldots, \frac{^-9}{3}, \frac{^-6}{2}, \frac{^-3}{1}, \frac{3}{^-1}, \frac{6}{^-2}, \frac{9}{^-3}, \ldots \right\}.$$

All the fractions in any one of these equivalence classes name the same number. (We call such numbers *rational numbers*.) It is quite natural, therefore, to identify the fractions in each equivalence class and to consider them all to be the same. In practice this is just what we really do. For example, if we take the fractions $^-9/6$ and $3/^-2$ (which are in the same equivalence class), we tend to think of them as equal rather than just equivalent, and we certainly write $\frac{^-9}{6} = \frac{3}{^-2}$ instead of some such thing as $\frac{^-9}{6}$ **R** $\frac{3}{^-2}$.

Exercise Set 9

1. Find the equivalence classes of 1, 2, 3, 9, and 10 formed by the equivalence relation has the same parity as, defined on the set N of natural numbers.

2. The relation **is coincident with or parallel to,** defined on the set of all straight lines in the coordinate plane, is an equivalence relation. Describe three of the equivalence classes formed by this relation.

3. Consider the equivalence relation **names the same number as** defined on the set F of all fractions. Find at least four members of the equivalence classes of each of the following fractions.

a. $\dfrac{1}{3}$ **b.** $\dfrac{^-2}{6}$ **c.** $\dfrac{^-4}{^-4}$ **d.** $\dfrac{0}{2}$

Two Special Equivalence Relations

We should not leave the subject of equivalence relations without mentioning the two simplest equivalence relations of all.

The first of these is the relation of *equality* (or *identity*) on any set S. As a set of ordered pairs, this relation is simply

$$\{(x, y) \mid x \in S, y \in S, \text{ and } x = y\}, \quad \text{or} \quad \{(x, x) \mid x \in S\}.$$

Checking that equality is reflexive, symmetric, and transitive, and is therefore an equivalence relation, is a simple mental exercise. This relation is also called the *diagonal* relation on S because of the appearance of its graph. To see how the graph does look, let us consider a specific set $S = \{a, b, c, d\}$. Written out, the equality relation on S is $\{(a, a), (b, b), (c, c), (d, d)\}$. If we graph this relation, using the method introduced, page 269, we get the set of heavy dots shown in Figure 26. The lighter dots represent open pairs not in the relation and have been included mainly to strengthen our case. Now, these sixteen dots form a square array, and the graph of the identity relation is a diagonal of the array. Hence the name "diagonal

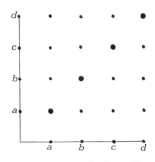

FIG. 26.—Δ on $\{a, b, c, d\}$.

relation." We often use the symbol Δ for this relation. (The symbol Δ is not a triangle, but the capital of the Greek letter "delta." Δ corresponds to our D, the initial letter of the word diagonal.)

Another simple relation that can be defined on any set S is the one relating each member of S to *every* member of S. This relation is called the *Cartesian product* of S with itself and is denoted by $S \times S$. (See Booklet No. 1: *Sets*, pp. 37–40.) Thus

$$S \times S = \{(x, y) \mid x \; \varepsilon \; S, y \; \varepsilon \; S\};$$

that is, $S \times S$ consists of *all* ordered pairs of members of the set S. (All the dots, light and heavy, in Figure 26 make up the graph of $S \times S$ in the case $S = \{a, b, c, d\}$.) As a relation, $S \times S$ is too "big" to be of much interest: everything is related to everything. But it does have the feature that every relation defined on S is a subset of $S \times S$. Indeed, we could have used this fact as a definition:

A relation on a set S is a subset of $S \times S$.

Pictorial Implications

Let us see what effects the reflexivity and symmetry of a relation have on its graph. Suppose we know that a relation $\mathbf{R}$ on a set S is reflexive. Then for every x in S, we have $x\mathbf{R}x$, or (x, x) ε $\mathbf{R}$. This means that $\mathbf{R}$ contains Δ (thinking of both relations as sets of ordered pairs). This

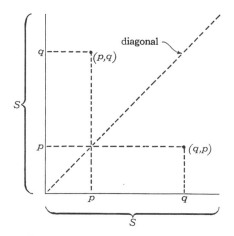

Fɪɢ. 27.—Reflexivity and symmetry.

means, in turn, that the graph of $\mathbf{R}$ must contain the graph of Δ, that is, the diagonal (Fig. 27) of $S \times S$. This situation is illustrated in Figures 28(a) and 28(c). Other graphs of reflexive relations are shown on pages 268–69, and 282, in Figures 18, 19(c), and 24. Notice in each case that the graph contains the diagonal, that is, all the dots on the 45° line through the origin.

If a relation **R** on a set S is symmetric, we know that if p**R**q, then q**R**p; that is, if (p, q) ε **R**, then (q, p) ε **R**. Figure 27 shows how the graphs of (p, q) and (q, p) look. It seems reasonable to say that they are symmetric in the diagonal, that is, symmetrically located, or mirror, images of each other with respect to the diagonal. If every point of a figure is paired with another point so that these two points are symmetric in the diagonal, then we say that the whole figure is symmetric in the diagonal. The graph of any symmetric relation must have this property. Figures 28(b) and 28(c) show graphs of symmetric relations. Others are to be found on pages 256–57, 269, and 282, in Figures 11, 12(a), 12(b), 19(c) and 24.

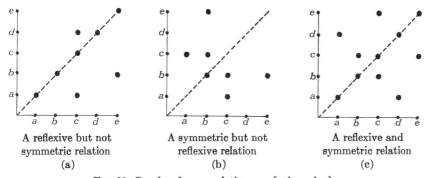

A reflexive but not symmetric relation	A symmetric but not reflexive relation	A reflexive and symmetric relation
(a)	(b)	(c)

FIG. 28. Graphs of some relations on {a, b, c, d, e}.

In view of the above remarks we see that if we have the graph of a relation before us, we can tell almost at a glance if the relation is reflexive or symmetric. There is a graphical test for transitivity, but since it is rather difficult to describe and apply, we shall not discuss it.

The arrow diagram tests for reflexivity, symmetry, and transitivity are very simple indeed. Recall that to construct the arrow diagram of a relation **R** on a set S, we put down and label a set of dots, one for each member of S. Then if (x, y) ε **R**, that is, if x**R**y, we draw an arrow from x to y. The above-named properties of the relation have the following effects on the arrow diagram:

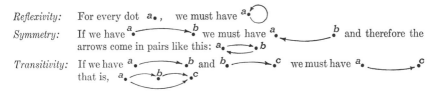

Figure 29 shows the arrow diagram of an equivalence relation on the set $\{a, b, c, d, e, f\}$, that is, a relation having all of the above properties.

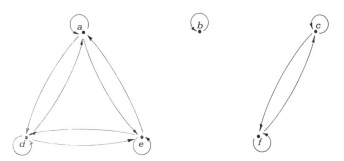

FIG. 29.—Arrow diagram of an equivalence relation.

Exercise Set 10

1. This exercise pertains to the relation whose arrow diagram is shown in Figure 29.
   a. Write out the relation as a set of ordered pairs.
   b. Construct the graph of the relation.
   c. Find the equivalence classes formed by the relation.

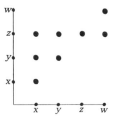

FIG. 30.—A relation.

2. The graph of a relation is shown in Figure 30.
   a. Is the relation reflexive?
   b. Is the relation symmetric?
   c. Write out the relation as a set of ordered pairs.
   d. Construct the arrow diagram of the relation.
   e. Is the relation transitive?

RELATIONS FROM ONE SET INTO ANOTHER

Most of the relations we have studied so far have related members of a certain set of things to other members of that *same* set. In talking about these in general, we have usually named the set S and have said that the relation in question is *on* *S*. There are many relations, however, that relate things in one set to things in a different set. For example, **was born in the year** relates persons to integers. (President Johnson was born in the year 1908; Julius Caesar was probably born in the year 102 B.C., that is, year ⁻102.) And the relation **was ridden by** relates the horses to the jockeys in a given race.

None of this changes our basic concept of a relation as a set of ordered pairs. But now if the first components of all the ordered pairs in a relation **R** are members of a set *S*, and the second components of all the ordered pairs in **R** are members of a set *T*, we say that the relation is *from S into T*. Thus, the above-mentioned relation **was born in the year** is from the set of all persons into the set *J* of integers. Two of the many ordered pairs in this relation are (President Johnson, 1908) and (Julius Caesar, ⁻102). The relation **was ridden by** is from a certain set of horses into a certain set of jockeys.

Reflexivity, symmetry, and transitivity are properties that do not make sense for relations from one set into a different set, so relations of this kind cannot be equivalence relations. (The most important relations from one set into another are functions, which we shall study later in this booklet.) We can, however, picture relations of this new kind both by graphs and by arrow diagrams. Let us illustrate with an example.

As you know, the alphabet we are now using was derived from the Latin. It contains five letters that are called vowels: *a*, *e*, *i*, *o*, and *u* (we shall not confuse things with *y*, which is not Latin anyway.) Now, there are other alphabets in use today. Let us consider the Greek alphabet. It contains twenty-four letters, seven of which are vowels. These are α, ϵ, η, ι, o, υ, and ω (named alpha, epsilon, eta, iota, omicron, upsilon, and omega). Anyone translating—or, more accurately, transliterating—from one alphabet to the other must know which Greek vowels correspond to which Latin vowels. He must know, for example, that to the Latin "*a*" there corresponds the Greek "α." That is, he must know the relation from the set *L* of the Latin vowels to the set *G* of Greek vowels; the ordered pair (*a*, α) is one of the members of this relation. Written out completely, the relation is

$$\{(a, \alpha), (e, \epsilon), (e, \eta), (i, \iota), (o, o), (o, \omega), (u, \upsilon)\}.$$

The graphing of this relation presents no difficulty. The only change we make in our established procedure is in the labeling of the horizontal and vertical lines. In this case we label the horizontal line with the names of the members of *L*, and the vertical line with the names of the members of *G*. We then proceed just as before and represent the pair (*e*, η), say, by a dot above *e* and opposite η. The graph is shown in Figure 31(a).

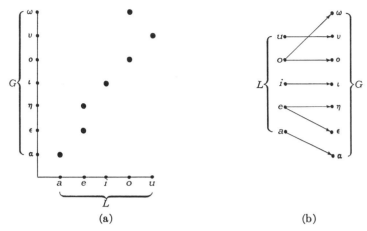

(a)   (b)

Fɪɢ. 31.—Transliteration relation.

To construct the arrow diagram for the relation, we now need to put down two sets of dots, one for the set L, the other for G, and label them. Then we draw the arrows as we did in the past: since (e, η) is in the relation, for example, we draw an arrow from dot e to dot η. The completed arrow diagram is shown in Figure 31(b).

FUNCTIONS

We sometimes hear the noun "function" used in casual conversation in such sentences as "Your weight is a function of how much you eat" and "Your tax rate is a function of your income." (It is also used in such phrases as "social function" and "the function of the liver," but in a different sense and one that will not concern us.) In mathematics and the sciences, the phrase "is a function of" is employed to express the idea that one "condition" or "state" depends on another. We hear such sentences as "Distance is a function of time," "Water pressure is a function of depth," and "The area of a circle is a function of its radius."

These sentences suggest the idea of relationships between pairs of things: distance and time, pressure and depth, and area and radius. In what follows we shall see that functions are indeed special kinds of relations.

The Word "Function" Defined

Let us consider the relation is a son of, defined on a set of men and boys. Suppose a name is placed in front of this phrase to give, say, "John is a son of." Because John has only *one* father, the name of only *one* person may correctly be placed at the end of the phrase. Thus if "John is a son of Mr. Smith" is true, then "John is a son of Mr. Jones," "John is a son of Mr. Kelly," and so on, are false. If we think of the relation **is a son of** as a set of ordered pairs, we see that we can have only one ordered pair with a given first component. Thus, not both of the ordered pairs (A, B) and (A, C), with $B \neq C$, can be in the relation. (For if they were, we would have "A is a son of B" and "A is a son of C," which is a biological impossibility.) We shall call relations of this type "functions."

For contrast, let us consider the relation **is a brother of**, also defined on a set of men and boys. Suppose this set contains three sons, X, Y, and Z, of the same parents. Then both of the statements "X is a brother of Y" and "X is a brother of Z" are true. Thus both of the ordered pairs (X, Y) and (X, Z) are in the relation. If, therefore, we are told that the first component of an ordered pair in **is a brother of** is X, we find that the ordered pair itself is not uniquely determined. The definition of "function," to be given below, rules out relations in which such ambiguity exists.

Our general definition is as follows:

> A *function is a relation in which no two different ordered pairs have the same first component.*

Let us illustrate this idea by considering a number of relations, some of which are functions and others not.

EXAMPLE 1

Each of the following sets of ordered pairs is, of course, a relation. Use the above definition to determine which of them are functions.

$$\mathbf{F} = \{(1, 1), (2, 2), (3, 3), (4, 4)\}$$
$$\mathbf{G} = \{(1, 1), (1, 2), (2, 1)\}$$
$$\mathbf{H} = \{(1, 1), (2, 4), (3, 9), (4, 16), (5, 25)\}$$
$$\mathbf{K} = \{(1, 1), (2, 1), (3, 2), (4, 2)\}$$

Of these four relations, only **G** is not a function. The relation **G** contains two different ordered pairs with the same first component, namely, 1. Notice that **K** contains different ordered pairs with the same *second* component. This is not ruled out by the definition of function.

EXAMPLE 2

Consider the relation, defined on the set W of whole numbers, that consists of all ordered pairs of the form $(m, 7 \times m)$. This relation can be thought of as the **multiplication table for 7**. Some of the ordered pairs in it are (0, 0), (1, 7), (2, 14), (5, 35), and (22, 154); you can find many more if you please. Is this relation a function? We know that when we multiply a number by seven there is a *unique* product. Hence for any whole number that we choose to use as the first component of an ordered pair, there is exactly one number that can serve as the second component, namely, seven times the first number. Thus the first component determines the ordered pair uniquely, and the relation *is* a function. This function written in set-builder notation is

$$\{(m, n) \mid m \ \varepsilon \ W, n \ \varepsilon \ W, \text{ and } n = 7 \times m\},$$

or, more simply, $\{(m, 7 \times m) \mid m \ \varepsilon \ W\}$.

EXAMPLE 3

Consider the following relation from the set of the fifty states into the set of letters of the alphabet:

$$\{(\Box, \triangle) \mid \triangle \text{ is the first letter in the name of } \Box\}.$$

Some of the ordered pairs in this relation are (Alabama, A), (Alaska, A), (New Mexico, N), and (Texas, T). You can supply some more. Since the name of each state is unique, it is quite clear that this relation is a function.

If we change the order of $\Box$ and $\triangle$ in each pair, we get a different relation:

$$\{(\triangle, \Box) \mid \triangle \text{ is the first letter in the name of } \Box\}.$$

This relation from the alphabet into the set of states is *not* a function. This is because it contains two different ordered pairs with the same first component: (T, Texas) and (T, Tennessee), 'for example. Can you find other examples?

EXAMPLE 4

We have seen how a relation can be described by its arrow diagram.

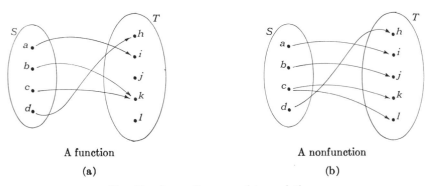

A function   A nonfunction

(a)   (b)

FIG. 32.—Arrow diagrams of two relations.

Let us consider two relations described in this way and decide whether they are functions or not. Figure 32 shows the arrow diagrams of two relations, both of them from the set $S = \{a, b, c, d\}$ into the set $T = \{h, i, j, k, l\}$.

Write out the relation depicted in Figure 32(a) as a set of ordered pairs. You will see that no two ordered pairs in this set have the same first component. This relation is therefore a function. Notice that the presence of the ordered pairs (b, k) and (c, k) in the relation is permitted by the definition of function.

In Figure 32(b) you see that there are arrows from c to k and from c to l. This means that the ordered pairs (c, k) and (c, l) are both in the corresponding relation. Since these two different pairs have the same first component, this relation is *not* a function.

EXAMPLE 5

Just as a relation can be described by its arrow diagram, it can be described also by its graph. In Figure 33 we show the graphs of two relations. One of these relations is a function, while the other is not. Do you see that the relations whose graphs are shown in Figure 33 are the same

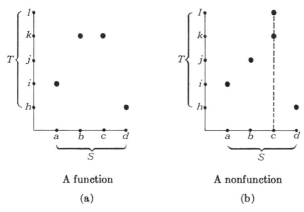

A function   A nonfunction

(a)   (b)

FIG. 33.—Graphs of two relations.

as those whose arrow diagrams were shown in Figure 32? Thus, in Figure 33(a) we see the graph of a function and in Figure 33(b), the graph of a relation that is not a function. Notice that in the latter picture there is a vertical dotted line that contains two points of the graph. This situation is typical of the graphs of relations that are not functions; it will be referred to again.

Most of the functions we have considered so far have contained only a finite number of ordered pairs. In mathematics and its applications the most important functions are those containing infinitely many pairs. Of these, functions defined on the set R of real numbers occur most frequently. In the remaining numbered examples it is to be understood that the relations discussed are all defined on R. We shall display the graphs of these relations. (Unfortunately, without using a branch of mathematics called analytic geometry, we cannot actually prove that these graphs are the correct ones.)

EXAMPLE 6

Is the relation $\{(x, y) \mid x < y\}$ a function? To show that it is *not*, we need only observe that if x is replaced by some number, then there are many possible replacements for y which will cause the resulting ordered pair to be in the relation. Thus for $x = 3$ such ordered pairs as $(3, 4)$, $(3, 5)$, and $(3, 17)$ are in the relation. Since these have the same first component, we conclude that the relation is not a function. (The graph of this relation appears in Figure 13.

EXAMPLE 7

The relation $\{(x, y) \mid y = (2 \times x) - 1\}$ *is* a function. It is certainly true that if we multiply a number by 2 and then subtract 1, we get a unique answer. Therefore, if we are given a number to serve as first com-

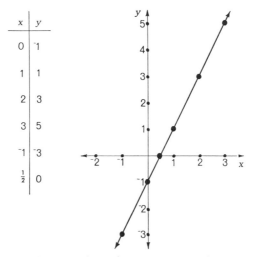

FIG. 34.—$\{(x, y) \mid y = (2 \times x) - 1\}$.

ponent, x, of an ordered pair, the second component, y, is uniquely determined. The graph of this function may be drawn by making a table giving some of the ordered pairs in the function, as shown in Figure 34. We then locate these points and observe that they appear to lie on a certain straight line. This line actually is the graph of the function.

EXAMPLE 8

The relation $\{(x, y) \mid y = x^2\}$ might be called the "squaring" relation, since the second component of each ordered pair in the relation is the square of the first component. The relation is a function, because if a number is squared, that is, multiplied by itself, the result is unique. Some of the ordered pairs in the function are (0, 0), (1, 1), (2, 4), (3, 9), (⁻1, 1), (⁻2, 4), (⁻3, 9), (1/2, 1/4), and (⁻1/2, 1/4). The graph of this function is the curve shown in Figure 35. (The curve is called a *parabola*.

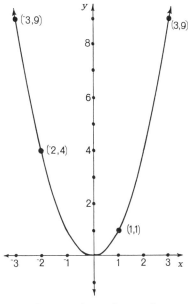

FIG. 35.—$\{(x, y) \mid y = x^2\}$.

It occurs both in nature and in technology: certain comets follow parabolic paths, and the cables of a suspension bridge hang approximately in the form of part of a parabola.)

EXAMPLE 9

The relation $\{(x, y) \mid x^2 + y^2 = 25\}$ is *not* a function. We can see this from the fact that both of the ordered pairs (3, 4) and (3, ⁻4) are in the relation. (Observe that $3^2 + 4^2 = 9 + 16 = 25$ and $3^2 + (⁻4)^2 = 9 + 16 = 25$.) We know that a function cannot contain two different ordered pairs with the same first component. You should try to find some more ordered pairs in the relation. If you graph the two ordered pairs we just obtained and others such as (0, 5), (0, ⁻5), (5, 0), (⁻5, 0), and (⁻4, ⁻3), you will see that the resulting points all appear to lie on the circle having radius 5 and with its center at the origin. This circle, pictured in Figure 36, is indeed the graph of the relation.

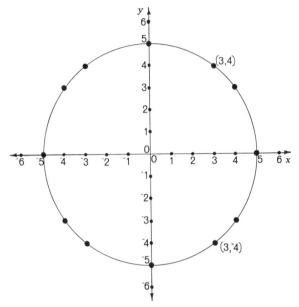

Fig. 36.—$\{(x, y)\,|\,x^2 + y^2 = 25\}$.

The Vertical-Line Test

Let us look at the graphs of the relations we have been considering in the foregoing examples. We notice that in the case of each relation that is *not* a function, it is possible to find a vertical line containing at least two points of the graph. This was pointed out explicitly in Example 5 on page 295. You can check for yourself that in Figure 36 there is a vertical line intersecting the graph of the nonfunction $\{(x, y) \mid x^2 + y^2 = 25\}$ at more than one point. (Indeed, there are many such vertical lines.) And you can do the same in Figure 13, page 258, which shows the graph of $\{(x, y) \mid x < y\}$.

On the other hand, we notice that no vertical line contains more than one point of the graph of a relation that *is* a function. Some vertical lines may contain no points of the graph, while others may contain one point. But *no* vertical line intersects the graph of a *function* in as many as two points. You should check this in the cases of the functions we discussed in the foregoing examples.

We therefore have a test enabling us to tell, by looking at the graph of a relation, whether that relation is a function or not:

If there is a vertical line that intersects the graph of a relation in more than one point, then the relation is not a function. If there is no such vertical line, then the relation is a function.

The reason this test works is easy to see: If there are two points of the graph of a relation on a certain vertical line, then the two corresponding ordered pairs in the relation have the same first component but different second components. This means that the relation is not a function, by the very definition of function.

Exercise Set 11

1. Which of the following relations are functions?

   a. $\{(1, 0), (2, 0), (3, 0)\}$

   b. $\{(0, 1), (0, 2), (0, 3)\}$

   c. $\{(a, b), (b, c), (c, d), (d, a)\}$

   d. $\{(x, y) \mid x \,\varepsilon\, R, y \,\varepsilon\, R, \text{ and } y^2 = x\}$

2. In this exercise, q stands for any number of the set of positive real numbers. Which of the following relations are functions?

   a. $\{(p, q) \mid p \text{ is a rectangle and } q \text{ is the area of } p\}$

   b. $\{(q, p) \mid p \text{ is a rectangle and } q \text{ is the area of } p\}$

   c. $\{(q, p) \mid p \text{ is a square and } q \text{ is the area of } p\}$

3. Figure 37 shows the graphs of two relations. Which of these relations is a function?

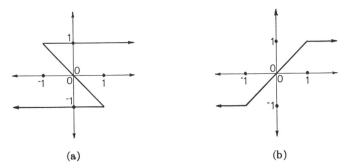

(a)   (b)

Fig. 37.—Two relations.

Functional Notation

In earlier sections of this booklet, we found it convenient to employ a single symbol as the name of a relation (we ordinarily used "**R**"). It is useful to do the same in the case of functions. In a given discussion about a function we can, of course, take as the name of the function any symbol that is not already being used. We often use the letter "**f**" for this purpose, however, because it is the initial letter of the word "function." Other popular names for functions are **g**, **h**, and φ (*phi*, the Greek equivalent of "**f**"). Functions are usually given italic-letter names, such as f, g, h, and ϕ, but in this booklet we shall use boldface-letter names for emphasis.

It is also useful to have a name for the set of all *first* components of ordered pairs in a given function: We call this set the *domain* of the function. Thus in the case of the function

$$\mathbf{f} = \{(1, 2), (2, 4), (3, 6), (4, 8)\},$$

the domain of **f** is the set $\{1, 2, 3, 4\}$. The set of all *second* components of ordered pairs in a function is called the *range* of the function. In the above example, the range of **f** is the set $\{2, 4, 6, 8\}$.

Let us look at the function

$$\mathbf{g} = \{(x, y) \mid x \; \varepsilon \; R, y \; \varepsilon \; R, \text{and } y = x^2\},$$

which we considered in Example 8. The set-builder notation contains the statement "$x \; \varepsilon \; R$," concerning the first components of ordered pairs in **g**. This tells us that the domain of **g** is the set R of real numbers. (Be careful not to confuse this "R," which stands for a set, with the "**R**" meaning "relation," which we used previously.) What is the range of **g**? The statement "$y = x^2$" tells us that the second component, y, of each ordered pair in **g** is the square of the first component, x. We know that the square of no real number can be negative, and therefore we conclude that the range of **g** can contain no negative numbers. It can be shown that the range of **g** consists of *all* real numbers that are not negative (see Booklet No. 11: *The System of Real Numbers*); that is, the range of **g** is $\{y \mid y \; \varepsilon \; R$ and $y \geq 0\}$.

It might be appropriate to point out some symbolism employed by mathematicians even though we shall not use it in this booklet. They use either of the notations

$$\mathbf{f} : S \to T \quad \text{or} \quad S \overset{\mathbf{f}}{\to} T$$

to convey all of the following information: **f** is a function, the domain of **f** is the set S, and the range of **f** is contained in the set T. Notice that the notation does not say that the range of **f** *is* T, only that it is a subset of T.

Let us now consider any function **f**, and let the domain of **f** be the set S. We know that for each member x of S there is exactly one ordered pair in **f** that has x as its first component. (That there is at least one ordered pair in **f** with first component x follows from our definition of what the domain of **f** is. That there is no more than one is a consequence of the definition of function.) It is convenient to have a symbol to name the second component of this unique ordered pair. We use $\mathbf{f}(x)$ for this purpose.

[Warning: $f(x)$ is *not* the product of f and x, although it looks a little like it; f is not even a number.] The symbol $f(x)$ is read "f of x." We often call $f(x)$ the *value* of the function f at x. We shall illustrate these ideas with some examples.

Let $f = \{(a, i), (b, k), (c, k), (d, h)\}$. This is the function we considered in examples 4 and 5 on pages 294–95. The domain of f is the set $\{a, b, c, d\}$, and the range of f is the set $\{h, i, k\}$. What is $f(a)$? It is the second component of the unique ordered pair in f that has a as its first component. Since this ordered pair is (a, i), we have $f(a) = i$. Similarly, since (b, k) is the only ordered pair in f having b as its first component, we see that $f(b) = k$. In like manner, we find that $f(c) = k$ and $f(d) = h$.

If we are considering a function that has a symbol other than f as its name, we must alter the rest of the notation accordingly. Thus, if the name of a function is g, we use $g(x)$ for the second component of the ordered pair in g having x as its first component. And if, in this case, we choose to call the first component z—say, instead of x—then the second component would be $g(z)$. (Recall the "what's-in-a-name" principle we used much earlier in this booklet: It does not matter what symbol we choose to use for the variable in an open sentence. But having chosen it, we must be consistent in its use. The situation is similar here.)

We have considered the function

$$g = \{(x, y) \mid x \, \varepsilon \, R, \, y \, \varepsilon \, R, \text{ and } y = x^2\}$$

in Example 8, page 297, and earlier in this section. We saw that some of the ordered pairs in g are $(0, 0)$, $(1, 1)$, $(2, 4)$, $(3, 9)$, $(^-2, 4)$, and $(1/2, 1/4)$. From these we see that $g(0) = 0$, $g(1) = 1$, $g(2) = 4$, $g(3) = 9$, $g(^-2) = 4$, and $g(1/2) = 1/4$. We do not really need a listing of ordered pairs to find $g(x)$ for a given x. We need only observe that the symbols $g(x)$ and y stand for the same thing, namely, the second component of the unique ordered pair in g whose first component is x. In this example we also know that $y = x^2$. Therefore, we have $g(x) = x^2$. This expression can be thought of as a "rule" enabling us to find the second component of an ordered pair in g, given the first component. The rule, therefore, essentially describes the function g. Once we have the rule, it is easy to find as many values of the function as we please. Simply by substituting numbers for the variable in $g(x) = x^2$, we find that

$$g(5) = 5^2 = 25, \quad g(^-3) = (^-3)^2 = 9, \quad g(1) = 1^2 = 1,$$

and so on.

In Example 7 on page 296, we considered the function

$$\varphi = \{(x, y) \mid x \, \varepsilon \, R, \, y \, \varepsilon \, R, \text{ and } y = (2 \times x) - 1\}.$$

We have now given the function a name, φ. In this case, just as before, we notice that both $\varphi(x)$ and y are symbols representing the second component of the unique ordered pair in φ that has first component x. In this example, however, it is given that $y = (2 \times x) - 1$. Therefore the rule, or formula, that enables us to find the second component when given the first, takes the form $\varphi(x) = (2 \times x) - 1$. We find by substitution that

$$\varphi(0) = (2 \times 0) - 1 = 0 - 1 = {}^{-}1,$$
$$\varphi(1) = (2 \times 1) - 1 = 2 - 1 = 1,$$
$$\varphi(2) = (2 \times 2) - 1 = 4 - 1 = 3,$$
$$\varphi(3) = (2 \times 3) - 1 = 6 - 1 = 5,$$
$$\varphi({}^{-}1) = (2 \times {}^{-}1) - 1 = {}^{-}2 - 1 = {}^{-}3,$$
$$\varphi(\tfrac{1}{2}) = (2 \times \tfrac{1}{2}) - 1 = 1 - 1 = 0.$$

Compare these expressions with those given in the table of Figure 34, page 296. The same information concerning the function is conveyed in both places.

Exercise Set 12

Describe the domain and range of each of the following functions. Find also the values asked for.

1. $f = \{({}^{-}3, 3), ({}^{-}2, 2), ({}^{-}1, 1), (0, 0), (1, 1), (2, 2), (3, 3)\}$. Find $\mathbf{f}(2)$, $\mathbf{f}({}^{-}2)$, $\mathbf{f}(0)$, and $\mathbf{f}({}^{-}1)$.

2. $g = \{(x, y) \mid x \,\varepsilon\, R \text{ and } y = x - 2\}$. Find $\mathbf{g}(5), \mathbf{g}(2), \mathbf{g}(0), \mathbf{g}({}^{-}2)$, and $\mathbf{g}(1)$.

3. $\varphi = \{(\square, \triangle) \mid \square \text{ is the } \triangle\text{-th letter of the English alphabet}\} = \{(A, 1), (B, 2), (C, 3), \cdots, (Y, 25), (Z, 26)\}$. Find $\varphi(N)$, $\varphi(C)$, $\varphi(T)$, and $\varphi(M)$.

Functions as "Rules"

In the examples at the end of the preceding section, we noted that the expressions $\mathbf{g}(x) = x^2$ and $\varphi(x) = (2 \times x) - 1$ essentially described the functions g and φ. These expressions can be thought of as "rules" telling us how to find the second component of the ordered pair that has a given first component. To have complete information about the function we must know, of course, what the permissible first components are; that is, we must know the domain of the function as well as the rule. In practice, most functions are described by rules rather than being given explicitly as a set of ordered pairs.

Suppose, for example, we are told that the domain of a certain function $\mathbf{f}$ is the set $\{1, 2, 3, 4\}$ and that for each x in this set, $\mathbf{f}(x) = x + 2$ (this is the rule). What is the function as a set of ordered pairs? We know that the first components of these pairs are the numbers in the domain. To find the corresponding second components, we need only substitute in the formula expressing the rule. Thus if we substitute 1, we find that $\mathbf{f}(1) =$

$1 + 2 = 3$, and therefore $(1, 3)$ is in **f**. Substituting 2 gives us $f(2) = 2 + 2 = 4$; hence $(2, 4)$ ε **f**. If we continue, we find that $f = \{(1, 3), (2, 4), (3, 5), (4, 6)\}$.

We cannot, of course, always write out all the ordered pairs in a function as we did above. But, given the information about its domain and its rule, we can write out as many permissible ordered pairs in a function as we please and can express the set of *all* ordered pairs in the function, using set-builder notation. The first sentence in the following paragraph illustrates the phraseology we use when describing a function by a rule.

Let the function **f** be defined on the set R of real numbers by $f(x) = 2 - x$. (Notice that both the domain of **f** and the rule are specified.) We may obtain values of this function by substitution in the formula expressing the rule. Thus we find that

$$f(0) = 2 - 0 = 2, \quad f(1) = 2 - 1 = 1, \quad f(2) = 2 - 2 = 0,$$

and

$$f(3) = 2 - 3 = {}^{-}1.$$

The expressions just obtained tell us that the ordered pairs $(0, 2)$, $(1, 1)$, $(2, 0)$, and $(3, {}^{-}1)$ are in the function **f**. These are only a few of the infinitely many ordered pairs in **f**. To express the function as the set of all ordered pairs in it, we use set-builder notation and write

$$f = \{(x, y) \mid x \text{ ε } R \text{ and } y = 2 - x\}.$$

It is not necessary to write y ε R, because if x is a real number, so is $2 - x$ and therefore y. We can, if we like, eliminate y entirely and write $f = \{(x, 2 - x) \mid x \text{ ε } R\}$.

The rule that describes a function need not be a mathematical formula like the foregoing cases. Thus, the rule that $h(p)$ is the height in inches of person p describes a function **h** defined on the set of all persons. We might call **h** the "height" function. Some ordered pairs in **h** are (Elizabeth II, 64) and (President Johnson, 74). The function itself in set-builder notation is

$$h = \{(p, q) \mid p \text{ is a person and } q \text{ is the height of } p \text{ in inches}\}.$$

In view of the fact that it is so convenient to describe specific functions by rules, you might well ask why we did not use this idea to give a *general* definition of function. Why not use something like the following as a definition?

*A function is a rule that makes a unique member of a set T correspond to each member of a set S. If **f** is the name of the function, then $f(x)$ is the member of T corresponding to the number x of S.*

This statement expresses quite well what we have observed in the preceding pages. Indeed, many books use statements very similar to this one as their definitions of functions. Such a "working definition" has considerable intuitive appeal and serves very well in many areas of mathematics.

In defining a function to be a rule, however, the question arises as to just what a "rule" is. "Rule" is certainly a more familiar word than "function" and might be considered elementary and primitive enough to be used as a basis for a definition. But a careful analysis of what we mean by a "rule" would probably lead us to the idea of "pairing" and ultimately to the idea of a "set of ordered pairs." It is for this reason that we chose to define a function as a certain kind of relation—that is, a certain kind of set of ordered pairs.

Of course, not everything can be defined without running into what is known as "circularity." A classic instance of circularity is found in a certain dictionary that contains the following definitions: "A turtle is a sea-going tortoise," and "A tortoise is a land-going turtle." Some things must remain undefined concepts, and other things must be defined in terms of these. Throughout this booklet we have chosen to use "set" and "ordered pair" as undefined concepts on the ground that they are very primitive and elementary ideas.

There is nothing wrong, however, if we choose to define specific functions by sentences in this form: "Let the function f be defined on a set S by (the rule) $f(x) = \cdots$," where the three dots stand for some expression involving x. We have seen that such a statement gives us complete information about what the function f is, as a set of ordered pairs.

Exercise Set 13

1. Let the function f be defined on the set $\{2, 4, 6, 8, 10\}$ by the rule $f(x) = x - 1$. Write out f completely as a set of ordered pairs.

2. Let the function g be defined on the set J of integers by $g(n) = 4 - n^2$. Find $g(^-2)$, $g(^-1)$, $g(0)$, $g(1)$, and $g(2)$.

3. Suppose $\varphi = \{(x, y) \mid x \, \varepsilon \, R$ and $y = x + 3\}$. Fill in the blanks in the following sentence: The function φ is defined on the set _____ by the rule _____.

Functions as "Mappings"

The word "mapping" is often used as a synonym for "function." This usage was probably inspired by cartography, which is the representation of a part of the earth's surface by a map. If we think of a map of the United States, for example, we see that to each point in the actual physical country there corresponds a point on the sheet of paper on which the map is printed. If we let x stand for the terrestrial point and let $\mathbf{f}(x)$ stand for the point on the map that represents it, we see that a function $\mathbf{f}$ is defined. We notice that $\mathbf{f}$ really is a function, not just a relation, because no one terrestrial point is represented by two different points on the map. (Two physical points, one directly above the other, would be represented by the same point on the map, but this does not violate the definition of function.)

Many people feel that the word "mapping" conveys the idea of a special kind of correspondence better than does the word "function." When a mathematician thinks of a function as a mapping, he usually has in mind a picture of two sets of objects and some indication of the correspondence, perhaps by arrows. This mental picture may look like the arrow diagram in Figure 32(a), page 294, or it may be less detailed such as the one shown in Figure 38. In Figure 38 the blob labeled S represents

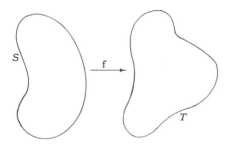

FIG. 38.—Schematic representation of a mapping.

the domain of the mapping $\mathbf{f}$, and the blob labeled T represents a set containing the range of $\mathbf{f}$.

In this connection the word "map" is sometimes used as a verb in such sentences as "The function $\mathbf{f}$ maps x into $\mathbf{f}(x)$." Suppose, for example, we are considering the mapping (function) $\mathbf{g}$ defined on the set N of natural numbers by $\mathbf{g}(x) = x^2$. We then say that $\mathbf{g}$ maps 1 into 1, 2 into 4, 3 into 9, and so on. These statements are just another way of saying that $\mathbf{g}(1) = 1$, $\mathbf{g}(2) = 4$, $\mathbf{g}(3) = 9$, and so on.

The "Function Machine"

A device that is sometimes found helpful in explaining the function concept is the so-called function machine. It can be described as follows: For a given function, $\mathbf{f}$, we visualize a box, the "$\mathbf{f}$-machine." The box has an "input" opening into which we may insert any member of the domain of $\mathbf{f}$. It also has an "output" opening. The actual mechanism inside the box need not concern us. We assume, however, that it has the ability to take whatever comes into the input—say x—to work on it, and then to eject from the output the value $f(x)$. Figure 39 shows a sche-

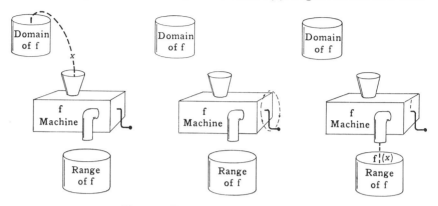

FIG. 39.—The f-machine in operation.

matic picture of the f-machine in operation. Each output quantity is a member of the range of the function f. (Recall the definition of range of a function given on page 300.)

Consider the function f defined on the set N of natural numbers by the rule $f(x) = x + 3$. The associated "machine" might well be called the "add-3 machine." If 2 is put into this machine, the output will be $f(2) = 2 + 3 = 5$; if the input is 7, the output will be $f(7) = 7 + 3 = 10$; and so on.

Modern computers are examples of function machines that actually exist. These have the ability to produce large numbers of values of complicated functions in very short times.

Exercise Set 14

1. If the function f is defined on the set R of real numbers by $f(x) = x^2$, the corresponding "f-machine" might well be called the "squaring machine." Find the output of the squaring-machine for each of the following inputs: 2, 0, ⁻3, ⁻2, 1/2, and ⁻1/2.

2. Repeat exercise 1, with the "cubing machine," or "g-machine," where $g(x) = x^3$, in place of the f-machine.

PROBLEMS INVOLVING FUNCTIONS

In this section we shall discuss three important types of problems that arise in connection with functions. First, however, let us recall that a general relation R, since it consists of a set of ordered pairs, can be written in set-builder notation. Namely, we might write $R = \{(x, y) \mid \cdots\}$, where the three dots following the vertical bar stand for some statement about x and y which enables us to decide whether a given ordered pair is in R or not. Because a function is a special kind of a relation, it, too, can be written in the form $\mathbf{f} = \{(x, y) \mid \cdots\}$, but now the statement about x and y that follows the vertical bar must be such that there are not two different pairs in $\mathbf{f}$ having the same first component.

When we look at

$$\mathbf{f} = \{(x, y) \mid \cdots\},$$

we see the three symbols $\mathbf{f}$, x, and y. The three types of problems referred to above can be roughly classified in terms of these symbols as follows:

Type 1. *Given $\mathbf{f}$ and x, find y.*
Type 2. *Given $\mathbf{f}$ and y, find x.*
Type 3. *Given some pairs (x, y), find $\mathbf{f}$.*

What we really mean by these problems will be explained below with the help of some examples. (The classification of these problems as Types 1, 2, and 3 is not a standard one; we introduce it here only as a convenience.)

Type-1 Problems

In this type of problem we assume that we have complete information as to what the function in question is. Perhaps we have it written out as a set of ordered pairs, but usually we have it described by a rule or formula. We also are given a definite first component of an ordered pair in the function. We wish to find the second component. In terms of functional notation this means that we are given a function $\mathbf{f}$ and a member x of its domain; we want to find $\mathbf{f}(x)$. This is precisely the kind of problem we have already considered in the sections entitled "Functional Notation" and "Functions as 'Rules.'" Let us consider two more examples.

Let $\mathbf{f}$ be the "area-of-a-square" function. That is, $\mathbf{f}(x)$ is the area (the number of square units) of a square with side of length x (the number of linear units). Since the length of the side of a square is positive, the domain of $\mathbf{f}$ is the set P of positive real numbers. Thus the function $\mathbf{f}$ is defined on the set P by the formula $\mathbf{f}(x) = x^2$. If we are now asked to find the area of a square, given the length of a side, we have a Type-1 problem: We know $\mathbf{f}$ and x, and we want to find $\mathbf{f}(x)$. The solution of the problem is simply a matter of substituting the given value of x in the defining formula $\mathbf{f}(x) = x^2$. Thus the area of a square of side 3 is $\mathbf{f}(3) = 3^2 = 9$; the area of a square of side $\frac{3}{2}$ is $\mathbf{f}(\frac{5}{2}) = (\frac{5}{2})^2 = \frac{25}{4} = 6\frac{1}{4}$, and so on.

Let us now consider a somewhat more complicated function, the "area-of-a-rectangle" function (Fig. 40). We know that the area of a rectangle

having base of length b and height of length h is $b \times h$. How shall we
express this in function language? We observe that the area of a rectangle
depends on a *pair* (b, h) of numbers and not on just one number, as in
the case of a square. If we use **g** as the name of the "area-of-a-rectangle"

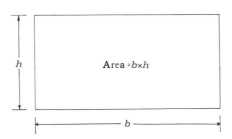

Fig. 40.—Area of a rectangle.

function, we see that **g** is defined on the set of all *ordered pairs* of positive
real numbers. (In this particular example it happens not to matter that
the pairs are ordered. In general, however, it does matter in which order
the numbers are taken.) If we let P be the set of all positive real numbers,
we then recall that the set of all ordered pairs of members of P is the
Cartesian product $P \times P$. See page 288 and Booklet No. 1: *Sets*, pages
37–40. Thus the function **g** is defined on the set $P \times P$ by the formula
$\mathbf{g}((b, h)) = b \times h$.

A function like **g** that is defined on a set of ordered pairs is sometimes
called a "function of two variables." It is conventional to omit the outer parentheses in such a symbol as $\mathbf{g}((b, h))$, so it appears in the simpler form
$\mathbf{g}(b, h)$; in this brief treatment, however, we shall not drop these parentheses.

Since the domain $P \times P$ of the function **g** itself consists of ordered
pairs, the members of **g** will have a somewhat unfamiliar look. The ordered
pairs in **g** have other ordered pairs as their first components, namely,
members of $P \times P$. Thus the ordered pair $((6, 2), 12)$ is in **g** because the
area of a rectangle of base 6 and height 2 is 12. Other ordered pairs in **g**
are $((4, 3), 12)$, $((1, 5), 5)$, and $((3, 3), 9)$.

Finding the area of a rectangle, given its base and height, is the Type-1
problem in this example. That is, we know the function **g** by its defining
formula $\mathbf{g}((b, h)) = b \times h$, and we are given b and h; hence we have
the member (b, h) of the domain of **g**. We want to find $\mathbf{g}((b, h))$. (If we
compare the foregoing with our original introduction of Type-1 problems
on page 71, we see that **g** plays the role of **f**; (b, h) plays the role of x;
and $\mathbf{g}((b, h))$ plays the role of y.) The solution of this Type-1 problem
is again seen to be just a matter of substitution in the formula defining **g**.
Thus, given $b = 5$ and $h = 2$, we find that $\mathbf{g}((5, 2)) = 5 \times 2 = 10$.

Type-2 Problems

In this type of problem we again suppose that we know the function **f**. It may be given as a set of ordered pairs, or it may be described by a rule or formula. Now, however, we are given a value that is to be the *second* component of an ordered pair in **f**, and we wish to find the *first* component. That is, we have **f** and a value for **f**(x), and we wish to find x.

We find that a Type-2 problem may have more than one solution. This is never the case with a Type-1 problem. Thus, suppose we are given the function **f** = {(1, 2), (2, 4), (3, 4), (4, 6)} and the value 4 for **f**(x). The Type-2 problem is to find x so that **f**(x) = 4. This problem has two solutions, namely, x = 2 and x = 3, because **f**(2) = 4 and **f**(3) = 4.

We see also that the value given for **f**(x) must be a member of the range of **f**. Thus, in the foregoing example there is no solution for the Type-2 problem of finding an x such that **f**(x) = 3. This is due to the fact that 3 is not the second component of any ordered pair in **f**; that is, 3 is not in the range of **f**.

The situations illustrated above can occur equally well if the given function is described by a rule or formula. As an example, let **f** be defined on the set R of real numbers by **f**(x) = x^2. Now, there are two solutions for the Type-2 problem of finding x such that **f**(x) = 9: x = 3 and x = ⁻3, since **f**(3) = 3^2 = 9 and **f**(⁻3) = (⁻3)^2 = 9. On the other hand, there is no solution to the problem of finding x such that **f**(x) = ⁻4. This problem is to find x such that x^2 = ⁻4, and we know that the square of no real number is negative.

In many applications a knowledge of the domain of the given function enables us to eliminate "extraneous" solutions. Thus, if the function **f** of the preceding paragraph were the "area-of-a-square" function considered earlier, it would still be described by the formula **f**(x) = x^2. But the domain of **f** is now the set P of positive real numbers, since the length of the side of every square is positive. In this case the solution x = 3 is unique for the Type-2 problem of finding x so that **f**(x) = 9, because the other solution, ⁻3, which we found in the above paragraph, is not in the domain P of the function **f** we are now considering. Actually, the functions considered in this paragraph and in the preceding paragraph are different functions. Although they are both described by the same formula, they have different domains and therefore are different sets of ordered pairs.

Let us consider Type-2 problems associated with the "area-of-a-rectangle" function **g** discussed above. The function **g** is defined by the formula **g**((b, h)) = $b \times h$, when both b and h are positive real numbers. The Type-2 problem that gives 12, say, as the value of **g**, is to find b and h such that **f**((b, h)) = 12, that is, $b \times h$ = 12. We find that there are many solutions: (2, 6), (4, 3), (12, 1), and (8, $1\frac{1}{2}$) are a few of them. This is to be expected, of course, since there are many rectangles having area 12.

Even if a Type-2 problem has only one solution, the solution may be difficult to find. If the formula defining the given function is a complicated one—say $f(x) = x^5 - x^3 + 2$—the finding of x so that $f(x) = 4$ leads to an extremely hard problem in *equation solving*. Mathematicians have worked for centuries on the problem of equation solving and have succeeded in showing that solutions of most equations can be obtained only approximately. From a practical point of view, this fact is no cause for concern. Solutions of equations arising in practical problems can usually be obtained by modern computers in a very short time.

Type-3 Problems

Let us introduce this type of problem with an example.

Suppose we are given the ordered pairs (1, 2), (2, 4), (3, 6), and (4, 8) and wish to find a function, f, defined on the set R of real numbers, such that these pairs are in f. The problem as stated has many solutions. For example, we could take for f the set of ordered pairs consisting of the four given ones, together with all pairs of the form $(x, 0)$, where x is any real number other than 1, 2, 3, or 4. This solution, however, seems to be unnatural and to lack aesthetic appeal.

If we study the four given ordered pairs, we notice that each second component is twice the corresponding first component. It therefore seems that the "best" function, in some sense, that contains the given pairs is the one in which the second component of *every* ordered pair is twice the first. This function, f, as a set of ordered pairs is $\{(x, y) \mid x \; \varepsilon \; R \text{ and } y = 2 \times x\}$. If we wished to describe f by a formula, we would say that f is the function defined on R by $f(x) = 2 \times x$. We observe that this function "fits" the given pairs; that is, we have

$$f(1) = 2 \times 1 = 2, \quad f(2) = 2 \times 2 = 4, \quad f(3) = 2 \times 3 = 6,$$

and

$$f(4) = 2 \times 4 = 8.$$

These statements are equivalent, respectively, to saying that (1, 2), (2, 4), (3, 6), and (4, 8) are in f.

A graphical interpretation of what we have just done is as follows: If we graph the given ordered pairs, we get the four points shown in Figure 41(a). The Type-3 problem is to find a function whose graph "fits" these points, that is, passes through them. We chose as the "best" solution to this problem the function f described in the preceding paragraph.

Its graph is shown in Figure 41(b). It is because of such graphical inter-

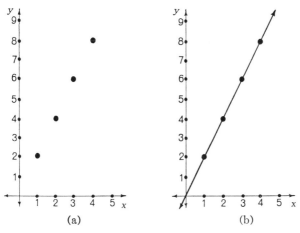

(a)   (b)

FIG. 41.—$\{x, y)|x \; \varepsilon \; R \; \text{and} \; y = 2 \times x\}$.

pretations that Type-3 problems are often referred to as *curve-fitting* problems. (In mathematics we extend the usual meaning of the word "curve" to make it include straight lines as "curves.")

We have not really answered the question of which of the many possible functions we should choose as the "best" solution of a given Type-3 problem. It appears that problems of this type usually occur in applications. In such cases we often have available further information that will help us make the choice.

A modification of this kind of Type-3 problem is particularly important in applications. This modification consists of choosing for the solution of a given problem a function that does not necessarily contain the given ordered pairs, but one that, in some sense, comes close to doing so. Graphically, this means that we pick a function whose graph comes close to the points representing the given pairs but does not necessarily pass through them.

Why should we make such a choice? In practice the given ordered pairs are usually obtained by observation of experiments, and these are subject to error. We are therefore not particularly concerned with having our function actually contain these pairs, which are probably not exactly correct anyway. By allowing ourselves some leeway, we may be able to find a function that is simple in form or that might be suggested by other considerations. An example may help to clarify these matters.

Let us suppose that a scientist is testing a certain diet on a rat and wishes to find a function relating the weight of the rat in ounces to its age in days. He weighs the rat each day and records his findings in a table:

Day number	1	2	3	4
Weight in oz.	1.7	1.8	2.3	3.2

This table gives a number of ordered pairs: (1, 1.7), (2, 1.8), (3, 2.3), and (4, 3.2). When these are graphed, the four points in Figure 42 result.

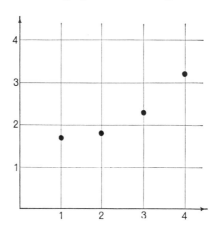

Fig. 42.—Graph of an experiment.

We can see that no straight line contains all of these points. This means that no function whose graph is a straight line can contain the observed ordered pairs. The scientist, however, may have good reasons for requiring a function of this type; and he may attribute the fact that there really is no function of this type to deficiencies in the observed data. This might be caused, for example, by inaccurate scales or perhaps an uncooperative rat. In this case he wishes to find a function whose graph is a straight line passing "close" to the four points. There is a standard procedure, called the *method of least squares*, that will produce such a function. If the method is applied in this case, there results the function **f**, defined by the formula **f**$(x) = 1.0 + (0.5) \times x$. The graph of **f** is shown in Figure 43(a).

It turns out that there is a fairly simple function, **g**, that actually contains all the ordered pairs in the example given above. It is defined by the formula

$$\mathbf{g}(x) = 2.0 - (0.5) \times x + (0.2) \times x^2,$$

and its graph is shown in Figure 43(b). The verification that **g** really does contain the four given pairs leads us to four Type-1 problems. Thus, if we substitute 3 in the defining formula, we find that

$$\mathbf{g}(3) = 2.0 - (0.5) \times 3 + (0.2) \times 3^2 = 2.0 - 1.5 + 1.8 = 2.3.$$

This means that the pair (3, 2.3) is in **g**. You may carry out the other three parts of the verification for yourself.

Even though there is this function **g** that "fits" the observed data exactly, the scientist may, for his own reasons, still prefer to use the simpler function **f** we found first. Let us suppose that the scientist decides that the function **f** defined by the formula $f(x) = 1.0 + (0.5) \times x$ is the one

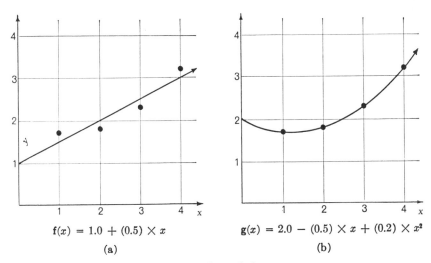

$f(x) = 1.0 + (0.5) \times x$ $g(x) = 2.0 - (0.5) \times x + (0.2) \times x^2$

(a)   (b)

Fig. 43.—Curve fittings.

that represents the growth of his rat. What can he do with this function? For one thing, he can use it for prediction purposes. Thus, to predict the weight of the rat when it is 5 days old, he needs only substitute 5 in the defining formula for **f** and obtain $f(5) = 1.0 + (0.5) \times 5 = 3.5$. (This is a Type-1 problem.) He therefore estimates that the rat will weigh 3.5 ounces when it is 5 days old. Or he might like to know when the rat will weigh 4.0 ounces. He now has a Type-2 problem: He wants to find x so that $f(x) = 4.0$—that is, so that $1.0 + (0.5) \times x = 4.0$. The value for x that makes this true is 6. Thus he predicts that the rat will weight 4.0 ounces when it is 6 days old. (In using the function **f** in this way, we must realize that there are limitations on its domain of validity, probably a relatively few days. Let us hope, at least, that the diet the scientist is testing is not so successful as to produce a two-year-old rat weighing 366 ounces.)

In this section we have considered three kinds of problems involving functions: Type-1 problems, which ordinarily reduce to *substitution in a formula*; Type-2 problems, which involve *equation solving*; and Type-3 problems, which are usually called *curve-fitting* problems. Much of higher mathematics is devoted to a study of functions, and the above types of problems do no more than scratch the surface of the subject. The most interesting and important functions are those satisfying certain conditions that we do not have space to discuss here. Analysis, for example, which is one of the major branches of modern mathematics, includes the study of the behavior of functions that satisfy certain "smoothness" conditions.

Exercise Set 15

1. Let the function **g** be defined on the set J of integers by $\mathbf{g}(n) = 4 - n^2$. Find two solutions of each of the following Type-2 problems:

    a. $\mathbf{g}(n) = 3$ **b.** $\mathbf{g}(n) = 0$

(Hint: See exercise 2 of Exercise Set 13 on page 304.)

2. Recall that the area of a triangle with base of length b and height h is given by the expression $1/2 \times b \times h$. Therefore, the "area-of-a-triangle" function is defined on the set of all ordered pairs of positive real numbers by the rule $\mathbf{f}((b, h)) = 1/2 \times b \times h$.

    a. Find $\mathbf{f}((5, 10))$, $\mathbf{f}((2, 6))$, $\mathbf{f}((4, 3))$, and $\mathbf{f}((12, 1))$.

    b. Find three solutions for each of the following Type-2 problems:
      i. $\mathbf{f}((b, h)) = 6$.   **ii.** $\mathbf{f}((b, h)) = 12$.

3. Suppose we are given the ordered pairs $(^-3, 3)$, $(^-2, 2)$, $(^-1, 1)$, $(0, 0)$, $(1, {}^-1)$, $(2, {}^-2)$, and $(3, {}^-3)$. What appears to you to be the "best" function **f**, defined on R, that contains all these ordered pairs?

SUMMARY

As mathematics has developed through the centuries it has expanded to include a large number of quite special and usually very complicated subjects. By studying these special subjects in order to discover what properties they have in common, mathematicians have discovered a number of unifying concepts during the last fifty years. Each of these concepts is based upon quite elementary ideas, and each contains as special cases a number of the apparently different traditional subjects.

In this booklet we have an example of such unification. Here, the unifying concept has been that of a *relation*. We have seen that the concept of relation is based on two very elementary ideas: *set* and *ordered pair*. Indeed, a relation is precisely a set of ordered pairs. We have seen also that the concept of relation embraces a number of different, more special, theories: we studied two of these, *equivalence relations* and *functions*, at some length, and we had a good deal to say about *order relations*. These subjects, in turn, contain innumerable special cases, which at first glance seem to have little in common but which all turn out to be relations.

—————————◆•◆—————————

For Further Reading

Among the various helpful references that deal with the subject here introduced are the following:

MAY, KENNETH O., and VAN ENGEN, HENRY. "Relations and Functions," in *The Growth of Mathematical Ideas, Grades K–12.* Twenty-fourth Yearbook of the National Council of Teachers of Mathematics. Washington, D.C.: The Council, 1959. Available from the National Council of Teachers of Mathematics, 1201 Sixteenth St., N.W., Washington, D.C. 20036.

McFADDEN, MYRA; MOORE, J. WILLIAM; and SMITH, WENDELL I. *Sets, Relations, and Functions: A Programmed Unit in Modern Mathematics.* New York: McGraw-Hill Book Co., 1963. Pp. 299. Available from McGraw-Hill Book Co., 330 W. 42nd St., New York, N.Y. 10036.

SELBY, SAMUEL M., and SWEET, LEONARD. *Sets—Relations—Functions: An Introduction.* New York: McGraw-Hill Book Co., 1963. Pp. 233. Available from the McGraw-Hill Book Co., 330 W. 42nd St., New York, N.Y. 10036

ANSWERS TO EXERCISES

Exercise Set 1

1. a. Open   **c.** Open

   b. False   **d.** True

2. True: **c, e, g, j**. False: **a, f.** Open: **b, d, h, i.**

3. a. {36}   **d.** {0}

   b. {0, 1, 2, 3}   **e.** { }, or $\emptyset$

   c. {3, 4, 5, $\cdots$}

4. a. {2, 3, 4}   **d.** {$\cdots$, ⁻4, ⁻3, 3, 4, $\cdots$}

   b. {0}   **e.** J

   c. { }, or $\emptyset$ **f.** {$\cdots$, ⁻2, ⁻1, 0, 1, 2, 3}

Exercise Set 2

1. a. {0, 1, 2}

   b. {⁻1, 0, 1, 2}

   c. {1, 2}

   d. {2}

   e. {2, 4, 6, 8, 10, 12}

   f. {Alabama, Alaska, Arkansas, Arizona}

2. a.

b., c.

d., e.

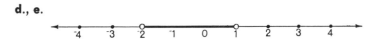

f.

Exercise Set 3

1. a., b. {(1, 4), (2, 3), (3, 2), (4,1)}

   c. {(0, 1), (0, 0), (1, 0)}

2. There are many acceptable answers to this exercise, but each must consist of at least four *ordered pairs*. Sample answers are given below:

a. (0, 0), (1, 1), (2, 2), (3, 3), ($^-$1, $^-$1), ($^-$2, $^-$2), ($\frac{1}{2}$, $\frac{1}{2}$), $\cdots$

b., c. (0, 2) (1, 1), (2, 0), (3, $^-$1), (4, $^-$2), ($^-$1, 3), ($^-$2, 4), $\cdots$

d. (0, 1), (0, 2), (0, 3), (1, 2), (1, 3), (2, 3), ($^-$3, 1), ($^-$1, $\frac{1}{2}$), $\cdots$

e. (0, 1), (0, 2), (0, 3), (1, 3), (1, 4), ($^-$1, 0), ($^-$1, $^-$1), $\cdots$

3. a.

x	y
1	4
2	3
3	2
4	1

b.

□	△
0	2
1	1
2	0
3	$^-$1
4	$^-$2
$^-$1	3
$^-$2	4

Exercise Set 4

1.

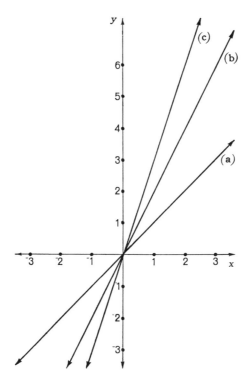

2. a. 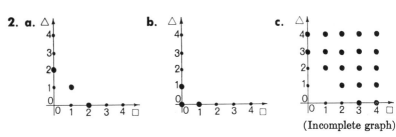 **b.** **c.**

(Incomplete graph)

3.   a. 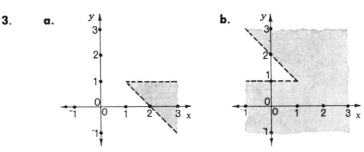 **b.**

Exercise Set 5

1. a. $\{(L, T), (L, E)\}$

b. $\{(T, E), (E, T), (T, L), (L, T), (E, L), (L, E)\}$

c. $\{(D, M), (D, T), (D, E), (D, L), (M, E), (M, L), (T, E), (T, L), (E, L)\}$

2. a. The complete relation is $\{$(Cleopatra, Columbus), (Cleopatra, Napoleon), (Cleopatra, Eisenhower), (Columbus, Napoleon), (Columbus, Eisenhower), (Napoleon, Eisenhower)$\}$.

b. Samples: (New York, Cleveland), (Cleveland, Chicago), (Denver, Reno), (Denver, San Francisco).

3. Samples: was built before, is located south of, is not as tall as.

Exercise Set 6

1.   a. 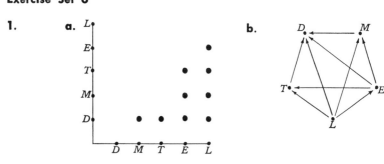 **b.**

2.

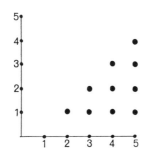

Exercise Set 7

1. a. No.

 b. Yes.

 c. $x\mathbf{R}y$, $y\mathbf{R}z$, $y\mathbf{R}y$, $z\mathbf{R}x$.

2. $\{(x, y), (x, z), (z, y), (y, z), (z, z)\}$

Exercise Set 8

1. Symmetry: If (x, y) ε R, then (y, x) ε R.
 Transitivity: If (x, y) ε R and (y, z) ε R, then (x, z) ε R.

2. a. This is an equivalence relation.

 b. This is not an equivalence relation, because we have
 $$z\mathbf{R}x \quad \text{and} \quad x\mathbf{R}y \quad \text{but not} \quad z\mathbf{R}y.$$

3. It is symmetric but not reflexive or transitive. (Note that $2 \neq 3$ and $3 \neq 2$, but $2 \neq 2$ is false.)

4. No. It is not reflexive.

5. Yes.

Exercise Set 9

1. The equivalence class of each of 1, 3, and 9 is H (p. 285); the equivalence class of 2 and of 10 is K.

2. The set of all vertical lines, the set of all horizontal lines, the set of all 45° lines.

3. Sample answers:

 a. $\dfrac{1}{3}, \dfrac{2}{6}, \dfrac{^-1}{^-3}, \dfrac{^-2}{^-6}, \dfrac{5}{15}$

 c. $\dfrac{^-4}{^-4}, \dfrac{1}{1}, \dfrac{2}{2}, \dfrac{^-1}{^-1}, \dfrac{21}{21}$

 b. $\dfrac{^-2}{6}, \dfrac{2}{^-6}, \dfrac{^-1}{3}, \dfrac{1}{^-3}, \dfrac{^-3}{9}$

 d. $\dfrac{0}{2}, \dfrac{0}{1}, \dfrac{0}{^-1}, \dfrac{0}{3}, \dfrac{0}{4}$

Exercise Set 10

1. a. $\{(a, a), (b, b), (c, c), (d, d), (e, e), (f, f), (a, d), (d, a), (a, e), (e, a),$
$(d, e), (e, d), (c, f), (f, c)\}$

b.

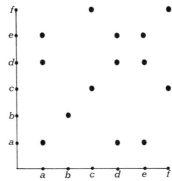

c. $\{a, d, e\}$, $\{b\}$, and $\{c, f\}$

2. a. Yes.

b. No.

c. $\{(x, x), (y, y), (z, z), (w, w), (x, y), (x, z), (y, z), (w, z)\}$

d.

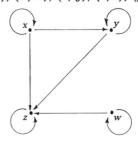

e. Yes. (This is best seen from the arrow diagram.)

Exercise Set 11

1. a and **c** are functions; **b** and **d** are not.

2. a and **c** are functions; **b** is not, because the length and width of a rectangle are not determined by its area.

3. b is the graph of a function; **a** is not.

Exercise Set 12

1. The domain of **f** is $\{^-3, ^-2, ^-1, 0, 1, 2, 3\}$, the range is $\{0, 1, 2, 3\}$.
$\mathbf{f}(2) = 2$, $\mathbf{f}(^-2) = 2$, $\mathbf{f}(0) = 0$, $\mathbf{f}(^-1) = 1$.

2. Both the domain and range of **g** are R. **g**$(5) = 3$, **g**$(2) = 0$, **g**$(0) = ^-2$, **g**$(^-2) = ^-4$, **g**$(1) = ^-1$.

3. The domain of φ is the set of letters of the English alphabet, the range is the set of the first 26 natural numbers. $\varphi(N) = 14$, $\varphi(C) = 3$, $\varphi(T) = 20$, $\varphi(M) = 13$.

Exercise Set 13

1. $\{(2, 1), (4, 3), (6, 5), (8, 7), (10, 9)\}$.

2. **g**$(^-2) = 0$, **g**$(^-1) = 3$, **g**$(0) = 4$, **g**$(1) = 3$, **g**$(2) = 0$.

3. $\cdots$ set R by the rule $\varphi(x) = x + 3$.

Exercise Set 14

1. The outputs are **f**$(2) = 4$, **f**$(0) = 0$, **f**$(^-3) = 9$, **f**$(^-2) = 4$, **f**$(\frac{1}{2}) = \frac{1}{4}$, and **f**$(^-\frac{1}{2}) = \frac{1}{4}$.

2. The outputs are **g**$(2) = 8$, **g**$(0) = 0$, **g**$(^-3) = ^-27$, **g**$(^-2) = ^-8$, **g**$(\frac{1}{2}) = \frac{1}{8}$, and **g**$(^-\frac{1}{2}) = ^-\frac{1}{8}$.

Exercise Set 15

1. a. $n = 1$ and $n = ^-1$.

b. $n = 2$ and $n = ^-2$.

2. a. **f**$((5, 10)) = 25$, **f**$((2, 6)) = 6$, **f**$((4, 3)) = 6$, and **f**$((12, 1)) = 6$.

b. Sample answers: **i.** $(2, 6), (4, 3), (1, 12), (3, 4)$.

ii. $(2, 12), (3, 8), (8, 3), (4, 6)$.

3. Did you choose the function **f** defined by **f**$(x) = -x$?

BOOKLET NUMBER FOURTEEN:

INFORMAL GEOMETRY

INTRODUCTION

As we look at the world around us, the physical objects we see have many shapes and sizes. We may observe some objects that seem to be alike in shape: an orange and a golf ball, a tree trunk and a tin can, a full moon and a silver dollar, and an ice cream cone and a funnel. Perhaps we notice that certain objects or parts of objects have the same size as well as shape: the petals of a daisy, the squares on a checkerboard, the tires of a car, and the black keys of a piano. Some objects have repeating patterns: wallpaper, the wings of a butterfly, and the fabric for a dress, to name just a few.

Notions of geometric figures are abstractions from such observations. The study of geometric figures and of their properties and relationships is known as *geometry*.

This booklet offers an informal introduction to some of the basic ideas in geometry. It starts with a discussion of certain fundamental notions about geometric lines, half-lines, rays, segments, and angles. Then it

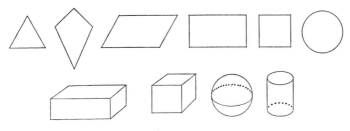

FIGURE 1

goes on to investigate some of the properties of various familiar plane and solid figures, such as those pictured in Figure 1, with which even very

323

young children have contact in their daily lives. Precise definitions of some of these geometric figures will be given, so that they can be identified accurately. In general, however, the treatment will be kept quite intuitive. The geometric relationships alluded to in the opening paragraph, known as similarity, congruence, and symmetry, will be dealt with in Booklet No. 18; they will be described in a way that is meant to appeal to your natural intuition. Both the text and the exercise sets of that booklet include numerous examples of paper-folding exercises and other do-it-yourself activities that will help you to visualize these relationships clearly.

THE LINE AND ITS SUBSETS

Historical Development

Historically, the number line as we know it is a relatively recent concept, originating with Pierre de Fermat and René Descartes, seventeenth-century French mathematicians.

In contrast, the geometric notion of a straight line is very old, dating back as far as 2000 B.C. with the Babylonians and 1300 B.C. or earlier with the Egyptians. Geometry (Greek $g\bar{e}$, "the earth," $+$ *metrein*, "to measure") played a very practical role in the lives of the Egyptians. They used their geometric know-how in the science of surveying and in the construction of buildings, bridges, and pyramids. The precision of measurement exhibited in the pyramids along the Nile River furnishes majestic evidence that the Egyptians were remarkably proficient geometers.

Before the rise of Greek civilization (approximately 600 B.C.) geometric knowledge was still basically empirical in nature. In contrast to the Egyptians, who used geometry mainly as a means for solving particular problems, the Greeks were interested in the science of geometry per se and in organizing its subject matter systematically. They did so by starting with a few simple, intuitive assumptions, called "axioms" or "postulates," and then proving all the remaining known facts from these basic assumptions by means of a logical chain of reasoning. Under the influence of the Greeks, geometry was developed to a high degree of perfection as a deductive science. Euclid's famous treatise, *The Elements of Geometry*, was written around 300 B.C., and it stood for over 2,000 years as the standard work in geometry.

Recent developments in the field of geometry include many imaginative ideas that are new both in the content and in the teaching of the subject. The so-called new mathematics, now widely used in the elementary curriculum, makes frequent use of these modern concepts.

The first part of this booklet includes a glimpse at some of the relationships between geometry and other topics in mathematics. For example,
it tells how the *geometric line* and its various subsets are related to the
number line and to the graph of an algebraic open sentence.

Lines and Points

The words "point" and "line" are undefined terms in geometry. The
abstract geometric concept of a line can be visualized in physical form
as a taut string extending infinitely far in opposite directions in space.
The arrowheads on the four geometric lines pictured in Figure 2 symbolize
this infinite property of the line. Using two adjacent edges of this page
as lines of reference, we can describe the four lines in Figure 2 as (a)
horizontal, (b) vertical, and (c) and (d) diagonal.

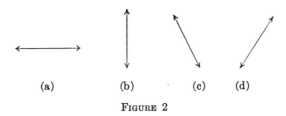

(a)   (b)   (c)   (d)

FIGURE 2

A geometric point is an abstract concept denoting position in space.
We draw a dot to represent a point in a geometric figure. A line can be
thought of as a set of points. The dots shown on the line in Figure 3
represent five points on the line.

FIGURE 3

How many points in all are contained on a line? It should be intuitively
clear that since a line extends infinitely far in both directions, any line
contains an unlimited number of points. This fact can be stated another
way:

There are infinitely many points on a line.

Often we are interested in considering only a few of the points on a
line at a time. It is helpful to have a way of distinguishing between these
points. We shall use capital letters to name points. It then becomes easy
to discuss the four points indicated on the line in Figure 4. For example,
to describe the relative position of point *B*, we could say that *B* is between

A and *C*. We can also say that *C* is between *D* and *A*. Can you make two more statements similar to these?

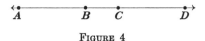

FIGURE 4

One of the basic assumptions in geometry is:

Two points determine one and only one[1] line.

Another way of stating this property is to say:

Exactly one[1] line passes through two points.

To visualize this fact intuitively, try the following experiment: Stick a straight pin through the middle of a drinking straw and press the pinpoint firmly against a sheet of paper on a table. Imagine that the straw represents a line passing through the pinpoint. Now rotate the straw slowly around the point and think of each different position it assumes as representing a different line through the point *P*. Figure 5(a) pictures three such lines. Next, mark another point, *B*, on the paper not far from *P*. Now rotate the straw so that it lies over *B*, as shown in Figure 5(b). Do you see that there *is* one, but *only* one, position of the straw that places it directly over *B*? That is, the two points *P* and *B* determine exactly one line.

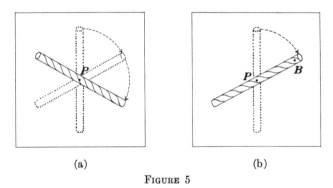

(a)   (b)

FIGURE 5

Perhaps the drawing in Figure 6 will clarify why the word "line" is reserved to mean "straight line." If we admitted the notion of a "curved line," we could draw infinitely many "lines" through the two points labeled *A* and *B*. This would contradict the basic assumption that exactly one line passes through two points.

---

[1] The phrases "one and only one" and "exactly one" mean the same thing in mathematics, namely, "one, and neither more nor less than that."

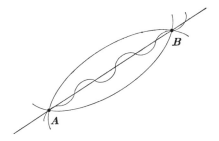

FIGURE 6

On the other hand, look at the drawing in Figure 7, in which three straight lines appear to be passing through the two points A and B. Can you figure out what is wrong? This is an example of the need to remember the limitation of our representing points visually with dots. *A geometric point has no size.* (Note: Use a sharp pencil in drawing geometric figures.)

Now let us draw two finer dots for the points A and B, and draw the line that passes through them (Fig. 8). This line can be denoted by a

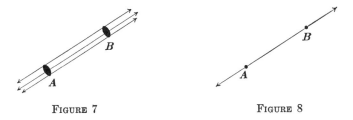

FIGURE 7   FIGURE 8

symbol that names the two points and has a little two-headed arrow over it, thus: $\overleftrightarrow{AB}$ (read "line AB").

Since a line can be identified by naming *any* two of its points in *either* order, the line in Figure 9 can be referred to in various ways, for example: $\overleftrightarrow{PR}, \overleftrightarrow{RS}, \overleftrightarrow{PS}, \overleftrightarrow{SR}$.

If we are not concerned with using particular points to determine a line, we sometimes name a line with a small letter, such as ℓ, m, or n (Fig. 10).

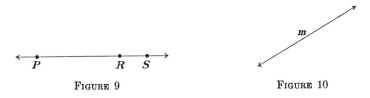

FIGURE 9   FIGURE 10

We have assumed that exactly one line passes through two points. It is also true that an infinite number of lines pass through one point, but how can we demonstrate this intuitively?

Let us begin by considering a point B on a line ℓ, and a single point A not on ℓ (Fig. 11). The two points A and B determine exactly one line, $\overleftrightarrow{AB}$, which intersects ℓ at B (Fig. 12).

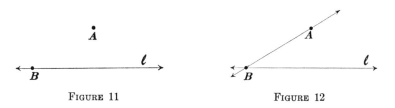

FIGURE 11   FIGURE 12

Since there are infinitely many points on ℓ, there must be an infinite number of different lines determined by A and this set of points. Figure 13 shows five such lines, namely, $\overleftrightarrow{AB}$, $\overleftrightarrow{AC}$, $\overleftrightarrow{AD}$, $\overleftrightarrow{AE}$, and $\overleftrightarrow{AF}$.

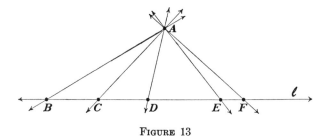

FIGURE 13

A fact about points and lines that is not so easy to explain intuitively is that there are infinitely many points *between* any two given points on a line. To see this, let us refer for a moment to the number line,[2] which serves as a numerical model of the geometric line. It is intuitively obvious that between any two distinct numbers we can always find another number by finding the average of the two original numbers. For example, if the two numbers are 1 and 5, then their average is $\frac{1+5}{2}$, or 3, which names the point halfway between the graphs of the two original points (Fig. 14).

Continuing with our example, we can locate two more points between the two original points, 1 and 5, by finding the average of 1 and 3, namely 2, and the average of 3 and 5, namely 4 (see Fig. 15).

[2] For a discussion of the one-to-one correspondence between the real numbers and the points on a number line, see Booklet No. 11: *The Real Number System*.

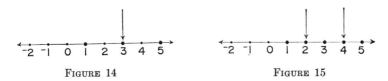

FIGURE 14   FIGURE 15

Clearly, we can continue ad infinitum this process of taking averages to get midpoints between midpoints, as indicated in Figure 16, even

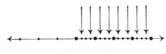

FIGURE 16

though it might look as if this process would eventually end when the dots start touching each other. This apparent impasse is due simply to the limitation of our having to represent points by dots, which do have physical size.

Since we could follow the same method with any two points on the line, we can assume that between any two points on the line there are infinitely many points.

Exercise Set 1

1. Draw a horizontal line. Choose two points on this line and label them X and Y.

   a. Now mark a third point, Z, on the same line so that Z lies between X and Y.

   b. Mark another point, W, on the same line so that Y lies between Z and W.

   c. One way of naming the line, which now has points X, Z, Y, and W marked on it, is $\overleftrightarrow{XY}$. Suggest six other names for this line.

2. Draw a horizontal line. On the line mark the points S, O, T, and P so *all* of these statements will be true.

   a. O is between S and P.

   b. T is between P and S.

   c. T is between O and S.

3. Consider three points, A, B, and C, as pictured below.

A •

B •   • C

These points determine three different lines. One of them is named $\overleftrightarrow{AB}$.

a. Name the other two lines.

b. Try to arrange the position of three points, A, B, and C, so that only one line is determined by them. (This line will have several names.)

c. Now try to arrange the position of three points, A, B, and C, so that two and only two lines are determined by them.

4. Consider four points, E, F, G, and H, as pictured below.

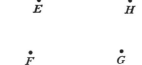

These points determine six different lines. Draw each line and name it.

5. On the number line below, what number corresponds to—

a. Point A?

b. Point B?

c. Point C?

d. Point D?

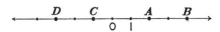

6. On the number line below, label points P, Q, and R so that P corresponds to $^-3$, Q to $2\frac{1}{2}$, and R to $^-3\frac{1}{2}$.

7. On the number line below, represent the set of even integers, $\{\cdots,\ ^-6,\ ^-4,\ ^-2,\ 0,\ 2,\ 4,\ 6,\ \cdots\}$.

Open Half-Lines

Consider a line ℓ and a point A on ℓ, as indicated in Figure 17. The point A separates the line ℓ into three subsets of points. One contains only the separation point A, while the other two consist of the infinite sets of points on either side of A. Each of these latter two subsets of ℓ is called a *half-line* with end point A. Since the end point is not included in either of these subsets, they are called *open half-lines*.

A half-line is named by its end point and one other point on it. In Figure 18 the point A separates the line ℓ into three disjoint sets consisting of A, the half-line AC, and the half-line AB. We use the suggestive symbol $\overset{\circ\rightarrow}{AB}$

FIGURE 17   FIGURE 18

to denote the open half-line AB. The little unshaded circle over the letter A indicates that the end point A is not included in the half-line. The arrow indicates that the half-line extends endlessly in the direction from A to B.

You will note that we always name the end point first. This is important in the case of half-lines, because even though $\overset{\leftrightarrow}{AB}$ and $\overset{\leftrightarrow}{BA}$ name exactly the same lines, $\overset{\circ\rightarrow}{AB}$ and $\overset{\circ\rightarrow}{BA}$ name two different open half-lines, as indicated in Figure 19.

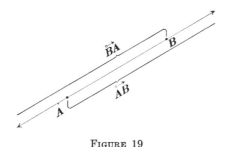

FIGURE 19

The real-number line offers an especially useful application of the notion of a half-line. The number line is ordinarily pictured in a horizontal position, with the points on the open half-line to the right of the origin associated with the positive real numbers and the points to the left with the negative real numbers. In fact, we often speak of the "positive half" and the "negative half" of the number line. Since the number 0 is neither positive nor negative, the point associated with it, called the *origin*, is a natural separation point. The set of real numbers can hence be thought of as the union of three nonoverlapping sets: the set consisting only of 0, the set of positive real numbers, and the set of negative real numbers (Fig. 20).

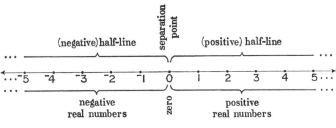

FIGURE 20

The Graph of an Open Number Sentence

The graph of the open sentence $x > 5$ (read "x is greater than 5"), where the replacement set for x is the set of real numbers, is the shaded half-line shown in Figure 21. Notice that the unshaded circle around the

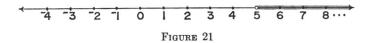

FIGURE 21

point labeled "5" indicates that this point is not included. Can you write the open sentence for the open half-line extending to the left from the graph of 5, as diagramed in Figure 22(c)?

We saw that the separation point and the two half-lines in Figure 20 form three disjoint subsets of the line and that their union is the line itself. Likewise, the solution sets of these three open sentences,

        (a) $x = 5$,

        (b) $x > 5$, and

        (c) $x < 5$ (read "x is less than 5"),

are three disjoint subsets of the real numbers, and their union consists of the set of all real numbers. These three subsets are indicated in Figure 22. In the same way, for any given real number, the set of real numbers can be separated into three disjoint sets: (a) the set consisting only of the

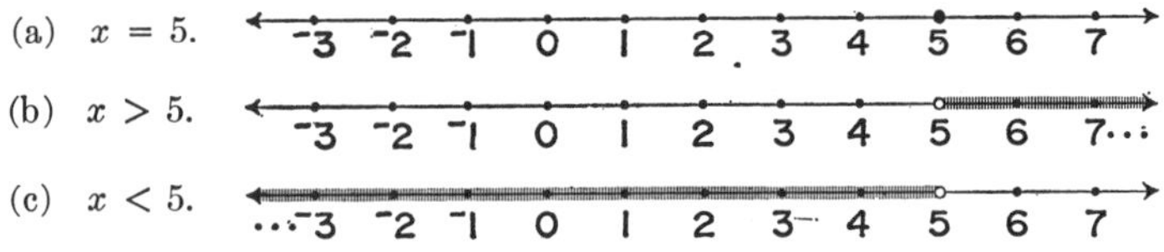

(a) $x = 5$.

(b) $x > 5$.

(c) $x < 5$.

FIGURE 22

given number, (b) the set of all numbers greater than the given number, and (c) the set of all numbers less than that number. The statement that any given real number belongs to exactly one of these three disjoint sets is called "the trichotomy law," *tri-* indicating the *three* possibilities.

If we were to rule out one of the two inequalities above, say $x > 5$, then we would have $x < 5$ *or* $x = 5$. We write this symbolically as $x \leq 5$ and represent this open sentence graphically as the *closed half-line* shown in Figure 23. Note that the end point, 5, is shaded to indicate that it is included in the closed half-line.

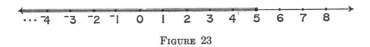

... ⁻4 ⁻3 ⁻2 ⁻1 0 1 2 3 4 5 6 7 8

FIGURE 23

Rays

A half-line that includes its end point—that is, a closed half-line—is called a "ray." Figure 24 shows a line ℓ with a shaded portion representing a ray with end point A and passing through B. This ray is denoted in symbols as $\overset{\bullet\longrightarrow}{AB}$, or more commonly just $\overrightarrow{AB}$ (read "ray AB").

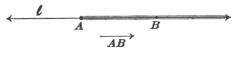

$$\overrightarrow{AB}$$

FIGURE 24

The notion of a ray is frequently encountered in everyday use, whenever an arrow is used to indicate a starting point and a given direction. Perhaps you have seen in a newspaper a diagram using an arrow to indicate the launching site of a missile and the direction in which the missile was fired. Any driver is familiar with the sign commonly used to indicate one-way traffic, like that in Figure 25(a). When we speak of the rays

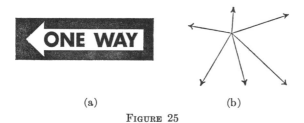

(a)   (b)

FIGURE 25

of the sun, we visualize the sun as a common end point for a set of rays pointing in all directions, much like Figure 25(b).

As you can see by the few examples cited, the intuitive notion of a ray is suggestive of its mathematical definition. In geometry, however, we must use precise notation and terminology so that we shall know exactly what set of points we are talking about. Thus in Figure 26, $\overrightarrow{AB}$ is not the same ray as $\overrightarrow{BA}$. A similar observation was made about the open half-lines of Figure 19. The fact that the arrowhead points to the right in the symbol is of course just a convention; the ray itself may point in any direction.)

FIGURE 26

Exercise Set 2

1. On the line $\overleftrightarrow{AB}$ below, regard point A as a separation point.

a. Does $\overset{\circ\rightarrow}{AB}$ contain the point A?

b. Place a point C on $\overleftrightarrow{AB}$ so that A lies between B and C.

c. Does $\overset{\circ\rightarrow}{AB}$ contain C?

d. Does $\overset{\circ\rightarrow}{AC}$ contain B?

2. Points A, B, and C are placed on a line as shown.

a. Is B on $\overset{\circ\rightarrow}{CA}$?

b. Is C on $\overset{\circ\rightarrow}{CA}$?

c. Is A on $\overset{\circ\rightarrow}{BA}$?

d. Is A on $\overset{\circ\rightarrow}{CA}$?

e. Is C on $\overset{\circ\rightarrow}{AB}$?

f. Is B on $\overset{\circ\rightarrow}{AC}$?

g. Place a point D on the given line so that D is on $\overset{\circ\rightarrow}{CA}$ but not on $\overset{\circ\rightarrow}{AB}$.

h. What point is on neither $\overset{\circ\rightarrow}{AC}$ nor $\overset{\circ\rightarrow}{AB}$?

3. Consider the number line below, with points A, B, and C corresponding to the numbers 0, 3, and $^-2$, respectively.

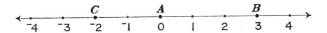

  a. The half-line $\overset{\circ\rightarrow}{AB}$, together with the point A, is the ray $\overset{\rightarrow}{AB}$. $\overset{\circ\rightarrow}{AB}$ is the graph of the open sentence $x > 0$. Write an open sentence which has $\overset{\rightarrow}{AB}$ as its graph.

  b. Name the ray that is the graph of the open sentence $x \leq 0$.

  c. Name the ray that is the graph of the open sentence $x \leq 3$.

  d. Write an open sentence that has $\overset{\rightarrow}{CA}$ as its graph.

4. Points A, B, C, D, E, F, and G are placed on a number line as shown.

A B C D E F G

$^-5$ $^-4$ $^-3$ $^-2$ $^-1$ 0 1 2 3 4 5

  a. Which of the seven labeled points are contained in $\overset{\rightarrow}{FE}$?

  b. Which of the seven labeled points are contained in the graph of the open sentence $x \leq 3$?

  c. The ray $\overset{\rightarrow}{FE}$ has several different names. Without labeling any further points, give four more names for $\overset{\rightarrow}{FE}$.

5. Draw a horizontal line. Place on it the five points T, G, R, E, and I in such a way that all of these statements are true:

  a. G is on $\overset{\rightarrow}{TE}$.

  b. T is on $\overset{\rightarrow}{EG}$.

  c. R is not on $\overset{\rightarrow}{GT}$.

  d. I is on both $\overset{\rightarrow}{TG}$ and $\overset{\rightarrow}{GT}$.

  e. R is not on $\overset{\rightarrow}{EG}$.

Segments

In the preceding sections we described two kinds of subsets of the line: open and closed half-lines. Closed half-lines were also called rays.

Another important subset of a line is a segment. By a *segment* we mean a

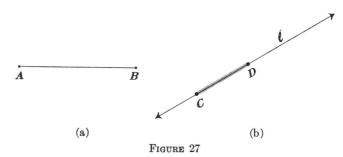

(a)   (b)

FIGURE 27

portion of a geometric line consisting of two points on the line, A and B, together with all the points lying between them. The two points A and B are called *end points* of the segment. The segment is denoted by the symbol $\overline{AB}$ (read "segment AB"). To be consistent with other symbols we have sometimes used for open and closed half-lines, we could use the symbol $\overset{\bullet\!-\!\bullet}{AB}$ to denote a segment. Actually, however, dots are not ordinarily used in the symbols for various subsets of the line.

We may draw a segment either without picturing the line of which it is a part—Figure 27(a)—or else by shading a portion of a line—Figure 27(b).

In naming a segment, the end points can be listed in either order. Thus in Figure 27(b), $\overline{CD}$ and $\overline{DC}$ name exactly the same segment, which consists of the two end points C and D together with all the points lying between them on the line.

In the case of segments, there is not the possible confusion with notation that we find with half-lines and rays. A few words of caution regarding terminology are nevertheless in order. The word "line" was used for a long time in mathematics in the sense of a segment with two end points. In fact, in the English translation of Euclid reference is made to drawing a "line," say from P to Q, and then extending the "line" to some point R. (See Fig. 28.) In most modern mathematics books, such figures are referred to

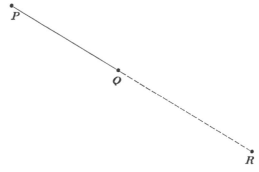

FIGURE 28

as segments, while the word "line" is reserved for a geometric figure that extends infinitely far in both directions. This distinction will be kept throughout our discussion.

As we look around us, we can see many physical representations of a geometric segment. For example, the edges of the pages you are reading represent segments. So do your pen and pencil. The intersection of two walls in a room and the intersection of a wall with the floor or the ceiling furnish more examples. From where you are sitting now, how many objects do you see that represent segments?

Line Segments as Graphs of Compound Open Number Sentences

Suppose that we wanted to write an open sentence to describe a subset of the real numbers consisting of all numbers that are (a) greater than or equal to 2 *and* (b) less than or equal to 6. The open sentence $x \geq 2$ (or alternatively, $2 \leq x$) would describe requirement (a), and $x \leq 6$ would describe (b). Now, we can combine these two open sentences and write a *compound open sentence*[3] like this: $2 \leq x \leq 6$. This sentence is read, "2 is less than or equal to x, and x is less than or equal to 6." To simplify this idea, we could say instead: "x is any number from 2 to 6, inclusive."

How shall we graph the solution set of the open sentence $2 \leq x \leq 6$, where the replacement set for x is the set of real numbers? We might approach the situation by considering one at a time the two separate conditions that must be fulfilled:

(a) $x \geq 2$,
(b) $x \leq 6$.

Let us build on our knowledge from the preceding section and graph the solution set of each of these open sentences separately. You will recall that the graph of the solution set of the open sentence $x \geq 2$ is a ray extending to the right from its end point, 2, on the number line. The graph of the solution set of the open sentence $x \leq 6$ is also a ray, directed to the left from its end point, 6.

Since we are looking for those numbers that satisfy *both* of the open sentences (a) and (b), let us represent the two rays on the same number line, as in Figure 29. In order to picture the set of points that fulfill both

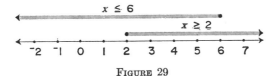

FIGURE 29

---

[3] For a more complete discussion of this subject, see Booklet No. 8: *Number Sentences*

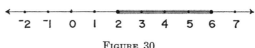

FIGURE 30

conditions, let us imagine lowering the two rays onto the number line to examine their overlap. The points that the two rays would have in common would be all the points between and including those labeled 2 and 6. Thus the graph of the compound open sentence $2 \le x \le 6$ can be represented as a segment on the number line with end points at the points labeled 2 and 6, as indicated in Figure 30.

Let us try another example: Graph the solution set of the open sentence $^-6 \le x \le 2$, where the replacement set for x is the set of real numbers. This time we might simply analyze the information in the given open sentence as "x is a number that can be anywhere from $^-6$ to 2, inclusive, on the real-number line." Then all we need to do is draw a number line and shade in a segment with end points at the points labeled $^-6$ and 2 (Fig. 31).

FIGURE 31

Exercise Set 3

1. Points A, B, and C are placed on a line as shown:

        A B C

    a. How many line segments can you name with end points chosen from A, B, and C?

    b. Is B on $\overline{AB}$?

    c. Is $\overline{AB}$ contained in $\overleftrightarrow{AB}$?

    d. Is $\overline{AB}$ contained in $\overrightarrow{AB}$?

    e. Is $\overline{AB}$ contained in $\overset{o\rightarrow}{AB}$?

    f. Is $\overline{BC}$ contained in $\overrightarrow{AB}$?

2. Draw a number line.

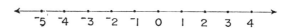

a. Graph the solution set of the open sentence $x \leq 3$ on the number line.

b. On the same number line, graph the solution set of the open sentence $x \geq {}^{-}4$. (See Figure 29 for a way to graph two solution sets on the same number line.)

c. Imagine sliding the two graphs you obtained in parts **a** and **b** down onto the number line to find the set of points that they have in common. Draw a separate number line and on it graph this set of points.

d. Is the set of points you obtained in part **c** a segment?

e. The set of points you obtained in part **c**, consisting of all those points that are common to the graphs of the open sentence $x \leq 3$ and $x \geq {}^{-}4$, is itself the graph of an open sentence. Write this open sentence.

3. a. Write an open sentence whose graph is the ray shown in this drawing:

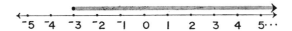

b. Write an open sentence whose graph is the ray shown here:

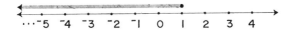

c. Using your results from parts **a** and **b**, write an open sentence whose graph is the segment shown below:

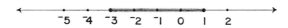

The Intersection and the Union of Two Rays

The fact that two rays may overlap in a segment can be stated more concisely in the terminology of sets.[4] Consider two sets, say X and Y.[5] The set consisting of all the elements that X and Y have in common is called the *intersection set*. We can denote this set by $X \cap Y$, read "the intersection of X and Y." Thus $X \cap Y$ stands for the set of elements that are common to *both X and Y*. For example, suppose that

$$X = \{0, 3, 6, 9, 12, 15, 18, 21, 24, 27, 30\},$$

and

$$Y = \{0, 5, 10, 15, 20, 25, 30\}.$$

---

[4] Refer to Booklet No. 1: *Sets*.
[5] Capital letters are also used to name sets. It is generally clear from the context whether a letter stands for a set or is being used to name a point.

Then

$$X \cap Y = \{0, 15, 30\}.$$

We could also find the *union set* of these two sets, denoted by $X \cup Y$ (read "the union of X and Y"). $X \cup Y$ stands for the set of elements that belong to either X or Y or to both. For the example above,

$$X \cup Y = \{0, 3, 5, 6, 9, 10, 12, 15, 18, 20, 21, 24, 25, 27, 30\}.$$

You should observe that while the elements 0, 15, and 30 belong to both X and Y, they are not listed twice in the union set.

Let us return to our geometric situation and consider the following problem: Given a line ℓ and two points A and B on ℓ (as shown in Figure 32), name the set of points described by $\overrightarrow{AB} \cap \overrightarrow{BA}$.

FIGURE 32

First of all, let us interpret the problem. We are asked for the intersection of two sets of points, each set being a ray; that is, we are back to our original problem of finding the set of points that two particular rays have in common. We shall follow a procedure similar to the one used in the preceding section.

1. Above the given line, sketch rays suggesting the rays $\overrightarrow{AB}$ and $\overrightarrow{BA}$, as shown in Figure 33.

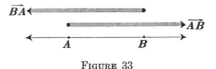

FIGURE 33

2. Imagine sliding both rays down onto the line so that you can see where the rays overlap—that is, where the two rays have a set of points in common.

3. Observe that they share points A and B and all the points in between; hence the intersection set is the segment $\overline{AB}$; that is,

$$\overrightarrow{AB} \cap \overrightarrow{BA} = \overline{AB}.$$

To find $\overrightarrow{AB} \cup \overrightarrow{BA}$, we start as before by sketching each ray above the line. Then imagine lowering both rays onto the line in order to see what points are on either $\overrightarrow{AB}$ or $\overrightarrow{BA}$, or both. Referring back to Figure 33, you

can see that every point on the line is included. Hence $\overrightarrow{AB} \cup \overrightarrow{BA} = \overleftrightarrow{AB}$
(or $\overleftrightarrow{BA}$).

Is the intersection set of two rays always a segment? Is the union set of two rays always a line? Consider the following examples to the contrary.

EXAMPLE 1: For the rays shown in Figure 34, find $\overrightarrow{AB} \cap \overrightarrow{BC}$ and $\overrightarrow{AB} \cup \overrightarrow{BC}$.

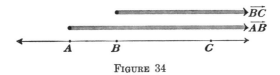

FIGURE 34

If we imagine sliding the two rays onto the original line, we see that they have the entire ray $\overrightarrow{BC}$ in common. Hence $\overrightarrow{AB} \cap \overrightarrow{BC} = \overrightarrow{BC}$. Similarly, the union of $\overrightarrow{AB}$ and $\overrightarrow{BC}$ is $\overrightarrow{AB}$; that is, $\overrightarrow{AB} \cup \overrightarrow{BC} = \overrightarrow{AB}$. This example illustrates that the intersection of two rays is not always a segment and the union is not always a line; the intersection and the union may in fact both be rays.

EXAMPLE 2: In Figure 35 find $\overrightarrow{BA} \cap \overrightarrow{BC}$ and $\overrightarrow{BA} \cup \overrightarrow{BC}$.

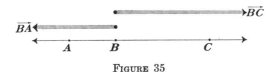

FIGURE 35

In this case, the intersection set is the set containing the single point B, and the union is the entire line. We write these results as $\overrightarrow{BA} \cap \overrightarrow{BC} = \{B\}$ and $\overrightarrow{BA} \cup \overrightarrow{BC} = \overleftrightarrow{AB}$.

EXAMPLE 3: In Figure 36 find $\overrightarrow{BA} \cap \overrightarrow{CD}$ and $\overrightarrow{BA} \cup \overrightarrow{CD}$.

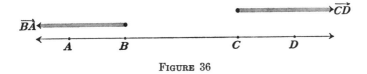

FIGURE 36

You can see that the rays $\overrightarrow{BA}$ and $\overrightarrow{CD}$, pictured in Figure 36, have no points in common; therefore, their intersection is the *empty set*, $\varnothing$. We indicate this by stating that $\overrightarrow{BA} \cap \overrightarrow{CD} = \varnothing$ (or { }). The union of the two rays is simply the set consisting of the two disjoint rays; we represent it simply as $\overrightarrow{BA} \cup \overrightarrow{CD}$.

The Intersection and the Union of a Segment and a Ray

Let us consider some situations involving segments and rays. In each case we shall refer to a horizontal line with the four points A, B, C, and D labeled in that order from left to right (Fig. 37). We suggest that you try each example before looking at the solution.

$$\overset{\longleftarrow}{\underset{A}{\bullet}\ \ \ \ \ \underset{B}{\bullet}\ \ \underset{C}{\bullet}\ \ \ \ \ \underset{D}{\bullet}\longrightarrow}$$

FIGURE 37

EXAMPLE 1: In Figure 37 find $\overrightarrow{AB} \cap \overline{BC}$.

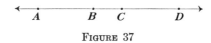

FIGURE 38

As illustrated in Figure 38, the set of points that the segment and ray have in common is the set containing B and C and every point between these two points—in other words, the segment $\overline{BC}$. In symbols, $\overrightarrow{AB} \cap \overline{BC} = \overline{BC}$ (or $\overline{CB}$).

EXAMPLE 2: In Figure 37 find $\overrightarrow{AB} \cup \overline{BC}$.

We need not draw another picture. The set of points that are in either $\overrightarrow{AB}$ or $\overline{BC}$ or both is a ray that we could name in three ways, $\overrightarrow{AB}$, $\overrightarrow{AC}$, or $\overrightarrow{AD}$. Hence $\overrightarrow{AB} \cup \overline{BC} = \overrightarrow{AB}$ (or $\overrightarrow{AC}$ or $\overrightarrow{AD}$).

EXAMPLE 3: In Figure 37 find $\overline{AC} \cap \overrightarrow{CD}$.

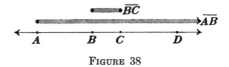

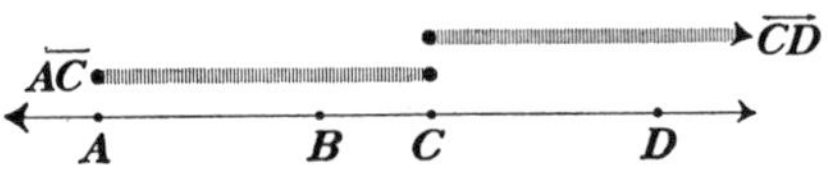

FIGURE 39

In Figure 39 we can see that the given segment and ray have only point C in common. Hence $\overline{AC} \cap \overrightarrow{CD} = \{C\}$.

EXAMPLE 4: In Figure 37 find $\overline{AC} \cup \overrightarrow{CD}$.

If we imagine sliding the segment and ray pictured in Figure 39 onto the line, we see that point A and all the points to the right of A on the line are included. This set is a ray with end point A, and the ray contains points B, C, and D. Hence we can name the union set by $\overrightarrow{AB}$, $\overrightarrow{AC}$, or $\overrightarrow{AD}$.

Exercises of this sort not only give practice in recognizing and naming points, rays, segments, and lines, but also provide an interesting application of the properties of sets. We have not taken time to mention these properties, but we hope that you may wish to further explore why the particular union and intersection sets result. The exercises that follow provide additional instances of situations that may occur. In particular, the problems in exercise 6 will treat the question: What is the intersection set of two segments?

Exercise Set 4

1. Let M be the set of positive odd integers, $\{1, 3, 5, 7, 9, \cdots\}$, and let N be the set of positive even integers, $\{2, 4, 6, 8, \cdots\}$.
   a. Find the union of M and N ($M \cup N$).
   b. Find the intersection of M and N ($M \cap N$).

2.
   a. How many points lie between point A and point B?
   b. How many points does $\overline{AB}$ contain?
   c. How many points lie between point A and $\overrightarrow{AB}$?

3. Draw a number line. Take two pencils and think of them as representing rays, with the eraser end as the end point of the ray and the pointed lead indicating the arrow. Experiment laying these "rays" along the line in various positions to see what kinds of "overlapping" you get. Can the intersection of these two "rays" be—
   a. A point?
   b. The empty set?
   c. A segment?
   d. A ray?
   e. The whole line?

4. Repeat exercise 3, this time considering the possible unions of the two
"rays" placed in various positions along the line. Can the union of
those two "rays" be—

a. A point?

b. The empty set?

c. A segment?

d. A ray?

e. The whole line?

5. Imagine all the segments pictured below as actually being stacked up
on the line. (In the picture we have shown them pried apart so that you

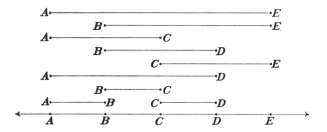

can see each individually.) Using ∪ for union and ∩ for intersection,
express:

a. $\overline{AC}$ in terms of $\overline{AB}$ and $\overline{BC}$.

b. $\overline{AD}$ in terms of $\overline{AC}$ and $\overline{BD}$.

c. $\overline{AD}$ in terms of $\overline{AC}$ and $\overline{CD}$.

d. $\overline{BD}$ in terms of $\overline{AD}$ and $\overline{BE}$.

e. $\overline{AD}$ in terms of $\overline{AB}$ and $\overline{BD}$.

f. $\overline{AD}$ in terms of $\overline{AB}$ and $\overline{BC}$ and $\overline{CD}$.

g. $\overline{BC}$ in terms of $\overline{AC}$ and $\overline{BD}$.

h. $\overline{BC}$ in terms of $\overline{AE}$ and $\overline{BC}$.

i. $\overline{AE}$ in terms of $\overline{AE}$ and $\overline{BC}$.

6. In the figure for exercise 5, are there two segments whose intersection is—

a. A point?

b. The empty set?

c. A segment?

d. A ray?

e. The whole line?

THE PLANE AND ITS PROPERTIES

Points and Lines that Determine a Plane

So far, we have been working with a line and some of its subsets: points, half-lines, rays, and segments. In analyzing the number line, we saw that a line is made up of infinitely many points.

In this section, we are going to extend our geometry to the plane. The word "plane," like the words "point" and "line," is an undefined term in geometry. Our intuitive notion of a geometric plane is that of a flat, smooth surface that extends infinitely far in all directions on the surface. A desk top, the floor, a sheet of paper, or a plate of glass—all suggest the abstract geometric idea of a plane (or, more precisely, of a portion of a plane). Just as a point is considered to have no size and a line no width, a plane is thought of as having no thickness.

A basic assumption concerning the plane is the following:

Any three noncollinear (not all on the same line) *points determine exactly one plane.*

Another is this:

If a plane contains two points of a line, then it contains the entire line.

As a consequence of these postulates we have this fact:

Through a line and a point not on the line there is exactly one plane.

You can visualize this situation intuitively by standing a rectangular piece of cardboard on one edge and holding it firmly against a table. Imagine that the cardboard represents a plane passing through the line determined by the end points of that edge, A and B (Fig. 40). Note that the plane of the table also passes through $\overleftrightarrow{AB}$. Just as infinitely many lines

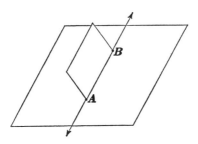

FIGURE 40

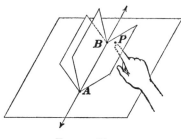

FIGURE 41

pass through a given point, likewise infinitely many planes pass through a given line. As you rotate the cardboard slowly about its edge $\overline{AB}$, think of each different position as representing a different plane through $\overleftrightarrow{AB}$. Now hold a fingertip somewhere near (but not touching) $\overline{AB}$ and somewhere *above* the plane of the table to represent a point P not on $\overleftrightarrow{AB}$. When you rotate the cardboard until it touches P (Fig. 41), you then have a representation of the unique plane that contains $\overleftrightarrow{AB}$ and P—that is, the plane that contains the three noncollinear points A, B, and P. (Dotted lines in the figure indicate portions that are hidden from view.)

Perhaps you can see now why a three-legged stool never wobbles when placed on the floor, since the three noncollinear tips of its legs will always fit exactly onto the plane of the floor. If there were a fourth leg, its tip might or might not lie on that plane. Repeat the experiment of Figure 41, using two fingertips and varying their positions by twisting your wrist in different directions. Sometimes both fingertips will touch the cardboard; sometimes only one will touch. Similarly, a four-legged chair will wobble if its four leg-tips do not all happen to fit onto the plane of the floor.

Figure 42 shows three noncollinear points, A, B, and C, and two lines,

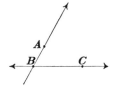

FIGURE 42

$\overleftrightarrow{AB}$ and $\overleftrightarrow{BC}$, that intersect at B. There is exactly one plane that contains points A, B, and C. You can see intuitively that this plane also contains the lines determined by any two of these points, for example, $\overleftrightarrow{AB}$ and $\overleftrightarrow{BC}$.

Hence we have the following:

If two lines intersect, exactly one plane contains both of them.

Exercise Set 5

1. $\overset{\bullet}{P}$

$\overset{\bullet}{Q}$ $\overset{\bullet}{R}$

Given any three noncollinear points, P, Q, and R, as shown above, draw three pictures to show how the points lie on two intersecting lines. (Hint: To show this, choose any one of the points as the point of intersection and make each of the other two points lie on a corresponding one of the lines.)

2.

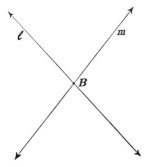

a. Starting with the two lines ℓ and m shown above, which intersect at point B, mark any other point A on line m and any other point C on line ℓ.

b. Are points A, B, and C collinear?

c. If you use the assumption that the two intersecting lines lie in exactly one plane, how many planes contain all three points, A, B, and C? Why?

3. In the room where you are sitting, turn your back to a doorknob. Then look at the horizontal line formed where the ceiling meets the top of the wall that you are facing. Try to imagine a plane that passes through both the top line and the point represented by the doorknob. Is such a plane possible?

4. In the room where you are sitting, pick two doorknobs and consider an

upper corner of the room. Try to visualize the plane that contains these
three "points." Is such a plane possible?

The Intersection of a Line and a Plane

In picturing a situation involving points and planes where all the points
lie in the same plane, we usually let our drawing paper itself represent that
plane. For example, in Figure 43 it is assumed that all four points, A, B,
C, and D, together with all six lines through these points, lie in the plane of
the paper. We could name this plane by naming any three of the points.

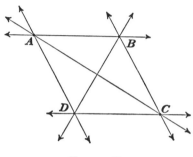

FIGURE 43

On the other hand, if one of those four points—say D—did not lie in
the plane of the other three, we might picture the situation as in Figure 44.
The lines $\overleftrightarrow{AB}$, $\overleftrightarrow{BC}$, and $\overleftrightarrow{AC}$ lie in the plane ABC. The lines $\overleftrightarrow{AD}$, $\overleftrightarrow{DB}$, and
$\overleftrightarrow{DC}$, however, do not lie in this plane. These lines are said to *intersect* the
plane in the points A, B, and C, respectively (Fig. 45). Let us now make
the following assumption:

> *If a line and a plane intersect, their intersection is either one
> point or the entire line.*

Thus we have three possible situations concerning a line and a plane:

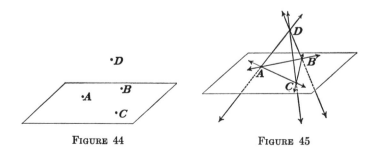

FIGURE 44   FIGURE 45

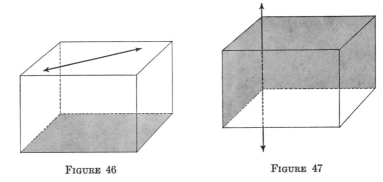

FIGURE 46   FIGURE 47

The line may lie in the plane; it may intersect the plane in exactly one point; or it may be *parallel* to the plane, so that the line and plane do not intersect. The latter case is illustrated by the example that any line in the plane of the ceiling will never intersect the plane of the floor (Fig. 46).

Parallel and Intersecting Planes

Two planes that have no points in common are called *parallel planes*. For example, the planes of the floor and ceiling are parallel planes, since they never intersect. We make a further assumption about two planes, namely:

If two planes intersect, they intersect in a line.

Figure 47 illustrates the line of intersection of the planes of two adjacent walls of a room.

Skew Lines

Perhaps you have looked up into the sky and observed two jet airplanes that look as if they were going to crash—one is traveling in a northerly direction and the other is traveling to the east (Fig. 48). But when they

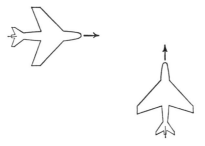

FIGURE 48

arrive at what appears to be the "same point," one slides gracefully under the other. The reason they do not meet is that their lines of flight are not in the same plane.

Any two lines that do not lie in a common plane are called *skew lines*. If two lines are skew, there is no plane that contains both of them. Hence skew lines have no points in common, since by a previous assumption any two lines that do intersect lie in exactly one plane and of course have this plane in common.

In the room pictured in Figure 49, lines ℓ and m are skew lines. Line ℓ lies in the plane of the ceiling, and line m lies in the plane of the floor. No single plane can be found that contains both of these lines. These lines have no points in common. Lines ℓ and k are also skew lines, as are lines ℓ and p.

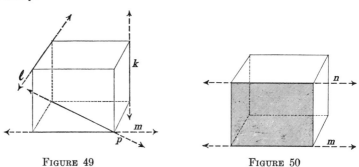

FIGURE 49   FIGURE 50

In fact, any line in the plane of the ceiling will never meet any line in the plane of the floor. For example, in Figure 50 lines n and m have no points in common. They are not skew lines, however, because they do lie in a common plane, namely, the plane of the front wall (which has been shaded). We shall focus our attention in the next section on the case in which two lines do lie in the same plane but have no points in common.

Exercise Set 6

1. Find a rectangular box of some sort (a shoebox or a cardboard carton, but not a cube) and place it upside down on the floor near you so that it looks like a solid block.

   a. Draw a picture of the box as it looks to you from where you are sitting.

   b. Did you draw a rectangle to represent the top of the box?

   c. Where could you place the box so that the top of the box looks like a segment?

   d. Where could you be so that the top of the box looks like a rectangle?

e. Could you move to where the top would look like a square?

2. Consider the table top as a portion of a plane and your pencil as a line segment.

    a. Hold the "line" so that it does not intersect the "plane" at all—that is, so the "line" is parallel to the plane. (Remember that even though the pencil stops, the line that it represents extends indefinitely in both directions.)

    b. Now hold the "line" so it intersects the "plane" exactly once.

    c. Can you hold the "line" so it intersects the "plane" in exactly two places?

3. In the room you are in, find twelve pairs of skew lines.

The Parallel Postulate

Is it possible for two lines in the same plane[6] to have no points in common? As we mentioned in the preceding section, the answer is "yes." Such lines are given a special name: *parallel lines.*

> *Two lines are parallel if and only if they lie in the same plane and do not intersect.*

In Figure 51, if we assume that lines ℓ and m lie on the plane of this page and have no points in common, we can say that lines ℓ and m are parallel. This fact can be expressed by the symbols "$\ell \parallel m$" (read "ℓ is parallel to m," "m is parallel to ℓ," or "ℓ and m are parallel to each other").

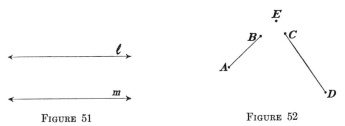

FIGURE 51   FIGURE 52

The rulings on a sheet of lined paper represent *parallel segments.* We have to be a little careful about defining what is meant by "parallel segments." Figure 52 shows two segments, $\overline{AB}$ and $\overline{CD}$, that lie in the same plane and do not intersect. Yet our intuition tells us that these segments are not parallel; we can visualize that the two lines containing these segments would intersect at about the point E. Hence, in defining parallel segments we cannot simply replace the word "line" by the word "segment"

---

[6] Lines that lie in the same plane are called "coplanar lines." For this entire section we shall limit our frame of reference to a single plane.

in the definition of parallel lines. Instead, we say that two segments are *parallel* if and only if the lines that contain the segments are parallel. In Figure 52, $\overline{AB}$ and $\overline{CD}$ are not parallel segments, because $\overleftrightarrow{AB}$ and $\overleftrightarrow{CD}$ are not parallel lines.

Similarly, any two rays (or a ray and a segment) are parallel if and only if the lines that contain them are parallel. In Figure 53, it is intuitively obvious that $\overrightarrow{AB}$ and $\overrightarrow{CD}$ appear to represent parallel rays; $\overrightarrow{EF}$ and $\overrightarrow{GH}$ do not intersect, but neither are they parallel, since the lines of which they are a part, $\overleftrightarrow{EF}$ and $\overleftrightarrow{GH}$, intersect at point I.

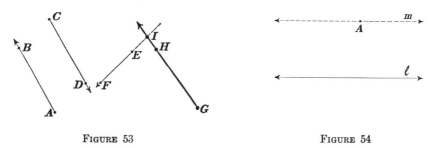

FIGURE 53   FIGURE 54

One of the basic assumptions on which our system of geometry rests is the property known as the Euclidean parallel postulate. The Euclidean parallel postulate can be stated as follows:

> *Given a line ℓ and a point A not on ℓ, there is one and only one line that contains point A and is parallel to ℓ.*

The situation is pictured in Figure 54. (Recall that in this section our frame of reference is a single plane.) Line m is parallel to the given line $ℓ$, and according to the postulate, there is only one such line m passing through the point A which does not intersect line $ℓ$.

We can summarize the relationship between any two lines *in a plane* by stating that exactly one of two situations can occur in our system of geometry:

> *Two lines intersect in exactly one point or else the lines are parallel.*

You might wonder what is meant by the phrase "in *our* system of geometry." Does this imply that there are other geometric systems as well? The answer to this question reveals one of the most interesting chapters in the history of mathematics.

"Our system of geometry" refers to the geometry with which most people are familiar, the Euclidean geometry that students learn in elementary and secondary school. Euclid based his development of geometry on five assumptions that seemed intuitively reasonable. Two of these postulates, which we have already used in this informal development, are the following: (a) exactly one line contains any two given points, and (b) exactly one plane contains any three noncollinear points.

After Euclid's *Elements* appeared, however, and for more than two thousand years, geometers felt that it should be possible to prove that the fifth assumption, the parallel postulate, was unnecessary because it could be derived from the other four. Many eminent mathematicians tried to prove that this was so, but all of them failed. In the futile attempt to prove this postulate superfluous, it was finally shown not only that the parallel postulate is indeed independent of the other postulates but also that there are other systems of geometry in which this postulate does not hold at all. These new systems have become known as *non-Euclidean geometries* because they do not assume Euclid's parallel postulate. Each of these systems has its own physical model.

It should not be surprising that Euclid apparently developed his geometry on the assumption that the world is a flat surface, with the Euclidean plane an abstraction of that physical observation. His postulate that any two points determine exactly one "line" is not valid on a uniformly curved surface such as a sphere, on which a "line" is a great circle. Thus, when you stretch a string tightly to form a "straight line" segment between the two points representing the North and South poles on a globe, you can see that an infinite number of such straight lines can pass through these two points, as indicated in Figure 55. The geometry used in navigation assumes that the ocean is not a flat, Euclidean plane surface but part of a spherical surface.

FIGURE 55

For 2,200 years the Euclidean assumption about geometric space went unchallenged, until the 1820's when the great Russian mathematician Nikolai Lobachevski conceived of a self-consistent geometric system in which Euclid's parallel postulate was not valid. With his bold and successful challenge of the unique "truth" of the Euclidean system of geometry,

Lobachevski made a tremendous impact on other mathematicians and scientists. They, too, were inspired to question so-called obvious truths that had been accepted for centuries; for example, Einstein challenged the assumption that *two events can truly occur in different places at the same time,* and thereby conceived his special theory of relativity.

Exercise Set 7

1. In this figure, name all the pairs of segments that appear to be parallel.

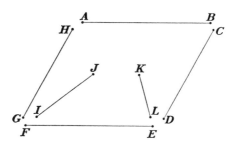

2. On a sheet of paper draw a line ℓ and a point A not on line ℓ. You can find the line that contains A and is parallel to line ℓ by the following procedure: Make a fold in the paper such that the line ℓ is folded back on itself and that A lies on the fold line. Unfold the paper and draw the fold line. Then make a second fold so that the first fold line is folded back on itself and so that A is on the second fold line. Does the second fold line appear to be parallel to line ℓ?

3. Suppose that we use as a model for a "non-Euclidean" geometry the following diagram, consisting of a plane set of points surrounded by a circle. Then a line segment becomes a "line." Show (by drawing) that there are several "lines" through point A that are "parallel" to "line" ℓ (that is, that do not intersect ℓ).

Half-Planes

When comparing the point–line relationship to the line–plane relationship, you may have observed some analogies. For example, just as two intersecting lines intersect in exactly one point, two intersecting planes intersect in exactly one line; just as two points determine a line, two intersecting lines determine a plane. There is one further analogy that we wish to make: A point on a line separates the line into three disjoint sets—the set consisting of the point itself, and the two sets consisting of the half-lines on each side of the point. In the same way, a line on a plane separates the plane into three disjoint sets—the set consisting of the line itself, and the *half-planes* on either side of the line.

To get an intuitive feeling of the notion of half-planes, let us imagine ourselves driving down a road with a center line, as in Figure 56. The "rule

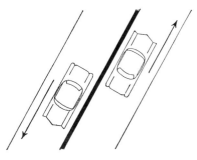

FIGURE 56

of the road" is to stay on your side of the line. In other words, the center line acts as a line of separation on the plane of the road. The line itself is no-man's-land.

In geometry, similarly, the dividing line lies in neither half-plane, even though it is the *boundary* line of each one. The line and the two half-planes, one on each "side" of the line, constitute the whole plane. Any single line in a plane separates the plane into these three disjoint sets.

As in the case of half-lines, we can distinguish between the two half-planes by naming a point in each. In Figure 57, the C side of $\overleftrightarrow{AB}$ has been shaded.

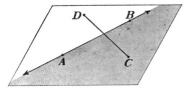

FIGURE 57

We assume that two points lie on opposite sides of $\overleftrightarrow{AB}$ (that is, in opposite half-planes) if the line segment connecting them intersects $\overleftrightarrow{AB}$

in one point. Point D in Figure 57 is not on the C side of $\overset{\leftrightarrow}{AB}$, since the segment $\overline{DC}$ intersects $\overset{\leftrightarrow}{AB}$. Can you place a point E in the diagram in Figure 57 so that segment $\overline{CE}$ does not intersect $\overset{\leftrightarrow}{AB}$? You will find that this point can be placed anywhere in the shaded half-plane containing C. To fulfill the requirement that $\overline{CE}$ does not intersect $\overset{\leftrightarrow}{AB}$, point E must lie on the C side of $\overset{\leftrightarrow}{AB}$.

The notion of half-planes will be important in the next sections to help us describe certain regions of a plane. The exercises in Exercise Set 8 will help prepare for this.

Exercise Set 8

1. Make a tracing of the figure shown below. Shade the part of the plane that is on the C side of $\overset{\leftrightarrow}{AB}$ with vertical shadings. Shade the part of the plane on the A side of $\overset{\leftrightarrow}{BC}$ with horizontal shadings. (Notice that you have doubly shaded the intersection of these two parts of the plane.)

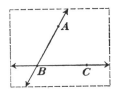

2. Make a tracing of the figure shown below. Shade the part of the plane that is on the A side of line ℓ and also on the A side of line m.

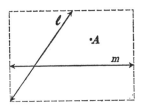

SUBSETS OF THE PLANE

Angles

In a plane, an unlimited number of lines pass through a given point. In Figure 58, three such lines, $\overset{\leftrightarrow}{BE}$, $\overset{\leftrightarrow}{CF}$, and $\overset{\leftrightarrow}{DG}$, are pictured passing through the point A. A second way of viewing the diagram in Figure 58 is to think of point A as a common end point for six rays, namely $\overrightarrow{AB}$, $\overrightarrow{AC}$, $\overrightarrow{AD}$, $\overrightarrow{AE}$, $\overrightarrow{AF}$, and $\overrightarrow{AG}$. Since there are infinitely many lines passing through

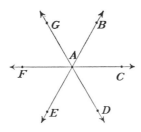

FIGURE 58

a given point, there are also infinitely many rays that originate at this point. Two rays such as $\overrightarrow{AB}$ and $\overrightarrow{AE}$ are said to be collinear because they lie on the same line, namely $\overleftrightarrow{BE}$, while two rays such as $\overrightarrow{AB}$ and $\overrightarrow{AC}$ are clearly noncollinear. The union of two noncollinear rays having a common end point is the familiar geometric figure called an angle.[7] The two rays are called the *sides* of the angle, and their common end point is called the *vertex*.

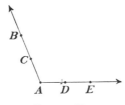

FIGURE 59

An angle can be designated by naming three of its points: its vertex and one other point on each of the rays. The vertex is always the second point named. Since any point on either ray may be used as the first letter in designating an angle, the same angle may be named in many ways. The symbol used to designate an angle is $\angle$. For example, in Figure 59, $\angle CAD$, $\angle CAE$, $\angle BAD$, or $\angle DAB$ are different names for the same angle. Can you name this angle in any other ways without labeling any more points?

---

[7] According to this definition of angle, a "straight angle" (180°) would not be considered as an angle but simply a straight line, since the two rays in this case are collinear.

An angle separates the plane into three sets of points: the angle itself, the set of points in the "interior" of the angle, and the set of points in the "exterior" of the angle. You have an intuitive notion about what the interior and exterior of an angle are. Thus, in Figure 60 the points B, A, and C are on the angle, $\angle BAC$, itself; points D and E are in the interior of this angle (the region shaded with vertical rulings); points F and G are in the exterior of this angle (the region shaded with horizontal rulings).

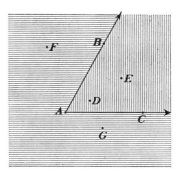

FIGURE 60

Now that we have confirmed our intuitive feeling for what is meant by the interior of an angle, let us define this region more precisely by using the notion of half-planes.

If we start with an angle—say $\angle BAC$ in Figure 61—we can observe that the rays $\overrightarrow{AB}$ and $\overrightarrow{AC}$ are parts of the lines $\overleftrightarrow{AB}$ and $\overleftrightarrow{AC}$, respectively. Now if we indicate these lines with dashes, as in the figure, we can visualize either

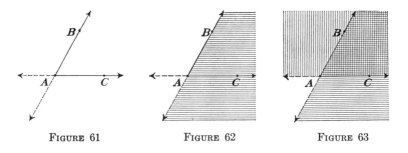

FIGURE 61   FIGURE 62   FIGURE 63

line as separating the plane into two half-planes. Let us consider $\overleftrightarrow{AB}$ first and with horizontal rulings let us shade the half-plane consisting of the

C side of $\overset{\leftrightarrow}{AB}$. The picture should look like the diagram in Figure 62. Now, on the same diagram let us consider $\overset{\leftrightarrow}{AC}$ as a separation line and shade in the B side of $\overset{\leftrightarrow}{AC}$ with vertical rulings. The result is shown in Figure 63. The crosshatched portion of the diagram represents the interior of $\angle BAC$. From this diagram you see that we can define the *interior* of $\angle BAC$ as the intersection of the two half-planes, one of them being the C side of $\overset{\leftrightarrow}{AB}$ and the other being the B side of $\overset{\leftrightarrow}{AC}$. The exterior of the angle is the set of points in the plane which includes neither the points of the angle nor those of its interior.

Angles will be important to our discussion of triangles in the next section.

Exercise Set 9

The picture below indicates the intersection of two streets. The points of interest are labeled as follows:

G, grocery store
S, stop light
P, park
D, drug store
B, bank
O, ocean
T, taxi stand
H, hotel
R, restaurant

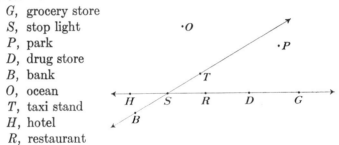

1. a. Name each of the four angles formed by the two streets $\overset{\leftrightarrow}{BT}$ and $\overset{\leftrightarrow}{HG}$.

b. What point do all four angles have in common?

c. Point P is in the interior of what angle(s)?

d. Point P is in the exterior of what angle(s)?

e. Point O is in the interior of what angle(s)?

f. Point O is in the exterior of what angle(s)?

g. Is point G on $\angle TSR$? on $\angle HSB$? on $\angle HST$? on $\angle DSB$?

h. Point H is in the exterior of what angle(s)?

2. a. To go directly from the park, P, to the ocean, O, you would need to cross the street represented by $\overset{\leftrightarrow}{BT}$. Are P and O in the same half-plane with respect to $\overset{\leftrightarrow}{BT}$?

b. Are H and O in the same half-plane with respect to $\overset{\leftrightarrow}{BT}$? Why?

c. Are P and O in the same half-plane with respect to $\overleftrightarrow{HG}$? Why?

d. Name all the points that are on the T side of $\overleftrightarrow{SG}$.

e. Name all the points that are on the G side of $\overleftrightarrow{ST}$.

f. What point(s) is (are) on both the T side of $\overleftrightarrow{SG}$ and the G side of $\overleftrightarrow{ST}$? What information does this give us?

Triangles

Let us consider any three noncollinear points, say A, B, and C, together with the segments $\overline{AB}, \overline{BC}$, and $\overline{AC}$ joining them. One such configuration is pictured in Figure 64. This is the familiar geometric figure known as a *triangle*. We can define a triangle as the union of the three segments that join three noncollinear points. The segments are called the *sides*, and their end points the *vertices* (singular: vertex), of the triangle. In Figure 64, the sides are $\overline{AB}$, $\overline{BC}$, and $\overline{AC}$, while points A, B, and C are the vertices. A triangle is denoted by the symbol $\triangle$ followed by the three vertices named in any order. Hence we can designate the triangle in Figure 64 by any of these names: $\triangle ABC$, $\triangle BCA$, $\triangle CAB$, $\triangle CBA$, $\triangle ACB$, or $\triangle BAC$.

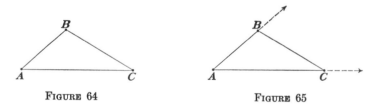

FIGURE 64   FIGURE 65

In Figure 65, vertex A is the vertex of $\angle BAC$, which contains the two sides $\overline{AB}$ and $\overline{AC}$ of the triangle. Even though the rays $\overrightarrow{AB}$ and $\overrightarrow{AC}$ of the angle BAC are not fully contained in the triangle, $\angle BAC$ is nevertheless called *an angle of* $\triangle ABC$. Hence we speak of a triangle as having three angles and of the vertex of each angle as a vertex of the triangle. One of the other two angles of $\triangle ABC$ could be named either $\angle BCA$ or $\angle ACB$, and the remaining angle either $\angle ABC$ or $\angle CBA$.

The triangle separates the plane into three disjoint sets: the set of points on the triangle, the set of points in its interior, and the set of points in its exterior. The *interior of the triangle* is the intersection of the interiors of the three angles of the triangle.

In Figure 66 the interior of $\triangle PQR$ is shaded with horizontal rulings and the exterior with vertical rulings. Each labeled point belongs to one

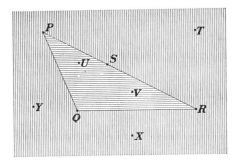

FIGURE 66

of these three sets. Thus, points P, Q, R, and S lie on the triangle; points U and V lie in the interior; and points T, X, and Y lie in the exterior.

Exercise Set 10

1. a. Name all the triangles in the figure below.

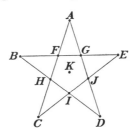

b. Point K is in the exterior of which of these triangles?

c. Point K is in the interior of which of these triangles?

d. Point K is on which of these triangles?

2. a. In the figure above, point A is in the exterior of which of the triangles?

b. Point A is in the interior of which of the triangles?

c. Point A is on which of the triangles?

3. Explain why any given triangle lies in exactly one plane.

Simple Closed Curves and Regions

A *curve* in a plane is merely a set of points that ideally can be traced without lifting the pencil from the paper. The drawings in Figure 67 are all examples of curves. Perhaps you can see intuitively why the figures in

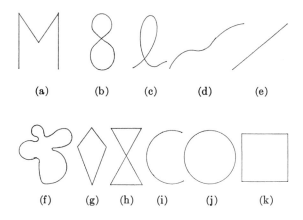

(a)   (b)   (c)   (d)   (e)

(f)   (g)   (h)   (i)   (j)   (k)

FIGURE 67

(a), (c), (d), (e), and (i) are called open curves; the others are called closed curves. To trace a *closed curve*, you can start at any point on the curve, continue along the curve, and return to that starting point without lifting your pencil from the paper. Figures (f), (g), (j), and (k) are simple closed curves. A *simple closed curve* starts and ends at the same point without ever crossing or retracing itself. Thus a triangle is a simple closed curve.

Any simple closed curve separates the plane into three sets of points: the curve itself, its interior, and its exterior. Considered together, a simple closed curve and its interior are sometimes called a *region*, and the curve itself is called the *boundary* of the region. In Figure 68 the triangle together with its interior is called a *triangular region*.

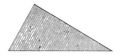

FIGURE 68

Some other examples of regions in the plane are pictured in Figure 69.

FIGURE 69

Let us look at each of the regions pictured in Figure 69 and ask the following question: Is it possible to locate two points, A and B, on the simple closed boundary curve so that at least part of $\overline{AB}$ lies *outside* the region?

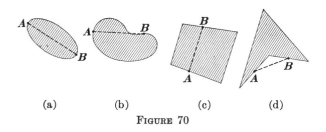

(a)   (b)   (c)   (d)

FIGURE 70

As indicated in Figure 70, the answers are (a) no, (b) yes, (c) no, (d) yes. In diagrams (a) and (c), no matter where the points A and B are placed on the simple closed curve, $\overline{AB}$ always lies fully *inside or on the boundary of* the region. Such regions are said to be *convex*, and the simple closed curves that form their boundaries are also classified as *convex*. Thus, all triangles are convex.

If, for some pair of points A and B on the simple closed curve, $\overline{AB}$ lies at least partly *outside* the region—as in (b) and (d)—then the region and also the simple closed curve that forms its boundary are classified as *concave*.

Exercise Set 11

1. Figures 67(f), (g), (j), and (k) are examples of simple closed curves. Which of these four simple closed curves are convex?

2. On each of the following simple closed curves you will find one point labeled A. Mark another point B on each simple closed curve to illustrate that each is concave.

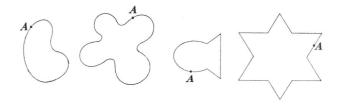

3. Draw a convex simple closed curve. Draw a triangle in its interior. Shade the entire region that is in the interior of the simple closed curve and that is also in the exterior of the triangle.

4. Make a tracing of the four points pictured below:

•   •

•   •

   a. Draw a convex simple closed curve that passes through the four points in your tracing.

   b. Draw a concave simple closed curve that passes through these same four points.

5. Can you place four points on your paper so that it would be impossible to draw a convex simple closed curve passing through them?

Polygons

A simple closed curve consisting of the union of line segments is called a *polygon*. In Figure 71, you can see that only (a), (b), (e), (f), and (h) are polygons. Regarding the other four, (c) and (d) are not *closed* curves; (i)

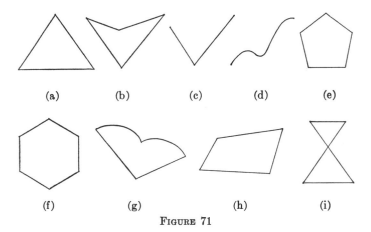

   (a)   (b)   (c)   (d)   (e)

   (f)   (g)   (h)   (i)

FIGURE 71

is not a *simple* closed curve; (g) is a simple closed curve, but it is not formed only of *line segments*. Thus you can see how our definition of a polygon gives a precise description of this particular class of geometric figures.

The line segments that form a polygon are called the *sides* of the polygon. (However, if consecutive segments are collinear, they are thought of as making up just one side.) A polygon is usually named according to the number of sides it has. A triangle is a polygon with three sides. A polygon with four sides is called a *quadrilateral*; five sides, a *pentagon*; six sides, a *hexagon*; seven sides, a *heptagon*; and eight sides, an *octagon*. Examples of these are pictured in Figure 72.

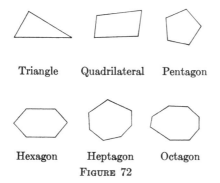

Triangle   Quadrilateral   Pentagon

Hexagon   Heptagon   Octagon
FIGURE 72

Any polygon together with its interior is called a polygonal region. We can specify the number of sides in its boundary by naming the particular kind of polygon; for example, a polygonal region bounded by six segments is called a hexagonal region.

All of the polygons shown in Figure 72 are convex. A concave polygon appears in Figure 71(b).

Exercise Set 12

1. The face of a familiar sort of bathroom tile could be described as a closed convex hexagonal region. Describe the region represented by the face of a standard "Stop" sign.

2. Draw a picture to represent each of the following:
   a. Concave quadrilateral
   b. Convex pentagon
   c. Concave hexagon
   d. Closed concave hexagonal region
   e. Closed convex octagonal region

3. Make a tracing of the following twelve points.

a. Construct a polygon with the twelve points as vertices.

b. Is your polygon convex or concave?

c. How many sides does your polygon have?

4. a. Draw a picture of a curve that is not closed.

b. Draw a picture of a closed curve that is not simple.

c. Draw a picture of a simple closed curve that is not a polygon.

d. Draw a picture of a simple closed curve that is the union of five segments.

SPACE AND THREE-DIMENSIONAL FIGURES

Geometric Space

So far in this booklet we have confined most of our discussion to figures that lie in one plane. Angles, triangles, quadrilaterals, circles, and polygonal regions are all examples of what are known as *two-dimensional* (or *plane*) *figures*—that is, figures that lie in a single plane. We have mentioned briefly some facts about points and lines that do not lie in the same plane and about intersecting planes, parallel planes, and lines that intersect planes. It is on these latter matters that we wish now to focus our full attention. Before we can develop these ideas adequately, however, we must define what we mean by geometric space.

Geometric space can be thought of as the set of all points in the physical universe. Since a geometric point represents position, space is represented by all possible positions in the universe. Every point lies in space; every line lies in space; every plane lies in space; in fact, we (our bodies) are contained in space.

Just as a point separates a line into two half-lines and a line separates a plane into two half-planes, a plane separates space into two *half-spaces*. Suppose we think of a plane as a sort of wall. The plane separates space into three disjoint sets of points: those in front of the plane, those in the

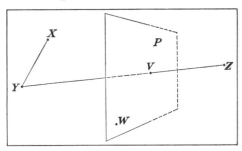

FIGURE 73

plane itself, and those behind the plane. The separating plane does not lie in either half-space; it is called the *boundary* of each half-space.

In Figure 73 the plane P separates space into two half-spaces. Since the segment joining X and Y does not intersect the plane P, points X and Y are in the same half-space with respect to the given plane P. Points Y and Z are in different half-spaces with respect to P, since the segment joining them, $\overline{YZ}$, intersects P at a point, V. Points V and W are in the boundary plane; hence they lie in neither half-space.

Drawing Spatial Diagrams

All of us are used to seeing figures that do not lie in a plane, such as tables, chairs, boxes, cans, balls, and so on. Such physical objects may or may not be solid; for example, consider a billiard ball versus a tennis ball. Difficulty arises when we come to draw such three-dimensional figures on the two-dimensional plane of a sheet of paper. We must use principles of perspective, just as an artist does, to convey the impression of an object as seen in space. In fact, even in drawing a *spatial diagram* of a two-dimensional figure, such as a circular disk or the portion of a plane such as that shown in Figure 73, we distort its true shape so as to give a realistic impression of how it appears in space. We know that a plate is generally round; nevertheless, in a spatial drawing we picture it as an ellipse to show how it would generally appear in space. We also

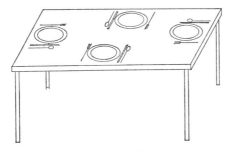

FIGURE 74

draw a rectangular table top with its left and right sides not parallel to the sides of the paper; that is, we draw the table top as a parallelogram in order to picture it as lying in a plane parallel to the floor (Fig. 74). In a *planar diagram*, on the other hand, a rectangle is always drawn with adjacent sides perpendicular to each other, and a circular region is always drawn as a round, rather than an elliptical, shape.

You will notice that we picture a plane by showing only a portion of it enclosed by four segments. If you hold a piece of cardboard in various

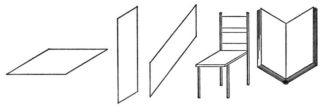

FIGURE 75

positions and draw what you see, you can illustrate planes oriented in horizontal, vertical, and slanted positions relative to the floor. Can you hold a piece of cardboard so that it appears a straight line to your eye?

The spatial diagrams in Figure 75 show a number of planes oriented in various positions in space.

Figure 76 illustrates techniques for drawing planes and lines in space. For each example follow the directions in parentheses; then compare your result with the spatial diagram shown.

(a)   A horizontal line intersecting a vertical plane
        (Stick a pencil through a piece of cardboard held vertically.)

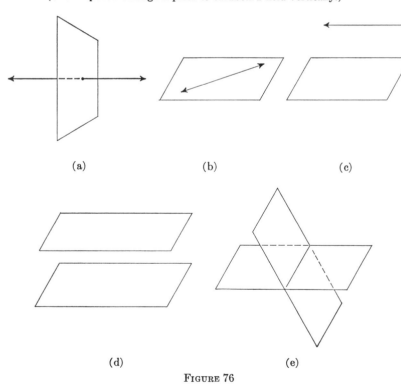

FIGURE 76

(b)   A line lying in a horizontal plane
        (Lay the cardboard flat on a desk; lay a pencil on top of it.)
(c)   A line in space parallel to a horizontal plane
        (Lay the cardboard flat on the desk; hold the pencil above, and parallel to,
        the plane of the desk.)
(d)   Parallel planes
        (Hold two pieces of cardboard so their planes do not intersect.)
(e)   Two intersecting planes
        (Cut two pieces of cardboard halfway through; then slide the pieces together
        at the slits.)

Analyzing Three-dimensional Rectangular Figures

Now let us analyze the geometric aspects of a room. We shall draw
a picture of a room, then label the corners in order to talk about the

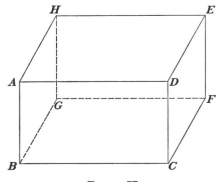

FIGURE 77

specific planes, lines, and points of the room. The eight corners of a room
represent geometric vertices. In Figure 77 these points are labeled with
the first eight letters of the alphabet.

As indicated by the shaded regions in the six drawings of Figure 78,
the room is bounded by six rectangular regions: the four walls, the floor,
and the ceiling. Since these geometric *faces* all lie in different planes, a
room is an example of a *three-dimensional* figure; and since the faces are
all rectangles, the room is called a three-dimensional *rectangular* figure.

The twelve segments that are sides of the six rectangles are called *edges*
of the rectangular figure. Looking at Figures 77 and 78, we see that the
four edges of the floor are $\overline{BC}$, $\overline{CF}$, $\overline{FG}$, and $\overline{BG}$. Can you name the eight
other edges of this figure? Notice that $\overline{BC}$ is also an edge of the front wall.
Thus each edge forms the intersection of two adjacent faces.

You will notice that some of the planes intersect and some do not. For
example, in Figure 78 the plane of the ceiling, $ADEH$,[8] does not intersect

---

[8] To identify a plane we need only name three noncollinear points, but for the purpose of this discussion
we designate any specific plane by naming the four vertices of the face that lies in that plane.

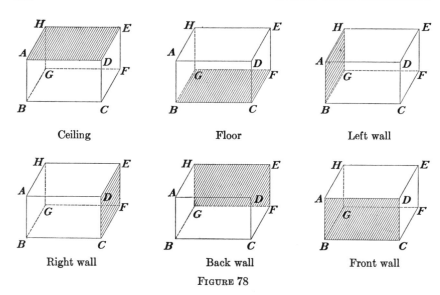

| Ceiling | Floor | Left wall |

| Right wall | Back wall | Front wall |

FIGURE 78

the plane of the floor, plane $BCFG$. These are parallel planes. There are two other pairs of parallel planes: $ABGH$ and $DCFE$, and also $HGFE$ and $ABCD$.

You also may have noticed that each plane intersects four other planes and is parallel to a fifth plane.

Let us concentrate for a moment on just the floor, $BCFG$, and the edge $\overline{AB}$, as pictured in Figure 79. We draw in $\overrightarrow{BC}$ and $\overrightarrow{BG}$. We know that $\angle ABC$ is a right angle, since it is an angle of a rectangle. Likewise, $\angle ABG$ is a right angle. Since $\overline{AB}$ does not lie in plane $BCFG$ but does form right angles with two rays that lie in plane $BCFG$ and pass through point B, we say that $\overline{AB}$ is perpendicular to the plane $BCFG$.

To generalize, a line—say $\overleftrightarrow{AB}$—is perpendicular to a plane at a given point—say P—in the plane if for any two rays $\overrightarrow{PC}$ and $\overrightarrow{PD}$ lying in the plane, $\angle APC$ and $\angle APD$ are right angles (Fig. 80).

Returning to our analysis of the room, notice that there are four seg-

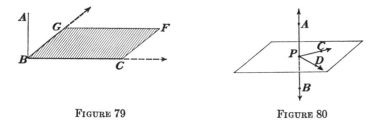

FIGURE 79   FIGURE 80

ments perpendicular to the plane of the floor: $\overline{AB}$, $\overline{CD}$, $\overline{EF}$, and $\overline{GH}$. These
four segments are also perpendicular to the plane of the ceiling, since the
planes of the floor and ceiling are parallel.

Our picture of a room gives us one further relationship between planes.
We can show that three planes may have a single point in common. Consider the plane of the front wall, $ABCD$; the plane of the left wall, $ABGH$;
and the plane of the ceiling, $ADEH$. These three planes have point A in
common; this is clear from the notation and is confirmed by the drawing
in Figure 77.

Exercise Set 13

1. Hold a circular piece of cardboard in front of you and rotate it slowly.
   Name three different geometric figures that appear as you see the disk
   in various possible positions.

2. In the room where you are, consider the plane determined by the ceiling
   and the plane determined by a slightly opened door.

   a. Where do these planes intersect?

   b. Open the door to various positions and consider what happens to
   the intersections.

3. Consider a four-story building.

   a. Are the planes of the first, second, and third floors all parallel to
   each other?

   b. Name another plane that is parallel to all of these.

4.

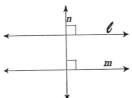

The three lines pictured have the following relationships: lines ℓ and m
are parallel; lines n and ℓ are perpendicular to each other; and lines
n and m are perpendicular to each other. The planes of the floor, the
left wall, and the ceiling of a room have similar relationships. Explain
what these relationships are.

Boxes, Cans, Cones, and Balls

In this final section we shall discuss some intuitive notions about a few
familiar solid figures: boxes, cans, cones, and balls. In geometry these are

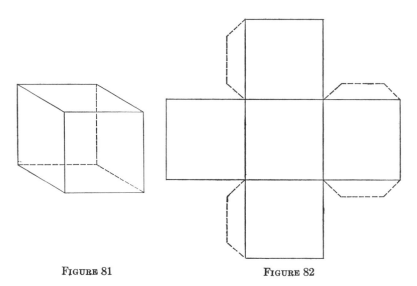

FIGURE 81   FIGURE 82

known respectively as rectangular prisms, right circular cylinders, right circular cones, and spheres.

BOXES

In the preceding section, we analyzed three-dimensional rectangular figures in some detail. Most boxes are rectangular. If each face of the box is a square region, as that in Figure 81, it is a special type of box called a *cube*. Unique among the general three-dimensional rectangular figures, a cube has faces that are all the same size and shape. The faces, then, are said to be *congruent* to each other (symbol: ≅). To learn more about this concept, see Booklet No. 18: *Symmetry, Congruence, and Similarity*.

Imagine that you take a cubical cardboard box and cut off its cover. Then visualize cutting the coverless box along enough of its edges so that it lies flat in a plane. What does the resulting figure in the plane look like? Try to draw it on a piece of paper. Figure 82 shows one of the possible figures you might have drawn (minus the broken lines that represent tabs). This is one of *eight* possible ways in which you could have cut the box. Now trace Figure 82, including the tabs, fold it, and glue it together to form a box without a cover. Next, cut the box in a *different* way so that it can again be flattened out. By constructing and cutting as many boxes as necessary, see how many of the eight ways you can find. We shall come back to this problem in Exercise Set 14.

CANS

What would you call the geometric relationship represented by the ends of a round can? By now you will readily answer: a pair of congruent circular regions. These regions, called the *bases* of the cylinder, lie in parallel planes.

Have you ever peeled off the label of a circular can? If you were to flatten the label on a plane surface, what shape do you think the paper would have?

A can (a right circular cylinder) is the union of two congruent circular regions and a curved surface that flattens into a rectangular region. (See Fig. 83.) The curved surface is called the *lateral surface* of the cylinder.

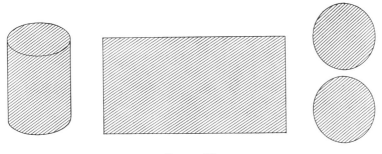

FIGURE 83

We can see how the lateral surface might be generated by carrying out the following activity: Cut a circular region out of a piece of cardboard and place it on a table. Now tie a small, weighted object to a piece of string about 6 inches long and hold the string above the region so that the weighted end just touches a point on the circular boundary. Then slowly rotate the weight all the way around the boundary. In Figure 84, the weighted string is shown in several of its positions. Each position represents a segment perpendicular to the planes of the bases of the cylinder. Such a segment is called an *altitude* of the cylinder. The lateral surface

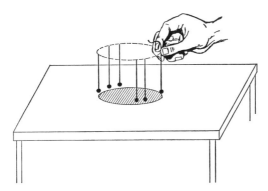

FIGURE 84

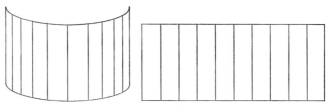

FIGURE 85

consists of the set of all such congruent segments. (See Fig. 85.) Since each segment is perpendicular to the two bases, the cylinder is called a *right* cylinder (suggested by the term "right angle").

CONES

A "cone" is a familiar figure in an ice-cream parlor, seen in the shape of the ice-cream cone itself and in the shape of the cups in which ice-cream sundaes are often served. Such a figure is known in geometry as a *right circular cone*, and it consists of a single circular region called the *base*, and a lateral, curved surface. Such a geometric cone is pictured in Figure 86.

The curved surface of a right circular cone can be generated in the following way: As in the case of a right cylinder, place a cutout of a circular region on a table to represent the base of the cone. Now hold a weighted

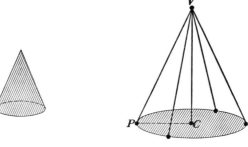

FIGURE 86　　　　　　　　　FIGURE 87

string at a point V above the table so that the weight just touches the center C of the circular region, as indicated in Figure 87. The segment $\overline{VC}$, perpendicular to the plane of the base, is called the *altitude* of the cone. Now, holding a second piece of string taut between V and any point P on the circular boundary, rotate the end point at P all the way around the circle. Each position of the string represents a segment called a *slant height* of the cone. Four such segments are shown in Figure 87. The set of all such congruent segments between V, the *vertex* of the cone, and points on the circular boundary of the base makes up the lateral surface of the cone.

The altitude of any cone is defined as the perpendicular segment from the vertex to the plane of the base. If the foot of the altitude coincides with the center of the base, as in Figure 87, then $\overline{VC}$ forms a right angle with each of the radii in the base. Hence this cone is called a *right* cone.

BALLS

A ball is a good representation of a three-dimensional figure called a *sphere*. The sphere in space is the counterpart of a circle in a plane. Let us recall the definition of a circle: A circle is a simple closed plane curve having

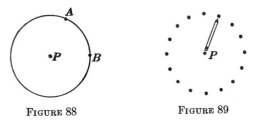

FIGURE 88   FIGURE 89

a point, say P, in its interior such that if A and B are any two points on the curve, then $\overline{PA} \cong \overline{PB}$. The point P is called the *center* of the circle. In Figure 88 we have represented a circle that lies in the plane of the paper.

We could generate a circle by holding one end of a pencil fixed at a point P on a piece of paper, and then rotating the other end into various positions on the paper, marking off each position with a dot. A number of such points have been marked in Figure 89. The set of all such points is a circle with center P and with radius congruent to the segment represented by the pencil.

If we follow a similar procedure in space, we can generate a sphere. Imagine that we are holding a small styrofoam ball in space and lightly sticking into the ball many toothpicks representing congruent segments. We then mold a piece of plastic bag around our configuration so that the end of each toothpick touches the plastic sheet. The plastic sphere that would result is pictured in Figure 90. The styrofoam ball represents the

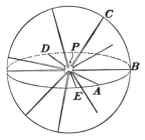

FIGURE 90

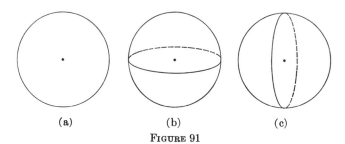

(a)   (b)   (c)
FIGURE 91

center, P, of the sphere, and the toothpicks represent the radii, $\overline{PA}$, $\overline{PB}$, $\overline{PC}$, and so on.

With this intuitive notion of a sphere, we can define a sphere as follows:

> *A sphere is a figure in space having a point, say P, in its interior and consisting of all points such that if A and B are any two of these points, then* $\overline{PA} \cong \overline{PB}$.

How can we picture a sphere in the plane of the paper? We generally distinguish a picture of a sphere from a picture of a circle, shown in Figure 91(a), by indicating on the spherical surface a *great circle*, which separates the sphere into two hemispheres (half-spheres), as drawn in Figure 91(b) and (c). Such a great circle has its center at the center of the sphere. One familiar physical representation of a hemisphere is the hollowed-out peel of half an orange.

Exercise Set 14

1. a. Which of the figures below are right cones?

   b. Which are right cylinders?

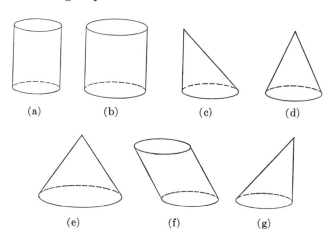

(a)   (b)   (c)   (d)

(e)   (f)   (g)

2. The configuration shown at the right folds to make a box without a cover. Of the various arrangements of five squares that are shown below, which could you also fold to make "coverless" boxes?

(a)   (b)   (c)   (d)

3. There are twelve different ways to arrange five squares of the same size, given the limitation that the sides must touch and that the touching sides of any two squares must exactly align—that is, excluding such arrangements as (a) and (b), at the right.

(a)   (b)

Five of the twelve are shown in exercise 2. See if you can find the other seven possibilities. Note, however, that two arrangements such as (c) and (d) are considered to be the same, since these shapes are congruent.

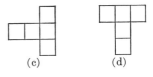

(c)   (d)

4. Circle the eight different arrangements of five squares that can be folded to make a box without a top. (You may wish to cut out each pattern and try folding it.) Put an **✕** on the square that will be the bottom of each box.

SUMMARY

In this booklet we have proceeded systematically from the geometry of a line to the geometry of a plane to the geometry of space, since it is essential to build up a language in order to write about geometric ideas. The language in itself, however, is by no means the most important element. With the presence of physical models and by means of actually pointing to the physical representations of the points, lines, segments, rays, planes, etc., that are under consideration, it is possible to communicate with very little terminology and notation. Hence it is not necessary to follow the sequence of the material given here; it is possible, rather, to start intuitively with any one of the geometric ideas developed in this booklet and to introduce precise language and terminology as the need arises.

For Further Reading

Among the various helpful references that deal with the subject here introduced are the following:

ANDERSON, RICHARD D. *Concepts of Informal Geometry.* ("Studies in Mathematics," Vol. V.) New Haven, Conn.: School Mathematics Study Group, 1960. Pp. 272. Available from A. C. Vroman, Inc., 367 S. Pasadena Ave., Pasadena, Calif. 91105.

BRUNE, IRVIN H. "Geometry in the Grades," in *Enrichment Mathematics for the Grades.* Twenty-seventh Yearbook of the National Council of Teachers of Mathematics. Washington, D.C.: The Council, 1963. Available from the National Council of Teachers of Mathematics, 1201 16th St., N.W., Washington, D.C. 20036.

EVES, HOWARD, and NEWSOM, CARROLL V. *An Introduction to the Foundations and Fundamental Concepts of Mathematics* (rev. ed.). New York: Holt, Rinehart & Winston, 1965. Pp. 398. Available from Holt, Rinehart & Winston, Inc., 383 Madison Ave., New York, N. Y. 10017.

FEHR, HOWARD F., and HILL, THOMAS J. *Contemporary Mathematics for Elementary Teachers.* Boston: D. C. Heath, 1966. Pp. 394. Available from D. C. Heath & Co., 285 Columbus Ave., Boston, Mass. 02116.

McFARLAND, DORA, and LEWIS, EUNICE M. *Introduction to Modern Mathematics for Elementary Teachers.* Boston: D. C. Heath, 1966. Pp. 406. See address above.

MITCHELL, BENJAMIN E., and COHEN, HASKELL. *A New Look at Elementary Mathematics.* Englewood Cliffs, N.J.: Prentice-Hall, 1965. Pp. 354. Available from Prentice-Hall, Inc., Englewood Cliffs, N.J. 07632.

MOISE, EDWIN E. *Elementary Geometry from an Advanced Standpoint.* Reading, Mass.: Addison–Wesley, 1963. Pp. 419. Available from Addison–Wesley Publishing Co., Inc., Reading, Mass. 01867.

VAN ENGEN, HENRY; HARTUNG, MAURICE L.; and STOCHL, JAMES E. *Foundations of Elementary School Arithmetic.* Chicago: Scott, Foresman & Co., 1965. Pp. 450. Available from Scott, Foresman & Co., 1900 E. Lake Ave., Glenview, Ill. 60025.

WHEELER, RURIC E. *Modern Mathematics, an Elementary Approach.* Belmont, Calif.: Brooks/Cole, 1966. Pp. 438. Available from Brooks/Cole, Belmont, Calif. 94002.

ANSWERS TO EXERCISES

Exercise Set 1

1. a.
   $X \quad Z \quad Y$

   b.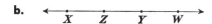
   $X \quad Z \quad Y \quad W$

   c. There are eleven more possible names:

   $\overleftrightarrow{XZ},\ \overleftrightarrow{XW},\ \overleftrightarrow{ZY},\ \overleftrightarrow{ZW},\ \overleftrightarrow{YW},\ \overleftrightarrow{YX},\ \overleftrightarrow{ZX},\ \overleftrightarrow{WX},\ \overleftrightarrow{YZ},\ \overleftrightarrow{WZ},$ and $\overleftrightarrow{WY}$.

2. The letters should spell STOP or POTS. (Note that statement **b** could have been omitted, since **a** and **c** alone give enough information to mark the points.)

3. a. $\overleftrightarrow{BC}$ (or $\overleftrightarrow{CB}$) and $\overleftrightarrow{AC}$ (or $\overleftrightarrow{CA}$)

   b. ⟵———•———•———•———⟶ *or* ⟵———•———•———•———⟶ *etc.*
   $\quad\quad A \quad B \quad C \quad\quad\quad\quad C \quad A \quad B$

   c. This is impossible. Three points determine either one or three lines.

4.

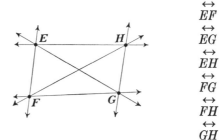

$\overleftrightarrow{EF}$ (or $\overleftrightarrow{FE}$)
$\overleftrightarrow{EG}$ (or $\overleftrightarrow{GE}$)
$\overleftrightarrow{EH}$ (or $\overleftrightarrow{HE}$)
$\overleftrightarrow{FG}$ (or $\overleftrightarrow{GF}$)
$\overleftrightarrow{FH}$ (or $\overleftrightarrow{HF}$)
$\overleftrightarrow{GH}$ (or $\overleftrightarrow{HG}$)

5. 2, 4, $^{-}$1, $^{-}$3

6.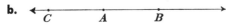

7. ⟵•—•⟶
   ···$^{-}$10 $^{-}$9 $^{-}$8 $^{-}$7 $^{-}$6 $^{-}$5 $^{-}$4 $^{-}$3 $^{-}$2 $^{-}$1 0 1 2 3 4 5 6 7 8 9 10···

Exercise Set 2

1. a. No.

   b. ⟵•————————•————————•————————⟶
   $\quad\quad C \quad\quad\quad A \quad\quad\quad B$

   c. No.

   d. No.

2. a. Yes.

b. No.

c. Yes.

d. Yes.

e. No.

f. No.

g. D must come between A and C.

h. Point A

3. a. $x \geq 0$.

b. $\overrightarrow{AC}$

c. $\overrightarrow{BA}$ (or $\overrightarrow{BC}$)

d. $x \geq {}^-2$.

4. a. A, B, C, D, E, F

b. A, B, C, D, E, F

c. $\overrightarrow{FD}, \overrightarrow{FC}, \overrightarrow{FB}, \overrightarrow{FA}$

5. The letters spell TIGER (or REGIT).

Exercise Set 3

1. a. Three $(\overline{AB}, \overline{BC}, \overline{AC})$

b. Yes.

c. Yes.

d. Yes.

e. No. (Point A is included in $\overline{AB}$ but not in $\overset{\circ\rightarrow}{AB}$.)

f. Yes.

2. a.

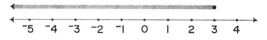

b.

c.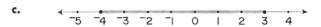

d. Yes.

e. $^-4 \leq x \leq 3$.

3. a. $x \geq \, ^-3$.

  b. $x \leq 1$.

  c. $^-3 \leq x \leq 1$.

Exercise Set 4

1. a. $M \cup N = \{1, 2, 3, 4, 5, 6, 7, 8, 9, \cdots\}$.

  b. $M \cap N = \varnothing$ (or $\{\ \}$). (That is, M and N have no elements in common, and hence the intersection set is the empty set.)

2. a. There are infinitely many points between any two different points on a line.

  b. Infinitely many

  c. None

3. a. Yes, for example:

  b. Yes, for example:

  c. Yes, for example:

  d. Yes, for example:

  e. No.

4. a. No.

  b. No.

  c. No.

  d. Yes, for example:

  e. Yes, for example:

5. a. $\overline{AC} = \overline{AB} \cup \overline{BC}$

  b. $\overline{AD} = \overline{AC} \cup \overline{BD}$

c. $\overline{AD} = \overline{AC} \cup \overline{CD}$

d. $\overline{BD} = \overline{AD} \cap \overline{BE}$

e. $\overline{AD} = \overline{AB} \cup \overline{BD}$

f. $\overline{AD} = \overline{AB} \cup \overline{BC} \cup \overline{CD}$

g. $\overline{BC} = \overline{AC} \cap \overline{BD}$

h. $\overline{BC} = \overline{AE} \cap \overline{BC}$

i. $\overline{AE} = \overline{AE} \cup \overline{BC}$

6. a. Yes, for example,

$$\overline{AB} \cap \overline{BC} = \{B\}, \qquad \overline{BC} \cap \overline{CD} = \{C\}, \qquad \overline{AC} \cap \overline{CE} = \{C\}.$$

b. Yes, for example,

$$\overline{AB} \cap \overline{CD} = \varnothing, \qquad \overline{AB} \cap \overline{CE} = \varnothing.$$

c. Yes, for example, **d, g, h** in exercise 5.

d. No.

e. No.

Exercise Set 5

1.

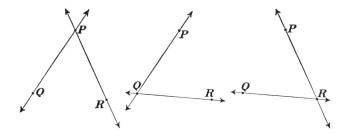

2. a.

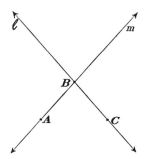

b. No.

c. Exactly one. Since A and B lie on line m, they lie on any plane that contains line m. Since B and C lie on line ℓ, they lie on any plane that contains line ℓ. But both of the lines ℓ and m lie in exactly one plane. Hence points A, B, and C all lie in this same plane and do not all lie in any other plane.

3. Yes.

4. Yes.

Exercise Set 6

1. a.

b. No.

c. Place the box so that its top is parallel to the floor and level with your eyes.

d. Looking directly down on top of the box.

e. No.

2. a.

b.

c. No.

3. Answers will vary but might include, for example, a pencil and a leg of a chair, or an edge of the cover of a book and an edge of the chalkboard.

Exercise Set 7

1. $\overline{AB}$ and $\overline{EF}$; $\overline{CD}$ and $\overline{GH}$

2. Yes.

3.

Exercise Set 8

1. 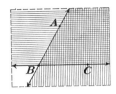 2.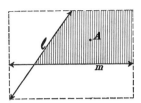

Exercise Set 9

1. a. $\angle HSB$ (or $\angle BSH$)

$\angle TSR$ (or $\angle TSD$, $\angle TSG$, $\angle DST$, $\angle RST$, etc.)

$\angle BSR$ (or $\angle BSD$, $\angle BSG$, etc.)

$\angle HST$ (or $\angle TSH$)

b. Point S

c. $\angle TSR$ (or $\angle TSD$, $\angle TSG$, $\angle RST$, etc.)

d. $\angle HST$, $\angle BSR$, $\angle HSB$

e. $\angle HST$

f. $\angle HSB$, $\angle TSR$, $\angle BSR$

g. Yes; no; no; yes.

h. $\angle TSR$, $\angle BSR$

2. a. No.

b. Yes, since $\overline{HO}$ does not intersect $\overleftrightarrow{BT}$; that is, you can go directly from the hotel, H, to the ocean, O, without crossing the street, $\overleftrightarrow{BT}$.

c. Yes, since $\overline{PO}$ does not intersect $\overleftrightarrow{HG}$.

d. O, T, P

e. R, D, G, P

f. Point P (Point P is in the interior of $\angle TSG$.)

Exercise Set 10

1. a. $\triangle AFG$, $\triangle BFH$, $\triangle CHI$, $\triangle DIJ$, $\triangle EGJ$, $\triangle ACJ$, $\triangle ADH$, $\triangle BDG$, $\triangle BEI$, $\triangle CEF$. (Each of the triangles could be named in six different ways.)

b. $\triangle AFG$, $\triangle BFH$, $\triangle CHI$, $\triangle DIJ$, $\triangle EGJ$

c. $\triangle ACJ$, $\triangle ADH$, $\triangle BDG$, $\triangle BEI$, $\triangle CEF$

d. None of them

2. a. $\triangle BFH$, $\triangle CHI$, $\triangle DIJ$, $\triangle EGJ$, $\triangle BDG$, $\triangle BEI$, $\triangle CEF$

b. None of them

c. $\triangle AFG$, $\triangle ACJ$, $\triangle ADH$

3. Suppose the vertices of the triangle are A, B, and C. We know that these are three noncollinear points and that three noncollinear points lie in exactly one plane. We can name this plane ABC. Now since A and B lie in plane ABC, so also does $\overleftrightarrow{AB}$. (If two points lie in a plane, then the line containing them lies in that plane.) Since $\overline{AB}$ is a subset of $\overleftrightarrow{AB}$, it must also lie in plane ABC. Similarly, since B and C lie in plane ABC, $\overleftrightarrow{BC}$ and hence $\overline{BC}$ do also; and since A and C lie in plane ABC, $\overleftrightarrow{AC}$ and hence $\overline{AC}$ do also. Since $\triangle ABC = \overline{AB} \cup \overline{BC} \cup \overline{AC}$, $\triangle ABC$ lies in the one plane ABC.

Exercise Set 11

1. (g), (j), (k)

2.

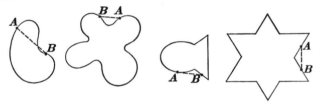

(Only one of many possible answers is given for each.)

3.

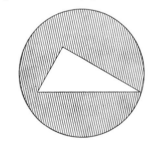

4. a.

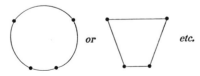

or   *etc.*

b.

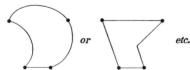

or   *etc.*

5. Yes, for example:

(Note that such a solution as this is not correct:
One of the four points must be in the interior of the triangle determined by the other three points.)

Exercise Set 12

1. Closed convex octagonal region.

2. a.

b.

c.

d.

e.

3. a. 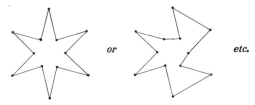   or   etc.

b. Concave

c. Twelve

4. a.    or   etc.

b.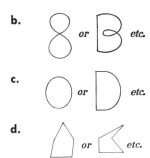

c.

d.

Exercise Set 13

1. Circular region, elliptical region, line segment
2. **a.** In a line that lies in the plane of the ceiling
   b. The intersections are all lines in the plane of the ceiling, passing through a common point, namely, the point where the line containing the hinges of the door intersects the ceiling.
3. **a.** Yes.
   b. The fourth floor
4. The floor and ceiling are parallel; the left wall and the ceiling are perpendicular to each other; and also the left wall and the floor are perpendicular to each other.

Exercise Set 14

1. **a.** (d) and (e)
   b. (a) and (b)
2. (a), (b), and (c)

3, 4.

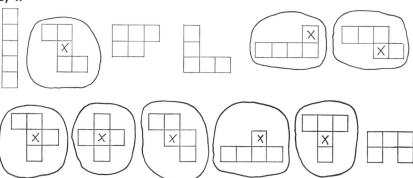

BOOKLET NUMBER FIFTEEN:

MEASUREMENT

INTRODUCTION

A group of first-grade children was asked, "What is arithmetic?" One of the most interesting responses was, "Arithmetic is measuring." Pursuing this unexpected viewpoint, the teacher asked, "What do you mean?"

"Like measuring to make a new dress. Sometimes my mother doesn't use a pattern. She uses me, and I have to stand still while she takes a lot of my measurements so she'll know how to cut the material to make it fit right."

"We measure when we buy shoes. I put my foot on that board like a ruler, and the man in the store moves it until it touches my toe. The man reads the size on the board."

"My mother puts my foot on a piece of paper and draws around my foot. Then she takes the picture to the shoe store."

Is arithmetic simply measuring? In science we observe, we identify, we compare. Is this measuring?

What is measurement?

"Measurement is one of the notions which modern science has taken over from common sense."[1] The commonsense use of the idea of measurement is so indigenous to man's behavior that it often goes unnoticed. What is this "common sense" that led to the concept of measurement?

The language of measurement is the language of comparison, and *measurement grows out of comparing.* Consciously or not, we are constantly comparing things within our awareness.

---

[1] Norman R. Campbell, "Measurement," *The World of Mathematics*, ed. James R. Newman (New York: Simon & Schuster, 1956), III, 1797.

Measuring is something that we all do many times each day. It involves much more than the narrow activity of making numerical measurements of length, area, or volume.

Jack was squeezing some toothpaste onto his toothbrush. Suddenly he stopped, because he had obtained enough.

Mrs. Smith was serving vegetables to her children. She put some of Martha's vegetables back, for she knew she had given Martha more than her daughter would eat.

The typist looked at the notes on her desk and decided that the letter on which she was working would be more than one page long.

Bill awoke and looked out the window. How light it was! He decided that he must have overslept.

These examples do not necessarily constitute one's usual concept of measurement, in which a ruler, scale, or other such instrument is involved. Nevertheless, some type of comparison is being made in each instance.

Jack used his toothbrush as a unit of measure. When the bristles of the brush were covered with toothpaste, he quit squeezing. Mrs. Smith remembered how much her daughter would eat. She adjusted Martha's portion to ensure that no vegetables would be left over. The typist knew how many lines of handwritten notes would fill a typed page. Bill judged the time of day by the intensity of the daylight.

Comparing things is as natural for man as breathing. Comparison is the basis for measurement. We make comparisons that range from very simple, general ones, such as "The string is as long as the ribbon" or "The elephant weighs more than the horse," to comparisons expressed in terms of precise numerical measurements.

Two unique features of measurement now begin to unfold. As we analyze the things we do every day, it becomes obvious that nearly everything we do involves comparing in some sense. Secondly, most of these comparisons are approximate in nature, involving some very simple ideas that have been in use since earliest times.

PROCEDURES FOR MAKING COMPARISONS

Can we identify the basic steps involved in the measurement process? Often we are unaware of the things we actually do in making comparisons, but an understanding of the process is important because we repeat the same steps again and again. Let us see if we can isolate the various procedures and bring them into sharper focus.

Making Qualitative Comparisons

In making a general comparison of two objects, we must first identify some common property that will furnish a basis for comparison. For example, we may wish to compare the *prettiness* of two flowers, the *size* of two buildings, and so forth. When a precise, quantitative comparison is not necessary or perhaps not feasible, then the degree of that property in one of the objects may be used as the basis, or unit of measure, for comparing it with the other. Thus, if we want to compare the prettiness of a daisy and a rose, we might use the prettiness of the rose as the basis for comparison. We could then say any of the following, depending on our personal evaluation of the matter:

The daisy is prettier than the rose.
The daisy is just as pretty as the rose, but no prettier.
The daisy is not as pretty as the rose.

We may select other properties for comparison, such as relative size. We might roughly compare two animals such as a dog and an elephant and use the size of the elephant as the basis for comparison. We might say:

The size of the dog is much less than that of the elephant.

We might even abbreviate that to:

The dog is much smaller than the elephant.

If the size of the dog were the basis, we would say:

The elephant is many times the size of the dog.

Again, we might abbreviate this to:

The elephant is much larger than the dog.

Exercise Set 1

Name the basis for comparison used in each of the following:

1. The beach ball is larger than the golf ball.

2. The cherry is smaller than the peach.

3. The shell is prettier than the rock.

4. The lion is fiercer than the mouse.

Making Quantitative Comparisons

A physical property we wish to measure must first be observed and identified. We sense, for example, the notions "cold" and "hot": snow is cold; fire is hot. From such simple observations we also identify "not cold" and "not hot." Thus we develop an awareness of *temperature* and its measurement.

Likewise, we can sense the notions "heavy" and "light" and compare two objects in terms of the characteristic known as *weight*.

Other physical properties that might occur to you for measuring include length, area, volume, density, viscosity, force, and velocity.

After we identify some common property of two things that we wish to compare, we then attempt to measure in some way the degree of likeness and difference. Ideas of amount, of position, of change, and of direction of change begin to come into focus.

Point of origin and *direction of change* are important ideas that we use in comparing and in making measurements. An awareness of variation or change involves also an awareness of the original state of being from which the change was made. It involves as well the awareness of change in one direction as opposed to change in another direction. Consider the directional changes expressed in these statements:

1. How far is it from *here* to *there?*
2. The sun will go down *later on.*

Within these simple situations we see the idea of a point of origin, or reference point, from which to measure and make comparisons.

In statement 1, the implied point of origin is "here." In 2, the clearly implied point of origin is "now," and the directional change alluded to is "after now," that is, *later on.*

Things that occur in nature help man to develop ideas concerning points of origin and to observe degrees of variation from those points.

For example, in the middle of the day the sun is directly overhead, and there is almost no shadow at all. In the morning the shadow is long in one direction; in the afternoon it is long in another direction.

There are times when day and night are almost equal. There are other times of the year when day is much longer than night, and at still other times night is much longer than day.

Events in nature, such as the equinoxes (points at which the sun crosses the celestial equator) and solstices (points at which the sun is at a maximum distance from the equator), helped man determine a point of origin from which to reckon time.

There are many examples of man's use of a point of origin and the direction of change. Any floor of a building, other than the top or bottom floor, serves as a point of origin from which the directions "up" and "down," or "upstairs" and "downstairs," are derived. Another example is the selection of the points on the equator as points of origin from which the directions "north" and "south" are measured along the meridians.

Some points of origin have been arrived at simply through general agreement. The International Date Line—a hypothetical, crooked "line" located approximately along the 180° meridian, halfway around the world from Greenwich, England—is an interesting example of a useful, man-made reference line that has become accepted everywhere by international agreement. By this agreement we have a point of origin at which each calendar day begins. Each day begins at midnight on the Date Line.

Exercise Set 2

1. Name the point of origin for each of the following:

   a. The seventh floor

   b. The 38th parallel

   c. 250 B.C.

   d. Twenty degrees below zero

   e. 19 years, 3 months, 27 days old

   f. $25.00 richer than at the end of January

2. How is each of the following used as a point of origin?

   a Today

   b. An empty container

   c. $100.00 in a saving's account

Using the Number Line

One of the most valuable uses for the ideas of a point of origin and direction of change is in constructing a number line. For example, an arbitrary point on a line may be selected and labeled 0 (see Fig. 1a).

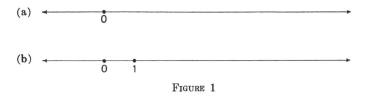

(a)

0

(b)

0 1

FIGURE 1

This is our point of origin. Another point on the line may be selected and labeled 1 (see Fig. 1b). If the line is horizontal, we ordinarily locate the point for 1 to the right of the origin. The distance from 0 to 1 is our basic unit of length, which is used to mark off consecutive unit segments on the line. We use numerals to label points on the number line in order to denote their distance from the point of origin (Fig. 2). One number, x, is said to be *greater than* another, y, if, on the number line, the numeral for x appears to the right of that for y.

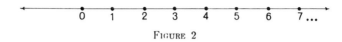

When we count on a number line, we use the ideas of a point of origin and of direction of change. When we count three units to the right from some point, say 4, and arrive at the point labeled 7, we are adding 3 to 4. When we count three units to the left from the point 4 to arrive at the point labeled 1, we are subtracting 3 from 4. Addition and subtraction are directional opposites as represented on the number line.

By the simple device of extending the whole-number line to the left of the zero point, marking off points at one-unit intervals in that direction, and then labeling them with negative numerals, we obtain the signed-number line representing the integers (Fig. 3). Numerals to the right of the origin might or might not be prefaced with a "$+$" sign.

Signed numbers are useful for indicating distances above or below sea level, temperatures above or below zero, and so on.

Thus it is that, starting with comparative terms such as "taller, shorter, same height" and "warmer, cooler, same temperature," we are led naturally to the mathematical notion of an ordered number scale as an instrument for sharpening and refining our comparisons. This scale provides a visual basis for interpreting the mathematical ideas of "less than," "greater than," and "equal to." When these ideas are expressed in mathematical language, we speak of them as inequalities and equations.

Some properties are not easy to measure on a numerical scale, and some may not be measurable. Can we actually measure beauty? Hardly. Can we measure intelligence? We often attempt to do so by giving standardized IQ tests and comparing scores with those on a scale of scores above and below a "normal" (average) score. The average score is our point of origin in this case.

Clothing manufacturers generally use a scale of S, M, L, and XL for labeling men's clothing. This scale is based on the approximate size of the "average man" (indicated by size M, medium). Using the S, M, L, and XL scale enables us to make the type of comparison we need in order to obtain something that is approximately our size.

In what follows, however, we shall be concerned only with numerical scales.

Using Standard Units

In early times, the span of a man's hand or the length of his foot was frequently used as a unit of measure, because these objects were not only convenient but also roughly of a standard size common to all men.

In modern times, various units of measure have become standardized by common usage and general agreement. For example, we have certain universally adopted linear units to measure distance, time units to measure time, and weight units to measure weight. The English system of weights and measures offers many examples of such standard units.

The necessity for standard units of measure can be illustrated in a situation such as the following. Suppose that you are asked to measure the length of a chalkboard with any object that you have available. The results of your measuring experiences might be as shown in Table I.

TABLE I

LENGTH OF CHALKBOARD

Unit of Measure	Measurement
pencil	15 pencils
stick	4 sticks
paper clip	103 paper clips
book	15 books
paper strip	17 paper strips
eraser	18 erasers

Can you visualize the length of the chalkboard from any of these measurements? We have a general awareness of the length of a paper clip, but few of us can visualize with any accuracy a length that is represented by 103 paper clips placed end to end. Since books are of many sizes, "15 books long" does not mean much as a measurement. Similar remarks can be made for each of the other measurements. Therefore, some *standard unit* is needed to provide *uniform interpretation* of measurements.

How do you know that the measurements were accurately performed? Actually, there is no way to tell this from the table of information on this page. The measurement with the pencil could be verified by having a number of persons measure the chalkboard with the same pencil and then comparing the results. If most of them have obtained a measure of 15, it could be agreed that the measurement is satisfactory. It is important to note that in order to verify a measurement, the same measuring unit must be used. Herein lies one of the basic reasons why standard units of measure are important.

Another reason for establishing standard units may be seen in the following situation. A friend of yours has just moved to a town that you have never visited. He writes a letter describing certain aspects of the town: "The grocery store is about twice as far from our house as the children's school." Does such a description enable you to picture the distance from his house to the grocery store? Suppose he had written, "It is nearly one mile to the nearest grocery store from our house." It is immediately evident just about how far it is to the grocery store, since the standard unit of a mile is a familiar term.

What do you think is the man-created basic unit of measure for the speed of an airplane that flies at supersonic speed (faster than the speed of sound)? A unit of measure for such speed is called "Mach," after a physicist by that name who contributed to the study of sound. We say that a plane is moving at Mach 1 if it is flying at the speed of sound. Thus, Mach 1 is the basic unit of measure. If the plane is flying at less than Mach 1, its speed can be named by subdivisions of the unit, such as Mach 0.10. The height at which the plane is flying is also considered, since the speed of sound varies with altitude. You may find it interesting to pursue further the ideas involved in the measurement of sound.

Although individual countries established standards of measure to be used by their own people, world trade made it necessary for them to come to some agreement about the standardization of measures for weight, length, volume, and time. In 1875 an international symposium was held in France, and as a result of that conference, the International Bureau of Weights and Measures was established. The group defined the standard units. Models of the standard units of measure were made. They are kept in France, but copies are available to other countries for purposes of comparison. Many countries have been given copies of these standard units, which they keep in their equivalents of our National Bureau of Standards in Washington, D.C.

Exercise Set 3

1. When the pencil and the book were used as units for measuring the chalkboard, the measurements were the same. What could you say about the length of each of these units?

2. Why is there such a difference in the measurements when a paper clip and an eraser are used?

3. Why do the numerical quantities for the measurements vary so widely?

4. What standard unit would be a practical one to select for measuring the following?

a. Distance between Omaha and Denver

b. Height of a building

c. Diameter of a bolt

d. Perimeter of a city block

e. Weight of an airplane

f. Annual growth in height of a child

g. Amount of carpet needed for a room

h. Volume of a water tank

i. Running time for the 50-yard dash

Developing a Measuring Instrument

After the property to be measured has been identified and an appropriate unit of measure has been selected, that unit may be used as the primary unit of a calibrated or graduated number scale. The scale, which can be bent to any convenient form we wish, forms part of a measuring instrument. Rulers, thermometers, clocks, and speedometers are examples of measuring instruments.

Each of the many kinds of measuring instruments has its own scale. Since the scale is a number line, measurements are read directly from

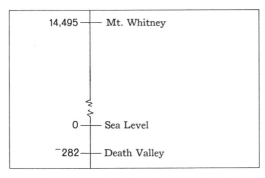

Fig. 4.—Height in feet above sea level.

the number line. For example, Figure 4 shows a scale that gives in standard foot-units the elevations above and below sea level of certain points on the earth.

Determining the scale and designing the measuring instrument are technical problems. Sometimes the scale is determined by observing certain constant physical phenomena. The compass scale is a good example. It was observed that a needle rubbed with a lodestone and then mounted to swing freely always points in a certain direction, which people agreed to call magnetic north. Accordingly, that particular direction is used as a point of origin to determine direction. The scale on the compass is used to determine the angular measure between a ray directed to the north and some other ray. One unit on the scale is the equivalent of one degree of angular measure.

A thermometer has two significant parts: a number line or scale and beside it a transparent tube containing an indicator substance (usually alcohol or mercury) that has the property of expanding with increasing temperature. Thermometers were developed because of a need to have some means of measuring relative temperatures.

Early attempts at temperature comparisons used two common things as standards for comparison. Ice was the one thing always associated with cold. Ice then became the standard of measure for coldness. On the other hand, what phenomenon in nature could be associated with warmth—fire? Yes, but it was not always available, nor could it be touched. The human body, however, represented something that was always warm and always available for making comparisons. Moreover, it represented something that normally was constant in temperature. Hence, man used the human body as his basis of comparison for warmth. It is interesting to note how these two temperature standards continued to be used for a very long period of time.

One of the earliest thermometers was made by Galileo, a Florentine physicist. The scale that was used on his thermometer had a unit interval based upon 1/1,000 of the volume of alcohol used in the tube. This thermometer gave inconsistent readings, however, because a column of alcohol in an open tube fluctuates with changes in air pressure. In 1612 Galileo invented the type of thermometer in use today, with the liquid contained in a hermetically sealed tube so that temperature readings would be unaffected by variations in air pressure.

An improved thermometer was made by Sir Isaac Newton, the great English physicist, in 1701. The scale he used was determined not by change in volume alone but by establishing two reference points. Newton used the temperature of freezing water and the temperature of the healthy human body for these two points. The height of the column of alcohol for each of these temperatures was scratched on the thermometer, and the interval between the two points was divided into twelve congruent parts, each of which represented a degree. The symbols 0° and

12° (zero degrees and twelve degrees) were assigned, respectively, to the two points.

In 1714 Gabriel Fahrenheit, a German physicist and maker of meteorological instruments, became interested in establishing a scale that would enable a person to make more precise temperature readings. After many different attempts, he assigned to the two aforementioned points—the temperature of water in which ice is forming and the temperature of the healthy human body—values of 32° and 98°, respectively.[2] The assignment of 32° to the freezing point of water, instead of 0°, which had been in common use, was arbitrarily chosen by Fahrenheit as a convenience to him in making meteorological reports. Each of the sixty-six congruent intervals between the referent points represented a degree. The scale was eventually extended, and 212° was noted to be the boiling point of water on this scale.

The Fahrenheit scale has 180 degrees between the boiling point of water and its freezing point. Scientists found it an awkward scale to use, however, especially in computations. The centigrade, or Celsius, scale was devised in 1742 to alleviate this problem. On this scale 0° is the freezing point of water, and 100° is the boiling point of water; the interval between these two reference points is divided into 100 congruent segments. This scale conforms to the decimal system of numeration used in the metric system of measurement.

Exercise Set 4

1. What type of scale is used to determine the depth of the ocean?

2. Does the word "scale," as used in music, refer to a measuring instrument?

3. Make a thermometer using a plastic straw, a container of colored liquid, and a board for mounting the straw and marking the scale. How would you calibrate this scale?

Summary

We have seen that in making quantitative comparisons certain definite procedures can be identified. These procedures are so simple and funda-

---

[2] A discrepancy occurs in the references. Some accounts list the temperature that Fahrenheit used for the human body as 96°. It was many years later that, with the boiling point of water fixed at 212°, the temperature of the healthy human body was determined to be about 98.6°

mental that they are frequently overlooked. The required steps are the following:

1. Identifying a physical property to measure
2. Selecting a point of origin
3. Using the number line
4. Using standard units
5. Developing a measuring instrument

THE THEORY OF MEASURE

The Mathematical Concept of Measure

What do the nouns *measure* and *measurement* mean to a mathematician? Like many another word in English, *measure* has many meanings. For example, in politics, it means a statute or law; in music, it denotes a subdivision of musical composition.

In mathematics,

> *measurement denotes the process of assigning a number to a physical property of some object or set of objects for purposes of comparison.*

The noun *measure* then denotes the number of units of the given property.

Some frequently measured physical properties are area, volume, weight, temperature, and density.[3] Can you name the property and the unit of measure in each of the following statements?

> The length of the table is 25 inches.
> The coffee pot holds 3 pints of water.
> The movie lasts 2½ hours.

Of course, we sometimes assign numbers to things as a way of naming or indexing them. Social security numbers and telephone numbers are examples of such labeling or indexing. These numbers, however, are not usually assigned by any measuring process.

Properties of a Measure

In the abstract mathematical field known as measure theory, a numerical association is a *measure* only if it has the following mathematical properties:

---

[3] Hassler Whitney, "The Mathematics of Physical Quantities," *American Mathematical Monthly*, LXX 1968), 115–38, 227–56.

A. In common language, we say that "the measure of the whole must be equal to the sum of the measures of all of its parts." For instance, if we were to weigh a dozen oranges, we would find that the weight is the same whether we weighed each orange separately and then added all the weights or whether we weighed them all together. The technical term for this property is "finite additivity."

B. Another property, which actually is implied by property A, is that the measure of "not any," or none, must be 0. The concept may seem less ridiculous if we think of measuring as counting. The number of elements in a set is a kind of measure of the set. We may meaningfully say that the number of elements in the empty set is 0.

C. The measure of a part of something should be not greater than the measure of the whole. For instance, the weight of half a cube of butter is less than that of the whole cube. This property is called "monotonicity." By properties A and B, property C is equivalent to the statement that measures are expressed by nonnegative numbers.

D. In any measuring experiment, if the measurement is done in a prescribed way under certain prescribed physical conditions, then repeated experiments should yield the same result.

In the language of Booklet No. 13: *Graphs, Relations, and Functions,* a measure is a function. Not every function, however, is a measure. Any function that has the particular properties described above is called a measure. Not all physical measurements fit this description, of course; temperature, for example, is not finitely additive in any immediate sense.

WAYS OF MEASURING

There are many things that are measurable and many ways of measuring. Procedures for measuring may be classified as follows:

1. Counting to find out how many
2. Measuring directly
3. Measuring indirectly

Counting

The set of counting numbers came into being to help us answer the question "How many?" We "measure" the cardinal number of a set by counting the number of elements in the set. We measure the cardinal number of the set of apples in a basket by counting. Counting, or determining the number of elements in a set of objects, is the only measuring procedure that yields an *exact* measure.

Direct Measurement

Direct measurement is usually a visual process that consists of making a direct comparison of some object with a suitable standard unit of measure. For example, we can measure the fluid capacity of a container by observing the number of standard pints of water required to fill it, and we can use a ruler to measure the number of inches in a given line segment.

Indirect Measurement

Many physical properties do not lend themselves to direct measurement, as for example: temperature, velocity, weight, brightness, and electrical energy. Instead, we have to use such ingenious, indirect measuring devices as the thermometer, speedometer, spring scale, watt meter, and so on for registering the quantity of these physical forces on a number scale.

Some things may be measured both by direct and by indirect methods. For example, we can measure directly to determine the perimeter of a square. It would be easier, however, to measure just one side and then find the perimeter indirectly by using the simple mathematical formula $p = 4s$, where p is the measure of the perimeter and s of the side. For example, if the measure of one side is 6 units ($s = 6$), then we know that the perimeter is $p = 4 \times 6 = 24$ units (see Fig. 5).

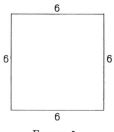

FIGURE 5

An instrument such as a ruler or yardstick is useful for measuring the length of a straight line segment, but much less useful for measuring the length of a curve. In the case of a circle we can find the circumference indirectly by measuring a diameter and then using a simple mathematical relationship between the diameter and circumference.

Very early in the history of geometry, it was discovered that the ratio of the circumference to the diameter of any circle is always the same. This fixed ratio is denoted by the Greek letter "pi" (π). Thus, if c denotes the circumference and d the diameter (see Fig. 6), then

$$\frac{c}{d} = \pi \quad \text{or} \quad c = \pi d.$$

We also know that the diameter of a circle is equal to twice its radius,

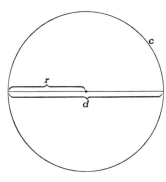

FIGURE 6

so the formula for the circumference in terms of the radius is

$$c = \pi \times 2 \times r, \quad \text{or} \quad c = 2\pi r.$$

There have been many interesting and unsuccessful attempts to express π as a rational number. (See Booklet No. 6: *The Rational Numbers.*) Mathematicians have shown that this is impossible; in fact, π is irrational. Instead, numbers such as 22/7 and 3.1416 have been used as rational *approximations* of π.

EXAMPLE:

Find the circumference, to the nearest 0.01 foot, of a circle having a radius of exactly 5 feet.

Solution: Substituting $r = 5$ in the formula above, we have

$$c = \pi \times 2 \times r = 10\pi.$$

Depending on the choice of the approximation of π, the *approximate lengths* of the perimeter would be as follows:

If $\frac{22}{7}$ is used for π, then $c = 10 \times \frac{22}{7}$, or 31.43 feet.
If 3.1416 is used for π, then $c = 10 \times 3.1416$, or 31.42 feet.

Let us consider another example of indirect measurement. Suppose that you wish to know the height of a certain tree that is too difficult to climb and hence to measure. On a sunny day the tree casts a dark shadow on the level ground. You can measure the length of a shadow. Now an idea occurs to you. Nearby there is a stick that you can make stand upright on the level ground. You make a drawing like Figure 7.

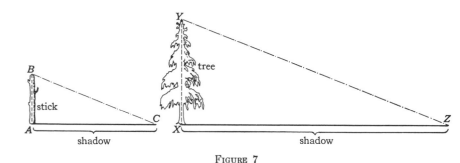

FIGURE 7

In Figure 7 let AB represent the length of the segment AB, etc. That is let

AB represent the height of the stick,
AC represent the length of the stick's shadow,
XY represent the height of the tree, and
XZ represent the length of the tree's shadow.

A mathematical relationship that you learned in geometry may come to mind:

The ratio of the height of the stick to the length of the shadow cast by the stick
is the same as
the ratio of the height of the tree to the length of the shadow cast by the tree.

This relationship can be used only if the measurements are made at the same time of the day and if the stick and the tree make the same angle with the ground, that is, only if triangles ABC and XYZ are similar.

A glance at Figure 7 shows that we can express this equality mathematically as

$$\frac{AB}{AC} = \frac{XY}{XZ}.$$

We can measure three of these quantities directly: AB, the height of the stick; AC, the length of the stick's shadow; and XZ, the length of the tree's shadow. Hence, to find the height of the tree, line XY, we simply solve for line XY and write

$$XY = XZ \times \frac{AB}{AC}.$$

Thus, if $AB = 3$, $AC = 4$, and $XZ = 16$, then we have

$$\frac{3}{4} = \frac{XY}{16},$$

$$XY = 16 \times \frac{3}{4}$$

$$= 12.$$

The preceding example of indirect measurement is a simple one. Properties such as weight, time, temperature, velocity, density, and viscosity are not so simple to measure indirectly. Consider such relatively complex instruments as:

odometers to measure distance traveled
speedometers to measure speed of travel
clocks to measure time
thermometers to measure temperature

The ideas of indirect measurement are an interesting part of the history of measurement. It is beyond the scope of this booklet to develop the topic further, but exploration by the reader should prove a rewarding experience.

Exercise Set 5

1. Using 22/7 for π, find the circumference of a circle that is 3 centimeters in diameter.
2. At a certain time of day, a building 30 feet high casts a shadow 50 feet long. If a man standing nearby casts a shadow 10 feet in length, how tall is the man?

HOW BRIGHT IS A STAR? HOW HARD IS A ROCK?

Measuring Brightness

"Star light! Star bright! First star I see tonight!" All stars shine by means of their own light. Some stars are brighter than others. Astronomers tell us that there are stars whose light is as much as 600,000 times brighter than our sun.

How is the brightness of a star measured? Establishing a unit of measure for brightness required much thought on the part of the astronomers. In order to measure apparent brightness (brightness as seen from the earth), astronomers use the fact that light behaves in the manner of both waves and particles. Scientists speak of these particles as photons of light. Star brightness is measured in terms of *magnitude*, which is obtained by counting photons with a very delicate instrument called a photometer. A scale of magnitudes is a way of showing relative brightness by a ranking procedure. Using magnitude as a unit of measure, astronomers speak of first-magnitude stars, second-magnitude stars, and so forth.

Because of the technical nature of the mathematics involved, the scale of magnitude is somewhat deceptive. For example, a first-magnitude star is approximately 2.5 times as bright as a second-magnitude star and 100 times as bright as a sixth-magnitude star.

Stars brighter than first-magnitude stars are ranked as zero-magnitude and as minus-magnitude stars. Vega is a zero-magnitude star. Venus is a celestial body of approximately minus-four magnitude. Its brightness is about 10,000 times as great as 76 Tauri, a sixth-magnitude star. A sixth-magnitude star is considered to be the faintest star visible to the unaided human eye. The measurement of the sun's brightness is magnitude minus–twenty-seven. The magnitudes of certain stars are listed in Table II.

TABLE II

MAGNITUDES OF STARS

Name of Star	Magnitude
Sun............................	−26.7
Sirius...........................	−1.4
Canopus........................	−0.8
Vega............................	0.1
Alpha Centauri..................	0.3
Betelgeuse......................	0.7
Pollux..........................	1.2
Castor..........................	1.6
76 Tauri........................	6.0

Does the representation on the scale in Figure 8 look like the familiar number line showing negative and positive values? On the ordinary num-

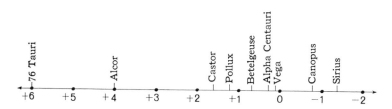

FIGURE 8.—Magnitude of certain stars.

ber line, starting from the origin, the graphs of the numbers increase positively as you go to the right, and negatively to the left. In general, one number is greater than another if its graph lies to the right of that of the other on the number line. Do the values for magnitudes of stars follow this same pattern? Even though the numbers representing magnitudes decrease as you go from left to right on the scale, the actual brightness increases because the less the magnitude, the greater the brightness. Using a directional (signed) number line facilitates interpretation of the measure of magnitude.

What determines the *apparent* brightness of a star? The two main factors are (*a*) the *luminosity* of the star, which is sometimes termed its *absolute brightness,* and (*b*) the *distance* of the star from the earth.

TABLE III

DISTANCE AND ABSOLUTE BRIGHTNESS OF STARS OF EQUAL
APPARENT BRIGHTNESS

TYPE OF MEASUREMENT	STAR			
	A	B	C	D
Distance from earth	d	$2d$	$3d$	$4d$
Absolute brightness (luminosity)	l	$4l$	$9l$	$16l$

What do we mean by the absolute brightness of a star? Differences in absolute brightness can be understood by comparing the light from a 500-watt light bulb with light from a 25-watt light bulb viewed from the same distance. As we increase the watts, we increase the amount of light. Similarly, when comparing two stars that are the same distance from the earth, the one with greater absolute brightness would have the greater apparent brightness.

Just how does distance relate apparent brightness to absolute brightness? Let us consider four different stars that have the same apparent-brightness rank but whose distances from the earth are not the same. Star A may be considered the basis for comparison. Star B is 2 times as far from the earth as Star A. Star C is 3 times as far as Star A. Star D is 4 times as far as Star A. In Table III, note the relationship of distance to absolute brightness. Remember that the measure of apparent brightness is the same for Stars A, B, C, and D.

In Table III note that Star B, which is 2 times as far from earth as

Star A, has an absolute brightness 4 times as great as Star A. Star C, which is 3 times as far as A, has an absolute brightness 9 times as great as that of Star A. Star D, which is 4 times the distance, has an absolute brightness 16 times that of Star A.

We can picture the idea on a scale, as in Figure 9. The point E rep-

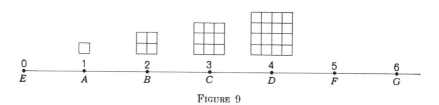

FIGURE 9

resents the earth and is a point of origin for the scale. Points A, B, C, D, F, and G represent the locations of stars. The distance from point E to point A is the basic unit of distance. The squares at points A, B, C, and D represent the amount of absolute brightness required in order for each of the stars to have the same apparent brightness from the earth. There appears to be a definite relationship between distance and absolute brightness for two stars when their apparent brightness is the same. What would you guess the absolute brightness would be for a star of the same apparent brightness but 5 times the distance from the earth as Star A? (If you guess 25, you are right.)

Reading the diagram for Figure 9, we can pair the numbers for distance and absolute brightness. That is, if the first number represents distance and the second absolute brightness, we have the set of ordered pairs

$$\{(1, 1), (2, 4), (3, 9), (4, 16), \cdots\}.$$

The dots suggest other ordered pairs. What ordered pair would you use to represent the relationship for point F? If you know the first number for the ordered pair (distance), can you find the second number (absolute brightness)? Let d stand for the first number and l for the second in the ordered pair (d, l), or (distance, absolute brightness). Can you state a mathematical formula to show the value of l compared with that of d? (Answer: $l = d^2$.) If you know the second number, can you find the first number by stating the formula for the value of d compared with l? (Answer: $d = \sqrt{l}$.)

The relationship of distance to absolute brightness, as presented here, is derived from the fact that for equal apparent brightness, absolute brightness varies as the square of the distance from the source. For purposes of comparison, the measure of luminosity, or absolute brightness, of a star is defined to be the magnitude that the star would have if it were approximately 32.6 light-years distant from earth.[4]

Measuring Hardness

What is the meaning of hard? How do we measure hardness? Some things are harder than others. We use a knife to cut bread, and the steel of the knife is harder than the bread. Everyone knows that a diamond is one of the hardest substances known to man. Can we make a scale of hardness?

Approximately a hundred years ago a scale of hardness was made by Friedrich Mohs. Ten common minerals were selected to serve as standard units. In accordance with the relative hardness of the ten minerals, a number was assigned to each of them. In this way a scale was made with "1" representing the softest mineral, "2" the next softest, and so forth through "10," which is the hardest. See Table IV.

TABLE IV

Scale of Hardness of Minerals

Number	Mineral
1	talc
2	gypsum (selenite)
3	calcite
4	fluorite
5	apatite
6	feldspar
7	quartz
8	topaz
9	corundum
10	diamond

A scratch test was used to establish this scale. The minerals are so arranged that each mineral from the hardest (10) to the softest (1) can scratch all the minerals that have a lower number on the scale. Similarly, each mineral could be scratched by a mineral with a higher number on the scale. Using the scratch test is a way of comparing or measuring. For example, a mineral whose hardness is in question is compared with the various specimens in the scale. If it is found that it will scratch numbers 1, 2, 3, and 4 but not 5, and if number 5 will scratch it, then it is given a hardness-ranking of 4.5.

Sets of specimen minerals that are classified by this scale can be pur-

---

[4] One light-year is the distance traveled by light in one year. It is about 5,880,000,000,000 miles. The distance from sun to earth is about eight light-minutes.

chased by persons wishing to identify and classify the hardness of rocks and minerals. The set then becomes the measuring instrument for determining the hardness of rocks.

An even simpler measuring device usually available to most people consists of one's fingernail, a copper penny, and a knife blade or a piece of steel. These items, with the scale shown in Table V as a reference, will enable one to measure the hardness of a rock or other substance.

TABLE V

A SIMPLE SCALE OF HARDNESS

Scratch Test	Rank on Scale
Fingernail will scratch the mineral	All minerals less than 2.5
Copper penny will scratch the mineral	All minerals less than 3.5
Steel knife blade will scratch the mineral	All minerals less than 5.5

In our improved technology we have developed much more refined methods of determining hardness. They involve very expensive instruments, however, and the two methods outlined here are still in common use.

How bright is a star? How hard is a rock? As we think of the systems of measuring that man has devised in order to find answers to these questions, we are reliving one of the many exciting chapters in man's attempt to organize his knowledge of the universe.

MEASURING AREA AND VOLUME

What Is Area?

When we measure the length of a line segment, we determine how many units of some standard linear measure are contained in it. Similarly, measuring the area of a plane region is a matter of determining how many of some standard unit of area measure the region contains.[5] The unit of measure selected should of course be small enough so that it will fit into the region to be measured. Then the area is equal to the number of times that the unit region is used in order to "cover" the surface completely.

Just as in linear measure, the smaller the square unit of measure we use, the more precise the measurement will be. Also, when an irregular or circular region is used as a unit of measure, we are not able to make

---

[5] A plane region is the interior of any simple, closed, plane curve, together with the curve itself.

a very accurate estimate of the area of a region because these units do not fit together compactly enough to cover the region that is being measured. Rectangular regions can be fitted together so that they "wallpaper" a region. These facts are illustrated in Figure 10, in which the

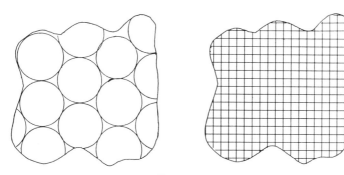

FIGURE 10

same plane region is measured first with a large circular unit and then with a small square as the unit of measure.

Area is measured in square units. A square region with side of length one linear unit has an area of one square unit. Such a region is called a *unit square* (Fig. 11).

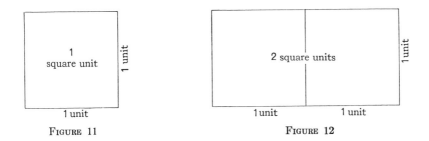

FIGURE 11   FIGURE 12

If the unit of length is one inch, then the unit square represents one square inch of area. If the unit of length is one mile, then the unit square represents one square mile of area. An area of two square units can be represented by a rectangular region with width one unit and length two units, as shown in Figure 12.

How is the area of a rectangular region determined? We could obtain a reasonable estimate by seeing how many unit squares with side of a suitable length, say 1 centimeter, are needed to cover the region. In

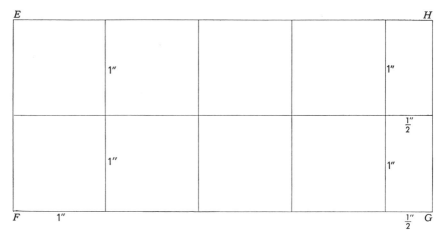

Figure 13 the unit of measure is the square inch. When you count the number of square inches in rectangle $EFGH$, you find that it has an area of

$$8 \text{ sq. in.} + \tfrac{1}{2} \text{ sq. in.} + \tfrac{1}{2} \text{ sq. in.} = 9 \text{ sq. in.}$$

Notice that the rectangle has base of length $4\tfrac{1}{2}$ inches and altitude of length 2 inches and that $4\tfrac{1}{2} \times 2 = 9$. Generalizing from this, you can see that the area A of a rectangular region with base of length b units and altitude of length h units is $b \times h$ square units; that is,

$$A(\text{rectangular region}) = b \times h, \text{ or } bh.$$

The use of this formula gives us a quick way of determining the area of a rectangular region simply by measuring its base and its altitude.

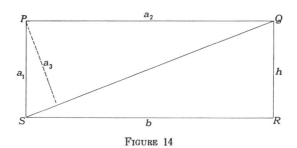

To find the area of a triangular region, we first recall that a diagonal of a rectangle (see diagonal $\overline{QS}$ in Fig. 14) separates the rectangular region into two congruent right-triangular regions. (See Booklet No. 14: *Informal Geometry*.) If the area of the rectangular region is $b \times h$ square units, then the area of each right-triangular region is $\frac{1}{2}(b \times h)$ square units; that is,

A(triangular region) $= \frac{1}{2}(b \times h)$, or $\frac{1}{2}bh$.

An altitude of a triangle is defined to be the perpendicular segment from a vertex to its opposite side or to its opposite side extended. Every triangle therefore has three distinct altitudes, one from each vertex to the side opposite that vertex. In a right triangle, such as $\triangle SPQ$ in Figure 14, with altitudes a_1, a_2, and a_3, two of the altitudes coincide with the legs $\overline{PS}$ and $\overline{PQ}$.

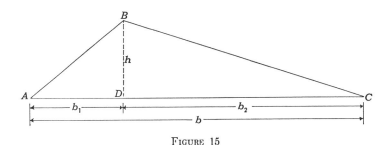

FIGURE 15

In Figure 15, the altitude $\overline{BD}$ is labeled with its length, h. The area of the triangular region ABC is the sum of the areas of the two smaller triangular regions ABD and BCD. That is, Area (ABC) = Area (ABD) + Area (BCD). Note that the length b of the base of triangle ABC is equal to the sum of the lengths b_1 and b_2 of the bases of the smaller triangles. Since the altitude $\overline{DB}$ is the same in all three triangles, we have

$(\frac{1}{2}h \times b_1) + (\frac{1}{2}h \times b_2) = \frac{1}{2}h(b_1 + b_2)$ (distributive principle)

$= \frac{1}{2}hb$,   or $\frac{1}{2}bh$ (since $b = b_1 + b_2$).

Therefore, the area of any triangular region can be found by using this formula, provided that the length of a base and a corresponding altitude can be determined.

The formula $A = \pi r^2$ for the area of a circular region with radius r can be derived by using calculus. The validity of this formula can be made plausible with the help of the following argument. First, draw and cut out a circular disc of paper. Then cut the disc along a diameter

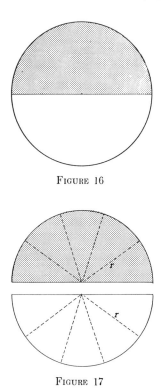

FIGURE 16

FIGURE 17

(Fig. 16), so that you have two half-discs. Shade the upper half. Now make cuts along the dotted lines as illustrated in Figure 17 and spread out the two half-discs as shown in Figure 18. Note that the sides of each pie-shaped wedge have length r, while the curved edge is part of

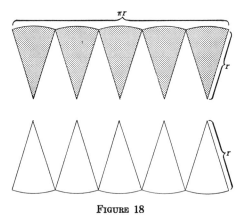

FIGURE 18

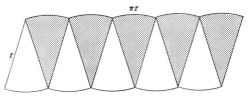

FIGURE 19

the circumference of the original disc. The wedges are all the same size. The sum of the lengths of the curved edges in each half-disc is equal to πr, half of the circumference. ($C = 2\pi r$; therefore, $C/2 = 2\pi r/2$, or πr.)

Now suppose that the two sets of pumpkin-teeth wedges are fitted together, as in Figure 19, to make a perfect "bite." The figure thus obtained resembles a parallelogram, but has a pair of scalloped sides.

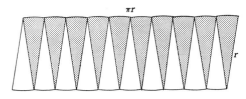

FIGURE 20

If we had used finer wedges, as in Figure 20 where each half-disc was cut up to make ten wedges of equal size, the straight sides would be more nearly vertical and the configuration would take on a more nearly rectangular shape.

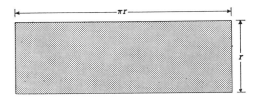

FIGURE 21

If instead of cutting each half-disc into ten wedges (Fig. 20) we were to cut each into a million wedges and fit the two halves together, we would get a geometric figure that would be approximately rectangular (Fig. 21). The length of the base of this almost-rectangle would be almost πr, and the height would be almost r. Using the formula for the area of a rectangle, $A = b \times h$, we get the limiting value

$$A = \pi r \times r$$
$$= \pi r^2.$$

Does the formula given here suggest an answer to the perfectly reasonable question, "Why is the area of a circular region given in *square* units?" When r is 5 inches, what would r^2 be? If in the preceding discussion we let r be 5 units, then the *exact* area of the circular region would be

$$A = \pi r^2 = \pi \times 5 \times 5 = 25\pi.$$

An approximation of the area of the circular region can be obtained by using either 22/7 or 3.1416 as the number for π. With $\pi = 22/7$, we have

$$A = \tfrac{22}{7} \times 5 \times 5 = 78\tfrac{4}{7}.$$

The area is approximately 78 4/7 square units.
With $\pi = 3.1416$, we get

$$A = 3.1416 \times 25 = 78.54.$$

The area is approximately 78.54 square units.
Let us look at the two regions called P and Q in Figure 22. Region

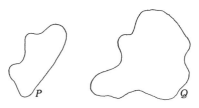

Figure 22

P has an area that we shall call A_P, and region Q has an area that we shall call A_Q. Since area is a number, it has the following properties.

1. If region P and region Q are two separate and distinct regions, then the combined area of the two regions is equal to the sum of their individual areas:

If $P \cap Q = \emptyset$, then $A_{(P \cup Q)} = A_P + A_Q$.

2. Area is expressed by nonnegative numbers. The numbers used to express area must be greater than or equal to zero:

$$A \geq 0.$$

3. If one region (P) is contained in the other region (Q), then the area of P is no more than the area of Q.

4. Congruent figures have equal areas.

Compare these properties of area with the properties listed on page 401.

Exercise Set 6

1. The following terms are often used in the classroom: work area, library area, play area. What is meant here by the word "area"?

2. Does perimeter determine area? Take four strips of cardboard $\frac{1}{2}$ inch by 4 inches and fasten them together with paper fasteners so that they make a square as shown in Figure 23(a).

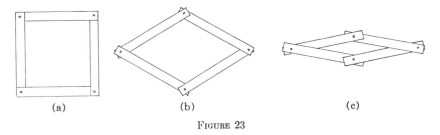

(a)　　　　　　(b)　　　　　　(c)

FIGURE 23

Adjust the frame to different positions as in (b) and (c) and trace the inside outline of the frame on coordinate paper. Estimate the area of each figure.

3. What is the area of a rectangular region whose length is $3\frac{1}{4}$ units and whose width is 12 units?

4. If the lengths of two rectangular regions are the same, how can you tell, without computing the area, which of the two will have the greater area?

5. Draw four different-shaped rectangular regions, each of which has an area of 24 square units.

What Is Volume?

We are frequently concerned with *volume* in one way or another. We make crude measurements of volume as we prepare foods. We are concerned with volume when we attempt to find a box that will hold a book we wish to send to someone. The gasoline gauge on our automobile gives us a ratio of the measure of the volume of gasoline in the tank to the measure of the total volume of the tank.

The lumber industry also uses volumetric measures. Lumber is usually measured by board feet. A *board foot* is a unit of volume; it is the volume of a piece of lumber that is 12 inches wide, 12 inches long, and 1 inch thick. Wood that is sold for use as fuel is sold by the *cord*. A cord is a unit of volume that is equivalent to a stack of wood 4 feet by 4 feet by 8 feet, or 128 cubic feet.

There are many units for measuring volume. The maritime industry uses a volumetric ton as a unit of measure in determining certain assessments and harbor fees. The *volumetric ton* is a measure that is equivalent to 100 cubic feet of enclosed space. However, cargo rates are based on the *measurement ton,* which is equivalent to 40 cubic feet of enclosed space; and the charges are determined both by weight and by the amount of space that the object occupies.

We are using "volume" to mean *capacity* as measured in cubic units. There are other meanings for the word: we speak about a "volume of business" on a particular day or look for "Volume IV" of a certain periodical. But for the measurement we are studying, volume and capacity are generally interchangeable terms, although "capacity" more strictly is used in referring to containers. We talk of one's capacity for eating watermelon. Or we may ask, "What is the capacity of this bucket?" and then proceed to measure the volume of liquid it will hold.

When we wish to measure the length of a line segment, we select a linear unit of measurement. When we wish to measure the area of a plane region, we select a square unit of measure. But now examine the box in Figure 24. The box has three dimensions: length (l), width (w),

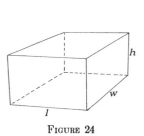

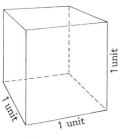

FIGURE 24   FIGURE 25

and height (h). If we wish to measure the capacity, or volume, of this box or the space it occupies, it will be necessary to select a unit of measure that also has these three dimensions.

The unit of measure that is used for measuring volume is a three-dimensional figure with sides one unit in length. For many of the same reasons that a unit square is selected for measuring area, we find a unit cube (Fig. 25) to be the best unit for measuring volume. If the

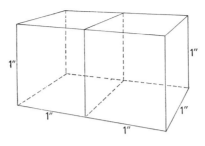

FIGURE 26

unit of length selected is an inch, then this unit cube has a volume of one cubic inch. If the unit of length is a centimeter, then the unit cube has a volume of one cubic centimeter.

Two cubic inches is the volume of a solid figure formed by placing two one-inch cubes side by side (see Fig. 26). Can we find some simple formula for obtaining the volume of *any* rectangular solid? First let us experiment with a cubical solid.

The large cube in Figure 27 has edges of length 2 centimeters. The smaller, shaded cube has edges of length 1 centimeter; it is therefore a unit cube with a volume of 1 cubic centimeter. Do you see that it takes *eight* of these cubic centimeters to fill the large cube? Note that this is the product of the length, the width, and the height of the large cube; that is, the volume in cubic centimeters is given by

$$V = l \times w \times h = 2 \times 2 \times 2 = 8.$$

Did this same formula work for Figure 26? There, $l = 2''$, $w = 1''$, $h = 1''$, so that the volume in cubic inches is

$$V = l \times w \times h = 2 \times 1 \times 1 = 2,$$

and the formula is valid for that case, also.

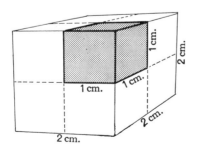

FIGURE 27

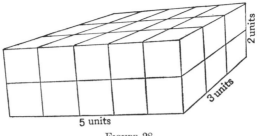

FIGURE 28

Now let us try a more complicated solid. In Figure 28 the stack of unit cubes is 5 units long, 3 units wide, and 2 units high. How many unit cubes are there altogether? One way to find out would be to think of the figure as consisting of two layers of blocks, each layer having 5 times 3 unit cubes in it. Since there are two layers, we have $(5 \times 3) \times 2 = 30$ unit cubes altogether. Here again, the formula $V = l \times w \times h = 5 \times 3 \times 2 = 30$ cubic units is valid.

Can the formula $V = lwh$ be used to find the volume of a container such as those shown in Figure 29? First of all, we need to observe that

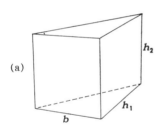
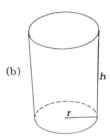

FIGURE 29

each of these represents a particular class of solid figures, one known as prisms (a) and the other as circular cylinders (b). Each of these solids has two *congruent, parallel* bases. The bases of a prism are polygonal, and those of a circular cylinder are circular. The perpendicular distance between the bases is called the height.

Secondly, we need to look at the formula itself. The product lw represents the area of the base in a rectangular prism such as that in Figure 28, so $lw \times h$ is the product of the base area and the height. Thus, the volume can be considered a function of two things: the area of the base and the perpendicular distance between the two parallel bases. We can now write a more general formula that can be used to determine the volume of the solids shown in Figure 29:

$$V = B \times h,$$

where B is the area of one of the bases and h is the height of the solid. To find the volume of (a) in Figure 29, we would first determine the area of the triangular region; second, determine the height; and third, multiply these two numbers together. You can see, then, why the formula for a triangular prism is often written in the following way:

$$V = \tfrac{1}{2}(b \times h_1) \times h_2,$$

where b is the length of the base of the triangle, h_1 is the length of the altitude to that base in the triangle, and h_2 is the height of the prism.

To find the volume of (b) or of any other circular cylinder, we must first determine the area of the circular base ($B = \pi r^2$) and then determine the perpendicular distance between the two parallel bases:

$$V = B \times h$$
$$= \pi r^2 h.$$

All measurements of volume are only approximations, since all linear measurements are necessarily approximate.

Is it possible to compare the size of two rectangular prisms without actually determining the volume of each? That is, can we compare corresponding linear dimensions and thereby reach any conclusions about comparative volume?

TABLE VI

VOLUMES OF RECTANGULAR PRISMS

Object	l	w	Area of Base	h	Volume
j	2	3	6	4	24
k	4	3	12	4	48

Examine the data in Table VI. We notice that the l measure of k is twice that of j, while the w and h measures are the same for both. Therefore, without calculating the volume we can reason that k will have the greater volume and that moreover the volume will be twice as great, since the length is greater by a factor of 2.

Suppose you have a rectangular container that has the same length and width as j but the measure of its height is 52. What statement could you make about the volume of this container as compared to that of j? Since l and w remain constant, only the h measurements would need to be compared. Therefore, since 52 is 13 times as great as 4, the volume will be 13 times as great.

When the dimensions that are required for determining the volume of two objects of the same class are known, a comparison of the two volumes can be made by comparing the measures of each dimension. If two of the dimensions such as length and width are the same, only the height needs to be compared. The volume of a container increases proportionately as any one dimension increases, provided that the other dimensions do not change.

Exercise Set 7

1. How many cubes of the sizes indicated below are needed to make one cubic unit?

   a. $\frac{1}{4}$ cubic unit

   b. $\frac{1}{8}$ cubic unit

   c. $\frac{1}{64}$ cubic unit

2. How many cubes with length of side as indicated below are needed to make one cubic unit?

   a. $\frac{1}{4}$ unit

   b. $\frac{1}{8}$ unit

   c. 4 units

THE ENGLISH AND THE METRIC SYSTEMS OF WEIGHTS AND MEASURES

Two different systems for the measurement of length, volume, weight, and temperature are used in the United States. We inherited the English system from colonial times; but we also use the metric system, which was adopted by Congress on July 28, 1866. The 1866 act reads, in part:

It shall be lawful throughout the United States to employ the weights and measures of the metric system, and no contract or dealing, or pleading in any court, shall be deemed invalid or liable to objection because the weights or measures expressed or referred to therein are weights and measures of the metric system.

Since 1893 all legal units of weights and measures in the United States have been defined in metric units or in numerical multiples and subdivisions of metric units.

In this section we shall take a look at the standard units and the calibrated scales for each of these systems.

The English System

You are familiar with the English system of weights and measures. The history of the selection of units and calibrated scales to express them is an interesting study. For example, an inch as a unit of measure of length is standardized today. Originally, an inch was the unit of measure equal to the width of a man's thumb. A more uniform unit of measure for the inch was desired, and three grains of barley became a unit of measure for length. After this unit had been in common use for hundreds of years, King Edward II of England declared a law making it compulsory to use the inch as a standard unit of length and defining the inch as the length of three grains of barley, round and dry, placed lengthwise end to end.

The commonly used units of measure were derived from parts of the body or from other familiar objects of approximately uniform size. Thus we have units such as the inch, the foot, the yard, the rod, the mile,[6] and the furlong.[7] The basic unit of length in the English system is the yard. That is why the term "yardstick" means "standard of measure," as for example in the statement "It all depends on what yardstick you are using." The names for the other terms give no clue to how many of each are contained in the basic unit. Table VII shows the relationship between the yard and the other units of length.

TABLE VII

UNITS OF LENGTH

Name of Unit	Multiple of a Yard
inch	$\frac{1}{36}$
foot	$\frac{1}{3}$
yard	1
rod	$5\frac{1}{2}$
furlong	220
mile	1,760

To convert a measure given in inches to a corresponding measure in feet, we divide by 12. We divide by 36 if we wish to convert a measure expressed in inches to a measure in yards. We note a similar irregularity among units in the familiar weights and measures, such as:

$$16 \text{ oz.} = 1 \text{ lb.}$$

$$2 \text{ pt.} = 1 \text{ qt.}$$

$$4 \text{ qt.} = 1 \text{ gal.}$$

In volume measures we have

$$1 \text{ cu. yd.} = 27 \text{ cu. ft.} = 46,656 \text{ cu. in.}$$

[6] From the Latin *milia passuum*, or "a thousand paces."
[7] A furlong originally was considered to be the length of a furrow in an ordinary field, or a furrow-long.

One may ask, "Why do we continue to use the cumbersome, complex denominations of English weights and measures?" The only logical explanation would be "Because of custom," since the simpler metric system, based on the decimal system of numeration, lends itself so easily to computation. The metric system is the standard one used in scientific work throughout the world.

The Metric System

In the metric system the *meter* is the basic unit for measure of length, the *gram* for measure of weight, and the *liter* for measure of capacity (liquid volume). Every other metric unit is some whole-number power of ten times the basic unit.

Table VIII shows the decimal relationship between the basic linear unit, the meter, and some other units of length. Note that Latin prefixes are used to name units that are negative power-of-ten multiples of the meter and Greek prefixes for units that are positive power-of-ten multiples.

TABLE VIII

METRIC UNITS OF LENGTH

Name of Unit	Multiple of a Meter
millimeter	$0.001, \dfrac{1}{1,000}$, or 10^{-3}
centimeter	$0.01, \dfrac{1}{100}$, or 10^{-2}
decimeter	$0.1, \dfrac{1}{10}$, or 10^{-1}
meter	$1.0,$ or 10^{0}
decameter	$10.0,$ or 10^{1}
hectometer	$100.0,$ or 10^{2}
kilometer	$1,000.0,$ or 10^{3}

The same system of prefixes is used for all types of units in the metric system. Thus, 1 kilogram = 1,000 grams, and 1 milliliter = 1/1,000 liter. There are other prefixes, but we shall mention at this time only myria-, meaning 10,000; mega-, meaning 1,000,000; and micro-, meaning 1/1,000,000. Actually, 1/1,000,000 of a meter is usually referred to as a *micron,* and is denoted by the Greek letter μ (mu).

In the metric system, converting one unit of measure into another is very simple. All that is needed is to relocate the decimal point in accordance with the new unit that one wishes to use. For example,

$$1.58 \text{ km.} = 1,580 \text{ m.} = 158,000 \text{ cm.,}$$

and

$$286 \text{ mg.} = 28.6 \text{ cg.} = .286 \text{ gm.} = 0.000286 \text{ kg.}$$

In the English system there is no such simple rule for changing measures from inches to feet, feet to yards, ounces to pounds, and so forth. The regular pattern of relationships among the units of length, volume, and mass is one of the great advantages of the metric system over the English system. A metric unit of volume can be matched with a related unit of mass. (*Mass* is a measure of *the amount of matter* in an object, while *weight* is the force of gravity acting on it. An astronaut in orbit is apparently weightless, but his mass is the same as it was on earth.) For example, the basic unit of mass in the metric system is the gram, and a gram is defined to be the mass of 1 cubic centimeter of pure water. A *liter* is defined to be the capacity of a container having a volume of 1,000 cubic centimeters; and so 1 liter of pure water has a mass of 1,000 grams, or 1 kilogram. The relationships in English weights are complex in comparison with the metric ones. In the English system the weight of 1 cubic foot of pure water is about 62.4 pounds; 1 liquid pint has a volume of 28.875 cubic inches, and a pint of water weighs 1.04 pounds.

Converting Units from One System to Another

It is sometimes desirable to convert measurements from one system to the other, since both systems are used in our country—the metric system in scientific work and the English system otherwise. The metric system is standard for all purposes in many parts of the world. Thus, if you are driving somewhere in Europe and see a sign that says "Maximum speed: 50 km/hr," you might want to convert to the more familiar English unit of miles-per-hour. Since the approximate equivalent of 1 kilometer in English units is 0.6 mile, you would calculate that 50 kilometers per hour is 0.6 × 50, or 30, miles per hour.

Tables of equivalent measures can be found in almanacs and textbooks.

Exercise Set 8

1. Which represents the greater quantity—
   a. 1 centigram or 1 milligram?
   b. 1 kilogram or 1 gram?
   c. 1 gram or 1 decigram?
   d. 1 deciliter or 1 dekaliter?

2. Fill in the missing numerals.

a. 16 meters = _____ decimeters = _____ centimeters = _____ millimeters.

b. 3.5 kilometers = _____ hectometers = _____ decameters = _____ meters.

c. 27 milliliters = _____ liters.

d. 100 grams = _____ centigrams = _____ milligrams.

3. When we use the liter as our basic unit, why is "10^{-3} × base" a valid way of identifying a milliliter? Why is "10^3 × base" a valid way of identifying a kiloliter?

4. Jim needed 6 grams of water for an experiment that he was doing, so he filled a graduated container with water up to the level marked 6 cc. Why was he right in doing so?

5. Which of these is the greatest measure—

a. 1 mile, 438 feet, or 126,700 inches?

b. 5,000 square yards, or 1 square mile?

c. 45,000 ounces, 4,000 pounds, or 1.1 tons?

d. 9 cubic feet, 1 cubic yard, or 46,656 cubic inches?

6. Why is it impossible to establish a "place-value system" for miles, yards, feet, and inches in the English system of linear measure?

PRECISION AND ACCURACY

Exact Measurement

It may be said that there are two kinds of measurement: exact and approximate. *Exact* measurements are necessarily the result of counting. For example, we can "measure" exactly the number of eggs in a crate or the number of dollar bills in our wallet simply by counting them. The property we are measuring in each case is the cardinal number of a given set of objects. Thus, we ordinarily compare the "size" of two auditoriums in terms of their relative seating capacity, that is, the number of seats in each.

On the other hand, measurements of physical properties other than "how-manyness" can only be approximations. Even with the finest measuring instruments that are available, an exact measurement cannot be determined; a certain amount of error will always exist.

Mistakes in Measurement

In measurement the words "error" and "mistake" have quite different connotations. A mistake implies carelessness on the part of the measurer. He may read the scale incorrectly. He may not place the measuring instrument at exactly the same place each time. He may record the readings incorrectly. Such mistakes can ordinarily be avoided if the individual is extremely careful. Nevertheless, the "human element" does contribute to the inevitable slight variation in results when a measurement is repeated.

The Precision of a Measurement

"Precision" and "accuracy" are not synonymous in measurement. "Precision" is a technical term and is defined as *the unit of measure* used. Precision is thus related to the measuring instrument. If you are measuring something to the nearest half of an inch, then the precision of your measurement is 1/2 inch. If a measurement is given as a decimal numeral, the placement of the numeral farthest to the right indicates the precision. A measurement of 35 feet was measured with precision of 1 foot; 3.5 feet has precision of 0.1 foot; 6.035 feet has precision of 0.001 foot. If you are given two measurements, *the one with the smaller unit of measure is the more precise.*

Since the precision is indicated by the numeral assigned to a given measurement, fractional units of measure should not be reduced to their simplest form. For example, a measurement of 6/8 of a unit should not be written as 3/4 of a unit, because that would not indicate the precision with which this approximate measurement was obtained. A measurement involving eighths of a unit (precision = 1/8 of a unit) is more precise than one involving fourths of a unit (precision = 1/4 of a unit).

Significant Digits

In scientific work, measurements are usually expressed as decimal numerals. Then each digit that serves to indicate how many units of measure are contained in the measurement is called a "significant digit." In the measurement 16.03 feet, the unit of measure (precision) is 0.01 foot, and there are 1,603 of these units in the measurement. Hence, the significant digits are 1, 6, 0, and 3. If, however, you were simply given a measurement of 16,000 miles, you could not be certain whether this was correct to the nearest mile unless it were specifically stated as such. If it were, then all five figures would be significant. Otherwise, you could assume only a precision of 1,000 miles. In that case, only the 1 and 6 would be significant digits.

Greatest Possible Error

Consider the measurements shown in Figure 30. In (a) the measure of $\overline{UV}$ *to the nearest unit* would be 3, since the point V is closer to the point named 3 than it is to the point named 2. The shaded interval between $2\frac{1}{2}$ and $3\frac{1}{2}$ shows the interval within which a measure given as 3, that is, with precision of 1 unit, must fall. The "greatest possible error" in any measurement is thus one-half of the unit of measure. Therefore, $\frac{1}{2}$ of 1 unit, or $\frac{1}{2}$ unit, is the greatest possible error in this case.

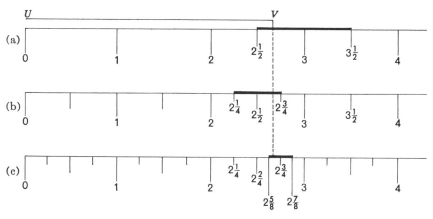

FIGURE 30

In (b) a more precise measurement is made. The unit of measure this time is $\frac{1}{2}$ unit, and so the greatest possible error is $\frac{1}{2}$ of $\frac{1}{2}$ unit, or $\frac{1}{4}$ unit. The measurement of $\overline{UV}$ to the nearest $\frac{1}{2}$ unit is $2\frac{1}{2}$ units, and the shaded interval of measure goes from $2\frac{1}{4}$ to $2\frac{3}{4}$ units.

In (c) the smaller unit of measure, $\frac{1}{4}$ unit, results in a still more precise measurement, with the greatest possible error equal to $\frac{1}{2}$ of $\frac{1}{4}$ unit, or $\frac{1}{8}$ unit. Now, the measure of $\overline{UV}$ to the nearest $\frac{1}{4}$ unit is $2\frac{3}{4}$ units, and the interval of measure extends from $2\frac{5}{8}$ to $2\frac{7}{8}$ units.

In general, the *greatest possible error of a measurement is one-half the precision*.

Relative Error and Accuracy

The "relative error" of a measurement is another technical term and is defined to be the ratio of the number of units in the greatest possible error to that in the measurement. Thus,

$$\text{relative error} = \frac{\text{number of units in greatest possible error}}{\text{number of units in the measurement}}.$$

A measurement reported as 12.5 units indicates that the precision of the measurement is 0.1 unit. Therefore, the greatest possible error would be 1/2 of 1/10, or 1/20, which would be 0.05. Accordingly, the relative error of the measurement is

$$\text{relative error} = \frac{.05}{12.5} = \frac{1}{250}, \quad \text{or} \quad 0.004.$$

Relative error furnishes a basis for comparing measurements. Of two measurements, the one with the lesser relative error is said to have the greater *accuracy*.

Which of the two measurements, 10.45 feet or 104 feet, is the more precise? Which has the greater accuracy? The calculations are summarized in Table IX.

TABLE IX

PRECISION AND ACCURACY

Measurement	10.45 Feet	104 Feet
Precision	0.01 ft.	1 ft.
Greatest possible error	$\frac{1}{2}$ of 0.01 ft. = 0.005 ft.	$\frac{1}{2}$ of 1 ft. = 0.5 ft.
Relative error (accuracy)	$\dfrac{0.005 \text{ ft.}}{10.45 \text{ ft.}} = 0.00048$	$\dfrac{0.5 \text{ ft.}}{104 \text{ ft.}} = 0.0048$

Since the measurement of 10.45 units had both the smaller unit of measure and the lesser relative error, it is the more precise and also has the greater accuracy. Note that if the precision of two measurements is the same (for example, 10.45 feet and 310.45 feet), then the numerator in the ratio for the relative error is the same for each, while the denominator varies with the size of the measurement. Since the greater the denominator is, the less the ratio will be, you can see why the greater of two measurements made with the same precision has the lesser relative error and hence the greater accuracy.

Each of the terms "precision," "accuracy," "relative error," and "mistake" has an important place in discussions of measurement. Correct use of these technical terms helps to clarify our understanding of measurement concepts.

Exercise Set 9

1. What is the precision of each of the following measurements?
   a. 2 feet
   b. $3\frac{9}{2}$ inches

c. 16.2 centimeters

d. 200 kilometers

e. 4.84 miles

f. $9\frac{5}{16}$ ounces

g. 1.00 tons

2. Determine the relative error for each of these measurements:

a. $2\frac{5}{16}$ inches

b. 4.14 centimeters

c. 705 miles

d. 75 miles

e. 30 seconds to the nearest 10 seconds

3. Determine the relative error in each pair of measurements and tell which measurement has the greater accuracy in each case.

a. 10 feet   or   **a'.** 10.00 feet

b. 155 inches   or   **b'.** 1.5 inches

c. 7 centimeters or   **c'.** 7.78 centimeters

d. 2.3 ounces   or   **d'.** 23 ounces

4. Name the unit of measure and the significant digits in each of the following measurements.

a. 137 feet

b. 2.025 inches

c. 0.03 feet

d. 200.5 kilograms

———————◆●◆———————

For Further Reading

Among the various helpful references that deal with the subject here introduced are the following:

BANKS, J. HOUSTON. "Concepts of Measurement," in *Enrichment Mathematics for the Grades.* Twenty-seventh Yearbook of the National Council of Teachers of Mathematics. Washington, D.C.: The Council, 1963. Available from the National Council of Teachers of Mathematics, 1201 16th St., N.W., Washington, D.C. 20036.

BELL, CLIFFORD; HAMMOND, CLELA D.; and HERRERA, ROBERT B. *Fundamentals of Arithmetic for Teachers.* New York: John Wiley & Sons, 1962. Pp. 389. Available from John Wiley & Sons, Inc., 605 Third Ave., New York, N.Y. 10016.

PAYNE, JOSEPH N., and SEBER, ROBERT C. "Measurement and Approximation," in *The Growth of Mathematical Ideas, Grades K-12.* Twenty-fourth Yearbook of the National Council of Teachers of Mathematics. Washington, D. C.: The Council, 1959. See address above.

WREN, F. LYNWOOD. *Basic Mathematical Concepts.* New York: McGraw-Hill, 1965. Pp. 398 Available from McGraw-Hill Book Co., 330 W. 42 St., New York, N.Y. 10036.

ANSWERS TO EXERCISES

Exercise Set 1

1. The size of the golf ball
2. The size of the peach
3. The prettiness of the rock
4. The fierceness of the mouse

Exercise Set 2

1. **a.** Ground floor
   b. Equator
   c. The year of the birth of Christ
   d. 0°
   e. Date of birth
   f. Financial state on January 31
2. **a.** In referring to yesterday, tomorrow, and so on
   b. In referring to "how full"
   c. In figuring how much can be withdrawn without closing the account, when this is the minimum balance allowed

Exercise Set 3

1. They were both about the same length.
2. Because of their difference in length.
3. Because the lengths of the different units of measure varied so widely.
4. **a.** Mile
   b. Foot
   c. Centimeter
   d. Foot
   e. Ton
   f. Inch
   g. Square yard
   h. Gallon or kiloliter
   i. A second

Exercise Set 4

1. A scale of fathoms is used.

2. No, it refers to a series of tones arranged in a sequence of rising (or falling) pitch.

3. Determine two known referent points.

Exercise Set 5

1. $\frac{6\,6}{7}$ centimeters

2. 6 feet

Exercise Set 6

1. An "area" in this instance is a designated place. Through common usage the word "area" has more than one meaning. In mathematics, area is a number that is a measure of a region.

2. The experiment shows that the area can change with adjustment of the sides, even though the perimeter remains the same.

3. The area is 39 square units.

4. By comparing the widths. The greater of the two widths will, in this instance, determine which area will be greater.

5. Drawings will vary, depending upon the selection of the two factors for length and width that will result in a product of 24. For example: 6×4, 3×8, 12×2, 1×24, $1/2 \times 48$.

Exercise Set 7

1. a. 4
   b. 8
   c. 64

2. a. 64
   b. 512
   c. $\frac{1}{64}$

Exercise Set 8

1. a. 1 centigram
   b. 1 kilogram
   c. 1 gram
   d. 1 dekaliter

2. a. 160 decimeters; 1,600 centimeters; 16,000 millimeters
   b. 35 hectometers; 350 decameters; 3,500 meters
   c. .027 liters
   d. 10,000 centigrams; 100,000 milligrams

3. A milliliter is 1/1,000 of a liter, and a kiloliter is 1,000 times as large as a liter.

4. Yes. In the metric system, 1 cubic centimeter weighs 1 gram, and 6 grams would be the equivalent of 6 cubic centimeters.

5. a. 126,700 inches

   b. 1 square mile

   c. 4,000 pounds

   d. 46,656 cubic inches

6. There is no simple decimal relation among the units. For example, 12 inches = 1 foot; 3 feet = 1 yard, etc.

Exercise Set 9

1. a. 1 foot

   b. $\frac{1}{2}$ inch

   c. 0.1 centimeter

   d. Not clearly indicated

   e. 0.01 mile

   f. $\frac{1}{16}$ ounce

   g. 0.01 ton

2. a. $\frac{1}{74}$

   b. 0.0012

   c. 0.0007

   d. 0.006

   e. 0.166

3. a. 0.05; **a′** 0.0005; **a′**.

   b. 0.003; **b′** 0.03; **b**.

   c. 0.07; **c′** 0.0006; **c′**.

   d. 0.02; **d′** 0.02; both the same.

4. a. 1 foot; 1, 3, and 7.

   b. 0.001 inch; 2, 0, 2, and 5.

   c. 0.01 foot; 3.

   d. 0.1 kilogram; 2, 0, 0, and 5.

COLLECTING, ORGANIZING, AND INTERPRETING DATA

A BRIEF LOOK AT STATISTICS

Why We Use Statistics

"How many students in the world are left-handed?" On the surface this question may seem to be merely a matter of idle curiosity. Yet in actual fact it has some very practical ramifications. The left-handed student faces certain unique problems that school planners need to consider. For example, when only armchair desks are available, someone— usually a principal or an architect—must be able to make a reasonable prediction about how many left-hand desks should be provided for a classroom of a given size. Even if desks suitable for either left- or right-handed students are available, the school planner still must have some way to determine how many desks must be placed with their light source to the right, so that the left-handed student will not be writing in his own shadow.

One might try to find an answer to the introductory question by conducting a complete survey of the total student population. Obviously, however, such an undertaking would be all but impossible. The question happens to be of a type that is best answered by collecting data[1] from a suitable sample of the total population and then organizing and interpreting this data in such a way as to obtain the most accurate answer possible.

Other questions of the same type are "What proportion of all elementary teachers read the *Arithmetic Teacher*?" and "Which state has the highest per capita divorce rate?" Although some questions of this kind may be of theoretical interest only, most of them are motivated by very real and practical considerations. All of them are examples of the sort of problem situation in which the collection, the organization, and

---

[1] This word is defined in the section on "Collecting Data."

the interpretation of data play an essential role in helping people to make wise decisions with limited information. These analytical methods simply furnish a technique for intelligent problem solving in the face of uncertainty. Basically, they constitute what is widely referred to as "the scientific method."

Four Stages in Problem Solving

Let us return now to the original question ("How many students in the world are left-handed?") and use it to illustrate the four stages generally associated with the problem-solving process. (See also Booklet No. 17: *Hints for Problem Solving*.)

1. *Observation:* Every teacher has observed that some students are left-handed. During a classroom writing assignment these students can often be spotted at a glance. Once the teacher is aware that there is one such student in the class, it is almost reflex action to look around the room for others and even to make a mental note of the number who are left-handed.

2. *Hunches and Hypotheses:* In a conversation with colleagues, or simply out of an idle remark, an explicit question might arise—"Do you have any idea what proportion of all students are left-handed?"— followed by a conjecture: "I had three out of thirty-two this year and five out of thirty-seven last year. One of the other teachers has six left-handed students in a class of thirty-five. Judging from these samples, I'd guess that about one in seven is left-handed."

"I'd guess about one in seven" is simply a hunch based on limited observation. In many situations we have to act largely on the basis of just such a hunch. In so doing, we have, on the basis of the observed data, formulated a hunch into a premise (hypothesis) concerning general patterns.

3. *Prediction:* "Working from the hypothesis that about one student in seven is left-handed, I would predict that I'll have about five left-handed students next year in my class of about thirty-five students."

The teacher made this deduction from the hypothesis that he had formulated on the basis of observations. Note that in this case the word "prediction" does not mean "foretelling a future event by mere guessing," but, rather, "deducing it by reasoning from observed facts."

4. *Verification:* The hunch that about one student in seven is left-handed can be substantiated or altered by gathering new data on the matter. These new facts can be used to check the prediction and then to test the original hypothesis. If the new facts differ too much or too

often from the prediction, the hypothesis should be revised to be consistent with the larger amount of data now available. Then the revised hypothesis should also be tested by steps 3 and 4.

Thus we have distinguished four fairly definite stages in problem solving:

1. Observation of facts
2. Formulation of a hypothesis concerning the facts
3. Prediction (deduction) from the hypothesis
4. Verification of the prediction by further observations

Often these stages are intertwined rather than sharply and clearly separated. The teacher's initial observation in the classroom led to subsequent speculation. This, in turn, led to collecting additional data from colleagues as well as from the teacher's own memory. Once all the data was collected, the organization and interpretation of it was, in this instance, a straightforward matter. Determining the best method for gathering the data is not, however, so simple a problem. The particular method used to collect and organize the data can affect the hypothesis considerably and may thereby influence the prediction. Clear thinking, careful work, and often some ingenuity must be applied in every case, to obtain information that will yield reliable conclusions.

EXAMPLE: "Theft of Finished Product"[2]

A certain business firm has to have a great deal of waste material hauled away. The waste material weighs considerably less per cubic foot than does the finished product. Some shortages have been observed in the finished product. The firm analyzed this mystery as follows:

1. *Observation:* The net weights of four different truckloads of waste, chosen at random, ranged between 14,200 and 14,500 pounds.

2. *Hypothesis:* The variation in weight from truckload to truckload is random (that is, strictly chance) and is within certain bounds—say, within 300 pounds of the least and the greatest weights observed above.

3. *Prediction:* Practically all future truckloads will fall between 13,900 and 14,800 pounds.

4. *Verification:* On further observation several truckloads were found to weigh 16,000 pounds. This tends to *contradict* the initial prediction and hence to contradict the original hypothesis.

2a. *Additional Hypothesis:* The unusually heavy truckloads might be associated either with certain trucks or with certain drivers.

1a. *New Observation:* The extra-heavy loads do coincide with one particular driver.

2b. *Further Hypothesis:* The fact that one driver is consistently taking out unusually heavy loads, together with the known fact that the finished product is sub-

and The following account is based on an example taken from *Statistics: A New Approach*, by W. A. Wallis
    [2] H. V. Roberts (Chicago: The Free Press of Glencoe, 1956), p. 9.

stantially denser than the waste, suggests the possibility that this driver may be smuggling out the finished product at the bottom of his load. More facts are needed, however, before one can safely conclude that this is true.

Exercise Set 1

1. The student-parking situation at many colleges is getting quite acute. A graduate student at a large midwestern university faced this problem every day. One day when he arrived late for class, he parked in a metered location and forgot to move his car. This happened again in the same parking place a few days later. Each time, he received a ticket. On reading the tickets he noticed that on both days his car had been ticketed at about the same time, namely 2:00 P.M. The next time he happened to park in that location, he put enough coins in the meter to cover his parking there until 2:30 P.M., although he planned to leave the car there for the rest of the afternoon. When he came back to his car at 6:15 P.M., it had not been ticketed. Identify and describe the various phases of the problem-solving process that the student used.

2. One day, in an emergency, the patrolman of exercise 1 happened to pass at 4:00 P.M. along the street that he ordinarily checked at 2:00 P.M. He noted an exceptionally large number of cars parked beside meters registering "time expired." The next day he altered his route to check this street at 4:00 P.M. and found he needed to issue several more tickets than usual. Thereafter, he varied his route from day to day in a random sort of way; and although he needed to issue only a few more tickets than he issued when checking at 2:00 P.M., more coins were found in the meters. Identify and describe the various phases of the problem-solving process that the patrolman used.

3. Devise a problem-solving story, using observation, hypothesis, prediction, and verification. *Story hints:* (a) "It rains every time I leave my umbrella behind"; (b) "Does she or doesn't she?"—the correlation between the times a woman's hair appears to be tinted and her visits to the hairdresser; (c) the story of the boy who cried, "Wolf!"

COLLECTING DATA

The origin of a word is often interesting because it can throw light on why certain concepts are associated with the word. Such is the case with the word "data" (singular: datum), which comes directly from a Latin word meaning "something given" and is now generally used to mean given information, or facts. ("Data" is often used as a collective noun and hence can be used with a singular verb form. For example, you might say, "This data was collected some time ago.") When we collect and organize numerical data, we are collecting and organizing numerical facts, usually with the aim of trying to infer certain general conclusions from them.

There is a general tendency for most people to react to the word "data" with the thought of formidable tables of figures, charts, and graphs. Yet as indicated above, numerical data are simply numerical facts, whether few or many. Such facts are not limited to books and ledgers but are part of our everyday experiences. Indeed, nowadays our lives are all but deluged with them, often incorporated in such slogans as, "Brush with Zest toothpaste and you'll have 40 percent fewer cavities." We use numerical facts in planning parties, determining taxes, manufacturing clothing, and myriad other ways.

We have seen how data collection fits into a general pattern of problem solving. Occasionally, data is collected simply as a matter of record. Records of births, deaths, and marriages were kept long before methods had been devised for deducing additional information from such data.

We might loosely classify the data we need for solving a problem as follows:

1. Firsthand, or original, data is that which we ourselves collect.
2. Secondhand, or "ready-made," data is that which has already been collected for some purpose by others.

Secondhand data can usually be obtained from such sources as almanacs, encyclopedias, textbooks, and research studies. In collecting data from a secondary source, the observer may have very little personal knowledge of how and why the data was originally collected or how it was used. He may therefore feel somewhat uneasy about any interpretations or decisions that he might make solely on the basis of this data.

In order to appreciate some of the uncertainty factors that can enter into the data-collecting process, let us consider a hypothetical example.

An Example of Data Collecting

Grown men are usually taller than grown women. *Are boys of a certain preadolescent age taller than girls of the same age?*

This question might stem from a very practical consideration. For example, in planning a school building it might be useful to know whether the shower heads should be installed higher on the wall in the boys' locker room than in the girls'. This question is clearly not the type that can be answered by reasoning deductively from any basic principle. Rather, it is of a sort to be answered by using methods that involve the collection, organization, and interpretation of numerical data. To find an answer to the foregoing question, suppose we begin by comparing height measurements for a group of twelve-year-old boys with those for a group of twelve-year-old girls. We might use the YMCA and the YWCA as sources for our data, asking someone at each of these places to obtain measurements for us. Suppose that we received the set of measurements shown in Table I from a Mr. Jackson at the YMCA.

TABLE I

HEIGHTS OF A GROUP OF TWELVE-YEAR-OLD BOYS

5 ft. 3¼ in.	5 ft. 4½ in.	4 ft. 11¾ in.
4 ft. 11½ in.	5 ft. 7¼ in.	5 ft. 2 in.
4 ft. 9¾ in.	5 ft. 7¼ in.	5 ft. 6 in.
5 ft. 3 in.	5 ft. 3⅜ in.	4 ft. 10 in.
5 ft. 5½ in.	6 ft. ½ in.	5 ft. 5½ in.
4 ft. 7 in.	4 ft. ½ in.	5 ft. ½ in.
5 ft. 4¼ in.	5 ft. 3¾ in.	5 ft. 3½ in.
5 ft. 6 in.	5 ft. 5⅞ in.	5 ft. 3 in.
5 ft. 2¾ in.	5 ft. 2¾ in.	5 ft. 2½ in.
5 ft. ⅝ in.	5 ft. ¾ in.	5 ft. 1½ in.
5 ft. 4 in.	5 ft. 4¾ in.	5 ft. 1 in.
5 ft. 3⅜ in.	5 ft. 2¾ in.	5 ft. 1½ in.
5 ft. 1 in.	5 ft. 1¼ in.	5 ft. 2½ in.
5 ft. 6½ in.	5 ft. 6¼ in.	1 m. 53 cm.*

* Note: The boys were playing around and broke the yardstick, so I had to use a meter stick for the last measurement.—[Signed] Stonehall Jackson

Now suppose that a lady at the YWCA sent the data shown in Table II, listing alphabetically the names of the girls opposite their respective heights.

When we count the number of measurements, we note that there are forty-two entries in the data for the boys and only thirty-five for the girls. On the other hand, the girls' list contains names, whereas the boys' list does not. For example, we can find the name of the tallest or the shortest girl in the group. But is this information pertinent to the original inquiry? Of course not. The question we want to answer asks only, "Are boys of a given preadolescent age taller than girls of that same age?" As far as our inquiry is concerned, it is not essential—nor even helpful—to be given the names of the girls.

We are now confronted with several decisions:

1. Should we include the last measurement for the boys—the measurement made with a meter stick?

TABLE II
Names and Heights of a Group of Twelve-Year-old Girls

Sandra Atkin	5 ft. 1 in.		Susan Boppe	5 in. $\frac{1}{2}$ ft.
Sandra Attkin	5 ft. 2$\frac{1}{2}$ in.		Susan Bue	5 ft. 7 in.
Sandra Atttkin	5 ft. $\frac{1}{4}$ in.		Susan Burk	5 ft. 8 in.
Sharon Baer	5 ft. 3 in.		Susan Burke	5 ft. 6 in.
Sharon Bar	4 ft. 10 in.		Cathy Caine	5 ft.
Sharon Barr	5 ft. $\frac{1}{2}$ in.		Cathy Cairne	5 ft. $\frac{1}{2}$ in.
Sharon Beer	5 ft. 1 in.		Cathy Carlsen	5 ft. 2 in.
Sharon Bier	4 ft. 11$\frac{3}{4}$ in.		Cathy Carlson	5 ft. 3 in.
Sharon Bird	4 ft. 11$\frac{3}{4}$ in.		Cathy Carrey	4 ft. 10 in.
Sharon Birge	5 ft.		Cathy Christie*	4 ft. 10$\frac{1}{2}$ in.
Sharon Birk	5 ft. 2$\frac{1}{2}$ in.		Cathy Christy	4 ft. 11 in.
Sharon Bjork	5 ft. 6 in.		Cathy Crnich	4 ft. 9$\frac{1}{2}$ in.
Sharon Bjorke	4 ft. 9 in.		Cathy Crnych	4 ft. 11$\frac{3}{4}$ in.
Sharon Bodie	5 ft. 3$\frac{1}{4}$ in.		Donna Daene	4 ft. 11 in.
Susan Book	5 ft. 1 in.		Donna Dana	5 ft. 6 in.
Susan Bookey	5 ft. $\frac{1}{4}$ in.		Donna Danar	5 ft. 2 in.
Susan Bookley	4 ft. 11 in.			

* Eleven years and eight months old.

2. Should we include the measurement of Cathy Christie, who was not yet of the stipulated age?

3. What should we do about the fact that there are more measurements for the boys (forty-two) than for the girls (thirty-five)? Could these complications have been avoided? Let us see.

Using Expert Advice

We have observed in the example above that rushing enthusiastically but thoughtlessly into an investigation can give rise to some possibly unnecessary complications. How could we have proceeded so as to avoid such problems?

Perhaps a bit of expert advice might be useful at this point. Were we faced with a legal problem, it would make sense to seek a competent attorney. If the problem were a medical one, we would try to consult a competent physician. Our present problem is to reach a conclusion from certain numerical information. Now, who is an expert at analyzing numerical facts so as to be able to draw certain conclusions from them? A mathematician? That would seem to be a natural choice; and we are interested here in a special kind of mathematician, one who is an expert at the job of collecting, organizing, and interpreting data. He is called a *statistician*. A statistician is a person who has been professionally trained in the scientific methods for collecting and analyzing data to obtain desired information from it. We would do well to seek his advice before plunging ahead.

Accordingly, suppose that we take our two samples of data to a competent statistician for some pointers on how to proceed. We call each set of data a *sample* because each list of heights represents only a tiny sampling of the heights of all twelve-year-old boys or girls in our country. A statistician would refer to the *totality of all the possible observations* (that is, the heights of *all* such children) as the *population*. Thus, each set of data is a sample of the population. Let us agree to distinguish between the two tables of measurements by calling the list for the boys "Sample 1" and that for the girls "Sample 2."

There are a number of things the statistician might tell us.

The first thing he would want us to note is that the two sets of measurements have been taken with two individual measuring instruments (in fact, with *three* different ones, if you include the meter stick). Since we shall be making comparisons based on these measurements, ideally we should use the same measuring instrument in obtaining the two samples. We should also try to use the most accurate instrument we can get.

He would probably remind us of another thing: that the measurements were made by two different persons. When taking measurements, some people will just naturally be more careful and precise than others. Moreover, even though the lady at the YWCA meticulously wrote down the names of all the girls she measured, the man at the YMCA *measured* more meticulously. He gave his measurements to the nearest one-eighth of an inch, whereas the lady recorded hers only to the nearest one-quarter of an inch. If we are not obtaining the data ourselves, we should be careful to give precise directions to those who are doing it for us.

Another thing: What about the boy who is six feet tall? Doesn't that make you wonder a bit? Was there a boy in the group who was really that tall? Since this height is so unusual for a twelve-year-old—and especially since there are more measurements of boys than of girls, anyway—you might feel that this measurement should be thrown out.

Yet even though that particular reading may appear extreme, it *was* one of the measurements. It belongs in the list of data just as much as any other measurement—unless, of course, there was some error made in measuring, or the boy was really much older, or he was wearing "elevator" shoes! If we are going to throw out any reading, we should do it in a way that is not selective. Otherwise, if we discard any data that seems extreme, simply because it does not conform to our preconceived notions of what is "normal," we may defeat the very purpose of our investigation. That is, we would be fitting the data to our preformed conclusion instead of reaching a conclusion that fits the data.

TABLE III

HEIGHTS OF A SECOND GROUP OF TWELVE-YEAR-OLD BOYS

5 ft. $7\frac{3}{8}$ in.	5 ft. $6\frac{1}{2}$ in.	5 ft. $5\frac{7}{8}$ in.	5 ft. $3\frac{7}{8}$ in.	5 ft. $1\frac{1}{2}$ in.
5 ft. $7\frac{1}{4}$ in.	5 ft. $6\frac{3}{8}$ in.	5 ft. $5\frac{7}{8}$ in.	5 ft. $3\frac{7}{8}$ in.	5 ft. $1\frac{1}{4}$ in.
5 ft. $6\frac{3}{4}$ in.	5 ft. $6\frac{1}{8}$ in.	5 ft. 5 in.	5 ft. $3\frac{3}{4}$ in.	5 ft. $\frac{7}{8}$ in.
5 ft. $6\frac{3}{4}$ in.	5 ft. $6\frac{1}{8}$ in.	5 ft. 4 in.	5 ft. $3\frac{1}{2}$ in.	4 ft. 10 in.
5 ft. $6\frac{5}{8}$ in.	5 ft. $6\frac{1}{8}$ in.	5 ft. 4 in.	5 ft. $2\frac{7}{8}$ in.	4 ft. 10 in.
5 ft. $6\frac{1}{2}$ in.	5 ft. 6 in.	5 ft. $3\frac{7}{8}$ in.	5 ft. $1\frac{1}{2}$ in.	4 ft. $9\frac{3}{4}$ in.

Let us pretend that our expert statistician has a friend who happens to be doing the same thing we are trying to do. Here are the friend's samples for the two groups of twelve-year-olds, boys and girls. Let's call them Sample 3 and Sample 4 (Tables III and IV) and compare his approach with ours.

TABLE IV

HEIGHTS OF A SECOND GROUP OF TWELVE-YEAR-OLD GIRLS

5 ft. $7\frac{7}{8}$ in.	5 ft. 1 in.	4 ft. $11\frac{7}{8}$ in.	4 ft. $10\frac{1}{2}$ in.	4 ft. $10\frac{1}{8}$ in.
5 ft. $5\frac{1}{2}$ in.	5 ft. $\frac{7}{8}$ in.	4 ft. $11\frac{3}{4}$ in.	4 ft. $10\frac{1}{2}$ in.	4 ft. 10 in.
5 ft. 5 in.	5 ft. $\frac{7}{8}$ in.	4 ft. $11\frac{1}{2}$ in.	4 ft. $10\frac{1}{2}$ in.	4 ft. 9 in.
5 ft. 3 in.	5 ft. $\frac{3}{4}$ in.	4 ft. 11 in.	4 ft. $10\frac{1}{2}$ in.	4 ft. $8\frac{1}{2}$ in.
5 ft. $2\frac{1}{2}$ in.	5 ft.	4 ft. $10\frac{1}{2}$ in.	4 ft. $10\frac{1}{2}$ in.	4 ft. 8 in.
5 ft. $2\frac{3}{8}$ in.	5 ft.	4 ft. $10\frac{1}{2}$ in.	4 ft. $10\frac{1}{4}$ in.	4 ft. 5 in.

Notice that both of his samples contain the same number of measurements. This is a good idea. We might do the same when we collect our data for making comparisons. Notice also that he rearranged the data in order of size. Such organization does not involve much more effort, and it enables us to read at a glance, directly from the data, some very useful information. For instance, looking at Tables III and IV, we can quickly comprehend the following:

The tallest boy is shorter than the tallest girl.
The shortest boy is taller than the shortest girl.
Half of the boys are taller than all but one of the girls.
More than half of the girls are under five feet, whereas only three boys are under five feet.

The heights in Sample 4 range from 4 feet 5 inches to 5 feet $7\frac{1}{8}$ inches, a spread of $14\frac{7}{8}$ inches.

The heights in Sample 3 range from 4 feet $9\frac{3}{4}$ inches to 5 feet $7\frac{3}{8}$ inches, a spread of $9\frac{5}{8}$ inches from the shortest boy to the tallest.

Random Samples

Let us continue with another important point the statistician would certainly want to explain. Does it seem reasonable that half of the boys in Sample 3 should be taller than all but one of the girls in Sample 4? Or that the spread of heights among the boys was only $9\frac{5}{8}$ inches, while that among the girls was $14\frac{7}{8}$ inches? Comparing the data in Sample 3 with that in Sample 1, you may also have noted something that might well make you wonder how Sample 3 was chosen: the average height for Sample 3 is several inches greater than the average for Sample 1. A possible explanation for this could be that although the boys in the two samples were indeed of the same age, the boys in Sample 3 might have been selected from a group of boys who turned out for basketball. If so, then this is a representative sample, *not* of the total population with which we are concerned, but only of a specially selected subset of it.

Our sample should be as representative as possible of the *total* population we are considering. That is to say, we want to collect our data in such a way as to obtain the most accurate reflection of the population that we possibly can. (Remember that the "population" consists of all the possible observations of whatever sort we are sampling.) There is a way of doing this. It is called *random sampling*. The word "random" in this case does not refer to the data in the sample, but to the process for obtaining the sample. A sample is a *random sample* of a given total population if it was obtained by a process that enabled it to have the same chance of being drawn from the total population as any other sample of that same size. Thus, since the YMCA and the YWCA were selected for Samples 1 and 2, these samples were by no means randomly selected from the total population.

Of the several compelling reasons for collecting data by random sampling, the main one is that statistical analysis makes extensive use of the mathematical laws of probability, which are valid only for samples that are random. Another reason is that random sampling usually gives a truer picture of the population. This does not mean that a random sample is a perfect miniature replica of the population, but only that it is more likely to be representative than one that is not random.

The following classic example shows what seriously misleading information may be extracted from a sample that is not accurately representative.

In 1936 the *Literary Digest,* a popular magazine of that day, mailed out 10,000,000 questionnaires to poll the electorate prior to the presidential election. On the basis of some 2,300,000 returns, the magazine predicted that the Republican candidate, Alfred M. Landon, would be elected. Instead, his Democratic opponent, Franklin D. Roosevelt, was reelected by one of the largest majorities in American presidential history!

A postmortem revealed, among other factors involved in this "blooper," that in the 1936 election there was a strong relation between income and party preference and that the sample of voters polled by the *Literary Digest* was overweighted with high-income people.

You may recall the remark that when we wish to compare some characteristic of two groups of objects, it is a good idea to use samples of the same size. Let us suppose that we decide to do this and that we want to reduce each one of our Samples 1 and 2 to just thirty measurements, as the statistician's friend did. We can do this in a nonselective way by means of *random drawing.* We would proceed more or less as follows:

1. First, we label the forty-two measurements in Sample 1 with the numbers from 1 to 42.
2. Next, we get forty-two Ping-Pong balls and number them also from 1 through 42. Then we put the balls in a container and mix them thoroughly.
3. Now we draw out twelve of the balls, one at a time. Each time a numbered ball is drawn, we cross out the measurement with the corresponding number on Sample 1. After making twelve drawings, we will have 42 − 12, or 30, measurements left.
4. We reduce the data in Sample 2 by the same method, using thirty-five Ping-Pong balls and drawing out five of them at random so that thirty measurements will remain.

The reason for this procedure is that it gives each measurement to be discarded the *same chance as any other* of being drawn from the total population of measurements. This is loosely what is meant by a random (or chance) drawing.

Recapitulation

The imaginary visit with the statistician has been profitable in many ways. With his professional training and experience, he could explain some of the fine points of the art of collecting data for statistical analysis, including the following:

1. The need for care and forethought in making preparations for collecting the data

If someone else collects the data for you, it is particularly important that he be given specific instructions on such matters as accuracy and precision, the number of items to be included in the sample, and any special equipment needed to obtain it.

2. The need for care in recording the data and for including any pertinent comments

3. The importance of selecting the sample of observations in such a way as to get an accurate cross section of the total population

Exercise Set 2

1. Define each of the following:
   a. Data
   b. Statistician
   c. Population
   d. Random sample

2. If you chose the children in your own classroom as a sample, would your choice be a random sample of any of these populations?
   a. All the children in your school
   b. All the children in your country
   c. All the children in the world

More About Sampling

Let us return to the idea of sampling and try to summarize a few of the reasons for using a sample. In our particular inquiry regarding heights of preadolescent children, we wanted to know whether, in general, boys of a given age are taller than girls of that age. The phrase "in general" means "on the average." Of course, the task of collecting data for all the boys and girls of that age throughout our country would be well-nigh impossible. Hence we restrict our sample size to something more manageable, even while trying to arrive at a conclusion that is as general and far-reaching as possible.

One of the most practical reasons for resorting to samples is the cost, because collecting a comprehensive set of data can be an expensive business both in money and in time. To be sure, our information would be more complete and precise if we were to observe the entire population. But this is neither practical nor even possible in many cases. Moreover, if data is collected too hurriedly because of the hugeness of the task, the results may be less accurate than if they were based on a carefully collected sample.

Then again, the population may happen to be unlimited or to extend indefinitely into the future, so that it would be impossible to collect a complete set of data. For example, almost everyone has seen a number of beautiful sunsets. It might be interesting to keep a record of how frequently they occur at some particular location—say at Chicago—in order to find out whether one is more likely to see a fine sunset there in January, for example, than in July. Such a collection of data would be a sample of an indefinite population, inasmuch as the total number of gorgeous sunsets is unknown and would certainly extend into the very future for which the predictions are to be made.

Sometimes the reason for using a sample is an obviously practical one, as the following illustration demonstrates.

Many structures such as radio-station antenna towers and airway beacons are equipped with powerful lights that are visible for long distances on clear nights. In some cases the towers are extremely tall, and near the top they look dangerously slender. Inasmuch as pole sitting went out of fashion some years ago, it is a rare person nowadays who has had the uncomfortable experience of looking down the length of such a tall, slender structure. Have you ever wondered how it would feel to be replacing a burned-out electric bulb in such a location? Whenever such a light bulb burns out—and of course they do—someone has to climb up and replace the bulb. Since this is a dangerous task, it is desirable to use the most reliable light bulbs possible, those with the longest life. But how can one test for such reliability?

A number of companies produce so-called long-life bulbs. Even though they all try to meet certain specifications, there are variations in the bulbs produced by different companies. (In fact, there are variations in the bulbs produced by any single company.) In order to determine the most reliable bulbs for the specific situation, certain carefully designed tests are carried out. The observations of the total population in this case would be measurements of the length of life of all "long-life" bulbs. Each observation (each measurement) would result in a burned-out bulb. Hence, observing the entire population in this case would result in destroying every available bulb—hardly a practical procedure!

Other Methods of Obtaining Firsthand Data

Data can be collected firsthand by methods other than direct measurement. For example, data can be obtained from interviews and from questionnaires. Both of these methods require effective communication with people, which of course involves "the human element" with its many complexities. Information collected by either of these means is highly susceptible to a variety of abuses both deliberate and sub-conscious.

The collection process in both cases involves questions and answers to questions. The reliability of the data thus obtained naturally depends in part on whether the questions were clearly stated and well under-stood. A question may seem perfectly clear and understandable to the inquirer, who may have deliberated a long time on the subject and be familiar with all aspects of it. Yet the question may be confusing to the responder or not well understood by him. Either he may lack knowledge of the subject, or, if he happens to be familiar with it, he may lack the time or the ability to give a thoughtful answer. Because of these facts, the questions, whether oral or written, are usually designed for a simple "yes" or "no" type of response.

Even certain characteristics of the interviewer himself may affect the response. For example, a woman might respond to a question posed by another woman in quite a different way than she might if it were posed by a man.

An interesting anecdote about the effect of the questioner on the responder was reported in the *University of Chicago Magazine* of April 1952: "When soldiers were asked if the army is unfair to them, 35 per-cent said 'yes' to interviewers of the same nationality as the soldier, but when asked by interviewers of a different nationality, only 11 per-cent said 'yes.' "

The neophyte data collector often resorts to interviews or question-naires, unaware of all the pitfalls in these methods of obtaining in-formation. Before attempting to collect data by either of these means, he would be well advised to seek the counsel of an expert statistician. (In fact, such advice should not be restricted to neophytes.)

Collecting Secondhand Data

Some inquiries require data that cannot easily be obtained firsthand—for example, data on the heights of mountains. In that case the data must be obtained from a secondary source, and it is important to try to evaluate the reliability of the source. Even supposedly reliable sources sometimes show discrepancies, as the example in Table V shows. The two sets of figures given in Table V were obtained from the 1950 editions of two well-known almanacs.

TABLE V

CONFLICTING DATA FROM TWO ALMANACS, 1950 EDITIONS

"Tabulation of Those Who Speak the Chief Languages" [From first source]		"Languages of the World" [From second source]	
Arabic	29,000,000	Arabic	58,000,000
Chinese	488,573,000	Chinese	450,000,000
Czech	7,500,000	Czech	8,000,000
Dutch	16,548,500	Dutch	10,000,000
German	78,947,000	German	100,000,000
Hungarian	8,001,112	Hungarian	13,000,000
Italian	43,700,000	Italian	50,000,000
Japanese	97,700,000	Japanese	80,000,000
Portuguese	48,800,000	Portuguese	60,000,000
Rumanian	19,400,000	Rumanian	16,000,000
Spanish	80,000,000	Spanish	110,000,000
Swedish	6,266,000	Swedish	7,000,000
Turkish	16,160,000	Turkish	18,000,000

Summary

The theory of statistics furnishes a scientific method for collecting and analyzing numerical data in the way that will best help us find answers or make wise decisions in the face of incomplete information. Whenever it is either impossible or impractical to obtain all the numerical facts relevant to a particular problem, we have to rely on a process called *sampling*. On the basis of the partial information furnished by a sample of data taken from the total population, which consists of the set of all possible data of the sort being considered, the statistician tries to deduce conclusions that are as general and reliable as possible.

Selecting a suitable and adequate sample requires expert judgment and know-how. The sample should be as representative as possible of the total population under consideration. To illustrate what is meant by an "adequate" sample, suppose that for some reason you wanted to determine what proportion of fifth graders in the United States have visual problems. Data collected from just three fifth-grade classes would hardly be an adequate sample on which to base any general conclusions. On the other hand, if one were interested in obtaining such information only for one rather small school district, then three classes might well furnish an adequate sample.

A sample of a given size is said to be *random* if it was obtained by a method that gave every other sample of that size in the total population the same chance of being selected. The data for a sample are drawn *at random* from the total population in much the same way as are the winners in a lottery, where the tickets are all mixed in a container and the winning numbers are drawn out.

There are several reasons why it is usually desirable for a sample to be a random one. For one thing, such a sample is likely to give a more accurate reflection of the total population. But the most important reason is that the mathematical laws of probability, on which the statistician relies, apply only to samples that are random.

Data for statistical analysis can be collected from direct observation, from questionnaires and interviews, or from secondary sources. Scientific experiments, weather reports, space trips, television programs, modes of transportation, and ticket sales are only a few examples of the many sources from which numerical data can be obtained.

Direct observation is likely to be the most accurate way of collecting data, assuming that the observer knows exactly what is wanted and what to look for.

Questionnaires should be used with caution. The accuracy of the data obtained in this way depends on the ability of the questioner to ask questions that cannot be misinterpreted. Questions that require the expression of opinion are less desirable than those designed for a simple "yes" or "no" response. Then, too, questionnaires are not always returned, so the sampling may be inadequate.

Data may also be obtained "ready-made" from almanacs, textbooks, and other reference works. Such data is, of course, no more accurate then the investigator's source.

The recording of data is an essential part of the collection process. The observer should try to make as complete and precise a recording of his data as is possible. Care in this matter will be well rewarded later on when the time comes to organize and interpret the data.

Suggestions for Sources of Data

Listed below are suggestions for data that can be collected right in the classroom.

1. Shoe sizes of the pupils in the classroom
2. Heights of the children
3. Weights of the children
4. Color of eyes or hair of the children
5. Enrollment in classes, clubs, or events
6. The favorite colors of the children
7. Cost of the same item in different stores, as determined from newspaper advertisements

8. TV programs seen the night before class
9. Record of the temperature for a week in a particular place in the room at three certain times each day
10. The number of automobiles that pass the classroom window during a five-minute period at the same time each day
11. High and low temperatures of cities, as found in a newspaper
12. First names of fifteen persons
13. Birthdays of the children
14. Weekly growth of a plant from seed to maturity
15. Number of blocks each child lives from school
16. Opinion polls
17. The time taken for each classroom activity during the day
18. Each pupil's favorite kind of meat
19. Where each child went on his vacation
20. Kinds of books read by the children

Exercise Set 3

1. Classify as firsthand or secondhand the data obtained by the following activities:
   a. Reading a thermometer
   b. Consulting an encyclopedia
   c. Reading baseball standings in the sports section of a newspaper
   d. Recording "heads" or "tails" as you flip a coin
2. Refer to the financial section of your local newspaper. List several sources of data that can be found there.

ORGANIZING DATA

Once data has been collected, the next step in a statistical analysis is to determine how it should be organized so that it will readily yield useful information. This is no simple feat, but one that calls for both imagination and experience. Just as an author uses words to create a novel, so the statistician uses tables and charts to create a "story" out of a mass of data.

The organization of numerical facts—that is, the method of telling the story—depends on the nature of the facts and the purpose for which they were obtained. (Of course, we are assuming that the data has been collected with care and thoroughness, for otherwise no amount of skillful organization can be expected to yield accurate information.) Although there is no simple recipe for eliciting answers from a collection of data, the statistician does have two useful devices for describing and summarizing his information: the *frequency distribution*, and certain *descriptive measures* of the distribution.

Organizing Qualitative Data: Charts and Pictograms

Suppose that the manager of a boarding home wants to put in an ice-cream order for a certain day, so that there will not be a surplus of some flavors and an insufficiency of others. Accordingly, she might ask the boarders to fill out the following questionnaire:

Mark an X in the space beside your favorite ice-cream flavor.

____ chocolate   ____ lemon   ____ vanilla

____ strawberry   ____ orange

Table VI shows how many votes each flavor received on one such occasion. The flavors have been arranged in decreasing order of preference so that the results may be readily grasped.

TABLE VI

PREFERENCES OF ICE-CREAM FLAVORS

Flavor	Number of Votes
Vanilla	15
Chocolate	14
Strawberry	9
Orange	6
Lemon	5

A *bar chart* provides a useful means for picturing relative frequencies of qualitative classifications, such as those for the ice-cream flavors. In Figure 1 the number scale denoting frequencies could equally well

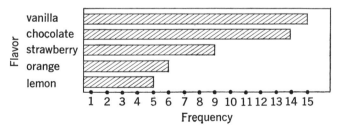

FIG. 1.—Preferences for five flavors of ice cream.

have been drawn vertically. In that case, the bars would have been vertical instead of horizontal. Note that the width of the bars has no significance; in fact, the relative frequencies could just as well have been denoted by line segments instead of bars, although the effect would be less striking.

A *circle graph*, or "pie chart," is another useful device for presenting a visual summary of qualitative-data frequencies. The circle is divided into pie-shaped pieces, or *sectors*, whose areas are proportional to the quantities that are to be represented.

For example, suppose that a family budgets its annual income as in Table VII.

TABLE VII

FAMILY BUDGET

Item	Percent of Income
Food	30
Clothing	20
Shelter	25
Savings	10
Miscellaneous	15
Total	100

In order to represent on a circle graph (Fig. 2) the percentage of total income allotted to food, we would use a protractor and construct a sector with central angle equal to 30 percent of 360°, or 108°. Table

FIG. 2.—Allocation of family budget.

VIII indicates the size of the central angle allotted to each of the five items of expense.

TABLE VIII

CENTRAL-ANGLE SIZES FOR SECTORS IN CIRCLE GRAPH

Item	Degrees in Central Angle
Food......................	$0.30 \times 360° = 108°$
Clothing...................	$.20 \times 360° = 72°$
Shelter....................	$.25 \times 360° = 90°$
Savings...................	$.10 \times 360° = 36°$
Miscellaneous..............	$0.15 \times 360° = 54°$
Total.....................................	$360°$

A more dramatic device for displaying frequencies of qualitative observations is the *pictogram*. A pictogram consists of a number of rows of small schematic pictures denoting the item (or items) being observed. Each picture represents some specified amount of that particular item. Each row is labeled according to its classification, just as are the bars in a bar chart.

For example, we might denote by means of a pictogram (Fig. 3) the number of satellite firings anywhere in the world during the three-year period 1957–59. (In this case, each symbol represents one satellite firing.)

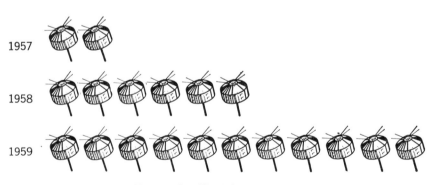

FIG. 3.—Satellite firings, 1957–59.

Pictographs are commonly used in those newspapers, magazines, and books whose readers are assumed to have a minimum of technical background for interpreting charts and graphs.

Organizing Quantitative Data:
Frequency Tables and Histograms

Now let us see how we might go about organizing a collection of data that is quantitative (numerical) in nature instead of qualitative. Suppose that we are given the set of heights of a group of forty twelve-year-old boys, as shown in Table IX. The heights are recorded to the nearest one one-hundredth of a foot. Note also that the heights as presented here are not raw (unorganized) data, but are in the form of an *array*, that is, arranged in order of magnitude.

TABLE IX

HEIGHTS (IN FEET) OF 40 TWELVE-YEAR-OLD BOYS

5.75	5.38	5.18	5.07
5.71	5.37	5.17	5.06
5.66	5.31	5.16	5.05
5.62	5.28	5.15	5.03
5.55	5.27	5.14	4.98
5.44	5.26	5.12	4.95
5.41	5.24	5.10	4.88
5.41	5.23	5.10	4.87
5.40	5.23	5.09	4.82
5.39	5.22	5.08	4.56

From this array we can comprehend at a glance which are the greatest and the least heights, how many are less than five feet, and so forth. What is not so easily observed, however, is the fact that there is more spread between numbers grouped at either end of the array than between numbers falling near the middle. Information of this latter sort is more easily visualized when the data is summarized in the form of a *frequency distribution*. To construct a frequency-distribution table from the above data, we might proceed in the following manner.

First, we find the *range*, or total spread, of the data. That is, we calculate the difference between the least number and the greatest. In this case, the range is $5.75 - 4.56$, or 1.19, feet.

Next, we separate the range into a set of equal intervals, called *class intervals*. Experience and common sense are the best guides for selecting the number of intervals to use—usually anywhere from six to fifteen. The aim is to summarize the data so that one can readily visualize the underlying distribution. For our sample of forty observations we might use six intervals, as follows: 4.56–4.75, 4.76–4.95, 4.96–5.15, 5.16–5.35, 5.36–5.55, 5.56–5.75. Note that in order to avoid ambiguity as to which interval a measurement falls into, the intervals are chosen so as not to overlap. Thus, a height of 4.75 feet belongs in the first interval, and one of 4.76 feet belongs in the second interval.

By counting the number of measurements in each interval, we obtain the frequency distribution shown in Table X. As we glance at the table we can immediately observe a tendency for the measurements to cluster in the middle intervals and thin out toward the ends of the distribution.

TABLE X

FREQUENCY DISTRIBUTION OF HEIGHTS OF
40 TWELVE-YEAR-OLD BOYS

Interval	Frequency
4.56–4.75	1
4.76–4.95	4
4.96–5.15	12
5.16–5.35	11
5.36–5.55	8
5.56–5.75	4

A still better visual impression of the frequency distribution in Table X can be obtained from a special type of graph known as a *histogram*. First we draw a horizontal line on which to scale the heights, marking off on this line the initial point of each of our chosen class intervals. Now we can indicate each measurement by putting a dot above the appropriate mark on the scale, thus obtaining what is called a *dot frequency diagram* (Fig. 4).

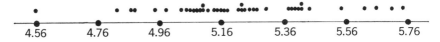

| 4.56 | 4.76 | 4.96 | 5.16 | 5.36 | 5.56 | 5.76 |

FIG. 4.—Dot frequency diagram of distribution in Table X.

When the number of measurements is large, however, or when there is a clustering at some part of the scale, so that many of the dots coincide or nearly coincide, then a diagram of this sort is impractical. Instead we add another dimension to the diagram by constructing over each interval a bar as wide as the interval. In the resulting histogram (Fig. 5) the height of each bar is proportional to the number (frequency) of measurements in its base interval. Thus, the height of the bar varies with the *density* of the dots along the horizontal scale. The area of a rectangle is the product of its width and height; so if the class intervals are of equal width, then the areas of the bars are proportional to their

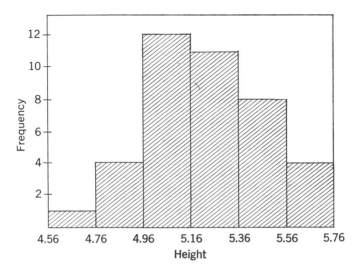

Fig. 5.—Histogram of distribution in Table X.

heights and hence to the density of the dots in their base intervals. Thus a histogram might be described as a sort of *density diagram* of a quantitative distribution of items.

Another way of graphing a frequency distribution is by means of a *frequency polygon,* which is formed by connecting the midpoints of the histogram bar tops with straight line segments. (See Fig. 6.) Notice how

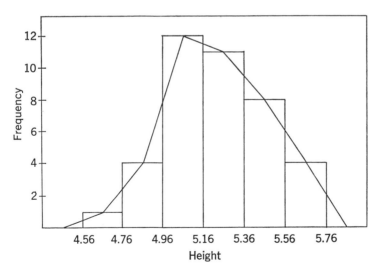

Fig. 6.—Frequency polygon of distribution in Table X.

the histogram is extended one class interval at each end and the polygon is continued to the horizontal axis at the midpoint of each of these intervals.

When several sets of data are being graphed for comparison, they can be visualized more clearly by superimposing their frequency polygons than by superimposing their histograms.

A frequency polygon suggests an idealized representation of a frequency distribution in the form of a smooth curve. This is easy to visualize if you think of graphing an extremely large sample of data so that the class intervals could be quite narrow and yet contain a large number of observations. Then, when the midpoints of the tops of the very narrow histogram bars are connected, the resulting frequency polygon usually is almost indistinguishable from a smooth curve. (See Fig. 7.)

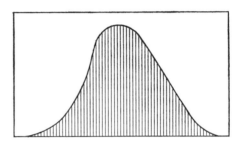

Fig. 7.—Idealized frequency polygon as a smooth curve.

It is a difficult problem in statistical analysis to try to infer which particular smooth curve most accurately represents the population from which the sample is drawn. This is why smooth curves should not ordinarily be substituted for actual histograms in an attempt to give a quick impression of a distribution.

Measures of Central Location:
The Mean, the Median, and the Mode

Graphic devices, such as the frequency histogram, are useful for offering a quick visual summary of a large collection of measurements. To paraphrase a familiar saying, one picture is worth a thousand numerical facts.

Suppose, however, that we wanted to compare the heights in a sample consisting of forty twelve-year-old boys with those in a sample of forty girls of the same age. How could we measure, or even try to express, the degree of similarity between their frequency distributions or their histograms? Although we could attempt to describe their similarities in words, we could summarize this information much more compactly and precisely with certain numerical descriptive measures that can be derived from the samples. In particular, we are usually interested in knowing where a distribution is centered on the total scale of values it assumes.

One of the most commonly used *measures of central location* is the *arithmetic mean* of the distribution. The arithmetic mean is most often referred to as the *average* and is defined as follows:

The arithmetic mean of a set of n measurements is simply their sum divided by n.

EXAMPLE:

If the weights, to the nearest pound, of five men are 160, 185, 210, 153, and 178 pounds, find their mean weight.

$$Solution: \frac{160 + 185 + 210 + 153 + 178}{5} = \frac{886}{5} \doteq 177.$$

Suppose that you have two samples and that you know the mean and also the number of observations for each one. Then it is a simple matter to calculate the mean of the two samples combined. Let A_1 be the mean and let n be the number of observations in the first sample. Then if S_1 is the sum of the n observations, we have:

$$A_1 = \frac{S_1}{n}, \quad \text{or} \quad nA_1 = S_1.$$

Similarly for the second sample, with mean A_2 and m observations,

$$mA_2 = S_2.$$

Then the mean, A_3, for the two samples combined is:

$$A_3 = \frac{S_1 + S_2}{n + m}$$

$$= \frac{nA_1 + mA_2}{n + m}.$$

One disadvantage of the mean as a numerical measure to describe the "center" of a distribution is that its value may be affected considerably by one or two extreme values in the set of observations. For example, suppose you wanted to determine how much income a young attorney would probably earn in Denver, Colorado. From interviews with a random sample of ten Denver lawyers under thirty-five years of age, you learn that the average income for eight of them is $15,000, but the average for the other two is $50,000. You determine the average for the entire sample of ten by using the formula for A_3:

$$\frac{8 \times 15,000 + 2 \times 50,000}{8 + 2} = \frac{120,000 + 100,000}{10}.$$

And you find that the average is $22,000! The young attorney wanting to practice law in Denver, who tries to weigh the income potential against the scenic and sporting attractions, might find such a high figure falsely reassuring.

The very fact that the mean *is* so sensitive to any extreme values in a distribution can also, for some purposes, be one of its advantages as a descriptive measure.

Another useful measure of central location is the *median* of an array of measurements. The median is the value of the middle observation; that is, half of the items have a value that is less than the median, and half have a greater value. If the array contains an even number of items, then there are two "middle" values, and the value halfway between these two is considered the median.

EXAMPLE 1:

Find the median of the following set of observations: 2, 7, 1, 5, 11.

Solution: First we array the numbers in order of magnitude: 1, 2, 5, 7, 11. Then we observe that the median is 5.

EXAMPLE 2:

Find the median of the following set of six observations: 8, 13, 2, 6, 17, 5.

Solution: Rearranging these items in an array, we have 2, 5, 6, 8, 13, 17. Since there are two middle items, 6 and 8, the median is the value halfway between them, namely 7.

Note that an extreme observation does not unduly affect the value of the median. For example, if the largest number in the array of Example 1 were, say, 53 instead of 11, the median would still be 5.

Since the median is relatively unaffected by a few extreme values in a distribution, it is sometimes described as being more accurately representative of a set of observations than some other descriptive measures. The median is also a preferable measure to use for a distribution that has open-ended intervals. For example, suppose that the previously mentioned sample of Denver attorneys' incomes were organized into a frequency distribution with the first class interval labeled "under $8,000" and the last one "over $25,000." Since we do not have the precise values of all the observations, we could not find their sum so as to compute the mean of the sample. In fact, we could not even specify the class interval into which it falls. From the frequencies for each interval, however, we could easily find the interval in which the median lies, and even compute its approximate value.

The median is a useful descriptive statistic for some purposes. Unlike the mean, however, it is not an algebraic measure. Hence the medians of two comparable samples cannot be combined to yield a composite median for the combined sample.

Another measure of central location is one called the *mode*. This is the value of the variable that occurs with the greatest frequency. Of course, a distribution may have more than one mode; that is, there may be several class intervals containing the same maximum number of observations. Such a frequency distribution is called *multimodal*. If Sample 3 were arranged in a frequency distribution, it would be found to be a *bimodal* one because there are two modes in the array: 5ft. $6\frac{1}{4}$ in. and 5 ft. $3\frac{7}{8}$ in., with maximum frequency $f = 3$.

In statistical studies, the mean, the median, and the mode of a sample are all referred to as "averages" because each in its way describes a "typical" value in the array of observations.

Measures of Variability:
Range and Percentiles

The branch of mathematics called descriptive statistics was at first concerned primarily with determining various averages of a frequency distribution. Soon after that, the emphasis shifted to a study of the *variability* in a distribution as an equally important characteristic of the sample. In particular, the statistician is interested in the degree of *dispersion*, or "scatter," about an average.

As we learned in the preceding section, neither the mean, the median, nor the mode gives any hint either of the extreme values that may be contained in a distribution or of the pattern of variation about these "centers" of the distribution.

The simplest measure of the variation in a distribution is its range, that is, the difference in value between the greatest and the least observation. For example, the range of heights in Table IX is $5.75 - 4.56$, or 1.19.

One trouble with using the range as a measure of the variation in a sample of observations is that the greater the number of values included in the sample, the greater the range tends to be. This means that if we are comparing the ranges of two or more samples of similar observations—for example, the heights of several groups of twelve-year-olds—we need to know, when we are interpreting the results, whether the samples are all of about the same size.

The range is very useful as a measure of variability in engineering problems, particularly in the field of statistical quality control of mass-produced items. Here the same sample size, usually quite small, is used repeatedly. Each sample item is observed for any excessive variation in some measurable characteristic—for example, in the diameter of the lug bolts of a certain model of automobile. Even a slight amount of variation in the dimensions of a particular component may be crucial in determining whether certain parts of a given product can be interchanged.

The range shows only the spread in an array and gives no picture of the pattern of distribution between the extreme values. A more sensitive measure of variability can be obtained by finding the *quartiles* of a distribution, that is, the three values of an array which separate the total frequency, from the lowest value to the highest, into four consecutive quarters. Thus, the *lower* (or *first*) *quartile* is the value that separates the lowest one-quarter of the measurements from the remaining three-quarters of the measurements. The *second quartile* is, of course, the median. The *upper* (or *third*) *quartile* separates the lowest three-quarters of the measurements from the remaining one-quarter of the measurements.

A measure of relative position finer than the quartile is *percentile*. Thus, the pth percentile in an array is the value such that p percent of the measurements are less than that value, and $100 - p$ percent are greater. The eightieth percentile in an array of data marks the boundary between the lowest 80 percent of the measurements and the remaining (higher-valued) 20 percent of the measurements.

The *interquartile range*, which is the difference between the first and third quartiles, is another useful measure of dispersion. Half of the observations lie in this range.

Any two or more positional measures provide some idea of the variation in a distribution. In fact, the more of such measures you have, the closer you come to reproducing precisely the frequency distribution from which they are derived. For example, consider two samples, S_1 and S_2, each consisting of the weights of forty people. Suppose that you are given the following information about the samples and wish to compare the two:

1. Both samples have the same median: 130.
2. In S_1 the least value is 95 and the greatest is 215.
   In S_2 the least value is 115 and the greatest is 155.
3. In S_1 the lower quartile is 125 and the upper is 160.
   In S_2 the lower quartile is 124 and the upper is 144.

From these facts you can compute the following:

1. The range in S_1 is $215 - 95 = 120$, while the range in S_2 is $155 - 115 = 40$. The two samples clearly have quite different-looking histograms, with S_1 having three times the amount of horizontal spread that S_2 has.

2. In S_1 the interquartile range is $160 - 125 = 35$, while in S_2 this range is $144 - 124 = 20$. Thus we know that in S_1 half of the weights are clustered in a relatively narrow region around the median, covering only about one-fourth of the range. In S_2 half of the weights fall into a region covering one-half of the range.

An idealized representation of their histograms is indicated in Figure 8.

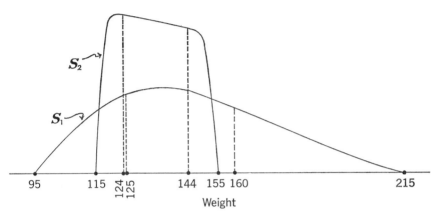

FIG. 8.—Comparative idealized histograms.

Measures of Variability:
Mean Deviation and Standard Deviation

As mentioned earlier, the mean of a set of observations is an algebraic measure, and hence it has computational properties that make it especially useful for purposes of statistical analysis.

The various amounts by which the measurements in a sample deviate from the mean obviously give an indication of the dispersion about this central measure. Hence it is desirable to devise a formula, involving all such deviations, that will provide some index of the variation in the sample. The average of all the deviations would seem a good measure to use. Let us try an example:

Consider a sample consisting of the following measurements: 1, 3, 3, 4, 6, 7. The mean, M, of this sample is:

$$M = \frac{1 + 3 + 3 + 4 + 6 + 7}{6} = 4.$$

Now let us list the values of the deviations from M and find their mean value. The first one is $1 - 4 = ^-3$. In similar manner we find the others to be $^-1$, $^-1$, 0, $^+2$, and $^+3$. Their mean, then, is:

$$\frac{^-3 + {}^-1 + {}^-1 + 0 + 2 + 3}{6} = \frac{0}{6} = 0.$$

It is not just coincidence that the algebraic sum of the deviations from the mean is zero. A bit of algebraic sophistication is needed to prove that this sum is *always* zero for any set of n observations. For the simple case $n = 2$, however, you can easily follow the proof. If we call the two observations a and b, then their mean is:

$$M = \frac{a + b}{2}.$$

The deviations of a and b from their mean are $a - \frac{a+b}{2}$ and $b - \frac{a+b}{2}$ respectively. The sum of the two deviations is:

$$\left(a - \frac{a + b}{2}\right) + \left(b - \frac{a + b}{2}\right).$$

Using the associative property of the real numbers under addition, we can rewrite this as:

$$(a + b) - 2\left(\frac{a + b}{2}\right) = (a + b) - (a + b) = 0.$$

To get around the zero-sum obstacle, we could use instead the average of the *absolute values* (the amounts without regard to sign) of the deviations from the sample mean. This average is known as the *mean deviation,* or the average deviation. It was at one time widely used as a measure of variation. In the sample above having $M = 4$, we find that:

$$\text{mean deviation} = \frac{3 + 1 + 1 + 0 + 2 + 3}{6} = \frac{10}{6} = 1\tfrac{2}{3}.$$

Another measure of deviation is the *standard deviation.* This is perhaps the most important measure of dispersion used in statistical theory.

To find the standard deviation of a sample, we must first calculate the *variance,* which is in itself a useful measure of the variation about the sample mean. The variance is simply the average of the squares of all the deviations from the mean. (Squaring deviations is another method for avoiding negative differences.) Thus, in the sample used above, consisting of 1, 3, 3, 4, 6, 7 and having $M = 4$ and mean deviation $= 1\tfrac{2}{3}$, the variance V is found as follows:

$$V = \frac{(^-3)^2 + (^-1)^2 + (^-1)^2 + 0^2 + 2^2 + 3^2}{6} = \frac{24}{6} = 4.$$

You can see from this example that the greater the absolute deviations are, the greater the variance will be. This makes the variance qualify as a good measure of the dispersion around the mean of a sample.

Now, to obtain the standard deviation, we simply take the square root of the variance. Note that this brings us back to the same units of measurement as those of the sample items. Then for the sample above with variance $V = 4$, we have:

$$\text{standard deviation} = \sqrt{4} = 2.$$

(In more advanced statistics there are methods to show that for small samples—that is, for n small—the variance of the sample tends to underestimate the amount of variance in the total population from which it is drawn. A better estimate of the actual population variance is obtained by dividing the squares of the sample deviations by $n - 1$ instead of n. Likewise, the formula for the standard deviation usually contains $n - 1$, rather than n, in the denominator.)

The sample, consisting of 1, 3, 3, 4, 6, 7, that we have been using can now be described as follows: Its mean is 4, its median is 3.5, and its mode is 3. Its range is 6 and its standard deviation is 2. Armed with a compact summary of this sort, we have a handy basis for comparing similar samples or for obtaining a quick impression of the salient features of a very large sample of observations.

Exercise Set 4

1. Arrange the following data (time after a given date) in chronological order:

6 yr. 2 mo.	7 yr. 9 mo.	8 yr. 8 mo.	3 yr. 2 mo.
9 yr. 6 mo.	6 yr. 5 mo.	6 yr. 4 mo.	7 yr. 11 mo.
14 yr. 0 mo.	4 yr. 1 mo.	11 yr. 7 mo.	10 yr. 3 mo.

2. Arrange these scores in order from the lowest to the highest and determine the median score.

158	62	3	47	92
95	78	56	82	9
125	32	97	41	50
145	14	26	58	102

3. There were 360 pupils enrolled in a school. The classification of pupils by grades was as follows: kindergarten, 40; first grade, 80; second grade, 90; third grade, 45; fourth grade, 35; fifth grade, 35; sixth grade, 35. Make a circle graph that will show the enrollment by grades.

4. Determine the mean, the median, and the mode for the following data:

83, 52, 63, 53, 75, 62, 82, 51, 75, 65, 85,
59, 78, 52, 80, 54, 97, 71, 85, 62, 84, 54,
99, 80, 92, 75, 87, 55, 53, 40, 94, 66, 87, 64.

5. Using the data in exercise 4, organize it to show the number of scores in each of the intervals 40–49, 50–59, 60–69, 70–79, 80–89, 90–99.

6. Make a histogram for the data in exercise 5.

7. For the following data,

6, 6, 6, 7, 7, 7, 7, 7, 7, 7, 8, 8, 8, 8, 8, 8, 8, 8, 8, 8,
9, 9, 9, 9, 9, 9, 9, 9, 9, 9, 10, 10, 10, 10, 10, 10, 10,
11, 11, 11,

find:

a. The mean
b. The mean deviation
c. The variance
d. The standard deviation correct to two decimal places

INTERPRETING DATA

Uncertainty

It was observed earlier that statistics can be used to help us make "wise" decisions in the face of uncertainty. It was also pointed out that care has to be taken in using statistical methods, if egregious conclusions are to be avoided. There is, however, a more fundamental difficulty inherent in the use of statistical methods than those of mere misapplication, misinterpretation, or blunder. The root of the problem lies in the fact that while statistics can give us some numerical guidance when we find ourselves in a situation of uncertainty, it *cannot* remove the uncertainty. Nevertheless, we can collect, organize, and analyze a random sample of data and then apply the mathematical concept of probability to select from among alternative courses of action the one that seems more likely to produce desired results.

Before turning our attention to the topic of probability, let us see if we can identify a little more clearly the nature of uncertainty in a situation. First, let us examine an example in the field of medical research and public health.

When testing a new drug for its effectiveness in curing a certain disease, the researcher must find some way to distinguish the effects of the drug from those of other possible factors contributing to a patient's recovery. For example, some persons might recover from the disease without medical aid of any kind. In testing a drug, one might treat a hundred persons in group A with the drug and another hundred persons in group B with a placebo (a known inactive substance). If 75 percent of the persons in group *A* recover and 62 percent of the persons in group *B* recover, can the difference definitely be attributed to the drug? Since you might reasonably expect (even in the absence of any treatment) variations in the number of recoveries from the disease in two different groups of one hundred patients, does the difference between 62 percent and 75 percent give any useful information about the worth of the drug? To answer this question, you need to know how likely it is that such a difference in recovery rates would happen by chance alone.

The foregoing example is typical of many kinds of situations in which we wish to determine whether or not some occurrence is due entirely to chance. Suppose that a person who claims to be clairvoyant correctly identifies the suit of 14 out of a total of 52 bridge cards in a blindfold test. Is such a "success" ratio attributable to his clairvoyance or just to luck?

Test scores for a group of children taught to read by method *A* averaged five points higher than the test scores for a comparable group of children taught to read by method *B*. Is method *A* really superior to method *B*, or is the difference in test scores just a matter of chance?

A quality-control check reveals that a certain manufacturing process produces ten faulty items out of a thousand, whereas an average of no more than eight out of a thousand is permissible. Should the plant cease production while the cause is sought?

These examples illustrate areas in which it is useful to be able to assess quantitatively the likelihood that a given event is occurring by chance alone.

Probability of an Outcome

Statements such as "It will probably rain today," "Mayor Jones is likely to win the election," and "The chance that Yale will beat Harvard in the football game is remote" all reflect uncertainty. It is intuitively clear that some things are less likely to occur than others. For example, the likelihood of rain is ordinarily much greater when the sky is cloudy and the barometer is falling than it is when the sky is clear and the barometer is rising. It is possible that it could rain in either event, but we should be less surprised if it did so in the first instance than in the second. One of the concerns of the branch of mathematics known as *probability theory* is to assign numerical values to such ideas.

There are two basic ways in which numbers are assigned to likelihoods. One way is to examine physical or other inherent properties in a situation and then make an assignment based on these properties. Such an assignment is called an *a priori* assignment. Another way is to examine what has happened in the past and then to make an assignment based on experience. Such an assignment is called an *a posteriori* or *empirical* assignment. Let us examine a priori probability first.

Children's games sometimes come equipped with "spinners," such as that pictured in Figure 9. By spinning the arrow, one determines how many spaces to move a marker on a board. If the arrow stops in the

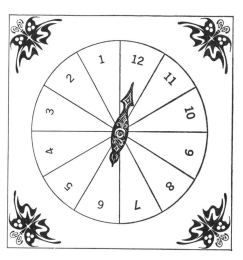

Fig. 9.—A spinner for a game of chance.

region of the circle marked "1," the marker can be moved one space; if the arrow stops at "2," the marker can be moved two spaces; and so on. If the spinner is "honest" in the sense that it is not defective or rigged in some way and if the sectors into which the circle is divided are all of equal size, we have no reason to suspect that on a given spin the arrow is more likely to stop in any one region than in any other. (Of course, it could also stop on one of the lines separating the spaces, but we suppose that these are negligibly thin.) We say then that the *outcomes* (numbers from 1 to 12) are *equally likely*, or *equally probable*. Because there are twelve outcomes, we might reasonably expect that, on the average, about one time in twelve the number 7, for example, would be selected by the arrow. It therefore makes sense to use the ratio $\frac{1}{12}$ to describe this likelihood. Accordingly, we say that the *probability* of getting 7 upon a spin of the arrow is $\frac{1}{12}$. Similarly, the probability of getting 8 upon a spin of the arrow is $\frac{1}{12}$, the probability of getting 9 is $\frac{1}{12}$, and so on. Some other examples of a priori assignments of probabilities are:

1. The probability that a "fair" coin will show heads after being flipped is $\frac{1}{2}$. This follows from the assumption that there are only two possible outcomes, a head or a tail, and that these are equally likely to occur.

2. The probability is $\frac{1}{52}$ that the bottom card in a well-shuffled bridge deck is the queen of hearts. This follows from the assumption that each card is equally likely to be shuffled to the bottom position in the deck and that there are fifty-two cards in a bridge deck.

3. The probability that any one of fifteen names will be selected in a drawing is $\frac{1}{15}$. This follows from the assumption that the name drawn is determined by chance alone and there are fifteen names.

An examination of the foregoing examples should suggest that, in general, if there are n possible outcomes in a situation of some kind and if each of the outcomes is equally likely to occur, then the probability assigned to each outcome is the ratio of 1 to n, or $\frac{1}{n}$.

A word frequently used in connection with equally likely outcomes is *random*. If a selection of equally likely outcomes is made by chance alone, we say that a random selection has been made or that the selection was made at random.

Notice that (from the definition of the probability of one of n equally likely outcomes) the fewer the possible outcomes, the greater the probability assigned to each. Indeed, if there is only one possible outcome from some occurrence, we say that the outcome is *certain* and its probability is 1. On the other hand, the more outcomes there are, the less likely it is for any given one of them to occur, and the probability assigned to each is less. As a special case, we say that the probability of an impossible outcome is 0.

Probability of an Event

Usually we are not as interested in the occurrence of a single outcome in some situation as we are in the occurrence of any one of a set of outcomes. For example, in the game involving a spinner it might be that we could win the game if any of the numbers 8, 9, or 10 resulted from a spin. How shall we assign a probability to the occurrence of any one of this set? Guided by our earlier thinking, we can see that there are three chances in twelve that a spin will result in one of these numbers. Accordingly, it makes sense to say that the probability that one of these numbers will result from a spin is $\frac{3}{12}$.

Similar reasoning in other examples suggests the following general definition for the occurrence of an event (in technical terms, an *event* is any set of outcomes in a given situation): The probability of the occurrence of an event in a situation where each outcome is equally likely is the ratio of the number of outcomes in the event to the total number of possible outcomes. To illustrate an application of this definition, we might assign a probability to the event "a heart is drawn" in a situation in which one card is selected at random from a standard bridge deck. Since there are thirteen hearts in a deck, the event "a heart is drawn" consists of thirteen outcomes out of fifty-two. Therefore, the probability of the occurrence of the event is $\frac{13}{52}$, or $\frac{1}{4}$.

Sometimes we are interested in the probability that an event will *not* occur and wish to assign a probability to this nonoccurrence. To help visualize this situation, you should observe that the total set of possible outcomes in a given situation can be separated into two sets by an event. One set, E, contains all outcomes in the event. The other set, called E' (read "E prime," or "the complement of E"), contains all outcomes not

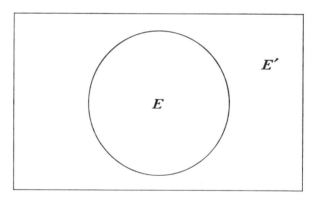

Fig. 10.—Schematic representation
of an event and its complement.

in E. Figure 10 depicts this situation. In the figure the region enclosed in the rectangle can be thought of as containing all of the possible outcomes. The circle can be thought of as containing all outcomes in E. Then the region outside the circle but inside the rectangle contains all of the outcomes not in E. This set can also be called an event, the "nonoccurrence of E."

Notice that the following things are true about this situation:

1. All possible outcomes are included in the rectangle.
2. No outcome in E is in E'.

These two facts imply that the sum of the probabilities of E and E' must be 1, since exactly one of these events is certain to occur. Therefore, if you know the probability of E, you can find the probability of E', and vice versa. For example, if the probability of an event's occurring is $\frac{3}{8}$, then the probability of its not occurring is $1 - \frac{3}{8}$, or $\frac{5}{8}$. Similarly, if the probability that an event will not occur is $\frac{5}{7}$, then the probability that it will occur is $1 - \frac{5}{7}$, or $\frac{2}{7}$.

Empirical Probability

Sometimes there is no way in which you can reasonably establish the probability of a particular outcome except from experience. For example, if you were interested in assigning a probability to the event that it would rain in Milwaukee on a given day three years in the future, you would have no basis for making such an assignment other than by looking at what has happened in Milwaukee on approximately the same date in the past. For example, if you found from its records that over the past twenty-five years it had rained on a given date in four of those years, you might arbitrarily assert that the probability that it would rain on the same day three years in the future would be $\frac{4}{25}$. As mentioned earlier, a probability of this kind is called an a posteriori, or empirical, probability.

Empirical probabilities are frequently encountered under other names. For example, a baseball player's batting average (ratio of the number of hits to the number of times the player has been at bat) can be looked at as the empirical probability that he will hit safely the next time he is at bat. Thus a batting average of 0.300 means that during a specified period in the past the player has on the average hit safely three times out of each ten times at bat. The empirical probability that he will hit safely his next time at bat is then $\frac{3}{10}$.

Empirical probabilities, unlike fixed a priori probabilities, are subject to change. A baseball player's batting average changes each time he officially is "at bat." For example, a player has been at bat ten times and has had three hits. The empirical probability of making a hit on the eleventh time is $\frac{3}{10}$. If out of 100 times at bat he has managed to hit twenty times, the empirical probability of a hit on the 101st time at bat will be $\frac{20}{100}$, or $\frac{2}{10}$. On the other hand, the probability that a fair coin will show heads on any given random toss remains at $\frac{1}{2}$ for each toss, even though heads may have resulted twenty times in a row.

Notice that neither an a priori nor an empirical probability p, $0 < p < 1$, tells you anything for certain about a given outcome. If the probability (either kind) that a given outcome will result from something is $\frac{3}{10}$, you cannot, for example, assert that the outcome will result three times out of the next ten chances. It *might* result three times out of the ten; but also, it might result seven times, ten times, or no times at all.

What both kinds of probability can be interpreted to mean (although for different reasons) is that as more and more outcomes occur, you can *expect* that the ratio of the number of times the given outcome occurs to the total number of outcomes will be close to the probability assigned. Of course, this expectation is based on an assumption, on the one hand, that an arbitrary a priori assignment of a probability is valid and, on the other hand, that what has happened in the past will continue to happen in the future. As you can see, the concept of the probability of an outcome or of an event can offer some help in navigating the shoals of uncertainty, but it does not remove the shoals.

Exercise Set 5

1. If there are 7 cards numbered 1 to 7, respectively, in a box, what is the probability that a card you draw at random will have a 6 on it?

2. If there are 5 red marbles and 4 green marbles in a bag, what is the probability that the first marble you draw out will be green?

3. What is the probability that the pointer of each spinner pictured below will stop on blue? On yellow? On red? Fill in the table with your data.

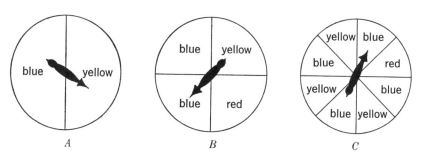

	Probability		
Spinner	Blue	Yellow	Red
A			
B			
C			

For Further Reading

Among the various helpful references that deal with the subject here introduced are the following:

College Entrance Examination Board. *Introductory Probability and Statistical Inference for Secondary Schools* (rev. ed.). Princeton, N.J.: The Board, 1959. Pp. 182. Available from College Entrance Examination Board, Box 592, Princeton, N.J. 08540.

Kemeny, John G.; Snell, J. Laurie; and Thompson, Gerald L. *Introduction to Finite Mathematics* (2d ed.). Englewood Cliffs, N.J.: Prentice-Hall, 1966. Pp. 465. Available from Prentice-Hall, Inc., Englewood Cliffs, N.J. 07632.

Page, David A. "Probability," in *The Growth of Mathematical Ideas, Grades K–12*. Twenty-fourth Yearbook of the National Council of Teachers of Mathematics. Washington, D.C.: The Council, 1959. Available from the National Council of Teachers of Mathematics, 1201 16th St., N.W., Washington, D.C. 20036.

Pieters, Richard S., and Kinsella, John J. "Statistics," in *The Growth of Mathematical Ideas, Grades K–12*. Twenty-fourth Yearbook of the National Council of Teachers of Mathematics. Washington, D.C.: The Council, 1959. See address above.

Smith, Rolland R. "Probability in the Elementary School," in *Enrichment Mathematics for the Grades*. Twenty-seventh Yearbook of the National Council of Teachers of Mathematics. Washington, D.C.: The Council, 1963. See address above.

ANSWERS TO EXERCISES

Exercise Set 1

1. *Observation:* Student received a ticket written at 2:00 P.M. on two successive occasions for parking overtime at the same location.

   Hypothesis: The parking meter is checked at 2:00 P.M. each day.

   Prediction: If coins sufficient to pay for parking until 2:30 P.M. are put in the meter, then no ticket will be written.

   Verification: The student put this amount of money in the meter, and no ticket had been issued at the end of the day.

2. *Observation:* Appreciably more cars were illegally parked at 4:00 P.M. than was ordinarily the case when cars were checked at 2:00 P.M.

   Hypothesis: Several individuals are taking advantage of the fact that parking in a given place is checked at the same time each day.

   Prediction: If the pattern is changed abruptly, then enough money may be collected in fines to make up for past violations; and if thereafter the pattern is varied randomly, then more money will be paid for parking.

   Verification: More tickets were issued for a while, and thereafter more coins were found in the meters.

3. Answers will vary. For the umbrella story, the analysis might be as follows:

   Observation: Yesterday I took my umbrella and it did not rain. Today I did not take my umbrella and it rained.

   Hypothesis: It never rains when I take my umbrella, but it always rains when I don't take it.

   Prediction: If I take my umbrella on the odd-numbered days of the month but not on the even-numbered days, then it will rain on the even-numbered days but not on the odd-numbered days.

   Verification: Subsequent events indicated that the hypothesis is faulty.

Exercise Set 2

1. **a.** Facts

   b. A person who is professionally trained in the scientific methods for collecting and analyzing data so as to obtain desired information from it

   c. The totality of all possible observations

d. A sample obtained by a process that enables it to have the same chance of being drawn from the total population as any other sample of the same size

2. a. No.   **b.** No.   **c.** No.

Exercise Set 3

1. Firsthand: **a, d**

Secondhand: **b, c**

2. Lists will vary but might include stocks, bonds, and securities that were bought and sold, real-estate transactions, automobile sales, and passenger traffic on airlines.

Exercise Set 4

1.

3 yr. 2 mo.	7 yr. 9 mo.	11 yr. 7 mo.
4 yr. 1 mo.	7 yr. 11 mo.	14 yr. 0 mo.
6 yr. 2 mo.	8 yr. 8 mo.	
6 yr. 4 mo.	9 yr. 6 mo.	
6 yr. 5 mo.	10 yr. 3 mo.	

2. 3, 9, 14, 26, 32, 41, 47, 50, 56, 58, 62, 78, 82, 92, 95, 97, 102, 125, 145, 158

$$\frac{62 - 58}{2} = \frac{4}{2} = 2; \qquad 58 + 2 = 60.$$

Median score = 60.

3. Kindergarten: $\frac{40}{360}$ (40°)

First grade: $\frac{80}{360}$ (80°)

Second grade: $\frac{90}{360}$ (90°)

Third grade: $\frac{45}{360}$ (45°)

Fourth grade: $\frac{35}{360}$ (35°)

Fifth grade: $\frac{35}{360}$ (35°)

Sixth grade: $\frac{35}{360}$ (35°)

Enrollment by Grades

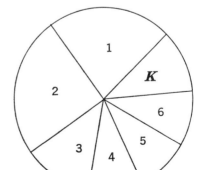

4. Mean: 71
Median: 73
Mode: 75

5.

Interval	No. of Scores
40–49	1
50–59	9
60–69	6
70–79	5
80–89	9
90–99	4

6.

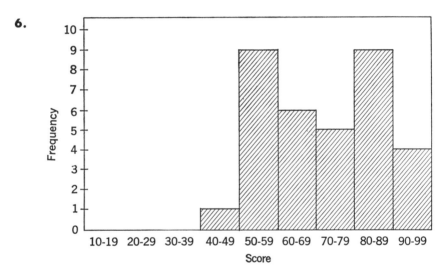

7. a. 8.5   **b.** 1.15   **c.** 1.85   **d.** 1.36

Exercise Set 5

1. $\frac{1}{7}$ **2.** $\frac{4}{9}$ **3.**

Spinner	Probability		
	Blue	Yellow	Red
A	$\frac{1}{2}$	$\frac{1}{2}$	0
B	$\frac{1}{2}$	$\frac{1}{4}$	$\frac{1}{4}$
C	$\frac{1}{2}$	$\frac{3}{8}$	$\frac{1}{8}$

BOOKLET NUMBER SEVENTEEN:

HINTS FOR
PROBLEM SOLVING

SOME THOUGHTS ABOUT PROBLEM SOLVING

What Is a Problem?

The ability to go round an obstacle, to undertake an indirect course where no direct course presents itself, raises the clever animal above the dull one, raises man far above the most clever animals, and men of talent above their fellow men.—George Pólya.[1]

The meaning of "problem" is often confused in the mathematics classroom. A teacher assigns a given set of problems from the text for classwork or homework. What sort of "problems" are these? In mathematics the usually accepted concept of a problem differentiates between situations such as this assignment and those that require certain behaviors beyond the routine application of an established procedure. A true problem in mathematics can be thought of as a situation that is novel for the individual called upon to solve it.

The first situation mentioned above generally involves working "exercises" rather than solving problems. Although such an assignment certainly may include some problems, an assignment from a mathematics textbook generally involves working a number of examples identical or nearly identical to ones that have been worked out by the teacher or completely explained within the text. This is not meant to imply that activities such as working exercises or drilling on basic facts are not useful; indeed, these

---

[1] *Mathematical Discovery* (New York: John Wiley & Sons, 1962), p. 118.

activities are extremely important and necessary. What is meant is that the opportunity should be provided for the student actually *to solve problems*. The importance of providing this opportunity is pointed out by George Pólya in his book *Mathematical Discovery*. Pólya states that solving problems is a practical art, like swimming or skiing or playing the piano: you can learn it only by imitation and practice, for there is no "magic key" that opens all doors and solves all problems. If you wish to learn how to swim, you have to go into the water; likewise, if you wish to become a problem solver, you have to solve problems.

One further comment is in order regarding what is, or is not, a true problem. Often a given exercise is merely routine for some individuals, while for others it becomes a task requiring careful thought and decision. It has been said, "One person's problem is another person's exercise and a third person's frustration." For this reason it is frequently difficult to determine beforehand whether or not a given situation is a problem for a particular individual. It is intended that many of the examples used later in this booklet will be unfamiliar to you so that they will indeed be true "problems."

How a Person Solves a Problem

It is considered that the existence of certain conditions determines whether a situation is a true problem for a particular individual:

1. The individual has a clearly defined, desired goal of which he is consciously aware.
2. The path to the goal is blocked, and the individual's fixed patterns of behavior, his habitual responses, are not sufficient for removing the block.
3. Deliberation must take place. The individual becomes aware of the problem, defines it more or less clearly, identifies various possible hypotheses (solutions), and tests these for feasibility.

In solving a mathematical problem it is important that an individual first determine what question is being asked of him and that he also feel motivated to answer the question. Statement 2 above, "The path to the goal is blocked," then determines whether or not the question is truly a problem. If you were asked to find the product $^-3 \times {}^-4$, would this be a problem? Let us assume that you are motivated to obtain the correct answer to this question. If you are familiar with multiplication of integers, have previously determined that the product of two negative integers is positive and, therefore, make the automatic response of 12, then no "blocking" has occurred, and this is not a true problem for you. If, on the other hand, you are familiar with the existence of negative numbers, but you do not know how to multiply them, then the situation certainly would be different. In this situation you would have to deliberate and probably check on the feasibility of the different alternatives; for example, you would probably assume that the answer must be either 12 or ⁻12 and would then try to see which choice was consistent with what you already knew.

The third condition mentioned above is also an essential ingredient to determine whether a question is a problem for a particular individual or merely an exercise. You must *deliberate* in order to reach a point at which you are satisfied that you have the correct solution. At this point you will have solved the problem.

It is regarding the third condition, deliberation, that we see many different kinds of behavior exhibited by the problem solver. These can be described in such terms as observing, exploring, decision-making, organizing, recognizing, remembering, supplementing, regrouping, isolating, combining, diagramming, guessing, classifying, formulating, generalizing, verifying, and applying. Most of the textbook examples in mathematics do not call for many of these behaviors on the part of the student. Rather, their solution depends almost entirely on simple recall. Note that while recognizing and remembering are important behaviors in problem solving, generally the recall of a specific process and then the direct application of the process and technique are not enough in themselves to permit us to consider a given situation to be a problem.

The specific behaviors often required for solving a problem will be illustrated further in the section entitled "Unusual Problem Solving." The examples used there are of a special type. You will not have an established procedure for obtaining the answer to a question. Therefore, you will have to devise a strategy for attacking each particular problem.

The examples used in this booklet are situations illustrating problems that are to be brought to some successful termination by *thinking*. The problems are solved by the use of previously learned principles, simple or complex. As educational psychologists point out, principles are the essential ingredients of thinking. Furthermore, while human beings use principles to achieve some goals, the results of using principles in problem solving are not confined to achieving goals. When a problem solution is achieved, something is also learned, in the sense that the individual's capability is more or less permanently changed. What emerges from problem solving is a "higher-order principle," which then becomes a part of the individual's repertory. When encountered another time, the same type of situation may be responded to with greater facility, since the individual need use only recall; thus, the situation no longer constitutes a problem. Problem solving can therefore actually be considered a form of learning.

Why Problem Solving Is Important

The Twenty-first Yearbook of the National Council of Teachers of Mathematics describes the importance of problem solving in the following way:

> If life were of such a constant nature that there were only a few chores to do and they were done over and over in exactly the same way, the case for knowing how to solve problems would not be so compelling. All one would have to do would be to learn how to do the few jobs at the outset. From then on he could rely on memory and habit. Fortunately—or unfortunately depending upon one's point of view—life is not simple and unchanging. Rather it is changing so rapidly that about all we can predict is that things will be different in the future. In such a world the ability to adjust and to solve one's problems is of paramount importance.
>
> The case for teaching students how to formulate and solve problems involving quantitative thinking is abundantly clear. Come graduation and/or employment, they will have to be able to solve the problems posed for them in their advanced education or in the job they hold. To be able to do this is the pay-off of their education. Because most, if not all, mathematics teachers hold this position, they expend considerable effort in teaching their students how to solve problems in the field of mathematics. There are few, if any, kinds of instruction that potentially have more value.[2]

From what we know about learning, the best way to learn problem solving is by working problems and studying the processes we used in working them. It is important to study the problem-solving process itself, not just the "answer." Our knowledge in mathematics consists of both information and "know-how." The ability to *use* information, which we can refer to as know-how, is actually much more important than the mere *possession* of information. Note, however, that it is necessary also to have an adequate amount of information to use. The know-how is dependent on computational skill and on an understanding of certain concepts and processes.

The Role of Word Problems in Problem Solving

Word problems—problems that are written or stated in English sentences—are a useful device for teaching problem solving. In working word problems, attention should be directed to the *process* employed in the solving of problems. Word problems are often used in mathematics to provide practice material upon which a student can apply the principles of problem solving he has learned. In many situations, however, the word "problem" is used for practice on a specific procedure (often referred to in mathematics

---

[2] Kenneth B. Henderson and Robert E. Pingry, "Problem-Solving in Mathematics," in *The Learning of Mathematics: Its Theory and Practice*, Twenty-first Yearbook of the National Council of Teachers of Mathematics (Washington, D.C.: The Council, 1953), p. 233.

as an algorithm or algorism) or for practice in applying a recently learned generalization. For example, consider a person working a number of word problems involving substitution in a given formula, such as $d = rt$ (the formula for the distance traveled by an object moving at a given constant rate for a given period of time) or $A = bh$ (the formula for the area of a rectangular region), after he has been given the procedure and the specific formula. In such cases, he needs only to identify from the written information the various numbers to be substituted in the formula and then do the necessary computation. It is generally true that such "problems" are not really problems at all but practice exercises.

In many of the word problems presented in mathematics textbooks, the initial problem posed for the student is "What is the mathematical translation of the word problem?" In other words, the most important aspect of most of the verbal exercises is the writing of a mathematical sentence (often an equation or inequality) that states the conditions of the word problem. The best way to learn how to write appropriate mathematical sentences is to practice with many problems. The ability to translate from the written situation to an appropriate mathematical sentence enables a person to cope with a large number of problems in mathematics in an orderly, logical manner, particularly if he has developed techniques for determining the solution sets of standard types of open mathematical sentences. The translation of given real-life situations into mathematical symbolism is considered *the most useful tool in problem solving.*

OPEN SENTENCES—THE MOST USEFUL TOOL IN PROBLEM SOLVING

Number Phrases

Open number sentences are useful in finding solutions of verbal problems. To write open sentences for problems, one must be able to translate verbal phrases and sentences into mathematical language. Mathematical sentences, much like English sentences, are made up of noun phrases and verbs. The combination of these phrases and verbs makes the mathematical sentence complete.

Let us first direct our attention to number phrases. Here, along with their mathematical translations, are some English noun phrases typical of those occurring in problems:

1. The result of adding a number to 7: $7 + x$
2. The sum of some number and 13: $\Box + 13$
3. The result of increasing 3 by some number: $3 + \triangle$

4. The result of decreasing a number by 2: $n - 2$

5. The result of diminishing 18 by some number: $18 - z$

6. Five times some number: $5 \times \triangle$

7. The product of 12 and some number: $12 \times \triangle$

8. Seventeen divided by some number: $17 \div y$, or $\dfrac{17}{y}$

9. Two-thirds of some number: $\dfrac{2}{3} \times n$

Some discussion of the examples given above might be helpful at this point in order to make the mathematical translations more meaningful. In each case, to transform the word phrase into mathematical language, we introduced symbols, such as x, $\square$, $\triangle$, n, z, or y, to stand for the unspecified number. Each of these symbols is called a *variable*. For the problems in this section, the replacement set for these variables will be thought of as the set of real numbers unless otherwise specified.

EXAMPLE 1

The result of adding a number to 7: $7 + x$

Let us first observe that the phrases $7 + x$ and $x + 7$ are mathematically equivalent; that is, for any real number x,

$$7 + x = x + 7.$$

This follows from the commutative property for addition. Notice, though, that the first phrase is the literal translation of the given word phrase; $x + 7$ would ordinarily be used to express the result of adding 7 to a number rather than adding a number to 7. In solving open sentences it is often useful to apply not only the commutative but also the other properties of the real number system. At this point, however, we are simply translating English phrases directly into mathematical phrases. It is important to be precise in translating into mathematical phrases. This is illustrated by Examples 4, 8, 10, and 11, where the necessity of properly stating subtraction and division problems will be explained. A precise translation is essential to the solution of many problems.

EXAMPLE 2

The sum of some number and 13: $\square + 13$

Notice that a mathematically equivalent phrase for $\square + 13$ is $13 + \square$, because of the commutative property.

EXAMPLE 3

The result of increasing 3 by some number: $3 + \triangle$

Since "increasing" implies the binary operation of addition, this example is similar to Examples 1 and 2. Actually, the English phrase is imprecise, since the number 3 is a definite mathematical entity that cannot be altered;

but the intent is clear. The translation $3 + \triangle$ expresses the intended meaning.

EXAMPLE 4

The result of decreasing a number by 2: $\qquad$ $n - 2$

"Decreasing" implies the binary operation of subtraction, and it is a "number" that is being decreased by 2. As in Example 3, the English phrase is imprecise, but the translation $n - 2$ expresses the intended meaning. Let us note that $n-2$ and $2-n$ are *not* mathematically equivalent phrases. For example, when $n = 5$, then $5 - 2 \neq 2 - 5$, since $5 - 2 = 3$ and $2 - 5 = {}^-3$. Subtraction is *not* a commutative operation. (The symbol $\neq$ is read "is not equal to," and acts as a verb does in an English sentence. Symbols such as $=$, $\sim$, $<$, $>$, appear below in Table I.) A word phrase for $2 - n$ might be "two decreased by some number," which is quite different from the expression "some number decreased by two." This example points out the need for an accurate translation.

EXAMPLE 5

The result of diminishing 18 by some number: $\qquad$ $18 - z$

This is like Example 4. "Diminishing" implies subtraction, and it is 18 that is being "diminished." Therefore, we write $18 - z$.

EXAMPLE 6

Five times some number: $\qquad$ $5 \times \triangle$

"Times" implies the binary operation of multiplication. A mathematically equivalent phrase for $5 \times \triangle$ is $\triangle \times 5$, since multiplication of real numbers is a commutative operation. For example, $5 \times 6 = 6 \times 5$ and $5 \times 17 = 17 \times 5$. The accurate translation of the given expression, however, is $5 \times \triangle$.

EXAMPLE 7

The product of 12 and some number: $\qquad$ $12 \times \triangle$

A "product" is the result of multiplication.

EXAMPLE 8

Seventeen divided by some number: $\qquad$ $17 \div y$, or $\dfrac{17}{y}$

Division is the stated operation. Since 17 is being divided by some number, the number phrase is $17 \div y$. Division, like subtraction, is not commutative. Thus $y \div 17$ is *not* an equivalent phrase for $17 \div y$.

EXAMPLE 9

Two-thirds of some number: $\qquad$ $\dfrac{2}{3} \times n$

Multiplication is implied. A mathematically equivalent phrase for $\frac{2}{3} \times n$ is $n \times \frac{2}{3}$, but the correct translation is $\frac{2}{3} \times n$.

Quite often the wording of certain English phrases can cause severe difficulties. Two examples follow; these will be stated and discussed in some detail.

EXAMPLE 10
    The difference between 10 and some number: ?

We know that "difference" implies subtraction. Could there be more than one possible translation of this expression? Should this phrase be represented by $10 - y$ or by $y - 10$? Since subtraction is not commutative, we know that these two phrases are not equivalent. Then which one should be used for the mathematical translation? We would find it difficult to justify either one of the translations over the other.

Perhaps what is meant is the absolute value of $10 - y$, written mathematically as $|10 - y|$. This is commutative; for example, you have

$$|10 - 8| = |2| = 2 \quad \text{and} \quad |8 - 10| = |^-2| = 2,$$

so that

$$|10 - 8| = |8 - 10|.$$

The fact is that we have insufficient information to make a decision. This difficulty can be avoided if the meaning is expressed unambiguously in the first place, as in the following:

(a)   The difference when some number is subtracted from 10 $10 - y$
(b)   The difference when 10 is subtracted from some number $y - 10$

EXAMPLE 11
    The quotient of some number and 8:   ?

This can cause complications similar to those in Example 10. The term "quotient" suggests the operation of division. Is the mathematical translation $n \div 8$ or $8 \div n$? From the discussion for Example 8, we know that the two translations are not equivalent, since division is not commutative. What is probably meant here is $n \div 8$. This intent would be expressed unambiguously by either of the following verbal phrases:

(a)   The quotient of some number by 8
(b)   The result when some number is divided by 8

Exercise Set 1

Translate each of the following word phrases into a number phrase.

1. Some number plus 7

2. A number divided by 6

3. Two-fifths of a number

4. The result when 17 is subtracted from some number

5. The sum of a number and twice the same number

6. The product of 3 and some number

7. The product of a number and 2 more than this number

8. The result when 1 more than some number is divided by the number itself

9. The result when 3 times some number is subtracted from 5 times the same number

10. Eight less than some number

Following Instructions

Going one step further in translations, let us first translate a verbal phrase to a number phrase and then write other number phrases related to this phrase.

EXAMPLE 1

Suppose a reference is made to some number. We can represent this number by $\square$ (usually read "box"). Express mathematically the result of each of the following.

Five more than the number:	$\square + 5$
Three less than the number:	$\square - 3$
Four times the number:	$4 \times \square$
The number divided by 6:	$\square \div 6$, or $\dfrac{\square}{6}$
Twice the sum of the number and 5:	$2 \times (\square + 5)$
Ten times 3 less than the number:	$10 \times (\square - 3)$
The quotient obtained when 4 times the number is divided by 7:	$\dfrac{4 \times \square}{7}$, or $(4 \times \square) \div 7$

For the most part, the example above displays operational procedure on a variable and is often used in "guess my number" drills.

EXAMPLE 2

Suppose a reference is made to Ed's age. Representing Ed's age today as n years, we can express each of the following in terms of Ed's age now.

Ed's age in 3 years:	$n + 3$
Joan's age if her age is one-half Ed's age:	$\dfrac{1}{2} \times n$, or $\dfrac{n}{2}$
Joan's age in 5 years:	$\dfrac{n}{2} + 5$
Joan's age in 5 years, subtracted from Ed's age in 3 years:	$(n + 3) - \left(\dfrac{n}{2} + 5\right)$

Joan's age 8 years ago: $\dfrac{n}{2} - 8$

Ed's age in 6 years, added to Joan's age 8 years ago: $\left(\dfrac{n}{2} - 8\right) + (n + 6)$

Three times Ed's age in 7 years: $3 \times (n + 7)$

Four times Joan's age 2 years ago: $4 \times \left(\dfrac{n}{2} - 2\right)$

Note that the difference between the ages of any two persons remains the same throughout their lifetimes. However, if one person's age at a given point in time is, for example, twice the age of another individual, this will not remain true as time passes. Suppose that Ed is now thirty years old and Joan is fifteen years old. The difference between their ages today is 15 years, and Ed's age is 2 times Joan's age. Five years from now Ed will be thirty-five, and Joan twenty. The difference between their ages will still be 15 years, but notice what change will have occurred in the ratio of their ages: in 5 years Ed's age will be only $\frac{7}{4}$ times Joan's age. In 30 years, when Ed is sixty and Joan is forty-five, Ed's age will be $\frac{4}{3}$ times Joan's age.

EXAMPLE 3

Candy costs m cents per pound.
   The cost in cents of 8 pounds of candy: $8 \times m$, or $m \times 8$
   The cost in cents of a pound of peanuts, which
      cost twice as much per pound as candy: $2 \times m$
   The cost in cents of 6 pounds of peanuts: $6 \times (2 \times m)$
   The cost in cents of 8 pounds of candy and
      6 pounds of peanuts: $(8 \times m) + [6 \times (2 \times m)]$

EXAMPLE 4

One pound of candy costs 60 cents. One pound of peanuts costs \$1.20.
   The cost in cents of x pounds of this candy: $x \times 60$, or $60 \times x$
   The cost in cents of y pounds of peanuts: $y \times 120$, or $120 \times y$
   The cost in cents of a mixture of x pounds of
      60-cent candy and y pounds of \$1.20 peanuts: $(60 \times x) + (120 \times y)$

Note that \$1.20 has been converted to 120, since the unit is cents and not dollars.

EXAMPLE 5

There are $\square$ pounds of candy included in a mixture containing 3 pounds of peanuts. Candy costs 60 cents per pound. Peanuts cost \$1.20 per pound.
   The total weight of the mixture: $\square + 3$
   The cost in cents of the candy portion
      of the mixture: $60 \times \square$
   The cost in cents of the peanut portion
      of the mixture: 120×3
   The total cost of the mixture: $(60 \times \square) + (120 \times 3)$

EXAMPLE 6

One dime is worth 10 cents.

The value in cents of 1 dime:	1 × 10, or 10
The value in cents of 2 dimes:	2 × 10, or 20
The value in cents of 3 dimes:	3 × 10, or 30
The value in cents of 14 dimes:	14 × 10, or 140
The value in cents of 72 dimes:	72 × 10, or 720
The value in cents of n dimes:	n × 10, or (n × 10)

Use this same technique to find the value in cents of one nickel, one quarter, and so on.

EXAMPLE 7

George has some dimes. Denote the number of dimes George has by △.

The number of dimes Mannie has, if Mannie has

2 more dimes than George:	△ + 2
The value in cents of George's money:	10 × △
The value in cents of Mannie's money:	10 × (△ + 2)
The *number* of dimes George and Mannie have together:	△ + (△ + 2)
The *value* in cents of George's money and Mannie's money, together:	(10 × △) + [10 × (△ + 2)],

$$\text{or}$$
$$10[\triangle + (\triangle + 2)]$$

The last two phrases in Example 7 are quite different. The first involves the *number* of coins, while the second involves the *value* of these coins. If you state that you have 2 coins, one can only guess at the amount of money you have. You might have 2 cents (2 pennies), 10 cents (2 nickles), 6 cents (1 nickle and 1 penny), or even 200 cents (2 silver dollars). Do you see that the numeral used to represent the *number of coins* does not, in general, represent the *value of the coins*?

EXAMPLE 8

Helen has some nickels. Denote the number of nickels Helen has by □.

The value in cents of Helen's nickels:	5 × □
The number of dimes Patricia has if Patricia has twice as many dimes as Helen has nickels:	2 × □
The value in cents of Patricia's dimes:	10 × (2 × □)
The number of quarters Doris has if Doris has 3 fewer quarters than Patricia has dimes:	(2 × □) − 3
The value in cents of Doris' quarters:	25 × [(2 × □) − 3]
The number of coins the three girls have together:	□ + (2 × □) + [(2 × □) − 3]
The value in cents of the coins the three girls have together:	(5 × □) + [10 × (2 × □)] + (25 × [(2 × □) − 3])

This example is closely related to Example 7. Notice once again the difference in the last two expressions.

Exercise Set 2

1. Let □ represent some number. Express the result of each of the following, using this number as the referent.

a. Seven more than the number

b. Three less than the number

c. Five times the number

d. The number divided by 10

e. Six times the number added to 4 times the number

f. Nine less than the number, divided by the number itself

2. Let △ represent Barbara's age now. Express the result of each of the following, using this number as the referent.

a. Barbara's age in 7 years

b. Her age 2 years ago

c. Five times her age in 7 years

d. Three times her age 2 years ago

e. Barbara's age in 6 years added to her age 3 years ago

f. One-half Barbara's age now

3. Cashews cost $1.50 per pound. Express the following, using this value as the referent.

a. The cost in cents of 1 pound of cashews

b. The cost in cents of 3 pounds of cashews

c. The cost in cents of x pounds of cashews

d. The cost in cents of $x + 3$ pounds of cashews

Number Sentences

In Examples 1 through 8 in the preceding section, we pointed out typical word phrases and their mathematical translations. Now we shall show how these phrases can be linked together with "verbs" to form what is known as a mathematical sentence.

A complete mathematical sentence uses a verb symbol to represent a relation. Consider the examples shown in Table I. These symbols are but a few of the mathematical "verbs" used in mathematical sentences.

For the moment, let us give our attention to statements of equality. A sentence that uses the "is equal to" symbol ($=$) is the assertion that the number (or set, etc.) represented by the expression on the left-hand side of the symbol *is equal to*, or *is another name for*, the number (or set, etc.)

TABLE I

Relation	Symbol	Example of Use	Read
is equal to	$=$	$\square + 2 = 5.$	"Some number plus two is equal to five."
is less than	$<$	$5 < 7.$	"Five is less than seven."
is greater than	$>$	$5 > 1.$	"Five is greater than one."
is similar to	$\sim$	$\triangle ABC \sim \triangle DEF.$	"Triangle ABC is similar to triangle DEF."
is congruent to	$\cong$	$\triangle XYZ \cong \triangle JKL.$	"Triangle XYZ is congruent to triangle JKL."

represented by the expression on the right-hand side. This type of sentence is called an "equation."

Since the main emphasis of this section is on the writing of mathematical sentences and not on their solution, little or no mechanics will be given for the solution. We suggest that the reader examine a few of the many available algebra books that do develop the techniques for solving equations.

Checking one's answer is part of any word problem, and this we shall do by going back to the original statement of the problem and noting whether or not the answer satisfies the given conditions. If we were to check the answer by using the open mathematical sentence, we would be justified in stating only that the answer satisfied the mathematical sentence. It is possible to write incorrect mathematical sentences. Since we want the check for a correct solution to the original problem, we can do this only by going back to the original problem.

PROBLEM 1

Bob had 15 baseball cards. David gave him some more. As a result, Bob now has 32 cards. How many cards did David give to Bob?

Analysis

You do not know how many cards David gave to Bob. Let x represent the number David gave to Bob: x

Number of cards Bob had at first: 15

Number of cards Bob now has: $15 + x$

It is also given that Bob now has 32 cards.

Since "$15 + x$" and "32" name the same number, we arrive at this number sentence: $15 + x = 32.$

Solution

By an educated guess and a subsequent substitution, you probably noted that the solution set for this problem is $\{17\}$. If you were to read the mathematical sentence in words, you might have asked yourself this question: "The sum of what number and 15 is 32?" The answer "17" is obvious. The truth set {17} indicates that David gave 17 baseball cards to Bob.

Check

Bob has 15 baseball cards:	15
David gave him 17 more:	$15 + 17$
Therefore, Bob should now have 32 cards,	$15 + 17 = 32.$
which agrees with the given information.	

PROBLEM 2

Joe had some marbles. After a game with Dean, he had 17 more marbles than when he started. If he now has 51 marbles, how many marbles did he start with?

Analysis

You do not know how many marbles Joe had at the start. Let y represent the number of marbles Joe had:	y
Joe won 17 marbles from Dean, so he now has 17 more than the number he had at the start:	$y + 17$
It is given that Joe now has 51 marbles. Since "$y + 17$" and "51" name the same number, the number sentence is:	$y + 17 = 51.$

Solution

Stating the mathematical open sentence aloud, you might ask yourself, "The sum of what number and 17 is equal to 51?" The truth set for this sentence is {34}. Therefore, Joe started with 34 marbles.

Check

Joe started with 34 marbles:	34
He won 17 from Dean:	$34 + 17$
He now has 51 marbles,	$34 + 17 = 51.$
which agrees with the given information.	

PROBLEM 3

Marguerite lost 19 jacks. She does not remember how many she originally had but does know she has 24 jacks left. How many jacks did she originally have?

Analysis

You do not know how many jacks she originally had. Let $\square$ represent the number of jacks Marguerite originally had:	$\square$
She lost 19 jacks:	$\square - 19$

It is given that she has 24 jacks left. Since "□ − 19" and "24" name the same number, the number sentence is: □ − 19 = 24.

Solution

□ − 19 = 24 is read, "If 19 is subtracted from some number, the result is equal to 24." What is this number? Another way to interpret this same sentence is, "Nineteen plus 24 is equal to what number?" The last suggestion comes from the definition of subtraction. The answer to each of these questions is 43. The truth set {43} indicates that Marguerite started with 43 jacks.

Check

Marguerite originally had 43 jacks:	43
She lost 19 jacks:	43 − 19
She now has 24 jacks,	43 − 19 = 24.
which agrees with the given information.	

PROBLEM 4

Bill and Walt together have 62 rabbits. If Bill has 40 rabbits, how many does Walt have?

Analysis

You do not know how many rabbits Walt has. Let

$\triangle$ represent the number of rabbits he has:	$\triangle$
Bill has 40 rabbits:	40
Number of rabbits they have together:	$\triangle + 40$
Since "$\triangle + 40$" and "62" name the same number, the number sentence is:	$\triangle + 40 = 62.$

Solution

The sentence $\triangle + 40 = 62$ is read, "Some number plus 40 is equal to 62." This might also be interpreted to read, "The difference when 40 is subtracted from 62 is equal to some number." What is the number? The answer in either case is 22. The truth set {22} indicates that Walt had 22 rabbits.

Check

Bill has 40 rabbits:	40
Walt has 22 rabbits:	22
Together	40 + 22
they have 62 rabbits,	40 + 22 = 62.
which agrees with the given information.	

PROBLEM 5

Lenore and Ed together have 75 coins. Ed has twice as many as Lenore has. How many coins does each person have?

Analysis

You do not know how many coins each of
them has. Let y represent the number of
coins Lenore has: y
Ed has twice as many coins as Lenore has: $2 \times y$
Number of coins they have together: $y + (2 \times y)$
Since "$y + (2 \times y)$" and "75" name the same
number, the number sentence is: $y + (2 \times y) = 75.$

Solution

The sentence $y + (2 \times y) = 75$ is read, "Some number plus twice itself
is equal to 75." A number added to twice itself is the same as three times
the number. The original sentence is equivalent to the sentence "Three
times some number is equal to 75." The answer is "25" because
$3 \times 25 = 75$. The truth set $\{25\}$ indicates that Lenore has 25 coins. Since
Ed has twice this number ($2 \times y = 2 \times 25 = 50$), Ed has 50 coins.

Check

Lenore has 25 coins: 25
Ed has twice as many coins: $2 \times 25 = 50.$
Together $25 + 50$
they have 75 coins, $25 + 50 = 75.$
which agrees with the given information.

PROBLEM 6

Elaine has some dolls. Debbie has 3 more dolls than Elaine has. Twice
the number of dolls Elaine has is equal to 21 more dolls than Debbie has.
How many dolls does each girl have?

Analysis

You do not know the number of dolls each
girl has. Let $\triangle$ represent the number
of dolls Elaine has: $\triangle$
Debbie has 3 more dolls than Elaine: $\triangle + 3$
Twice the number of dolls
Elaine has $2 \times \triangle$
is equal to $=$
21 more dolls than
Debbie has: $(\triangle + 3) + 21$
The number sentence is: $2 \times \triangle = (\triangle + 3) + 21.$

Solution

The solution set for this open sentence can be obtained by using substitution. You will find that the solution set is $\{24\}$. This indicates that
Elaine has 24 dolls. Since Debbie has 3 more dolls than Elaine, Debbie
must have $\triangle + 3 = 24 + 3$, or 27, dolls.

Check

Elaine has 24 dolls:	24
Debbie has 3 more dolls than Elaine:	$24 + 3 = 27.$
Twice the number of dolls Elaine has	2×24, or 48
is equal to	=
21 more dolls than Debbie has,	$27 + 21 = 48.$
which agrees with the given information.	

PROBLEM 7

Beverly and Sharon have some cutouts. Together they have 80 cutouts. Three times the number of cutouts Beverly has is equal to 5 more than twice the number of cutouts Sharon has. How many cutouts does each girl have?

Analysis

In this problem, we do not have an obvious connection between the numbers of cutouts that Beverly and Sharon have. It is given, however, that together they have 80 cutouts. If Beverly has 10 cutouts, then Sharon has $80 - 10$, or 70, cutouts. If Beverly has 27 cutouts, then Sharon has $80 - 27$, or 53, cutouts. If Beverly has 62 cutouts, then Sharon has $80 - 62$, or 18, cutouts. If Beverly has z cutouts, then Sharon has $80 - z$ cutouts.

Let z represent the number of cutouts Beverly has:	z
Together they have 80 cutouts, so the number of cutouts Sharon has would be:	$80 - z$
Three times the number of cutouts Beverly has	$3 \times z$
is equal to	=
five more than twice the number of cutouts Sharon has:	$2 \times (80 - z) + 5$
The number sentence is:	$3 \times z = 2 \times (80 - z) + 5.$

Solution

The solution set for this problem is $\{33\}$. The truth set $\{33\}$ indicates that Beverly has 33 cutouts. Since together they have 80 cutouts, Sharon has $80 - z = 80 - 33$, or 47, cutouts.

Check

Beverly has 33 cutouts:	33
Sharon has 47 cutouts:	47
Together	$33 + 47$
they have 80 cutouts,	$33 + 47 = 80.$
which agrees with part of the given information.	

Three times the number
Beverly has 3×33, or 99
is equal to   =
five more than twice the
number Sharon has, $(2 \times 47) + 5 = 94 + 5 = 99.$
which agrees with the remaining
information.

PROBLEM 8

A farmer has chickens and horses. These animals together have 50 heads and 140 legs. How many chickens and how many horses does the farmer have?

Analysis

Some logical assumptions will have to be made about the given information. You can first assume that each of his animals has exactly one head. You can also assume that each chicken has the usual number of legs for a chicken, namely 2, and that each horse has the usual number of legs for a horse, namely 4. You do not know the number of chickens and you do not know the number of horses, but you do know there are 50 altogether.

Let □ represent the number of
horses: □
The number of chickens is: $50 - □$
The other bit of information
involves the number of legs.
If one horse has 4 legs, then
□ horses have this number
of legs: $4 \times □$
Using the same reasoning for
the chickens, you see that
the number of their legs is: $2 \times (50 - □)$
There are 140 legs altogether;
therefore, the number sen-
tence is: $(4 \times □) + 2 \times (50 - □) = 140.$

Solution

Through substitution, one finds that the truth set is {20}. This indicates that there are 20 horses, and from this information one can easily determine the number of chickens: $50 - □ = 50 - 20 = 30$.

Check

There are 20 horses: 20
There are 30 chickens: $50 - 20 = 30.$
Together $20 + 30$
they have 50 heads: $20 + 30 = 50.$

Total number of horses' legs: $4 \times 20 = 80.$
Total number of chickens' legs: $2 \times 30 = 60.$
Together $80 + 60$
they have 140 legs, $80 + 60 = 140.$
  which agrees with the given information.

Exercise Set 3

1. Translate each of the following word sentences into a number sentence.

a. The sum of 4 times a number and 6 is equal to 38.

b. If 17 is subtracted from some number, the result is equal to 18.

c. Three times some number, plus 2 more than the number, is equal to 34.

d. Twice some number, minus 2 more than the number, is equal to 26.

e. If 3 less than some number is divided by 5, the quotient is equal to 1.

f. Four times the sum of some number and 3 is equal to 44.

2. Here are some open sentences. For each sentence, make up a verbal problem for which the sentence expresses the number relations.

a. $\square + 6 = 37.$

b. $\dfrac{1}{6} \times n = 21.$

c. $(2 \times \Delta) - 3 = 19.$

d. $\dfrac{x + 4}{x} = 1\dfrac{1}{2}.$

3. Solve the following verbal problems. For each problem, follow the procedure given in the sample problems analyzed above. Write the number sentence, find the solution set, and then write a sentence to interpret your answer. The last three problems are difficult, but try them anyway.

a. Dorothy has some baby chicks. For her birthday she received twice the number she originally had. She now has 27 chicks. How many did she originally have?

b. The sum of twice some number added to 3 more than the number is equal to 24. Find the number.

c. The combined cost of a baseball and bat is $1.05. If the bat cost 5 cents more than the ball, how much did each item cost?

d. Alice and Bernadine together have 50 cents. Alice has 4 more coins than Bernadine has. If Alice's coins are nickles and Bernadine's coins are dimes, how many coins does each girl have?

e. Mary Jane is 20 years older than her daughter. Twice Mary Jane's age this year is equal to 3 times what her daughter's age will be in 10 years. Find the age of each.

f. A mixture of two grades of coffee is being prepared. How many pounds of 80-cent coffee must be mixed with 5 pounds of $1.20-coffee to make a mixture of 90-cent coffee?

Inequalities

Not all word problems are translated into mathematical sentences involving *equations*. Some deal with *inequalities*. Such problems can be expressed by number sentences in much the same way as we express problems dealing with equality. The translations are sentences instead of phrases, because of the inclusion of such mathematical verb phrases as "is less than" and "is greater than."

Some word sentences typical of those occurring in inequality problems, along with their mathematical translations, are given below.

1. Some number is less than 16. $\square < 16$.
2. Five is greater than some number. $5 > x$.
3. The sum of some number and 3 is greater than 17. $y + 3 > 17$.
4. Seven plus some number is less than 12. $7 + \square < 12$.
5. Some number is less than *or* equal to 9. $x \leq 9$.
6. Some number is greater than *or* equal to 9. $z \geq 9$.

In solving inequalities we proceed much as we did in solving equalities. Let us now analyze some situations involving inequalities, starting with the ones stated above. The replacement set for each example will be the set of positive integers $\{1, 2, 3, \cdots\}$ except when explicitly specified otherwise.

EXAMPLE 1

Some number is less than 16. The inequality
for this verbal statement can be read in
two ways. Since some number is less than 16, $\square < 16$.
it is also true that 16 is greater than
some number: $16 > \square$.
Since the replacement set is the set of positive
integers, the truth set for either sentence is: $\{1, 2, \cdots, 13, 14, 15\}$

EXAMPLE 2

Five is greater than some number: $5 > x$.
Can you write this statement in another way? $x < 5$.
The truth set is: $\{1, 2, 3, 4\}$

EXAMPLE 3

The sum of some number and 3 is greater than 17: $y + 3 > 17$.
Can you write this statement in another way? $17 < y + 3$.

Note that it is the number named by $(y + 3)$ that is greater than 17; or, stated in another way, 17 is less than the number named by $(y + 3)$.

The truth set is: $\{15, 16, 17, \cdots\}$

EXAMPLE 4

Seven plus some number is less than 12: $7 + \square < 12$.
Can you write this in another way? $12 > 7 + \square$.
The truth set is: $\{1, 2, 3, 4\}$

EXAMPLE 5

Some number is less than *or* equal to 9: $z \leq 9$.

As explained earlier,[3] two conditions are being suggested here. Some number is *less than* 9 $(z < 9)$, *or* the number is *equal to* 9 $(z = 9)$. The word "or" means "either one or both" conditions are to be satisfied.

The truth set is: $\{1, 2, \cdots, 7, 8, 9\}$

EXAMPLE 6

Some number is greater than *or* equal to 9: $z \geq 9$.
Can you write this in another way? $9 \leq z$.

What are the two conditions here? Either $z > 9$ or $z = 9$.

The truth set is: $\{9, 10, 11, \cdots\}$

Let us now consider a few verbal problems involving more complicated inequalities.

PROBLEM 1

Four times the sum of 6 and some number is greater than or equal to three times the sum of the same number and 14. What number or numbers satisfy these conditions?

Analysis

Some number: $\square$
The sum of this number and 6: $\square + 6$
Four times this sum: $4 \times (\square + 6)$
The sum of the same number and
14: $(\square + 14)$
Three times this sum: $3 \times (\square + 14)$
The sentence is: $4 \times (\square + 6) \geq 3 \times (\square + 14)$.

Solution and Check

Substituting values you think might work is a good method here. This eventually will lead to the fact that 18 and greater counting numbers make the sentence true. That is, $\square \geq 18$. Therefore, the truth set consists of all counting numbers equal to, or greater than, 18; that is, the truth set is $\{18, 19, 20, \cdots\}$. *A partial check for this problem involves substituting values*

---

[3] See Booklet No. 8: *Number Sentences.*

in the initial problem situation. A complete check for this type of problem would involve algebraic techniques beyond the scope of this booklet.

PROBLEM 2

A boy is 6 years older than his sister. If the sum of their ages is less than 24, how old might the sister be?

Analysis

You do not know how old the sister is. Let

the sister be *a* years old:	*a*
A boy is 6 years older than his sister:	$a + 6$
The sum of their ages:	$a + (a + 6)$
The sentence is:	$a + (a + 6) < 24.$

Solution and Check

Through experimentation we find that the solution set of this sentence is {1, 2, 3, 4, 5, 6, 7, 8}. This indicates that the sister must be less than nine years old to satisfy the conditions that (1) her brother is six years older than she is, and (2) the sum of their ages is less than 24.

PROBLEM 3

The area of a rectangular region is to be not more than 12 square feet. The length is 5 feet. What conditions are imposed on the width? (For this problem, consider the replacement set to be the set of positive real numbers.)

Analysis

The area of a rectangular region is given by the formula $A = l \times w$. The problem implies that the area may be 12 square feet or any number of square feet less than 12. The length is set at 5 feet. Notice that as the width changes, the area also changes.

The area	A, or $(l \times w)$
is not more than (that is, it is less than or equal to)	$\leq$
12 square feet:	12
The sentence is:	$l \times w \leq 12.$
Substituting the value 5 for the length, we get:	$5 \times w \leq 12.$

Solution and Check

The inequality $5 \times w \leq 12$ reads, "Five times some number is less than or equal to 12." One might correctly guess that if this relation holds for 5 times some number, a comparable relation might hold for one-fifth of these values. In this instance, if $5 \times w \leq 12$, then we have w (or $\frac{1}{5}$ of $5 \times w$) $\leq \frac{12}{5}$ (or $\frac{1}{5}$ of 12), or $w \leq \frac{12}{5}$. Check some values to convince yourself that the truth sets are indeed the same. The inequality $w \leq \frac{12}{5}$ indicates that to make the sentence true, the width must be "less than" or "equal to" $\frac{12}{5}$. Try some values on either side of $\frac{12}{5}$, and also $\frac{12}{5}$ itself, in order to verify the last statement. For instance, if you choose $\frac{12}{5}$ for the width, the sentence will be true, since the length (5) times this value $(5 \times \frac{12}{5})$ will equal 12 and this is one of the conditions contained in the statement of the problem. If you had chosen 2 for the width, the sentence would still be true, since $5 \times 2 = 10$, which is not greater than 12. If you had chosen 3 for the width, the sentence would be false, since $5 \times 3 = 15$, which is greater than 12.

PROBLEM 4

Write an open sentence expressing the fact that a certain positive number is less than its reciprocal. Find the number. (For this problem consider the replacement set to be the set of all positive real numbers.)

Analysis

A certain positive number $\quad\quad\quad\quad\quad\quad\quad\quad z$

is less than $\quad\quad\quad\quad\quad\quad\quad\quad\quad\quad\quad <$

its reciprocal: $\quad\quad\quad\quad\quad\quad\quad\quad\quad\quad \dfrac{1}{z}$

The sentence is: $\quad\quad\quad\quad\quad\quad\quad\quad z < \dfrac{1}{z}.$

Here, $z > 0$.

Solution and Check

We are looking for a positive real number that is less than its reciprocal. Let us try some guesses and, with the guesses, write their reciprocals. For instance:

Number	Reciprocal	
1	$\dfrac{1}{1} = 1.$	Is $1 < 1$? No.
2	$\dfrac{1}{2}$	Is $2 < \dfrac{1}{2}$? No.
$3\dfrac{1}{2} = \dfrac{7}{2}.$	$\dfrac{1}{7/2} = \dfrac{2}{7}.$	Is $\dfrac{7}{2} < \dfrac{2}{7}$? No.

It appears that all our guesses, which were 1 and above, are not working out. Since the replacement set is the set of positive real numbers, let us try some values less than 1.

Number	Reciprocal	
$\dfrac{1}{2}$	$\dfrac{1}{1/2} = 2.$	Is $\dfrac{1}{2} < 2$? Yes.
$\dfrac{3}{4}$	$\dfrac{1}{3/4} = \dfrac{4}{3}.$	Is $\dfrac{3}{4} < \dfrac{4}{3}$? Yes.
$\dfrac{11}{12}$	$\dfrac{1}{11/12} = \dfrac{12}{11}.$	Is $\dfrac{11}{12} < \dfrac{12}{11}$? Yes.

Thus it appears that the numbers making up the solution set are the positive real numbers between 0 and 1, exclusive. The solution set for this problem can be shown graphically by means of the number line (Fig. 1). Notice that the solid section is between, but not including, the graphs of the points 0 and 1

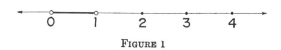

FIGURE 1

Exercise Set 4

1. Translate each of the following word sentences into a number sentence.

   a. A number is greater than 13.

   b. A number is less than 7.

   c. The sum of a number and 3 is greater than 32.

   d. Six times a number is less than or equal to 83.

   e. The sum of a number and 4 is greater than 3 times the number.

2. Here are some open sentences. For each sentence, make up a verbal problem for which the sentence expresses the number relation.

   a. $n + 8 > 32$.

   b. $(2 \times \square) + 3 \leq 19$.

   c. $y - 4 \geq 12$.

   d. $x + 8 < 2 \times x$.

3. Solve the following verbal problems. For each problem, first list the numbers involved and write the number sentence. Then find the solution set and write a sentence to interpret your answer. Take the set of counting numbers to be the replacement set.

   a. The sum of a number and 8 is greater than 32. Find the solution set of numbers that satisfy this condition.

   b. Find the solution set of numbers that satisfy the condition that a number is less than or equal to 4.

UNUSUAL PROBLEM SOLVING

The primary concern of this section is to pose situations that will further develop the problem-solving ability of the reader. The section deals with problems that are of a different nature from those of the preceding section. In general, the problems will not lend themselves to the immediate writing, and subsequent solution, of mathematical sentences. The basic objective of these problems is that the individual should *discover* and *generalize* from certain given information. This is one of the most important objectives of mathematics instruction.

A generalization can be thought of as a synthesis of two or more previously learned concepts. It is often much more than just the synthesis of these concepts, however, since it involves some *new learning*. While the "level" of generalization by individuals may vary a great deal in verbalization, symbolization, and applicability, the psychology of learning suggests that discovering a generalization is of much more value to the learner than merely being told it by others. Emphasis on discovery and generalization makes the learning more permanent and provides for ease in transfer to specific problems. A learner's success in unusual problem solving is partly dependent on his possession and recall of generalizations that "suit" the situation under consideration.

Some Sample Problems

The discussion that follows is somewhat unusual. The emphasis is on how to use nontraditional topics and techniques to learn about the structure of problem solving. Let us note that there is no standard key or procedure that will lead to the solution of all problems. Hence, our discussion will center around many examples. We shall attempt to point out various ways of attacking a given problem. In addition, the emphasis will be on the behavior exhibited by the problem solver. Let us proceed with our first problem. In this example, we shall first set up an actual solution to the problem. After our solution is complete, we shall briefly discuss the various steps within our solution.

PROBLEM 1

Given any counting-number value for n, such as 100, find a simple expression for the sum of the first n members of the set $\{1, 2, 3, 4, \cdots\}$ of counting numbers: Sum $= 1 + 2 + 3 + 4 + \cdots + n$.

Analysis

This problem involves a situation quite unlike any we have previously discussed. The situation is not one where we can immediately write down a mathematical sentence and then solve it to find the truth set. Rather, we are asked to discover and generalize a mathematical expression, or formula, that will enable us to compute quickly the sum of a given sequence of consecutive counting numbers, starting with 1.

It has been said that Karl Friedrich Gauss (1777–1855) solved this problem at the age of ten. He greatly astonished his teacher by being able to sum a long list of counting numbers almost as soon as the statement of the problem was given. Each problem involved a sequence of counting numbers such that the difference between any two consecutive numbers was the same. Let us see if, for our problem, we can duplicate Gauss's feat. If n is a definite counting number, say 5, how would we find the sum? The sum can be determined by writing down the first five counting numbers and adding them in order:

$$\text{Sum} = 1 + 2 + 3 + 4 + 5 = 15.$$

But as stated earlier, our problem is to see if we can find a simple and general formula for determining the sum. For example, to find the sum of the first 100 counting numbers by adding them one by one certainly involves a lot of adding, whereas a general formula for finding such a sum might considerably lessen the work. If we are going to search for a general formula, what should we do first? It might be useful to write down a few of the easier sums and see if any type of pattern develops.

$n = 1,$ Sum $= 1.$
$n = 2,$ Sum $= 1 + 2 = 3.$
$n = 3,$ Sum $= 1 + 2 + 3 = 6.$
$n = 4,$ Sum $= 1 + 2 + 3 + 4 = 10.$
$n = 5,$ Sum $= 1 + 2 + 3 + 4 + 5 = 15.$
$n = 6,$ Sum $= 1 + 2 + 3 + 4 + 5 + 6 = 21.$
$n = 7,$ Sum $= 1 + 2 + 3 + 4 + 5 + 6 + 7 = 28.$
$n = 8,$ Sum $= 1 + 2 + 3 + 4 + 5 + 6 + 7 + 8 = 36.$

At this point it should be noted that there is nothing sacred about our approach to this problem. The procedure being followed here is just one of the many possible ways of attacking the problem. You may have some ideas of your own about how to proceed next. If so, try them. Check your result against the final generalization.

The information given in the preceding sums can be examined for a *pattern*. It would probably be easier to examine this information if it were in tabular form. Organizing the information in a way that will make the work easier is a very important aspect of problem solving.

From Table II can you see some pattern? Make a guess at it and then check the pattern against some further sums. Were you right? You should not be afraid of making an incorrect guess. If your first guess was incorrect, make another. If your guess seems to work, try to state it in mathematical terms.

One thing you might try is to divide each Sum by the corresponding n and record the entries in a third column in Table II. The successive entries are 1, $1\frac{1}{2}$, 2, $2\frac{1}{2}$ 3, $3\frac{1}{2}$, 4, $4\frac{1}{2}$, or $\frac{2}{2}$, $\frac{3}{2}$, $\frac{4}{2}$, $\frac{5}{2}$, $\frac{6}{2}$, $\frac{7}{2}$, $\frac{8}{2}$, $\frac{9}{2}$. A pattern has emerged!

From the pattern, we can see one relationship that appears to exist be-

TABLE II

n (Number of Counting Numbers Being Summed)	Sum (Sum of the First n Counting Numbers)
1	1
2	3
3	6
4	10
5	15
6	21
7	28
8	36

tween the n and Sum (which we shall now refer to as S) values. It is the following:

The sum S of the first n counting numbers is one-half the product of n and the next greater counting number, $n + 1$.

Thus, if $n = 1$, then $n + 1 = 2$; and $\frac{1}{2} \times (1 \times 2) = 1$, which is the S value corresponding to $n = 1$. If $n = 2$, then $n + 1 = 3$; and $\frac{1}{2} \times (2 \times 3) = 3$, which is the S value corresponding to $n = 2$. Try this for $n = 3$. Did you find that the S value for $n = 3$ was one-half the product of 3 and 4? Use this same notion to find the sum of the first seven counting numbers, $1 + 2 + 3 + 4 + 5 + 6 + 7$. What must you do? You have $n = 7$. Then $n + 1 = 8$, and $S = \frac{1}{2} \times (7 \times 8) = 28$, which is the same value as the one given in the table.

While the technique described above seems to work, we have not really *proved* our result. At this point, however, we may feel that we have checked enough examples to satisfy ourselves that the technique *might* hold for any counting number n. (You should try some more values.) We should be aware, though, that there is a danger in making hasty generalizations. This fact will be illustrated in a later example dealing with primes.

Now let us see if we can mathematically represent the technique described above. In every case, we took an n value and a value one higher than n, namely, $n + 1$. We then multiplied the product of the two numbers, n and $n + 1$, by $\frac{1}{2}$, and this result was equal to the appropriate S. Can you write the mathematical sentence that represents this? If you proceed carefully, you should obtain the following sentence:

$$S = \frac{1}{2} \times [n \times (n + 1)], \quad \text{or} \quad S = \frac{n \times (n + 1)}{2}.$$

Check this formula for a few more values of n, such as 8, 9, and 10. The case for $n = 10$ is as follows:

$$S = \frac{1}{2} \times (10 \times 11),$$

or

$$S = \frac{10 \times (10 + 1)}{2},$$

$$= 55.$$

You might wish to check your answers by addition.

Could you now find the sum of the first 100 counting numbers? This sum is 5,050. Every example you do should lend support to the intuitive guess that this formula will work in all cases. It should be reemphasized that we have *not* proved the formula. The formula is indeed true, however, and can readily be proved, using special algebraic techniques. A mathematical proof shows that the formula holds for the general case.

It is interesting at this point to look at a different solution to the problem we have been considering—a solution that perhaps gives a deeper understanding of why the formula *must* be true in general. Gauss, it is said, noted that in adding an even number of consecutive counting numbers, the sum of the first and last is equal to the sum of the second and the next to last, and so on. For example, consider this technique applied to the sum of the first six counting numbers:

Gauss noted that the number of such pairs is one-half the number of counting numbers; in this case, we have ½ of 6, or 3, pairs. Thus, to find the sum, we need only to multiply the sum of each pair by the number of pairs. In our example this is 3 × 7 = 21.

If an odd number of counting numbers is given to sum, the same situation exists except for the "middle" number. But this number is always equal to one-half the common sum. For example, suppose we wish to find the sum of the first seven counting numbers:

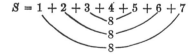

In this case the common sum is 8. We have three pairs that add to 8, and we have "half of an 8," or "half of a pair," because the middle number is 4. Thus we can say that we have $(3 \times 8) + (\frac{1}{2} \times 8)$, or $3\frac{1}{2} \times 8$, for a total sum of 28. Study this carefully to be sure you understand how it works. The following diagram shows this technique applied to the first *n* con-

secutive counting numbers. Note how we can represent the number just
before n by $(n - 1)$:

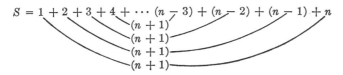

$$S = 1 + 2 + 3 + 4 + \cdots (n - 3) + (n - 2) + (n - 1) + n$$

Do you see how we can generalize this to obtain the formula we developed
previously? How many pairs are there that have $(n + 1)$ as their sum?
We have $\frac{1}{2}$ times the number of counting numbers, or actually $\frac{1}{2} \times n$ such
pairs. Thus we can write the formula in the following way:

$$S = \left(\frac{1}{2} \times n\right) \times (n + 1),$$

which is the same as

$$S = \frac{1}{2} \times [n \times (n + 1)],$$

or

$$S = \frac{n \times (n + 1)}{2}.$$

Note that our formula holds whether n is even or odd. A rigorous discussion
here would involve the process called *mathematical induction*.

Discussion

While the final step in the solution of Problem 1 was to state the general
formula, this was not, in itself, the most important aspect of the problem.
In solving the problem the important thing was *how the solution was obtained*. If you briefly review our analysis, you will note that certain special
techniques were used.

One of the things you probably had to do after first reading the statement of the problem was to *reread the problem* to be sure you understood
what was being asked. After this the problem was simplified by restating
it for a number of specific cases. Also, you were asked a number of questions
to help you *understand the nature of the problem*. A table was then set up to
organize the information that had already been obtained. At this point, you
were called upon to make an extremely important step: you were asked to
search for a pattern and to *make a guess as to what might be a solution* or what
might lead to a formula. You were encouraged to be flexible in your guess
and to *check it for accuracy*. If in the check you found your original guess
to be incorrect, then you had to revise your guess or make a new one.

For this particular problem a relationship was presented that seemed to be true. Then the attempt was made to generalize this relationship in mathematical language so that it could easily be used in other situations. (The general formula $S = \frac{1}{2} \times [n \times (n + 1)]$ was established.) This generalization was checked for a number of values of n, and then it was applied to the special case of $n = 100$. Finally, we sought to make the formula seem reasonable in the general case by pairing the terms to obtain $\frac{1}{2} \times n$ sums, each of which was equal to $n + 1$.

Different techniques were involved in the steps toward the solution of this problem. While not all problems can be solved in exactly the same way, many of these same procedures may be useful in other situations. To illustrate this, let us now consider another example.

PROBLEM 2

Find a simple expression for the sum of the first n members of the set $\{2, 4, 6, 8, \cdots\}$ of even counting numbers.

Analysis

Since we have just solved a similar problem, it seems that the methods of attack we used there might be useful here. If we write a few examples and tabulate the results (see Table III), we have the following:

$$n = 1, \qquad S = 2.$$
$$n = 2, \qquad S = 2 + 4 = 6.$$
$$n = 3, \qquad S = 2 + 4 + 6 = 12.$$
$$n = 4, \qquad S = 2 + 4 + 6 + 8 = 20.$$
$$n = 5, \qquad S = 2 + 4 + 6 + 8 + 10 = 30.$$

(Note that in this case the nth addend is not n; that is, the first addend is not 1 but 2; the second addend is not 2 but 4; the third addend is not 3 but 6; and so on.)

TABLE III

n (Number of Even Counting Numbers to Be Summed)	S (Sum of the Even Counting Numbers)
1	2
2	6
3	12
4	20
5	30

If we now search the table for a pattern, we can make an intuitive guess just as we did in the first problem. Is there a relationship between n—the number of even counting numbers to be added—and the sum S? The relationship appears to be that the sum S is the product of n and the next counting number, $n + 1$. If this is correct, then to find the sum of the first 5 even counting numbers, you need only consider the product of 5 and 6:

If $n = 5$, *then the next consecutive integer is* 6, *and* $S = 5 \times 6 = 30$.

Does this result check with our table? Yes, it does. Now, as in Problem 1, it would be useful to state this generalization mathematically. Can you do this? You need only consider the phrases for the given number n and one more than the number, $n + 1$. Then write the sentence asserting that the sum S is equal to the product of these two numbers:

$$S = n \times (n + 1).$$

After checking this with a few more examples, you should see if you can find the sum of the first 10 even counting numbers. Did you get 110?

The generalization we obtained for this problem could have been derived in a number of different ways. Do you see that if we had used Gauss's technique of adding the first and last addends, then the second and next to last, and so on, we would still have obtained a formula equivalent to $S = n \times (n + 1)$? This may not be quite so apparent unless we use a little algebra. (Do not worry if you cannot follow all of the algebra.)

We first must be able to represent the last addend in some way. How can the nth addend be written? The first addend has a value of 2, the second addend has a value of 4, the third addend has a value of 6, and so on. Thus, what is the value of, say, the sixth addend? Yes, it is 12. More generally, the nth addend (or the nth even counting number) has the value $2 \times n$. Therefore, the sum of the first addend and the last must be $2 + (2 \times n)$. The sum of the second and the next-to-last addends is $4 + [(2 \times n) - 2]$. This sum can also be simplified, by using the associative and commutative properties, to $2 + (2 \times n)$ and then to $(2 \times n) + 2$. Each pair of addends will have this sum:

$$S = 2 + 4 + 6 + \cdots + (2 \times n - 4) + (2 \times n - 2) + (2 \times n)$$
$$[(2 \times n) + 2]$$
$$[(2 \times n) + 2]$$
$$[(2 \times n) + 2]$$

How many of these pairs of addends do we have? We have $\frac{1}{2} \times n$ pairs of them (including one "half of a pair" if n is odd). The sum can be written:

$$S = \left(\frac{1}{2} \times n\right) \times [(2 \times n) + 2].$$

But by the distributive property of multiplication, we see that $(2 \times n) + 2$ is equal to $2 \times (n + 1)$. Thus,

$$S = \left(\frac{1}{2} \times n\right) \times [2 \times (n + 1)].$$

The associative and commutative properties of multiplication allow us to write this as:

$$S = \left(\frac{1}{2} \times 2\right) \times [n \times (n + 1)],$$

$$S = 1 \times [n \times (n + 1)],$$

$$S = n \times (n + 1).$$

One further approach to solving this particular problem deserves mention here. You might have noticed that each term in this sequence of addends is actually twice that of each term in the sequence of addends in our first problem:

Problem 1: $S = 1 + 2 + 3 + 4 + 5 + \cdots + n.$
Problem 2: $S = 2 + 4 + 6 + 8 + 10 + \cdots + (2 \times n).$

Does this suggest any way to find the sum of the first n consecutive *even* counting numbers? Could we use our first formula and multiply it by 2? For our present sum we would have:

$$S = 2 \times \left(\frac{1}{2} \times [n \times (n + 1)]\right).$$

By the commutative property of multiplication this can be written as:

$$S = 1 \times [n \times (n + 1)] = n \times (n + 1).$$

Discussion

We have considered just three ways of solving this problem. Two of the solutions employed the same types of procedures used in Problem 1. The third technique was slightly different, since we used the result of a previous problem to simplify our work. This points out another important aspect of problem solving: the *recall of information obtained from related problems.*

Let us consider one more problem dealing with sums of counting numbers.

PROBLEM 3

Find a simple expression for the sum of the first n members of the set $\{1, 3, 5, 7, 9, \cdots\}$, the odd counting numbers.

Analysis

The techniques used in the previous problems might also be useful for this example. Let us consider a number of specific sums and then put these in a table. (See Table IV.)

$$
\begin{array}{ll}
n = 1, & S = 1. \\
n = 2, & S = 1 + 3 = 4. \\
n = 3, & S = 1 + 3 + 5 = 9. \\
n = 4, & S = 1 + 3 + 5 + 7 = 16. \\
n = 5, & S = 1 + 3 + 5 + 7 + 9 = 25.
\end{array}
$$

Does a relationship exist between any value for n and its corresponding S value? At this point the pattern seems too nice to be true. But it is true: to find S, *all you need to do is square n*. Thus the formula for this case can be written:

$$S = n^2.$$

Check this for other specific values of n.

TABLE IV

n (Number of Odd Counting Numbers Being Summed)	S (Sum of First n Odd Counting Numbers)
1	1
2	4
3	9
4	16
5	25

The following problem also involves the sum of a number of addends.

PROBLEM 4

Consider the rational numbers of the form $\frac{1}{n \times (n+1)}$, where n is a counting number. Find the sum of the first 3 such rational numbers, the first 6 such rational numbers, the first k such rational numbers.

Analysis

First we must consider what a rational number of the form $\frac{1}{n \times (n+1)}$ is like. If we let $n = 1$, then the number is:

$$\frac{1}{1 \times (1 + 1)} = \frac{1}{1 \times 2} = \frac{1}{2}.$$

If $n = 2$, then the number is:

$$\frac{1}{2 \times (2 + 1)} = \frac{1}{2 \times 3} = \frac{1}{6}.$$

If $n = 3$, then the number is:

$$\frac{1}{3 \times (3 + 1)} = \frac{1}{3 \times 4} = \frac{1}{12}.$$

Summarizing this data to find the sums of 1, 2, and 3 terms, we have the following:

$$k = 1, \qquad S = \frac{1}{2}.$$

$$k = 2, \qquad S = \frac{1}{2} + \frac{1}{6} = \frac{4}{6} = \frac{2}{3}.$$

$$k = 3, \qquad S = \frac{1}{2} + \frac{1}{6} + \frac{1}{12} = \frac{9}{12} = \frac{3}{4}.$$

Thus the answer to the first part of our problem is $\frac{3}{4}$. We can continue in this same manner to find the sum of the first 6 terms. If you substitute 4, 5, and 6 for n in the general formula, you obtain $\frac{1}{20}$, $\frac{1}{30}$, and $\frac{1}{42}$, respectively, for the individual fractions. Adding these to the first 3 terms, $\frac{1}{2}$, $\frac{1}{6}$, and $\frac{1}{12}$, you see that the sum of the first 6 terms is $\frac{6}{7}$. This technique will work for the sum of a small number of terms, but what happens when k becomes large? It would be quite tedious to find the sum of the first 20 or 30 such fractions by direct addition. Therefore, we must look at the problem more closely and attempt to detect any pattern that may exist. What should we do first? As in our previous examples, it may be helpful to put some information in tabular form and to search for a pattern. For practice, fill in the two missing values in Table V. Did you supply $\frac{4}{5}$ and $\frac{5}{6}$ for the two

TABLE V

k (Number of Addends)	S (Sum of the Addends)
1............................	$\frac{1}{2}$
2............................	$\frac{2}{3}$
3............................	$\frac{3}{4}$
4............................	–
5............................	–
6............................	$\frac{6}{7}$

missing values in the table? With the information in the table before you, what do you think would be the result of summing the first 7 such fractions? Did you guess $\frac{7}{8}$? If so, you probably have noted a pattern. Check your guess against some further examples. You have probably noticed by now that the sum is a fraction whose numerator is the same as the number of terms and whose denominator is one more than this number; for example, if $n = 6$, then the sum is $\frac{6}{6+1}$, or $\frac{6}{7}$. Can you write the mathematical sentence that states the relationship between the sum and the number of terms? Using k for the number of terms and $k + 1$ for a number that is one greater than k, we can write the generalization as follows:

$$S = \frac{k}{k + 1}.$$

Check this formula, using the examples in Table V. Although we have not given a rigorous proof, this formula actually is valid for all counting numbers k. With this generalization it is now easy to find the sum of the first 20 rational numbers of the form $\frac{1}{n \times (n+1)}$. We need only substitute in the formula to obtain:

$$S = \frac{k}{k + 1} = \frac{20}{20 + 1} = \frac{20}{21}.$$

Discussion

This example further illustrates the variety of numerical problems available for practice. The *search for patterns* is a fascinating and important part of problem solving.

A Word of Caution

Before we continue, a word of caution is in order. In each of the previous examples, we have generalized from a number of specific examples. This has been pointed out as an important aspect of problem solving. The conjectures we have formed have been much more than the usual "guess." They might be called intuitive guesses. This kind of intuitive guess usually follows from some *implicit perception* of the total problem situation, and it generally follows a very careful perusal of the essential characteristics of the problem. The final generalization in each of our problems has come from a process of reasoning that went from the particular to the general. This pattern of thinking, which leads one to examine special cases intuitively for some "thread" of similarity and then to generalize from these cases, is referred to as induction. Great care must be exercised in drawing conclusions from an inductive process. Such conclusions must be stated as conjectures; for as we have already said, they have not actually been proved for all possible cases. Much of what we know in science is accepted because of induction; that is, when every observation has satisfied the generalization, it is assumed that the result holds in all cases. Therefore, the pattern of inductive thinking is extremely important.

To point out the danger of hasty generalization, however, let us consider the following situation.

Mathematicians have been trying for many years to develop a "prime generator," that is, a formula such that if a particular value for the counting number n is substituted in the formula, then the result will in every case be a prime number and, furthermore, that each different substitution for n will give a different prime number. (Remember that a prime number is a counting number greater than 1 that has only itself and 1 as factors.) One of the first formulas presented was the following:

$$p = n^2 - n + 11.$$

Start with $n = 1$ and substitute successive values for n in this formula to see if the results are actually primes. A set P consisting of the first 26 primes is given below so you can check your result quickly.

$$P = \{2, 3, 5, 7, 11, 13, 17, 19, 23, 29, 31, 37, 41, 43,$$
$$47, 53, 59, 61, 67, 71, 73, 79, 83, 89, 97, 101.\}$$

If we consider $n = 1$, we obtain

$$p = 1^2 - 1 + 11 = 11.$$

Since 11 is a prime, we do obtain a prime in this case. What about 2? In this case, we get $p = 13$, and this is also a prime. For $n = 3$ we have $p = 17$, and 17 is a prime. Check a few more, say 4, 5, and 6. In each of these cases, we obtain a prime number, namely 23, 31, and 41, respectively. Do you think the formula will give a prime number for all n? Fill in the values missing from Table VI.

TABLE VI

n	p
1	11
2	13
3	17
4	23
5	31
6	41
7	—
8	—
9	—
10	101

Now, after checking 10 specific situations do you feel that the formula will *always* give a prime? It certainly seems reasonable to assume so. Actually, in this problem we have checked more specific cases than in any previous problem. Let us try one more substitution. Consider the case $n = 11$. Here we get the following:

$$p = 11^2 - 11 + 11 = 11^2 = 121.$$

Is 121 a prime number? Is it divisible by some counting number other than 1 and 121? Certainly it is: Since $11^2 = 121$, 11 must be a factor. Therefore, our formula is *not* a prime generator.

Other formulas for prime generators have also been suggested. Consider the two given below:

$$p = n^2 - n + 41,$$

and

$$p = n^2 - (79 \times n) + 1,601.$$

Each of these fails. The first holds for all values of n up through 40 but does not hold when $n = 41$. (Do you see why?) The second is much more difficult to check out, but it fails at $n = 80$, since 1,681 is not a prime number. Mathematicians have not been able to prove that a prime generator formula does not exist, nor have they been able to find a formula that works for all counting numbers n.

In all inductive situations, one must be very careful about making a hasty generalization. What appears to be true may not be so. Thus it is important to check enough examples to satisfy oneself that a given pattern or generalization will hold. More than this, we must recognize that it is only after a conjecture has been *proved* true that it can be called a theorem, or a valid proposition.

This should not stop us from searching for patterns and making generalizations, for this is ordinarily the first step toward arriving at a theorem. It is *after* an intuitive guess that the mathematician attempts to prove or disprove his idea.

Exercise Set 5

Given: A set of rational numbers such that the nth rational number is of the form $\frac{1}{2^n}$.

1. Find the sum of the first 4 such rational numbers.

$$\left(\text{Hint: For } n = 1, \frac{1}{2^n} = \frac{1}{2^1} = \frac{1}{2} ; \quad \text{thus} \quad S = \frac{1}{2}. \right.$$

$$\left. \text{For } n = 2, \frac{1}{2^n} = \frac{1}{2^2} = \frac{1}{4} ; \quad \text{thus} \quad S = \frac{1}{2} + \frac{1}{4} = \frac{3}{4}. \right)$$

2. Make a conjecture about the sum of the first n such rational numbers.

3. Use the result of your conjecture to find the sum of the first 7 such rational numbers.

Sample Problems in Geometry

The field of geometry is rich in the type of problems we have been discussing. The three sample problems in this section are examples that require only an intuitive understanding of some of the vocabulary of geometry:

point, line, angle, polygon, and area. The first problem given below poses an interesting question regarding the relationship between points and lines. You might like to see if you can work out a solution on your own before reading the discussion that follows.

PROBLEM 5

Given a set of two or more points, no three of which lie in the same straight line, how many different straight lines are determined? (Note that any two points determine a straight line; that is, precisely one straight line passes through two given points.)

Analysis

Let us proceed as before by considering some specific situations. Given two points (call them P and Q), how many different lines can be drawn through them? Only one, of course. How about three points? Four points? These cases are difficult to visualize mentally. It is quite helpful, therefore, to use a pictorial representation to organize our data. For two points, see Figure 2.

FIG. 2.—Two points, one line.

Now consider three points, P, Q, and R (Fig. 3). Remember that the three points are not to be in one straight line. (Mathematicians use the word "noncollinear" to express the idea that points are not all in one straight line.)

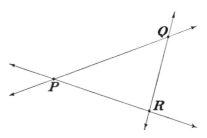

FIG. 3.—Three points, three lines.

Let us examine a few more pictures (Fig. 4). Now, as in our earlier problems, it would be helpful to put our information in a table. In Table VII we let n represent the number of points and S the number of different straight lines. Do you notice anything familiar about the table?

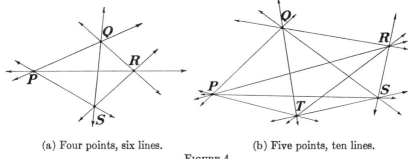

(a) Four points, six lines.   (b) Five points, ten lines.

FIGURE 4

Have you seen the same table, or one very much like it before? This table resembles the one we made up to find the sum of the first n counting numbers. It differs in only one respect. (You might wish to refer

TABLE VII

n	S
2	1
3	3
4	6
5	10

back to Table II. The numerals in the S column have been pushed down one position.

The method used in the summing of the first n positive integers was to note the relationship between one-half the product of two consecutive n-values and the corresponding S-value of the first n-value, $S = \frac{1}{2} \times [n \times (n + 1)]$. Will this same relationship apply here? Since the tables are not exactly the same, you might correctly surmise that the same relationship does not apply. But at the same time, you might guess that a relationship very similar to the one used before might well apply here. This is correct. Instead of taking one-half the product of two consecutive values in the n-table and comparing this with the S-value of the *first* n-value, as we did before, let us compare the product with the S-value of the *second* n-value. Let us denote the second n-value by n; then the first is $n - 1$. Thus for $n = 2$, we have $n - 1 = 1$; and $\frac{1}{2} \times (2 \times 1) = 1$, which is the correct value of S for $n = 2$. For $n = 3$, we have $n - 1 = 2$; and $\frac{1}{2}(3 \times 2) = 3$, which is the correct value of S for $n = 3$. More generally, we conjecture that in the case of n points, no three of which are collinear, the number of lines that are determined is given by

$$S = \frac{1}{2} \times [n \times (n - 1)].$$

Check this against a few more examples, such as $n = 6$ and $n = 7$. What if $n = 100$? In this case, we have:

$$S = \frac{1}{2} \times [n \times (n - 1)],$$

$$S = \frac{1}{2} \times [100 \times (100 - 1)],$$

$$S = \frac{1}{2} \times (100 \times 99),$$

$$S = \frac{1}{2} \times 9{,}900,$$

$$S = 4{,}950.$$

Thus 100 points, no three of which are on the same straight line, determine 4,950 different straight lines.

Discussion

Solving this problem involved using some valuable techniques. First, the use of *diagrams* was very important in obtaining our solution. Then we discovered that we could employ our *previously acquired knowledge* to help generalize a solution. As always, though, we should remember that we have not strictly proved the result.

PROBLEM 6

What is the sum of the measures of the angles of an n-sided convex polygon?

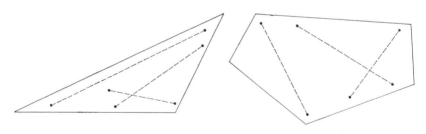

FIGURE 5

Analysis

To understand what is being asked in this problem, you need to know what is meant by a "convex" polygon.[4] A polygon is *convex* if for each pair

---

[4] See Booklet No. 14: *Informal Geometry*.

of points in the interior (inside) of the polygon the entire line segment joining the points lies in the interior of the polygon. Examples of convex
polygons are shown in Figure 5.

To show that a particular polygon is not convex, you need only find one
pair of points in the interior such that the line segment between them is

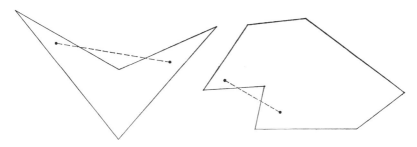

FIGURE 6

not entirely in the interior. Examples of polygons that are not convex are
given in Figure 6.

In order to try to determine an answer to the question stated in the
problem, it would be helpful to consider some specific examples of convex
polygons. Let us start with a triangle, as shown in Figure 7(a). Do you see
that every triangle is a convex polygon? The sum of the measures of the
angles in this case is 180°, as you probably know. You could obtain an
approximate experimental verification of this fact by tracing some triangles,
cutting the three angles from each, and fitting them together to see that
they seem to form a straight line. See Figure 7(b).

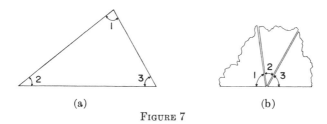

(a)   (b)

FIGURE 7

The next figure to consider is one with 4 sides, or a quadrilateral. If we
consider the figure to be a rectangle and draw such a diagram, we can see

that the sum of the measures of the angles must be 360° (Fig. 8). This is true: Each of the angles is a right angle, we know that the measure of a right angle is 90°, and 4 × 90° = 360°.

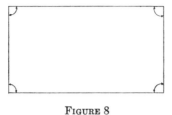

FIGURE 8

Do you suppose that the sum of the measures of the angles must be 360° for all 4-sided convex polygons? Consider the one shown in Figure 9.

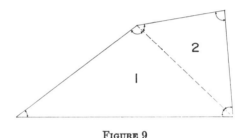

FIGURE 9

Notice what happens when a diagonal is drawn. (A diagonal is a segment joining two nonadjacent vertices.) Two triangles are formed. The sum of the angles in each triangle is 180°, and the sum of all the angles in the quadrilateral is accordingly 2 × 180°, or 360°. Study the diagram carefully, particularly the corners at the ends of the diagonal, to see why this is so.

The figure with 5 sides is a little more difficult. We have no previous information about the angles. Thus we must try to discover some technique for finding the sum of the measures. What do you think might help? Try something. One possible approach is again to divide the interior into triangular regions by drawing some diagonals. Consider the polygon in Figure 10, for which diagonals have been drawn from one vertex to all the other nonadjacent vertices.

We see that the sides of the polygon can be used along with the diagonals to construct 3 triangles. As indicated in the figure, the 3 triangles contain angles whose measures all add up to the same sum as the measures of the

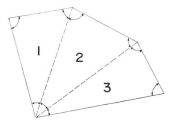

FIGURE 10

angles of the original polygon. Since the sum of the measures of the angles of a triangle is 180°, we need only take 3 × 180° to obtain the sum for the original polygon, which is 540°. Do you think this technique of dividing a convex polygonal region into triangular regions will work for a 6-sided convex polygon? Try it and see. Your diagram should look something like the one shown in Figure 11.

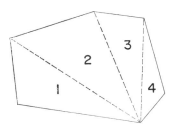

FIGURE 11

Since the number of triangles is 4, we see that the sum of the measures of the angles is 4 × 180°, or 720°. Let us make a table of the information we have obtained. (See Table VIII.) In this case we might actually like to include all three pieces of information: the number of sides, n; the number

TABLE VIII

n	$\triangle$	S
3	1	180°
4	2	360°
5	3	540°
6	4	720°

of triangles, $\triangle$; and the sum of the measures of the angles, S.

From this table we may make a number of observations. You might have noted that in each case the number of triangles is 2 less than the number of sides in the polygon; that is, if you have an n-sided convex polygon, you can divide it into $(n - 2)$ triangles. How does this help us to generalize to the sum of the measures of the angles of the n-sided polygon? Do you see that all we need to do is multiply 180° by the number of triangles? Thus, we can write the following mathematical statement for the sum, S, of the degree measures of the angles of an n-sided convex polygon:

$$S = (n - 2) \times 180°.$$

To find the sum of the measures, in degrees, of the angles of a convex polygon with 12 sides, we need only substitute in the formula:

$$S = (12 - 2) \times 180°,$$
$$S = 10 \times 180°,$$
$$S = 1,800°.$$

An interesting extension of this problem is the following: How do you find the measure of one of the angles in an n-sided "regular" polygon? Since the angles of a regular polygon all have the same measure, what do you have to do to find the measure of one of the angles? Certainly all you need do is to divide the sum of the measures by the number of angles, which is the same as the number of sides. In our last example, if the 12-sided figure were a regular polygon, each of the 12 angles would be 1,800° ÷ 12, or 150°. With this information it becomes an easy task to use a ruler and protractor to construct reasonably accurate diagrams of regular polygons.

Discussion

As in each of our previous problems, we find that the final example involved techniques that were somewhat different. After constructing our diagrams, we actually changed the problem from one of looking for the sum of the measures of the angles to one of finding how many triangles we could construct by drawing diagonals. We used an *auxiliary problem* to help us reach our solution to the initial problem. After reaching the solution, we noticed that we had almost solved another related problem. We then *extended* our solution to provide us with more information, and at the same time this gave us the tools to make some interesting constructions. The problem solver should be cognizant of logical extensions of his work.

Exercise Set 6

A diagonal is a line segment joining any two nonadjacent vertices of the figure.

1. How many diagonals are there in a six-sided convex polygon?

2. How many diagonals are there if the convex polygon has the following number of sides?

a. Three

b. Five

3. Develop a formula that expresses the sum of the diagonals for an n-sided convex polygon.

Let us now consider one more example from geometry. The solution to this problem is another example of the type of thinking and reasoning that is so valuable in problem solving.

PROBLEM 7

Imagine a piece of plywood with an array of evenly spaced nails forming small squares (Fig. 12) and consider that each side of each square has a length of one unit.

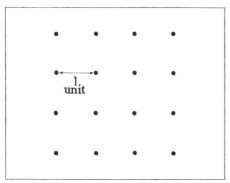

FIGURE 12

We are going to interweave some geometry with our arithmetic by asking this question: If you know the number of nails used in the perimeter, can you predict the number of units of the region you can surround with a rubber band? One unit of area is, of course, the area of a square with sides of length one unit each, as shown in Figure 13.

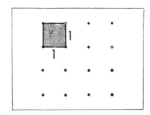

FIGURE 13

Before attempting to answer the foregoing question, two general ground rules will be made:

    1. Our surrounded region must be void of unused inside nails.

For example, in Figure 14(a) the diagram is accepted. On the other hand, diagram 14(b) is not accepted, since there is a nail inside the figure that is not part of the perimeter.

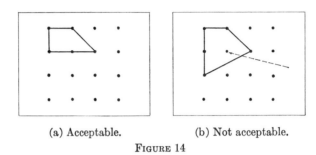

        (a) Acceptable.   (b) Not acceptable.

FIGURE 14

    2. The boundary of our figure must not cross itself, that is, it must be a simple closed curve.

The diagram in Figure 15 is *not* acceptable, since it violates this second ground rule.

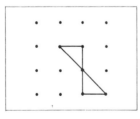

FIGURE 15

Abiding by rules 1 and 2, we may construct many types of simple closed curves. Using the same number of nails, we may make many different figures. The diagrams in Figure 16(a) through (e) are all acceptable, since they follow our two ground rules.

Analysis

Probably our first task in attempting to answer the posed problem would be to categorize our information in some meaningful way. A table might again be useful. For this table let us consider x to represent the *number of nails* used on the perimeter. In diagrams (a), (b), and (c) of Figure 16 we

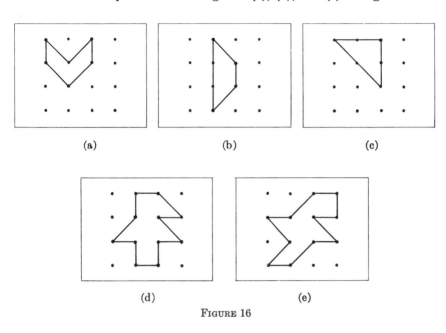

(a)   (b)   (c)

(d)   (e)

FIGURE 16

used 6 nails; in diagrams (d) and (e) we used 11 nails. By y we shall designate the *number of units of area* we obtained by using x nails for the perimeter. But do we get the same value of y for each of two *different* figures

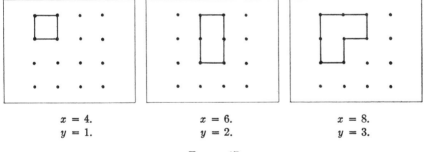

$x = 4.$ $x = 6.$ $x = 8.$
$y = 1.$ $y = 2.$ $y = 3.$

FIGURE 17

having the same value of x, such as in diagrams (b) and (c) or diagrams (d) and (e)? Let us see. Consider the examples shown in Figure 17.

Here the diagrams can all be subdivided into squares whose areas are easily computed. For triangular-shaped regions (Fig. 18), you should recall that the area is equal to one-half the product of the base and the altitude.

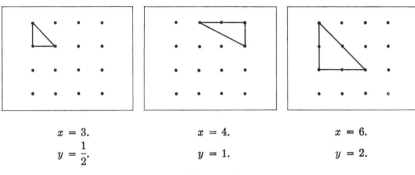

$x = 3.$ $x = 4.$ $x = 6.$

$y = \dfrac{1}{2}.$ $y = 1.$ $y = 2.$

FIGURE 18

Can you see a relationship between the number of nails used and the area of the resulting region? Do different regions with the same x-value have also the same y-value? If we set up a table, arranging x-values in numerical order, we might observe a pattern that the corresponding y-values follow. Considering values for x and y from the above examples, we can construct Table IX. We shall also assume that using 2 nails gives us 0 square units. Do you see why?

TABLE IX

x	y
2	0
3	$\dfrac{1}{2}$
4	1
5	
6	2
7	
8	3

We do not have any examples of figures using 5 nails or 7 nails for their perimeters. What would you guess would be the number of square units for each? Intuitively and with little or no trouble, you probably selected

$y = 1\frac{1}{2}$ for $x = 5$, and $y = 2\frac{1}{2}$ for $x = 7$. The pattern for y seems to be an increase of $\frac{1}{2}$ with every increase of 1 for x. At this point you might test your notion by making a figure that uses 9 nails on the perimeter and checking to see if the area of the region is $3\frac{1}{2}$ square units. Examples of this are shown in Figure 19.

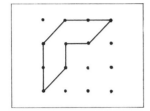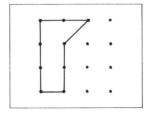

FIGURE 19

Try some others. Do they all have $3\frac{1}{2}$ square units of area? Once again our intuition seems to be correct. After we have filled in the additional information, we obtain Table X. At this point our approach might be to

TABLE X

x	y
2	0
3	$\frac{1}{2}$
4	1
5	$1\frac{1}{2}$
6	2
7	$2\frac{1}{2}$
8	3
9	$3\frac{1}{2}$

see if this table looks like any of the tables previously constructed. Comparing them, we notice that this is not like any of the others. Thus some other approach is necessary if we are to obtain a generalization. In order to arrive at a y-value of 0 for $x = 2$, we would need only to subtract 2 from the x-value. This appears easy enough—but will it work for the succeeding values of x? For $x = 3$, when we subtract 2, we obtain $3 - 2 = 1$; but this is not the correct y-value, which is $y = \frac{1}{2}$. In fact, the value we want for y is one-half the value obtained. What if we were to take the x-value, subtract 2, and then take one-half of this? This technique works for $x = 3$: If $x = 3$, then $3 - 2 = 1$; and $\frac{1}{2} \times 1 = \frac{1}{2}$. Hence $y = \frac{1}{2}$.

Does it work for $x = 2$? In this case, $2 - 2 = 0$; and $\frac{1}{2} \times 0 = 0$. Hence $y = 0$. Yes, it works!

Does it work for $x = 4$? In this case, $4 - 2 = 2$; and $\frac{1}{2} \times 2 = 1$. Hence $y = 1$. It appears that we have found a satisfactory generalization. Let us try $x = 8$; we need to arrive at $y = 3$. Now $8 - 2 = 6$, and $\frac{1}{2} \times 6 = 3$. Hence $y = 3$, and again this method works.

Can you write the mathematical sentence for this relationship? We take the x-value, subtract 2 from it, and then take one-half of this difference. Thus the general formula is:

$$y = \frac{1}{2} \times (x - 2), \quad \text{or} \quad y = \frac{x - 2}{2}.$$

Applying the formula for $x = 10$, we get:

$$y = \frac{10 - 2}{2},$$

$$y = \frac{8}{2},$$

$$y = 4.$$

If you check this answer by drawing a figure using 10 nails on the perimeter, you might have a diagram that looks like the one in Figure 20. By counting carefully we can see that the figure contains 4 square units. This is also consistent with the pattern in the table.

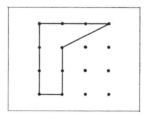

FIGURE 20

This certainly looks like the answer to our question, and without going into the idea of "proof" we shall agree that this is a correct formula.

Now let us extend our problem by omitting the first ground rule. We shall allow any type of simple closed figure. Thus the ones shown in Figure 21 are now acceptable; but the one shown in Figure 22 is not, since its bound-

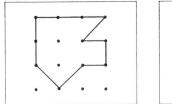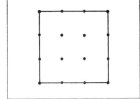

FIGURE 21

ary "crosses" itself and violates our second ground rule. The only way the acceptable figures differ from our previous ones is that nails are now allowed inside the figure, and these particular nails are not being used to form part of the perimeter.

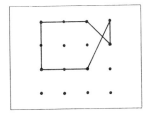

FIGURE 22

Does our generalization still hold? We need only to consider the example in Figure 23 to see that our previous generalization no longer holds. To

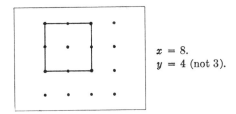

$x = 8$.
$y = 4$ (not 3).

FIGURE 23

work our way out of a very perplexing situation, let us consider some figures with 4 or more nails on the perimeter. We shall categorize these figures by the number of nails inside that are not being used. For example, consider the diagrams in Figure 24.

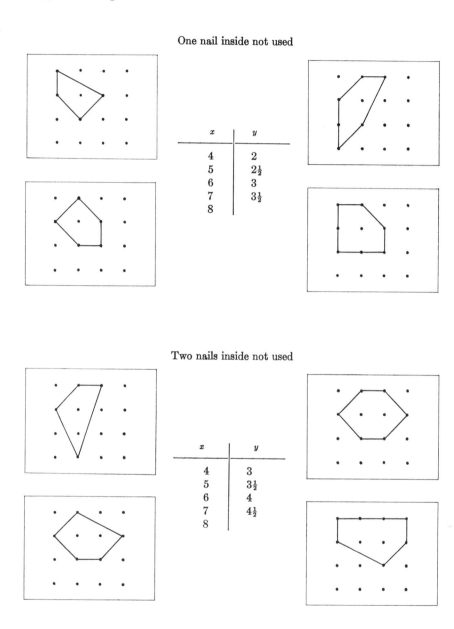

FIGURE 24

Try some other figures like those in the diagrams. Now what would you guess for $x = 8$ in each of the two situations (one nail inside or two nails inside)? Placing our three tables side by side and categorizing them by the number of nails inside, not used on the perimeter, we have Table XI.

TABLE XI

(a) ALL NAILS USED		(b) ONE NAIL INSIDE NOT USED		(c) TWO NAILS INSIDE NOT USED	
x	y	x	y	x	y
4	1	4	2	4	3
5	$1\frac{1}{2}$	5	$2\frac{1}{2}$	5	$3\frac{1}{2}$
6	2	6	3	6	4
7	$2\frac{1}{2}$	7	$3\frac{1}{2}$	7	$4\frac{1}{2}$

Remember, we do have a sentence that expresses y in terms of x for part (a) of Table XI. Do you notice any relationship between parts (a) and (b), parts (a) and (c), parts (b) and (c)?

1. For any given value of x, the y-value in part (b) is 1 greater than that in part (a); in part (c), each y-value is 2 greater than the corresponding y-value in part (a).

2. The numeral representing the differences in the value of y is exactly the same as the number of unused nails inside. This seems to imply that if we add the number of nails inside to the right-hand side of our original sentence, we shall again arrive at a correct sentence.

Let us try it; but first we need to use two symbols to differentiate between the nails used on the perimeter and the nails on the inside that are not used. We have already designated x to represent the number of nails on the perimeter. We shall choose z to represent the number of nails inside the figure, and we shall continue to use y to designate the number of square units. From this and the idea expressed in item 2 above, our sentence takes on a new form, namely,

$$y = \frac{x-2}{2} + z.$$

This sentence can be translated, "Count the number of nails used for the perimeter of the figure, subtract 2 from this number, divide the difference by 2, and then add to the quotient the number of unused nails inside the figure. This will yield the number of square units in the figure." For example, consider the case for $x = 11$ and $z = 4$ (Fig. 25).

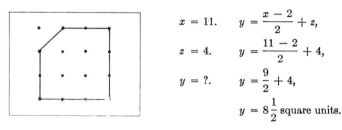

$$x = 11. \qquad y = \frac{x - 2}{2} + z,$$

$$z = 4. \qquad y = \frac{11 - 2}{2} + 4,$$

$$y = ?. \qquad y = \frac{9}{2} + 4,$$

$$y = 8\frac{1}{2} \text{ square units.}$$

FIGURE 25

Do you believe it? Count the squares.

If someone said that he made a figure using 36 nails on the perimeter and leaving 15 unused nails inside the figure, could you tell him the number of square units contained in his figure? In this case,

$$x = 36. \qquad y = \frac{x - 2}{2} + z,$$

$$z = 15. \qquad y = \frac{36 - 2}{2} + 15,$$

$$y = ? \qquad y = \frac{34}{2} + 15,$$

$$y = 32 \text{ square units.}$$

Discussion

This last problem has presented some unusual ideas. It illustrates how one often has to break a given problem into smaller parts. In addition, the formulas derived in the analysis certainly illustrate an unusual method for finding area. Since we arrived at our generalizations quite hastily, you may wish to study the problem further. You should convince yourself that the generalizations do indeed hold for all cases.

While we have looked at a number of examples, we have considered only a relatively small portion of possible problem situations. There are many puzzle books on the market today with some interesting and challenging problems. In particular we have not discussed the so-called logic problems that occur frequently in books and magazines. It is hoped, however, that you will continue to learn more about problem solving as you seek and solve more problems. You may find that many of the problems are appropriate for your own students. In solving problems, be sure to utilize the various techniques with which you are familiar and to seek new ones. This will help strengthen and increase your repertoire of techniques. Each problem you solve makes you a better problem solver.

SUMMARY

The purpose of this discussion on problem solving was to make you aware of what a true problem really is and to suggest some useful tools and techniques for solving problems in mathematics. Care was taken to suggest many important facets of problem solving:

1. The attempt was made to establish the proper *attitude* toward problem solving. Problems were related to puzzles and intellectual curiosities. In addition, you were warned of possible frustration, for there is no real problem if the solution is too easy, and there is a great deal more satisfaction in the solving of a difficult problem. We hope that the problems provided were on such a level, and at a slow enough pace, as to assure some satisfaction for every reader.

2. Inherent in each of the situations in the booklet was a concern for providing ways to extend the *understanding of the nature of the problem*. Such helpful aids as rereading the problem, restating the problem, or stating related problems were continually suggested or implied. You were asked questions to ensure that you understood the problems and that you knew what kind of mathematical situation was involved—computational, algebraic, or geometric.

3. In the problems presented in the section "Unusual Problem Solving" a major concern was to point out the need for *variety* and *flexibility* in your approach to problems. You were urged to make guesses. Experimentation, trial and error, estimation, and intuition were encouraged.

4. The need for visualizing, diagramming, organizing, and charting was illustrated in some of the examples. These are extremely important activities, and they enable a person to get started even though they often involve nothing more than a restatement of the problem in another form that is sometimes much easier to understand.

5. An attempt was made to encourage you to *ask questions* of yourself. This is an important part of problem solving. You should ask yourself such things as these: What do I know? What facts are given? What do I want to find out? What further information do I need? (Often problems occur with irrelevant information, and it is necessary to have the solver select the pertinent facts or conditions.)

6. Throughout the discussion in this booklet the emphasis was on the *method of solution*. Several methods were suggested for some of the prob-

lems, since this seemed more beneficial than just solving additional problems.

7. In the method of solution, it was important to be careful in the *analysis, organization,* and *communication* of the results. Solutions were written in a logical, orderly form.

8. It would be desirable to keep a supply of problems,[5] since it is necessary to provide adequate practice to develop and maintain skill in problem solving. Problem situations can be used to *discover* new mathematical concepts, principles, or relationships. They can be used as a basis for practice and as a substitute for excessive drill exercises.

9. You should *evaluate* your ability by considering your performance on the different aspects of problem solving.

It is hoped that these points suggest some ideas for your own teaching of problem solving.

[5] See, for example, Martin Gardner, *The Scientific American Book of Mathematical Puzzles and Diversions* (New York: Simon & Schuster, 1959).

For Further Reading

Among the various helpful references that deal with the subject here introduced are the following:

HENDERSON, KENNETH B., and PINGRY, ROBERT E. "Problem-Solving in Mathematics," in *The Learning of Mathematics: Its Theory and Practice,* Twenty-first Yearbook, The National Council of Teachers of Mathematics. Washington, D.C.: The Council, 1953. Available from The National Council of Teachers of Mathematics, 1201 16th St., N.W., Washington, D.C. 20036.

HILDEBRANDT, E. H. C. "Mathematical Modes of Thought," in *The Growth of Mathematical Ideas, Grades K-12,* Twenty-fourth Yearbook, The National Council of Teachers of Mathematics. Washington, D.C.: The Council, 1959. Available from The National Council of Teachers of Mathematics, 1201 16th St., N.W., Washington, D.C. 20036.

POLYA, G. *How to Solve It* (2d ed.). Garden City, N.Y.: Doubleday & Co., 1957. Pp. 253. Available from Doubleday & Co., Inc., 277 Park Ave., New York, N.Y. 10017.

WARD, MORGAN, and HARDGROVE, C. E. *Modern Elementary Mathematics.* Reading, Mass.: Addison-Wesley Publishing Co., 1964. Pp. 420. Available from Addison-Wesley Publishing Co., Inc., Reading, Mass. 01867.

ANSWERS TO EXERCISE SETS

(Answers given in each exercise set are suggested answers.)

Exercise Set 1

1. $\square + 7$

2. $\dfrac{x}{6}$, or $x \div 6$

3. $\dfrac{2}{5} \times n$

4. $\square - 17$

5. $y + (2 \times y)$

6. $3 \times n$

7. $\triangle \times (\triangle + 2)$

8. $\dfrac{x + 1}{x}$

9. $(5 \times \square) - (3 \times \square)$

10. $x - 8$

Exercise Set 2

1. a. $\square + 7$ **d.** $\dfrac{\square}{10}$, or $\square \div 10$

 b. $\square - 3$ **e.** $(4 \times \square) + (6 \times \square)$

 c. $5 \times \square$ **f.** $\dfrac{\square - 9}{\square}$, or $(\square - 9) \div \square$

2. a. $\triangle + 7$ **d.** $3 \times (\triangle - 2)$

 b. $\triangle - 2$ **e.** $(\triangle - 3) + (\triangle + 6)$

 c. $5 \times (\triangle + 7)$ **f.** $\dfrac{1}{2} \times \triangle$

3. a. 1×150 **c.** $x \times 150$

 b. 3×150 **d.** $(x + 3) \times 150$

Exercise Set 3

1. a. $(4 \times n) + 6 = 38.$ **d.** $(2 \times y) - (y + 2) = 26.$

 b. $\square - 17 = 18.$ **e.** $\dfrac{n - 3}{5} = 1.$

 c. $(3 \times \triangle) + (\triangle + 2) = 34.$ **f.** $4 \times (\square + 3) = 44.$

2. a. The sum of some number and 6 is equal to 37.

  b. One-sixth of some number is equal to 21.

  c. Three less than 2 times some number is equal to 19.

  d. Four more than some number divided by the number itself is equal to $1\frac{1}{2}$.

3. a. Let x represent the number of chicks Dorothy
  originally had: x
  She received as a present twice this number: $2 \times x$
  She now has 27 chicks. Since "$x + (2 \times x)$"
  and "27" name the same number, the
  sentence is: $x + (2 \times x) = 27.$

 Solution: $x = 9$. The truth set $\{9\}$ indicates that Dorothy originally had 9 baby chicks.

  b. Represent the number by: $\square$
  Twice the number $2 \times \square$
  added to $+$
  three more than the number $\square + 3$
  is equal to $=$
  24:          24
  The sentence is: $(2 \times \square) + (\square + 3) = 24.$

 Solution: $\square = 7$. The truth set $\{7\}$ indicates that 7 is the number in question.

  c. Represent the cost in cents of the
  baseball by: $\triangle$
  The bat costs 5 cents more than
   the baseball: $\triangle + 5$
  The total cost, in cents $\triangle + (\triangle + 5)$
  is equal to $=$
  105 cents.   105
  The sentence is: $\triangle + (\triangle + 5) = 105.$

 Solution: $\triangle = 50$. The truth set $\{50\}$ indicates that the baseball costs 50 cents. Since the bat costs 5 cents more than this, its cost in cents is $\triangle + 5 = 50 + 5 = 55.$

  d. Let $\square$ represent the number of coins
  Bernadine has: $\square$
  Alice has four more coins than
   Bernadine has: $\square + 4$

The value of Bernadine's dimes is: $10 \times \square$

The value of Alice's nickles is: $5 \times (\square + 4)$

The value of their coins together: $(10 \times \square) + [5 \times (\square + 4)]$

The sentence is: $(10 \times \square)$
$$+ [5 \times (\square + 4)] = 50.$$

Solution: The truth set $\{2\}$ indicates that Bernadine has 2 coins, so the number of coins Alice has is $\square + 4 = 2 + 4$, or 6.

e. Let z represent her daughter's age: z

Mary Jane is 20 years older than her daughter: $z + 20$

Twice Mary Jane's age now: $2 \times (z + 20)$

Her daughter's age in ten years: $z + 10$

Three times this: $3 \times (z + 10)$

The sentence is: $2 \times (z + 20)$
$$= 3 \times (z + 10).$$

Solution: $z = 10$. The daughter is ten years old, and Mary Jane is $z + 20 = 10 + 20$, or thirty years old.

f. Let $\triangle$ represent the number of
    pounds of 80-cent coffee needed: $\triangle$

Number of pounds of \$1.20 coffee: 5

Weight of total mixture: $\triangle + 5$

Value of 80-cent coffee, in cents: $80 \times \triangle$

Value of \$1.20 coffee, in cents: 120×5

Value of the mixture, in cents: $90 \times (\triangle + 5)$

The sentence is: $(80 \times \triangle) + (120 \times 5)$
$$= 90 \times (\triangle + 5).$$

Solution: $\triangle = 15$. The truth set $\{15\}$ indicates that 15 pounds of the 80-cent coffee must be mixed with every 5 pounds of the \$1.20 coffee in order to make a mixture of 90-cent coffee.

Exercise Set 4

1. a. $\square > 13$.

    b. $\triangle < 7$.

    c. $x + 3 > 32$.

    d. $6 \times n \leq 83$.

    e. $y + 4 > 3 \times y$.

2. a. The sum of some number and 8 is greater than 32.

    b. Two times a number plus 3 is less than or equal to 19.

    c. Four less than some number is greater than or equal to 12.

    d. The sum of some number and 8 is less than twice the same number.

3. a. Let x represent some number: x
The sum of some number and eight $x + 8$
is greater than $>$
thirty-two.   32
The sentence is: $x + 8 > 32.$

Solution: $x > 24$. The solution set is $\{25, 26, 27, \cdots\}$.

b. Let y represent some number: y
Some number y
is less than or equal to $\leq$
four.   4
The sentence is: $y \leq 4.$

Solution: The solution set is $\{1, 2, 3, 4\}$.

Exercise Set 5

1. $n = 4$, $\dfrac{1}{2^n} = \dfrac{1}{16}$, $S = \dfrac{1}{2} + \dfrac{1}{4} + \dfrac{1}{8} + \dfrac{1}{16} = \dfrac{15}{16}.$

2.

n (Number of Rational Numbers Used)	S (Sum of the Rational Numbers)
1	$\dfrac{1}{2}$
2	$\dfrac{3}{4}$
3	$\dfrac{7}{8}$
4	$\dfrac{15}{16}$

The denominator of each sum is the number 2 raised to its respective counting-number power, n. For example:

when $n = 1$, the denominator of S is $2^1 = 2$;
when $n = 2$, the denominator of S is $2^2 = 4$;
when $n = 3$, the denominator of S is $2^3 = 8$.

The numerator of each sum is one less than the denominator. Therefore, if we designate the denominator as 2^n, we can name the numerator $2^n - 1$, yielding a formula for the sum of the first n terms: $S = \frac{2^n-1}{2^n}$.

3. For $n = 7$, $S = \dfrac{2^7 - 1}{2^7} = \dfrac{128 - 1}{128}$,   or $\dfrac{127}{128}.$

Exercise Set 6

1. 9

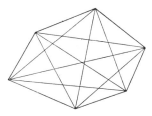

6 sides, 9 diagonals

2. a. 0   **b.** 5

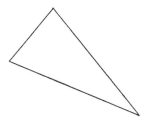   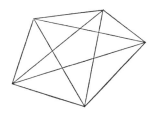

3 sides, 0 diagonals   5 sides, 5 diagonals

3. To seek a formula expressing the sum for an n-sided convex polygon, make a table and try to reason from the figures.

n (Number of Sides)	d (Number of Diagonals)
3	0
4	2
5	5
6	9

The formula is $d = \frac{n \times (n-3)}{2}$.

BOOKLET NUMBER EIGHTEEN:

SYMMETRY, CONGRUENCE, AND SIMILARITY

INTRODUCTION

In Booklet No. 14: *Informal Geometry* we gave an elementary introduction to some of the basic ideas in geometry. Starting with a discussion of fundamental notions about geometric lines, half-lines, rays, segments, planes, and angles, we went on to investigate some of the properties of various familiar plane and solid figures—figures with which even very young children have contact in their daily lives.

The present booklet is aimed at reinforcing and extending these notions through an intuitive description of the geometric relationships of symmetry, congruence, and similarity. Both the text and the exercise sets include numerous examples of paper-folding exercises and other do-it-yourself activities that will help you to visualize these relationships clearly. Since you will be asked to participate in a great deal of tracing and folding, you will need at hand several sheets of thin paper, a pencil, and some scissors.

SYMMETRY

Lines of Symmetry

In this section we are going to explore a geometric concept known as *symmetry*. Trace the closed region pictured in Figure 1, cut out the tracing, and then fold it on the broken line so that the bottom segment bends back on itself. You should find that the two polygonal regions on either side of the line fit together exactly. The dotted line is called a *line of symmetry*.

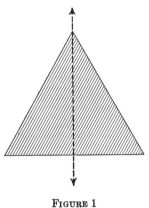

Follow the same procedure for each of the closed regions pictured in Figure 2. In which of the diagrams do the broken lines indicate lines of symmetry? You should have found that the broken lines in (b) and (d)

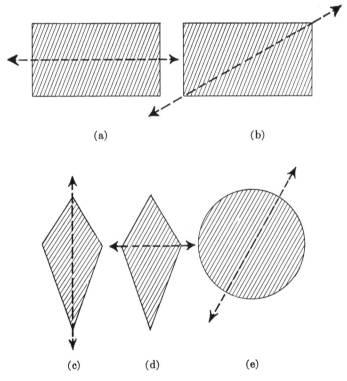

FIGURE 2

are not lines of symmetry, since in each case the two regions on either side do not coincide exactly when folded together along the line.

Before we ask you to produce lines of symmetry for various figures, let us give you a little more practice in recognizing these lines. In Figure 3, which of the broken lines are lines of symmetry? The lines have been numbered, since you will be testing more than one line with some of the

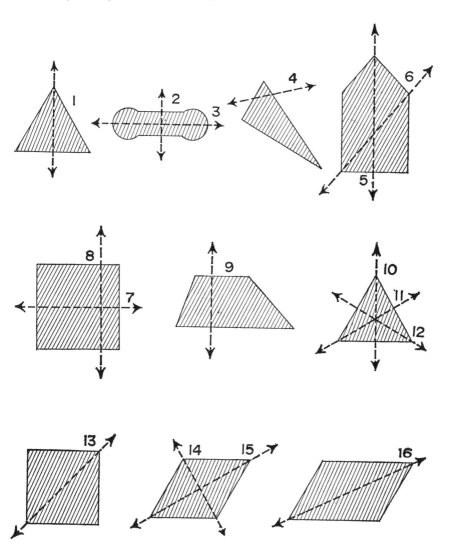

FIGURE 3

closed regions. You should be able to visualize the answer in most cases without actually tracing the closed region and folding it about the given line to see how the two sides fit.

The following number lines represent lines of symmetry: 1, 2, 3, 5, 7, 10, 11, 12, 13, 14, 15. The remaining lines are not lines of symmetry.

If you look around, you will probably see many lines of symmetry— perhaps in the pattern of the wallpaper, perhaps in the placement of doors and windows on the wall of a room, or perhaps on a picture of a human face with very regular features. (See Fig. 4.)

FIGURE 4

The notion of a line of symmetry suggests a shortcut method for making cutouts of symmetrical figures. For example, to cut out a heart-shaped figure, you might fold a sheet of paper, as indicated in Figure 5, and draw half of a heart so that the line of symmetry of the heart would coincide

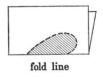

fold line

FIGURE 5

with the fold line of the paper. Then when you cut through the doubled sheet along the dotted outline and unfold it, the result will be a "whole-hearted" success!

Which of the objects pictured in Figure 6 could you make by a similar method? On a copy of each object, use shading to indicate the portion that you would actually draw. Also, dot in the line of symmetry that you

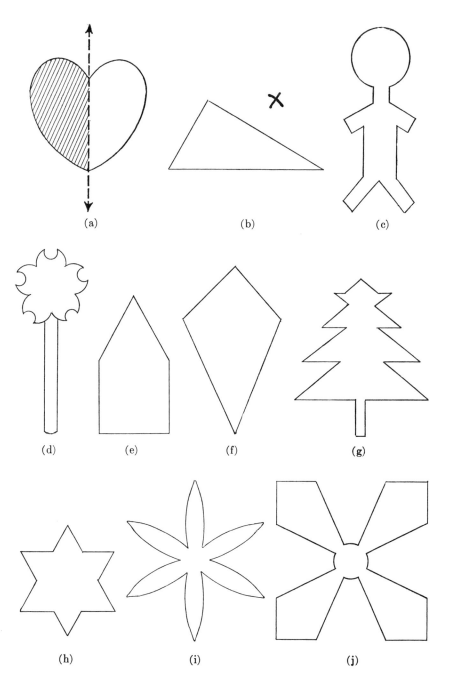

(a) (b) (c)

(d) (e) (f) (g)

(h) (i) (j)

FIGURE 6 [*cont. next page*]

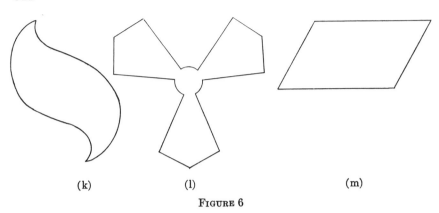

(k)   (l)   (m)

FIGURE 6

would employ as the fold line of the paper. If you cannot find such a line of symmetry, put an ✗ next to the picture. The first two, (a) and (b), have been done for you. Now place the "line of symmetry" against the fold line of another sheet of paper and, using the shaded portion as a pattern, cut through the doubled sheet. Did you get any surprises? Place your finished product on top of the corresponding picture in Figure 6. They should match. One possible solution is given in Figure 7.

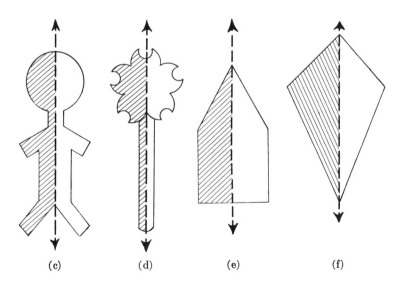

(c)   (d)   (e)   (f)

FIGURE 7 [cont. next page]

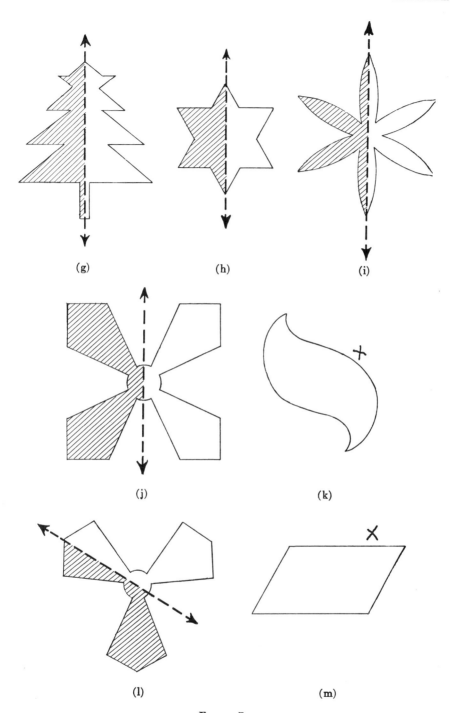

(g)   (h)   (i)

(j)   (k)

(l)   (m)

FIGURE 7

You can use symmetry to find the midpoint of a given segment and the bisector of a given angle. Let us discuss the case of the segment first. Trace the segment $\overline{AB}$, shown in Figure 8. Fold the paper so that points A and B coincide. In Figure 9 the point C, where the fold line $\overleftrightarrow{DE}$ intersects the segment $\overline{AB}$, is the *midpoint* of $\overline{AB}$. That is, C separates $\overline{AB}$ into two segments, $\overline{AC}$ and $\overline{CB}$, that are exact replicas of each other (Fig. 10).

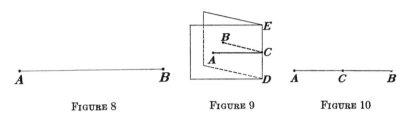

FIGURE 8   FIGURE 9   FIGURE 10

In analogous fashion, we can trace the angle $\angle CAB$ in Figure 11 and fold the paper in such a way that $\overrightarrow{AC}$ and $\overrightarrow{AB}$ coincide. Then the line of the fold—call it $\overleftrightarrow{AD}$—is actually a line of symmetry of $\angle CAB$, which we call the *bisector* of $\angle CAB$. The two angles, $\angle CAD$ and $\angle DAB$, in Figure 11 are exact replicas of each other.

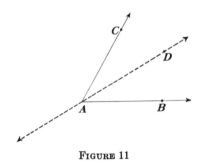

FIGURE 11

After one more paragraph on symmetry we shall introduce the word that is used in geometry to describe figures that are exact replicas of each other and then shall expand on the general notion of this important geometric concept.

Center of Symmetry

Let us look again at segment $\overline{AB}$ and its midpoint C, shown in Figure 10. You can see intuitively that for every point on $\overline{AB}$ there is another

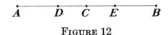

FIGURE 12

point on $\overline{AB}$ such that C bisects the segment joining the two points. Figure 12 shows a pair of such points, D and E. The midpoint C is accordingly called a *center of symmetry* for $\overline{AB}$ because $\overline{AB}$ is symmetrical with respect to C. A geometric figure is symmetrical with respect to a point O if and only if for each point A on the figure there is some point B on the

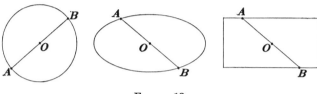

FIGURE 13

figure such that O bisects (is the midpoint of) $\overline{AB}$. The point O is a center of symmetry for each of the drawings in Figure 13.

Exercise Set 1

1. Draw dashed lines to show all the lines of symmetry for tracings of each closed region shown below. If a closed region has no line of symmetry, place an $\times$ next to it.

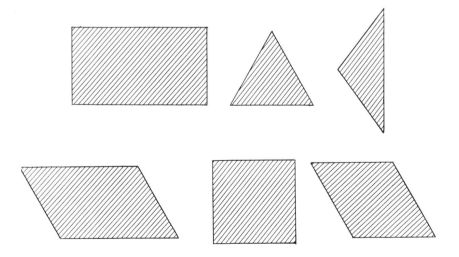

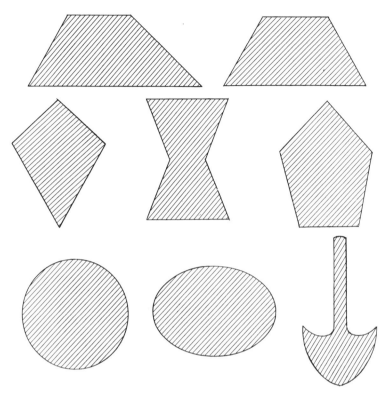

2. So far, we have considered the possible lines of symmetry only for various *regions*. Generalize our work on lines of symmetry by drawing all the lines of symmetry on copies of the following *configurations*.

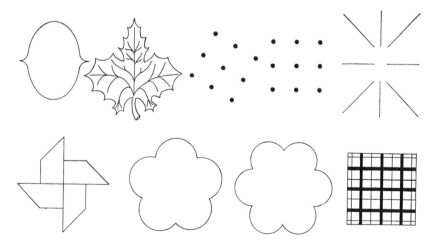

3. Complete a tracing of each figure shown below so that it is symmetric about *both* of the given dashed lines.

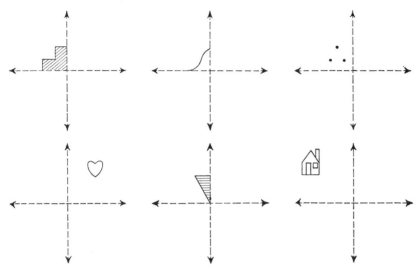

4. Each of the following objects could be cut from a piece of paper that has been folded twice. On a tracing of the outline make two dashed lines to indicate the two fold lines you might use; assuming the paper has been folded, shade the portion of the picture that you would actually have to draw on the paper to cut around.

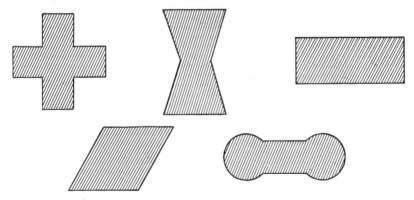

5. In each quadrilateral below, is the *O* a point of central symmetry?

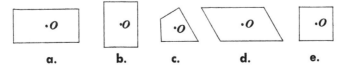

    a.   **b.**   **c.**   **d.**   **e.**

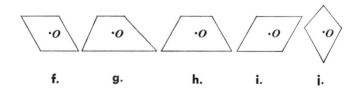

f.   **g.**   **h.**   **i.**   **j.**

6. Draw a figure that has infinitely many lines of symmetry.

CONGRUENCE

The Notion of Congruence

Any two objects that are exact replicas of each other are said to be *congruent.* Physically, two plane geometric figures can be tested for con-

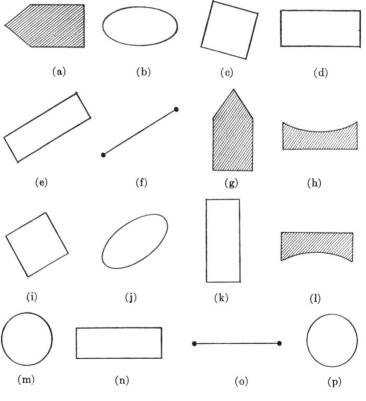

FIGURE 14

gruence by seeing if they can be fitted together so that they exactly coincide. We can describe this situation intuitively by stating that congruent figures have the same size and shape. See if you can match pairs of congruent figures in Figure 14.

The congruent pairs are as follows: (a) and (g), (b) and (j), (c) and (i), (d) and (k), (e) and (n), (f) and (o), (h) and (l), (m) and (p).

The notion of congruence is familiar to everyone. The pages of this booklet are congruent to each other, as are all of the lowercase c's on this page. Assembly lines in factories are constantly turning out "congruent" objects, which must meet certain specifications as to size and shape. Perhaps you can give some other examples.

Congruent Segments

The simplest geometric figure with which to illustrate the notion of congruence is a line segment. We foreshadowed this discussion at the end of the previous section, where we defined the midpoint, C, of $\overline{AB}$ to be the point that separates the segment into two segments, $\overline{AC}$ and $\overline{CB}$, that are exact replicas of each other. This rather cumbersome definition of a midpoint can be stated much more concisely in terms of congruence:

The midpoint of a segment is the point that separates the segment into two congruent segments.

If C is the midpoint of $\overline{AB}$, then $\overline{AC}$ is congruent to $\overline{CB}$. We can use the symbol $\cong$ and express this relationship as $\overline{AC} \cong \overline{CB}$ (read "segment AC is congruent to segment CB"). Of course, two line segments need not be part of the same line in order to be congruent.

A useful means of determining whether or not two segments are congruent is to use a compass. If the points of the compass are set at the end points of the first segment and if on being transferred to the second segment they also fall exactly at the end points of the second segment, then the two segments are congruent. The compass is also used in a similar manner to *construct* a segment congruent to a given segment.

Which of the five segments in Figure 15 are congruent? Whether you

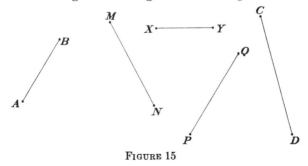

FIGURE 15

TOPICS IN MATHEMATICS

use tracing paper or a compass, you will find that there is only one pair of congruent segments: $\overline{MN} \cong \overline{PQ}$.

Before proceeding further, we should distinguish between the use of the symbol $=$ and the symbol $\cong$ in geometry. In Figure 16 we see that $\overline{AB}$ and $\overline{BA}$ are obviously equal because they name the *same* segment.

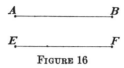

FIGURE 16

We express this as $\overline{AB} = \overline{BA}$. It is *not* correct, however, to say that "$\overline{AB} = \overline{EF}$," because $\overline{AB}$ and $\overline{EF}$ name two *different* segments. The way to express the fact that $\overline{AB}$ and $\overline{EF}$ are exact replicas of each other is to say that $\overline{AB} \cong \overline{EF}$; that is, segment AB is congruent to segment EF. Of course, any segment is an exact replica of itself and therefore is congruent to itself as well as being equal to itself. Hence, in Figure 16 both of the following are true:

$$\overline{AB} = \overline{BA} \quad \text{and} \quad \overline{AB} \cong \overline{BA}.$$

Congruent Angles

In Figure 17, if $\overleftrightarrow{AD}$ bisects $\angle CAB$, we can state simply that $\angle CAD \cong \angle DAB$. The bisector of an angle and the two sides of the angle form two

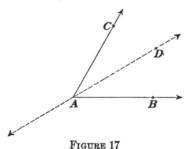

FIGURE 17

new congruent angles. We can consider either the line $\overleftrightarrow{AD}$ or the ray $\overrightarrow{AD}$ as the bisector of $\angle CAB$, although only the ray $\overrightarrow{AD}$ is actually a side of $\angle CAD$ and of $\angle DAB$.

Next let us discuss the congruence relation for any two angles. Suppose that we are given two angles, say $\angle PQR$ and $\angle XYZ$ in Figure 18. To see if $\angle PQR$ is congruent to $\angle XYZ$, trace $\angle PQR$ and lay the tracing, $\angle P'Q'R'$, on $\angle XYZ$ so that vertex Q' coincides with vertex Y and $\overrightarrow{Q'R'}$ coincides with $\overrightarrow{YZ}$.

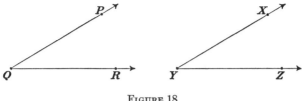

FIGURE 18

Now if $\overrightarrow{Q'P'}$ coincides with $\overrightarrow{YX}$, as indicated in Figure 19, the two angles are exact replicas of each other, and we write " $\angle PQR \cong \angle XYZ$."

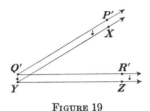

FIGURE 19

In a more formal treatment of geometry the congruence of two angles is usually defined in terms of their *measure*. That is, two angles are congruent if and only if they have the same measure.

Just as every line is an exact replica of every other line, so is every ray congruent to every other ray. In Figure 20(a), however, the two rays

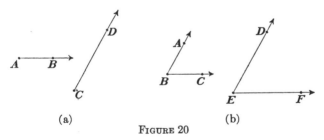

(a)   (b)

FIGURE 20

$\overrightarrow{AB}$ and $\overrightarrow{CD}$ may not *appear* to be congruent because of the way they were drawn. Likewise, in Figure 20(b) the two congruent angles, $\angle ABC$ and $\angle DEF$, may give the illusion of not being exact replicas. In general, it is helpful to draw congruent figures in such a way as to make them appear as true replicas.

An important kind of angle frequently mentioned in the study of geometry is a right angle. A simple way to construct a right angle is to draw a line $\overleftrightarrow{AB}$ on a piece of transparent paper and then fold the paper so that $\overleftrightarrow{AB}$ is doubled back on itself.

Now unfold the paper and draw a broken line, $\overleftrightarrow{CD}$, along the line of
the fold. You will then have four congruent angles with a common vertex
at E, the point of intersection of $\overleftrightarrow{AB}$ and $\overleftrightarrow{CD}$ (Fig. 21). We write this fact
as $\angle AEC \cong \angle CFB \cong \angle BED \cong \angle DEA$. Each of these angles is a
right angle. The symbol $\daleth$ at the vertex of one of them, $\angle CEB$, is often
used in a drawing to indicate a right angle.

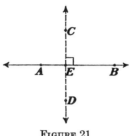

FIGURE 21

In Figure 21 the line $\overleftrightarrow{CD}$ is said to be *perpendicular* to $\overleftrightarrow{AB}$. The
symbol $\perp$ denotes the notion of perpendicular, so we write $\overleftrightarrow{CD} \perp \overleftrightarrow{AB}$.
To generalize, two intersecting lines are perpendicular if and only if the
four angles formed at their point of intersection are right angles. Two
rays, two segments, or a segment and a ray are perpendicular to each
other if the two lines of which they are a part are perpendicular to each
other.

To produce a line that is perpendicular to a given line and that passes
through a given point not on the given line, you could proceed as follows:
Draw a line $\overleftrightarrow{AB}$ and a point C not on $\overleftrightarrow{AB}$, as in Figure 22(a). Now fold
the paper so that C lies on the fold line and $\overleftrightarrow{AB}$ bends back on itself, as

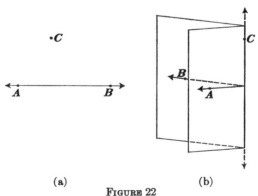

(a)   (b)

FIGURE 22

shown in Figure 22(b). When you unfold the paper, the fold line through C will be perpendicular to $\overset{\leftrightarrow}{AB}$.

Congruence Versus Symmetry

The notion of symmetry is closely related to that of congruence, but congruence does not depend at all on symmetry. That is, two figures having the same size and shape are congruent regardless of whether they

FIGURE 23

are located so as to be symmetric with respect to some line or point. For example, the triangles in Figure 23 are congruent simply because they are exact replicas of each other.

The following example illustrates further how congruence does not depend on symmetry. If you trace the rectangle pictured in Figure 24

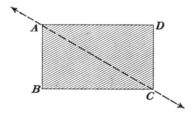

FIGURE 24

and fold it on the broken diagonal line, $\overset{\leftrightarrow}{AC}$, you will find that the two triangular regions do not fit exactly on each other. In fact, the result would look like the diagram in Figure 25, which shows clearly that $\overset{\leftrightarrow}{AC}$ is not a line of symmetry. Yet, the two triangular regions bounded by triangles $\triangle ABC$ and $\triangle CDA$, respectively, are congruent. We can place

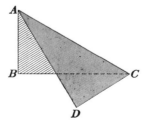

FIGURE 25

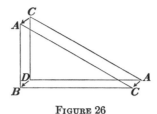

FIGURE 26

$\triangle CDA$ on $\triangle ABC$ so that they will fit exactly: we only need to rotate $\triangle CDA$ in a clockwise direction until vertex D coincides with vertex B and vertex C of $\triangle CDA$ coincides with vertex A of $\triangle ABC$, as indicated in Figure 26. This pairing of vertices of $\triangle ABC$ and $\triangle CDA$ establishes a *one-to-one correspondence* between pairs of congruent angles and of congruent sides. Thus, in Figure 26 $\angle ABC \cong \angle CDA$, $\angle BCA \cong \angle DAC$, and $\angle CAB \cong \angle ACD$. Likewise, corresponding sides are congruent, as follows: $\overline{AB} \cong \overline{CD}$, $\overline{BC} \cong \overline{DA}$, and $\overline{CA} \cong \overline{AC}$. To generalize, two triangles are congruent if, for some pairing of their vertices, corresponding parts (angles and sides) are congruent.

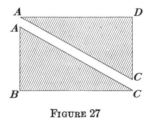

FIGURE 27

The original region can be considered as the union of two congruent triangular regions (Fig. 27).

Exercise Set 2

1. Give examples of congruent objects that you might encounter in a supermarket, in an automobile factory, on a farm, or in a kitchen.

2. Draw a horizontal line ℓ and draw point A not on line ℓ. First find the line that contains A and is parallel to line ℓ by making a vertical fold in the paper so that line ℓ is folded back on itself and so that A lies on the fold line; then make a horizontal fold so that the first fold line is folded back on itself and so that A is on the second fold line. The second fold line should then be parallel to line ℓ. Note that the first fold line, say m, is perpendicular to the given line ℓ and that the second fold line, say n, is perpendicular to the first fold line, m, as pictured below. Observe further that the parallel lines n and ℓ are both perpendicular

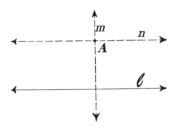

to line *m*. Does it appear that if two lines in a plane are both perpendicular to the same line, then they are parallel to each other?

3. Trace the figure below:

Find the midpoint of the segment $\overline{AB}$ by paper folding.

a. If the midpoint is *C* and if *D* is any other point on the fold line, what is the relationship between the two lines $\overleftrightarrow{AB}$ and $\overleftrightarrow{CD}$?

b. What kind of an angle is $\angle ACD$?

c. Name another right angle formed by these lines. (The line $\overleftrightarrow{CD}$ is called the perpendicular bisector of the segment $\overline{AB}$.)

4. Given any triangle, such as the one at the right, $\triangle ABC$, we can construct a triangle congruent to it in the following way:

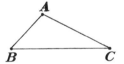

(a) Draw a line on your paper. Mark any point *B'* on the line:

(b) Set the two pointers of a compass so that they fall on *B* and *C* and mark a segment $\overline{B'C'}$ on your line so that $\overline{B'C'} \cong \overline{BC}$:

(c) Reset the two pointers of your compass so that they fall on *A* and *B*. With *B'* as center, draw a circle:

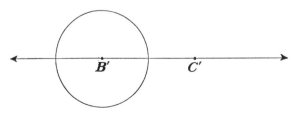

(d) Again reset the two pointers of your compass so that they fall on A and C. With C' as center draw a circle. These two circles will intersect at two points. Label either one of these points A'. Draw segments $\overline{A'B'}$ and $\overline{A'C'}$. Then $\triangle A'B'C' \cong \triangle ABC$.

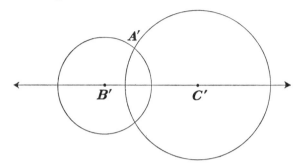

a. Name the three pairs of sides that are congruent.

b. Name the three pairs of angles that are congruent.

5. Construct a triangle congruent to $\triangle DEF$.

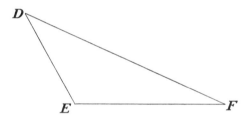

CLASSIFICATION OF PLANE FIGURES

Classification of Triangles

Now that we have defined congruence for segments and angles, we can use this notion in classifying triangles, as follows:

(a) If three sides of a triangle are congruent, the triangle is called *equilateral* (from the Latin word for "equal sides").

(b) If two sides of a triangle are congruent, the triangle is called *isosceles* (from the Greek word for "equal legs").

(c) If no side of a triangle is congruent to any other side, the triangle is called *scalene* (from the Greek word for "unequal" or "uneven").

(d) If three angles of a triangle are congruent, the triangle is an *equiangular* one.

(e) If a triangle has two congruent sides and a right angle in it, the triangle is called an *isosceles right triangle*.

It can be shown that if a triangle is isosceles, then the two angles opposite the congruent sides are congruent. Conversely, if a triangle has two congruent angles, then the two sides opposite those angles are congruent, and the triangle is isosceles. From this it easily follows that if a triangle is equilateral, it must be equiangular, and conversely. It can also be shown that if a triangle is scalene, then it has no congruent angles, and conversely.

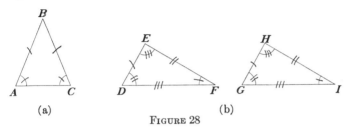

(a)   (b)

FIGURE 28

In drawing a geometric figure, it is customary to indicate congruent parts with similar markings. This is also a helpful device when comparing the corresponding parts of two congruent figures. For example, in Figure 28(a) the congruent sides of isosceles triangle ABC are indicated by a single slash on each. Likewise, the congruent angles opposite these sides have a single slash through each arc symbol. In Figure 28(b), $\overline{DE}$ and $\overline{GH}$ have like markings—a single slash—to indicate that these are corresponding congruent sides in the two congruent triangles DEF and GHI. The double slashes on $\overline{EF}$ and $\overline{HI}$ indicate that $\overline{EF} \cong \overline{HI}$. The triple-slashed arcs indicate that $\angle DEF \cong \angle GHI$.

The notion of a line of symmetry furnishes an interesting method for classifying triangular boundaries of closed regions. For example, if a triangular region has three lines of symmetry, its boundary is an equilateral triangle. In fact, establishing that there are two lines of symmetry is sufficient to ensure that there are actually three. In Figure 29(a),

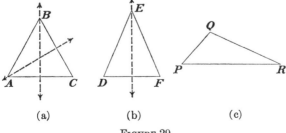

(a)   (b)   (c)

FIGURE 29

when $\triangle ABC$ is folded on the dashed vertical line of symmetry, $\overline{AB}$ coincides exactly with $\overline{BC}$; when $\triangle ABC$ is folded on the other dashed line of symmetry, $\overline{AB}$ coincides with $\overline{AC}$. Thus it is intuitively clear that $\overline{AC}$ and $\overline{BC}$ can be made to coincide, since $\overline{AB}$ can be made to coincide exactly with each of them. In Figure 29(b) there is only one line of symmetry, which means that only $\overline{DE} \cong \overline{EF}$ and $\triangle DEF$ is isosceles. In Figure 29(c) there is no line of symmetry, so $\triangle PQR$ is scalene.

Exercise Set 3

1. Using your compass, construct an equilateral triangle XYZ so that each of its sides is congruent to $\overline{AB}$.

A B

2. **a.** Can an equilateral triangle have a right angle?
   b. Can an isosceles triangle have a right angle?
   c. Can a triangle have more than one right angle?

3. The three lines of symmetry of the closed region bounded by the equilateral triangle XYZ meet at a point. Cut a tracing of this triangular

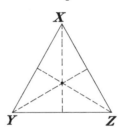

region out of a piece of stiff cardboard and try to balance it at that point on the tip of a compass leg. Try balancing it on any other point of the closed region. What do you observe?

4. Trace the equilateral triangle XYZ from exercise 3. By paper folding, find the midpoint, W, of $\overline{YZ}$.
   a. Does the fold line pass through point X?
   b. Is $\overleftrightarrow{XW}$ the same line as the fold line?
   c. Is $\overleftrightarrow{XW}$ the perpendicular bisector of YZ?
   d. Does $\overleftrightarrow{XW}$ bisect $\angle YXZ$?

5. By paper folding, find the midpoint, W, of $\overline{YZ}$ of the scalene triangle, $\triangle XYZ$, given below and then answer for this triangle the questions in exercise 4a–d.

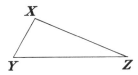

6. a. Draw a picture of a closed region that has two lines of symmetry.

b. Draw a picture of a closed region that has four lines of symmetry.

Classification of Polygons

Not only triangles but many other polygons can be classified according to certain properties of their sides and angles. In Booklet 14: *Informal Geometry* we named polygons according to the number of their sides— triangles, three; quadrilaterals, four; pentagons, five; hexagons, six; heptagons, seven; and octagons, eight. We also classified them as convex or concave.

Another property very often considered in describing a polygon is that of regularity.

A polygon is regular if and only if all of its sides are congruent and all of its angles are congruent.

An equilateral triangle is an example of a regular polygon, since it has three congruent sides and three congruent angles.

We mentioned in the preceding section that if a triangle has all of its sides congruent, then it follows that all of its angles are also congruent. This is not the case for polygons in general. For example, Figure 30 shows

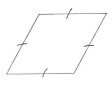

FIGURE 30

a convex polygon called a *rhombus*, in which the four sides are congruent but the four angles need not be. Conversely, we have the familiar polygon known as a *rectangle* (Fig. 31), in which the four angles are congruent but

FIGURE 31

the four sides need not be. Hence neither of these polygons has to be regular.

Some examples of regular polygons are pictured in Figure 32, with the common name given below each one. As indicated in Figure 32, the

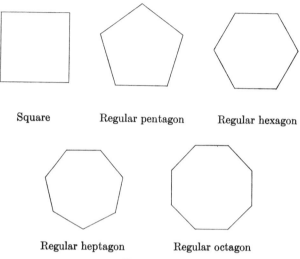

Square   Regular pentagon   Regular hexagon

Regular heptagon   Regular octagon

FIGURE 32

common name for a regular quadrilateral is a square. In the next section we shall classify quadrilaterals in general, according to certain properties of their sides and angles, just as we did for triangles in the preceding section.

Exercise Set 4

1. Draw all the lines of symmetry for each of the closed regions bounded by the regular polygons pictured in Figure 32. Can you suggest a rule that relates the number of lines of symmetry with the number of sides of a regular polygon?

2. Is it possible for a polygon to have more lines of symmetry than it has sides?

3. It is true that all regular polygons are convex. Show that the converse statement, "All convex polygons are regular," is false, by drawing a convex polygon whose sides (or angles) are not all congruent.

4. Is it possible for a hexagon to have—

   a. Exactly two lines of symmetry?

   b. Exactly four lines of symmetry?

   c. Exactly six lines of symmetry?

Classification of Quadrilaterals

As we mentioned earlier, a quadrilateral is a polygon that is the union of four segments. These four segments determine four angles. For example, in Figure 33, quadrilateral $ABCD$ (sometimes denoted by the symbol $\square \, ABCD^1$) determines four angles: $\angle ABC$, $\angle BCD$, $\angle CDA$, and $\angle DAB$.

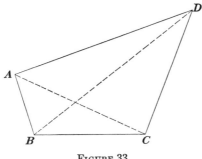

FIGURE 33

The points A, B, C, and D are called *vertices* of the quadrilateral; they are also the vertices of the four angles. The segments $\overline{AB}$, $\overline{BC}$, $\overline{CD}$, and $\overline{AD}$ are called *sides* of the quadrilateral. Any two sides (segments) that do not have a common end point (vertex) are said to be *opposite*; any two sides that do intersect at a vertex are called *adjacent* sides. Similarly, any two angles that do not have a side in common are said to be *opposite* angles, for example: $\angle DAB$ and $\angle BCD$, $\angle ABC$ and $\angle CDA$. Any two angles that do have a common side are called adjacent angles, such as $\angle DAB$ and $\angle ABC$, $\angle ABC$ and $\angle BCD$. The dashed segments, AC and BD, are called the *diagonals* of the quadrilateral. A diagonal of a polygon is a segment that joins the vertices of two nonadjacent angles.

Quadrilaterals can be classified according to notions of parallelism and congruency of their opposite sides and angles:

(a) *Scalene quadrilateral:* A quadrilateral in which none of the sides are congruent or parallel

(b) *Kite:* A quadrilateral in which two pairs of adjacent sides are congruent

(c) *Trapezoid:* A quadrilateral in which exactly[2] one pair of opposite sides are parallel

(d) *Isosceles trapezoid:* A trapezoid whose nonparallel sides are congruent

---

[1] We should note that the "$\square$" in the notation $\square$ABCD does not mean that the quadrilateral is a square, any more than the "$\triangle$" in the notation $\triangle$XYZ means that the triangle is equilateral; $\square$ABCD and $\triangle$XYZ denote *any* quadrilateral and triangle, respectively, until we ascribe further properties.

[2] In some definitions, "exactly" is replaced here with "at least."

(e) *Parallelogram:* A quadrilateral in which both pairs of opposite sides are parallel

(f) *Rhombus:* A parallelogram with four congruent sides

(g) *Rectangle:* A parallelogram with four congruent angles

(h) *Square:* A rectangle with four congruent sides

An example of each type of quadrilateral is pictured in Figure 34.

Each quadrilateral pictured in Figure 34 has been labeled with the little

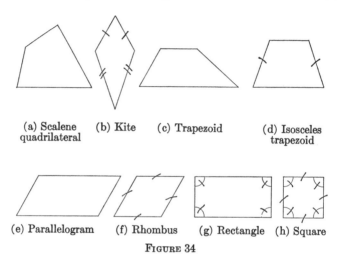

(a) Scalene   (b) Kite   (c) Trapezoid   (d) Isosceles
quadrilateral   trapezoid

(e) Parallelogram   (f) Rhombus   (g) Rectangle   (h) Square

Figure 34

markings that show congruent sides and angles. Some additional properties beyond those necessary for classification should be mentioned:

In a kite, the opposite angles are congruent.

In an isosceles trapezoid, two pairs of adjacent angles are congruent

In a parallelogram, both pairs of opposite sides are congruent; and also both pairs of opposite angles are congruent.

In a rectangle, all the angles are right angles.

Now let us go back to the quadrilateral regions pictured in Figure 34(a)–(h). Trace each closed region and draw all the lines of symmetry for each. Your drawings should look like those in Figure 35. In each case the number of lines of symmetry is indicated under the picture of the closed region. Do you notice any relationship between the congruent parts and the lines of symmetry?

We can summarize the results for the various types of quadrilaterals by observing some interesting patterns. You will recall that when a figure is folded along a line of symmetry, the two parts will exactly fit. Hence, in

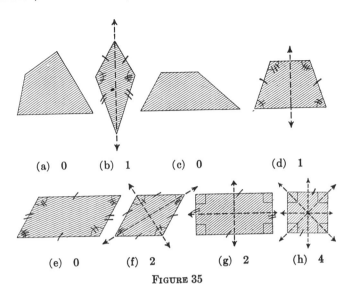

(a) 0   (b) 1   (c) 0   (d) 1

(e) 0   (f) 2   (g) 2   (h) 4

FIGURE 35

order for a quadrilateral region to have a line of symmetry, its boundary must have at least one of the following properties:

1. Two pairs of adjacent sides and the included angles are congruent as in Figure 35(b), (f), (h).
2. Two pairs of adjacent angles and the included sides are congruent as in Figure 35(d), (g), (h).

For property 1 the line of symmetry passes through vertices; for property 2 the line of symmetry passes through the midpoints of opposite sides. We should note that in either case the line of symmetry places the members of a pair of congruent parts on opposite half-planes, so that when the figure is folded on that line, these congruent members will coincide.

Let us refer again to Figure 35. It follows that since (a) and (c) have no congruent sides or angles, there are no lines of symmetry. The closed region in (e) bounded by a parallelogram also has no lines of symmetry since no adjacent sides or angles are congruent.

Exercise Set 5

1.

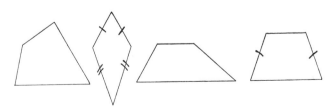

a. Name (state a classification of) each quadrilateral pictured above.

b. Make a tracing and draw all the lines of symmetry for each quadrilateral.

c. Which of the shapes have a line of symmetry that goes through a vertex (diagonal symmetry)?

d. Which of the shapes have a line of symmetry that goes through the midpoints of a pair of opposite sides (mediator symmetry)?

2. Which of the quadrilaterals in exercise 1 have a point of central symmetry?

3.

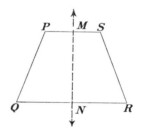

Quadrilateral $PQRS$ has only one mediator symmetry, as shown.

a. If you fold along the line of symmetry, what point falls on point S? On point R?

b. Is $\overline{PQ} \cong \overline{SR}$? Can you tell without measuring?

c. What segment is congruent to $\overline{PM}$? To $\overline{NR}$?

d. Does this quadrilateral have a point of central symmetry?

e. Name (state a classification of) the quadrilateral $PQRS$.

4.

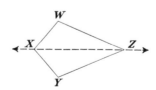

Quadrilateral $XYZW$ has only the one diagonal symmetry, as shown.

a. If you fold along the line of symmetry, what point falls on point W?

b. Is $\triangle XYZ \cong \triangle XWZ$? Can you tell without measuring?
c. What segment is congruent to $\overline{XY}$? To $\overline{WZ}$?
d. Does this quadrilateral have a point of central symmetry?
e. Name (state a classification of) the quadrilateral $XYZW$.

Circles

In Booklet 14: *Informal Geometry* we discussed and defined "simple closed curve." A type of simple closed curve deserving special attention is the circle. As in Booklet 14, we define a circle as follows:

A circle is a simple closed curve in a plane, having a unique point—say P—in its interiors such that if A and B are any two points on the curve, then $\overline{PA} \cong \overline{PB}$.

The point P is called the center of the circle. Note that a circle is symmetrical with respect to its center. You will recall that a simple closed curve separates the plane into three disjoint sets: the curve itself, its interior, and its exterior. Thus you can see that the center of a circle is not a point of the circle, since it lies in the interior.

A line segment with one end point at the center and the other end point on the circle is called a *radius* of the circle. In Figure 36, $\overline{PA}$, $\overline{PB}$, $\overline{PC}$, and $\overline{PD}$ are all radii (plural of radius) of the circle. From the definition of a circle and of a radius, it follows that all radii of a circle are necessarily congruent; that is, $\overline{PA} \cong \overline{PB} \cong \overline{PC} \cong \overline{PD}$, and so on.

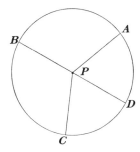

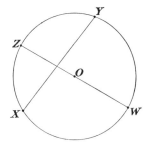

FIGURE 36   FIGURE 37

A *diameter* of a circle is a line segment having end points on the circle and containing the center of the circle. In Figure 36, $\overline{BD}$ is a diameter of the circle. A *chord* of a circle is any line segment whose end points lie on the circle. In Figure 37, $\overline{XY}$ and $\overline{ZW}$ are both chords of the circle with center O. $\overline{ZW}$ is a special kind of chord, namely, a diameter.

Any two points on a circle separate the circle into two *arcs*. For example, points X and Y in Figure 37 separate the circle into the arc containing point Z and the arc containing point W. These arcs are denoted, respectively, by the symbols $\overparen{XZY}$ and $\overparen{XWY}$.

A circle together with its interior is called a *circular region*. A round coin or the cover of a soup can are physical representations of circular regions.

Exercise Set 6

1. a. Draw a circle and draw any chord, $\overline{AB}$. By paper-folding tactics, find the perpendicular bisector of this chord.

b. Does the fold line contain the center of the circle?

c. What special kind of a chord of the circle does the fold line contain?

d. Is this special kind of chord a line of symmetry for the circle?

2. a. How many lines of symmetry does a circle have?

b. What do you observe about all of the lines of symmetry of a circle?

3. If you were given any circle and did not know where its center was located, how could you use paper-folding tactics to find the center?

SIMILARITY

Similar Figures

In the section on congruence we were concerned mainly with objects that have the same size and shape. In this section we are going to consider objects that have the same shape but not necessarily the same size. Such figures are called *similar* figures. The four circles at the top of Figure 38 are clearly similar, since all circles are certainly shaped alike, whether or not they are of the same size. The same is true of all squares.

Each of us has many intuitive notions of what we mean by similarity between objects. In ordinary conversation we tend to say that two objects are similar if they are alike in one or more obvious respects, as for example, if they have the same color, or if they are made of the same material, or if they are of the same sex. In geometry the term "similar" is used in a more precise sense, because it always denotes "having the same *shape*."

We know that congruent figures are the same in size as well as shape; hence all figures that are congruent are similar as well. Thus the two congruent triangles shown in Figure 39 are of course similar. But now suppose we look at one of them, say $\triangle ABC$, under a magnifying glass. Each side of

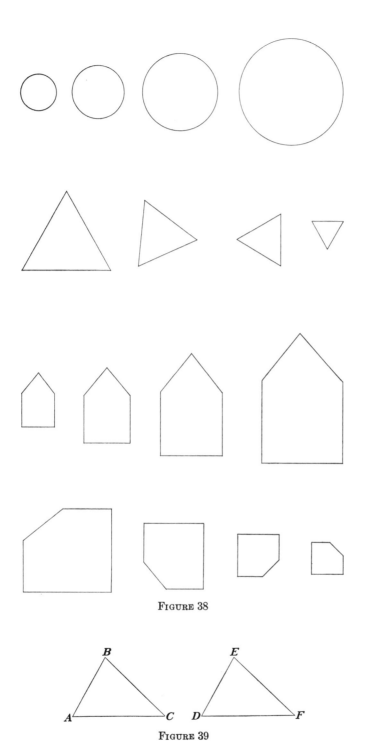

FIGURE 38

FIGURE 39

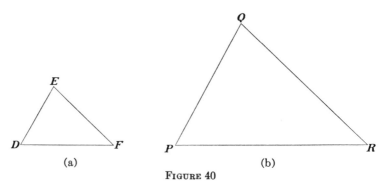

(a)   (b)

FIGURE 40

$\triangle ABC$ in Figure 40(a) was *magnified by the same amount* to produce $\triangle PQR$ in Figure 40(b). Hence the magnifying process uniformly increased the size of $\triangle ABC$ while preserving the original shape. Accordingly, we say that the two triangles in Figure 40 are similar.

Suppose that now we are given any two geometric figures, such as the regions pictured in Figure 41(a) and (b). These two regions look alike in shape, but they are not congruent, since region (a) obviously is much smaller than region (b). Do you think that by magnifying region (a) you

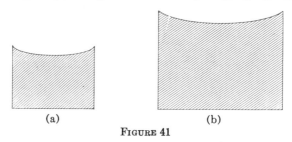

(a)   (b)

FIGURE 41

could obtain a region that would be congruent to the one pictured in (b)? If the answer is "yes" (as it is in this case), then the two figures, (a) and (b), are similar.

Let us try another example. Do the two simple closed curves in Figure 42(a) and (b) appear to be similar? Again the answer is "yes." This time,

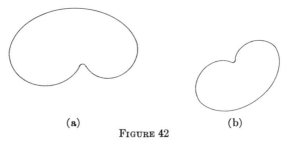

(a)   (b)

FIGURE 42

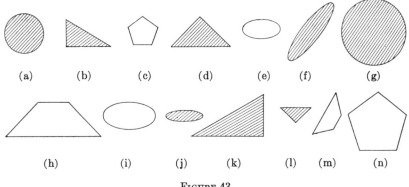

FIGURE 43

we would imagine magnifying the simple closed curve in (b) to produce one congruent to the one pictured in (a). We should note that the difference in orientation of the two figures does not matter.

See if you can match pairs of similar figures pictured above in Figure 43. Using our intuitive idea of magnifying, we can identify (a) and (g), (b) and (k), (c) and (n), (d) and (l), (e) and (i), (f) and (j), and (h) and (m) as pairs of similar figures.

All line segments are similar to one another because they all have the same "shape," even though they are of different size. In Figure 44, $\overline{CD}$ is

A B C   D

FIGURE 44

three times as long as $\overline{AB}$, so the ratio of the length, CD, of $\overline{CD}$ to the length, AB, of $\overline{AB}$ is 3 to 1. In symbols we write:

$$\frac{CD}{AB} = \frac{3}{1}.$$

Similar Triangles

Now let us compare the pair of triangles, $\triangle ABC$ and $\triangle DEF$, in Figure 45. You may observe intuitively that these triangles appear to be similar,

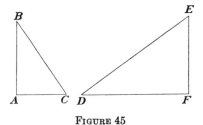

FIGURE 45

but in Euclidean geometry there is a precise way of testing whether they
have exactly the same "shape."

Suppose we let vertex A in $\triangle ABC$ be the one that corresponds to vertex
F in $\triangle DEF$, since the corresponding angles, $\angle A$ and $\angle F$, appear to have
equal measure. (They both appear to be right angles.) Then since $\overline{AC}$
seems to be the shortest side in $\triangle ABC$, and $\overline{EF}$ in $\triangle DEF$, let us pair
vertices C and E, and vertices B and D. You can perhaps visualize the
correspondence better if you imagine rotating $\triangle DEF$ clockwise one-
quarter of a complete turn so that $\triangle ABC$ and $\triangle DEF$ are lined up as in
Figure 46.

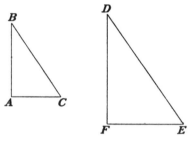

FIGURE 46

Now if we measure with a protractor and find that $\angle BAC \cong \angle DFE$,
$\angle ABC \cong \angle FDE$, and $\angle ACB \cong \angle FED$, then corresponding angles of
$\triangle ABC$ and $\triangle DEF$ are congruent. Does it appear that the length of each
side of $\triangle DEF$ is about $\frac{3}{2}$ times the length of the corresponding side of
$\triangle ABC$? If measuring shows this to be so, then we can write three ratios
to describe that fact:

$$\frac{FD}{AB} = \frac{3}{2}, \quad \frac{DE}{BC} = \frac{3}{2}, \quad \text{and} \quad \frac{EF}{CA} = \frac{3}{2}.$$

We can combine these ratios and write:

$$\frac{FD}{AB} = \frac{DE}{BC} = \frac{EF}{CA} = \frac{3}{2}.$$

We describe this equality of the ratios of corresponding sides by stating
that *the lengths of corresponding sides of the two triangles are proportional*,
in the ratio of 3 to 2 for this example.

Now we can give a precise test for the similarity of triangles:

> *Two triangles are similar if, for some pairing of their vertices,
> corresponding angles are congruent and the lengths of cor-
> responding sides are proportional.*

Similar Polygons

The foregoing test can be extended to include polygons of any number of sides. That is, two polygons are similar if, for some pairing of their vertices in order around the polygons, corresponding angles are congruent and corresponding sides are proportional in length. For three-sided polygons (triangles), however, it happens that *either one* of these two conditions is sufficient to establish similarity. That is, two triangles are similar if it is true *either* that corresponding angles are congruent *or* that corresponding sides are proportional in length.

You will recall that a polygon is regular if all its sides are congruent and all its angles are congruent. Hence we see that any two regular polygons having the same number of sides are similar, because no matter how their vertices are paired, corresponding angles will always be congruent and

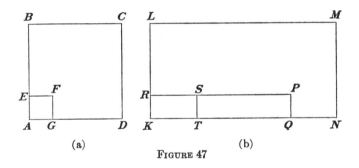

(a)   (b)

FIGURE 47

corresponding sides proportional in length. All squares are similar to one another, but not all rectangles. In Figure 47(a), you can see that the two squares $ABCD$ and $AEFG$ are similar because

$$\angle B \cong \angle C \cong \angle D \cong \angle A \cong \angle E \cong \angle F \cong \angle G,$$

and (approximately)

$$\frac{AB}{AE} = \frac{BC}{EF} = \frac{CD}{FG} = \frac{AD}{AG} = \frac{4}{1}.$$

But now look at the three rectangles with vertex K in Figure 47(b), namely: $KLMN$, $KRPQ$, and $KRST$. Since all the angles are right angles, we can safely assume that no matter how the vertices are paired in any two of these rectangles, corresponding angles will be congruent. When we compare the sides of rectangles $KLMN$ and $KRPQ$, however, it appears that $\frac{KN}{KQ} = \frac{4}{3}$, while $\frac{MN}{PQ} = \frac{4}{1}$. Therefore $\frac{KN}{KQ} \neq \frac{MN}{PQ}$. Here we have two pairs of corresponding sides with lengths that are *not* in the same proportion. Also, $\frac{KN}{PQ} = \frac{8}{1}$, while $\frac{MN}{KQ} = \frac{4}{6} = \frac{2}{3}$, so $\frac{KN}{PQ} \neq \frac{MN}{KQ}$

Thus the corresponding sides are not proportionate in any order, and the two rectangles $KLMN$ and $KRPQ$ are not similar.

A glance at rectangles $KLMN$ and $KRST$ will show that they *do* appear to be similar, with

$$\frac{KL}{KR} = \frac{LM}{RS} = \frac{MN}{ST} = \frac{NK}{TK} = \frac{4}{1}.$$

Exercise Set 7

1. a. Give examples of similar objects that you might encounter in a supermarket, in an automobile factory, on a farm, and in a kitchen.

  b. Is it possible that some of these similar objects might also be congruent?

2. a. Are all squares similar?

  b. Are all triangles similar?

  c. Are all rectangles similar?

  d. Are all regular pentagons similar?

  e. Are all hexagons similar?

  f. Are all tin cans similar?

  g. Are all (round) balls similar?

3. Explain why the two rectangles pictured below are *not* similar

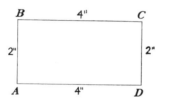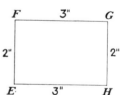

4. The figures below illustrate two similar quadrilaterals.

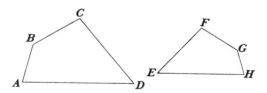

How would you pair the vertices in $ABCD$ with those in $EFGH$ so that corresponding angles would be congruent?

THREE-DIMENSIONAL FIGURES

The notions of symmetry, congruence, and similarity that we have developed for plane figures apply equally well to three-dimensional figures. You might note that exercise 1 in Exercise Set 2 is concerned with congruent three-dimensional figures, and exercise 1 in Exercise Set 7 with similar three-dimensional figures.

In three dimensions (space), figures might have not only points and lines of symmetry but planes of symmetry as well. Thus while the *picture* in Figure 4 of a girl with very regular features has a vertical *line* of symmetry, the girl herself would have a vertical *plane* (from front to back) of symmetry. You and your "mirror image" in an ordinary mirror are symmetrical with respect to the plane of the mirror. A sphere has infinitely many lines of symmetry and infinitely many planes of symmetry, namely all the lines and planes through the center of the sphere; but the center of the sphere is the sphere's only *point* of symmetry.

We can classify three-dimensional figures in much the same way that we classified plane figures. In doing so, we are led to many interesting considerations and discoveries. For example, while there are any number of regular polygons (since the number of sides may be any number greater than or equal to three; see Fig. 32), there are only five regular *polyhedra* (singular, *polyhedron*): regular tetrahedron, hexahedron (or cube), octahedron, dodecahedron, and icosahedron (Fig. 48). The number V of vertices, E of edges, and F of faces for these regular polyhedra are tab-

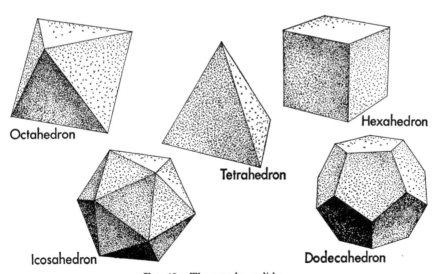

Octahedron

Hexahedron

Tetrahedron

Icosahedron

Dodecahedron

Fig. 48.—The regular solids.

TABLE I

Regular Polyhedron	V	E	F
Tetrahedron	4	6	4
Hexahedron	8	12	6
Octahedron	6	12	8
Dodecahedron	20	30	12
Icosahedron	12	30	20

ulated in Table I. It is interesting to note in the table that for the regular tetrahedron the numbers occur in the same order forward as backward (4, 6, 4) and that they occur in the same order forward for the regular hexahedron and dodecahedron as they do backward for the regular octahedron and icosahedron, respectively. Because of these relations the regular hexahedron and octahedron are said to be *dual* figures, as are the regular dodecahedron and icosahedron; the regular tetrahedron is its own dual.

You might note also that the numbers specified in Table I illustrate *Euler's theorem* that for *any* simple polyhedron you have

$$V - E + F = 2.$$

SUMMARY

In this booklet you have been asked to consider many geometric objects by imagining, observing, and constructing. It is hoped that this activity has clarified and reinforced your geometric intuition, so that you can more easily convey geometric notions to your students.

Although three-dimensional figures are more difficult to represent on the chalkboard than are plane figures, the fact is that we live in space and, from the day we are born, are used to touching solid objects. Accordingly, many of us actually develop a stronger intuitive feeling for three-dimensional figures than for plane figures. For example, even preschool children can sort their blocks into piles of those having the same shape and size. In teaching geometry to young children, it is a good idea to start with situations for which they have an intuitive feeling.

For Further Reading

Among the various helpful references that deal with the subject here introduced are the following:

BRUMFIEL, CHARLES F., and KRAUSE, EUGENE F. *Elementary Mathematics for Teachers*. Reading, Mass.: Addison-Wesley, 1969. Available from Addison-Wesley Publishing Co., Inc., Reading, Mass. 01867.

SENSIBA, DANIEL E. "Geometry and Transformations," in *Enrichment Mathematics for the Grades*. Twenty-seventh Yearbook of the National Council of Teachers of Mathematics. Washington, D.C.: The Council, 1963. Available from the National Council of Teachers of Mathematics, 1201 Sixteenth St., N.W., Washington, D.C. 20036.

SMART, JAMES R. *Introductory Geometry; An Informal Approach*. Belmont, Calif.: Brooks/Cole, 1967. Pp. 224. Available from Brooks/Cole, Belmont, Calif. 94002.

WEAVER, JAY D., and WOLF, CHARLES T. *Modern Mathematics for Elementary Teachers* (2d ed.). Scranton, Pa.: International Textbook Co., 1968. Pp. 274. Available from International Textbook Co., Scranton, Pa. 18515.

ANSWERS TO EXERCISES

Exercise Set 1

1.

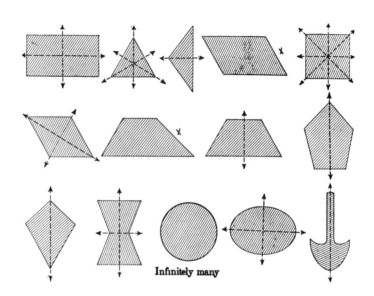

Infinitely many

2.

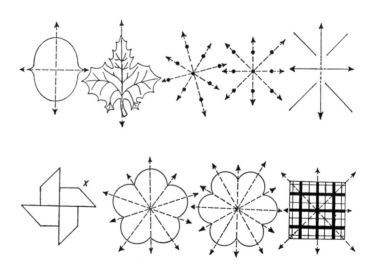

3.

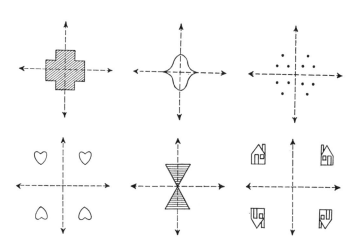

4.

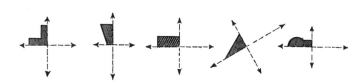

5. a. Yes.   **f.** Yes.
   b. Yes.   **g.** No.
   c. No.   **h.** No.
   d. Yes.   **i.** Yes.
   e. Yes.   **j.** No.

6.  or

Exercise Set 2

1. All eight-oz. cans of the same brand of tomato soup, all coins in the dime section of a cash register, all Brand-X half-gallon boxes of ice cream, etc.; screws, windshields, bolts, fenders, wrenches, knobs, etc., for the same make, model, and year of a particular car; milk cans, tools, grain bags, stancheons, etc.; teaspoons, dinner plates, tumblers, spice bottles—these and many more objects that have the same size and shape are congruent.

2. Yes.

3. a. They are perpendicular to each other.
   b. A right angle
   c. $\angle BCD$

4. a. $\overline{AB} \cong \overline{A'B'}$, $\overline{BC} \cong \overline{B'C'}$, $\overline{AC} \cong \overline{A'C'}$.
   b. $\angle ABC \cong \angle A'B'C'$, $\angle BAC \cong \angle B'A'C'$, $\angle ACB \cong \angle A'C'B'$.

5. See exercise 4.

Exercise Set 3

1.

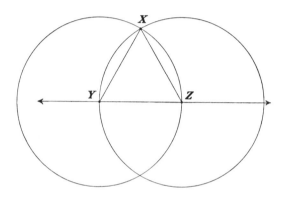

2. a. No. You can verify this by marking a segment, $\overline{YZ}$, congruent to $\overline{AB}$. Then fold the paper so as to get a fold line perpendicular to $\overline{YZ}$ at point Y. Mark point X so that $\overline{XY} \cong \overline{AB}$. Set the compass points on A and B, and draw a circle with Z as center. This circle will not intersect $\overleftrightarrow{XY}$ at X, so no equilateral triangle XYZ can be formed.

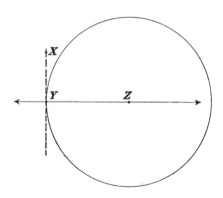

b. Yes, for example:

c. No. (The verification is very similar to the one given in **a.**)

3. The triangular closed region will balance at this point but at no other point.

4. a. Yes.   **c.** Yes.
   b. Yes.   **d.** Yes.

5. a. No.   **c.** No.
   b. No.   **d.** No.

6. a.

  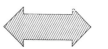 etc.

b.

 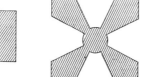 etc.

Exercise Set 4

1.

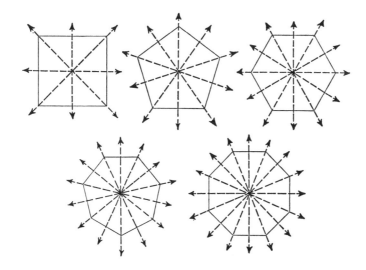

The number of lines of symmetry for a closed region bounded by a regular polygon equals the number of sides of the regular polygon.

2. No.

3.

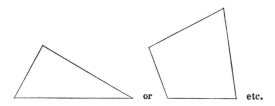

4. a. Yes.

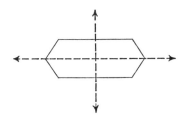

  b. No.

  c. Yes, if it is regular.

Exercise Set 5

1. a. See Figure 34.

  b. Same as for the corresponding closed regions pictured in Figure 35

  c. Kite, rhombus, square

  d. Isosceles trapezoid, rectangle, square

2. Parallelogram, rhombus, rectangle, square

3. a. $P; Q$

  b. Yes. Yes; since $\overleftrightarrow{MN}$ is a line of symmetry, these two segments must coincide when the fold is made.

  c. $\overline{MS}; \overline{QN}$

  d. No.

  e. Isosceles trapezoid

4. a. Y

  b. Yes. Yes, since these two angles must coincide when the fold is made along the line of symmetry, $\overleftrightarrow{XZ}$.

c. $\overline{XW}$; $\overline{YZ}$

d. No.

e. Kite

Exercise Set 6

1. a. The fold line is the perpendicular bisector of $\overline{AB}$. The paper is folded so that B falls on A.

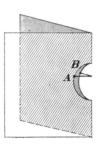

b. Yes.

c. A diameter

d. Yes.

2. a. Infinitely many

b. They all pass through the center of the circle. (Each contains a diameter of the circle.)

3. Fold to obtain any two of the lines of symmetry. They intersect at the center of the circle.

Exercise Set 7

1. a. Dimes, nickels, and quarters; cans that have the same shape, boxes, etc.; all square nuts, the wrenches in a set, tires, etc.; pails, tools, etc.; covers to jars, teaspoons and tablespoons; dinner and luncheon plates, cooking pots, etc., that have the same shape.

b. Yes. (Note further that all the congruent objects that you listed in Exercise Set 2 could be included here as being similar.)

2. a. Yes.

b. No; for example, these are not similar triangles:

c. No; for example, these are not similar rectangles:

d. Yes.

e. No; for example, these are not
similar hexagons:

f. No; for example, a soup can and
a tuna-fish can are not similar:

g. Yes.

3. Because the vertices cannot be paired in such a way as to make the
lengths of the corresponding sides proportional; you have

$$\frac{AB}{EF} = \frac{2}{2} \quad \text{and} \quad \frac{AD}{EH} = \frac{4}{3}, \quad \text{and} \quad \frac{2}{2} \neq \frac{4}{3};$$

you also have

$$\frac{AB}{EH} = \frac{2}{3} \quad \text{and} \quad \frac{AD}{EF} = \frac{4}{2}, \quad \text{and} \quad \frac{2}{3} \neq \frac{4}{2}.$$

4. A, B, C, D correspond to H, G, F, E, respectively.